CW00746947

# THE BOOK OF BEETLES

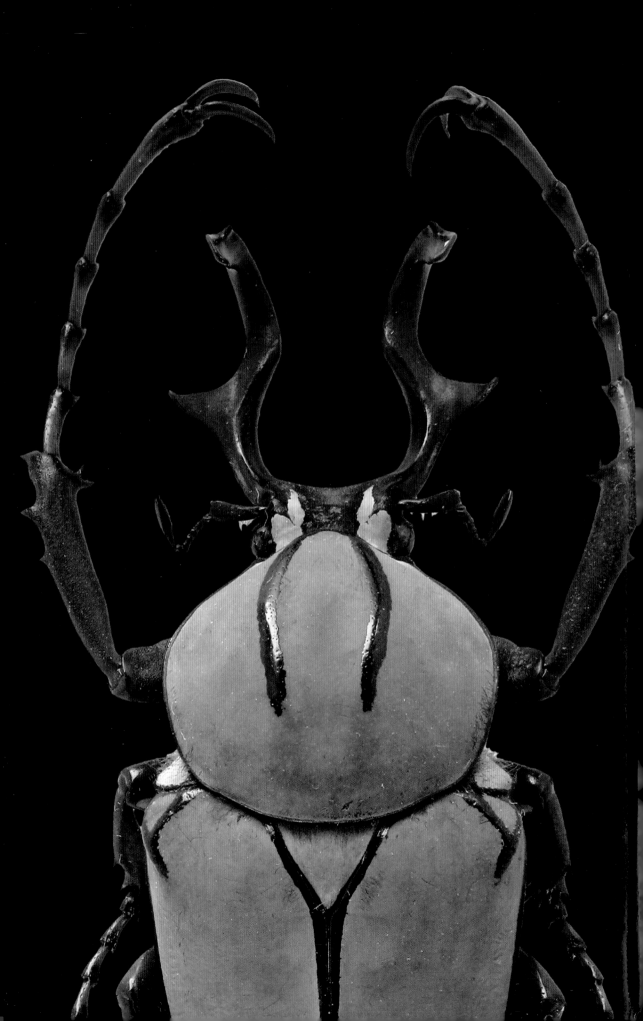

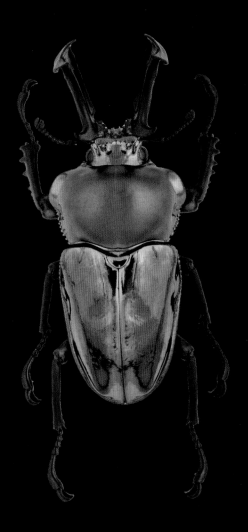

# THE BOOK OF BEETLES

## A LIFE-SIZE GUIDE TO SIX HUNDRED
## OF NATURE'S GEMS

**EDITOR**
PATRICE BOUCHARD

**CONTRIBUTORS**
PATRICE BOUCHARD, YVES BOUSQUET, CHRISTOPHER CARLTON,
MARIA LOURDES CHAMORRO, HERMES E. ESCALONA, ARTHUR V. EVANS,
ALEXANDER KONSTANTINOV, RICHARD A. B. LESCHEN,
STÉPHANE LE TIRANT, STEVEN W. LINGAFELTER

**Ivy Press**

PATRICE BOUCHARD is a research scientist and curator of Coleoptera at the Canadian National Collection of Insects, Arachnids, and Nematodes, Ottawa.

YVES BOUSQUET is a research scientist at the Canadian National Collection of Insects, Arachnids, and Nematodes, Ottawa.

CHRISTOPHER CARLTON is a research scientist and director of the Louisiana State Arthropod Museum, Louisiana State University Agricultural Center, Baton Rouge.

MARIA LOURDES CHAMORRO is a research entomologist and curator of Curculionoidea at the Systematic Entomology Laboratory (USDA) in the National Museum of Natural History in Washington, D. C.

HERMES E. ESCALONA is a visiting scientist at the Australian National Insect Collection-CSIRO, Canberra.

ARTHUR V. EVANS is a research collaborator at the Department of Entomology, National Museum of Natural History, Smithsonian Institution, Washington, D. C.

ALEXANDER KONSTANTINOV is a research entomologist and curator of Chrysomelidae at the Systematic Entomology Laboratory (USDA) in the National Museum of Natural History in Washington, D. C.

RICHARD A. B. LESCHEN is a researcher at Landcare Research and curator of Coleoptera at the New Zealand Arthropod Collection, Auckland.

STÉPHANE LE TIRANT is curator of the Montreal Insectarium.

STEVEN W. LINGAFELTER is a research entomologist and curator of Cerambycidae at the Systematic Entomology Laboratory (USDA) in the National Museum of Natural History in Washington, D. C.

First published in Great Britain in 2014 by
**Ivy Press**
210 High Street, Lewes
East Sussex BN7 2NS
United Kingdom
www.ivypress.co.uk

Copyright © 2014 The Ivy Press Limited

British Library Cataloguing-in-Publication Data
A CIP catalogue record for this book is available from the British Library.

ISBN 978-1-78240-049-3

Colour origination by Ivy Press Reprographics
Typeset in Fournier and News Gothic

Printed in China

10 9 8 7 6 5 4 3 2 1

Distributed worldwide (except North America) by
Thames & Hudson Ltd., 181A High Holborn,
London WC1V 7QX, United Kingdom

This book was conceived, designed, and produced by
**Ivy Press**
Creative Director PETER BRIDGEWATER
Publisher SUSAN KELLY
Art Director MICHAEL WHITEHEAD
Editorial Director TOM KITCH
Senior Project Editor CAROLINE EARLE
Commissioning Editor KATE SHANAHAN
Designer GINNY ZEAL
Illustrator SANDRA POND

JACKET AND LITHOCASE IMAGES
Klaus Bolte: *Agrilus planipennis, Timarcha tenebricosa*; Jason Bond and Trip Lamb: *Onymacris bicolor*; Lech Borowiec: *Cetonia aurata, Dytiscus marginalis, Pachylister inaequalis, Sphaerius acaroides*; Karolyn Darrow © The Smithsonian Institution: *Akephorus obesus, Eucamaragnathus batesi, Pasimachus subangulatus, Solenogenys funkei, Tetracha carolina*; Anthony Davies, copyright © Her Majesty the Queen in Right of Canada as represented by the Minister of Agriculture and Agri-Food: *Anomalipus elephas, Borolinus javanicus, Brachycerus ornatus, Calognathus chevrolati eberlanzi, Cheirotonus macleayi, Cossyphus hoffmannseggii, Cupes capitatus, Dinapate wrightii, Dineutus sublineatus, Erotylus onagga, Eupatorus gracilicornis, Gagatophorus draco, Geotrupes splendidus, Goliathus regius, Graphipterus serrator, Helea spinifer, Heliocopris gigas, Heterosternus buprestoides, Hexodon unicolor, Hister quadrinotatus quadrinotatus, Lasiorhynchus barbicornis, Lucanus elaphus, Macrolycus flabellatus, Mecynorhina torquata, Necrophilus subterraneus, Nicrophorus americanus, Notolioon gemmatus, Pleocoma australis, Rhipicera femorata, Ripiphorus vierecki, Sandalus niger, Saprinus cyaneus, Spilopyra sumptuosa, Strategus aloeus, Strongylium auratum, Syntelia westwoodi, Taurocerastes patagonicus, Tricondyla aptera, Zarhipis integripennis*; Henri Goulet, copyright © Her Majesty the Queen in Right of Canada as represented by the Minister of Agriculture and Agri-Food: *Amblycheila cylindriformi, Broscus cephalotes, Calosoma sycophanta, Cychrus caraboides, Damaster blaptoides, Elaphrus viridis, Helluomorphoides praeustus bicolor*; Vitya Kubáň and Svata Bilý: *Juniperella mirabilis*; René Limoges: *Acrocinus longimanus, Chalcosoma atlas, Chrysophora chrysochloa, Phalacrognathus muelleri*; Kirill Makarov: *Lethrus apterus*; R. Salmaso, Archives of the Museo di Storia Naturale of Verona: *Crowsoniella relicta*; Udo Schmidt: *Batocera wallacei, Hydrophilus piceus, Loricera pilicornis, Megasoma elephas, Paranaleptes reticulata, Siagona europaea*; Maxim Smirnov: *Chiasognathus grantii, Dicronocephalus wallichi, Mormolyce phyllodes, Sagra buqueti, Sulcophaneus imperator*; Laurent Soldati: *Prionotheca coronata*; Christopher C. Wirth: *Alaus zunianus, Amblysterna natalensis, Calodema regalis, Catoxantha opulenta, Cometes hirticornis, Euchroma giganteum, Isthmiade braconides, Oncideres cingulata, Sternocera chrysis, Thrincopyge alacris, Temognatha chevrolatii*.

# CONTENTS

# INTRODUCTION

"*From the small size of insects, we are apt to undervalue their appearance. If we could imagine a male* Chalcosoma *with its polished, bronzed coat of mail, and vast complex horns, magnified to the size of a horse or even of a dog, it would be one of the most imposing animals in the world.*"

CHARLES DARWIN, *THE DESCENT OF MAN, & SELECTION IN RELATION TO SEX*, 1871

ABOVE **Beetles are** an exceptionally diverse group of organisms that impact our agriculture, forestry, culture, and science. Their seemingly endless variations in structure (e.g., the male Atlas Beetle, *Chalcosoma atlas*) and adaptations to microhabitat have captivated humans for centuries.

Beetles of the order Coleoptera, with nearly 400,000 described species, comprise one of the most diverse and important groups of animals on Earth. As such, *coleopterists*, biologists who specialize in the study of beetles, have a view of the natural world with a degree of resolution that is seldom seen through the study of other organisms.

One out of every five species of plants and animals is a beetle. Despite their riot of forms, colors, patterns, and behaviors, all beetles share a select suite of physical attributes, the most conspicuous of which are the leathery or hardened forewings, or *elytra* (singular *elytron*). Depending on the species, elytra can help stabilize beetles in flight, protect their delicate hind wings and internal organs, conserve precious bodily fluids, capture bubbles of air underwater, and insulate them from extreme temperatures. Combined with their small and compact bodies and numerous other morphological and behavioral adaptations, beetles exploit and thrive in niches unoccupied or underutilized by other animals in widely diverse terrestrial and freshwater habitats.

Although the sheer number of species prevents all but the most common or economically important beetles from having a meaningful and widely accepted common name, each known species does have a scientific name consisting of a *genus* (plural *genera*) and *species* (singular and plural) epithet that is universally recognized. To manage information effectively, coleopterists file each species into a nested system of hierarchical groups, or *taxa* (singular *taxon*), based on their shared evolutionary characteristics. Species is the most exclusive taxon, while the order Coleoptera is the most inclusive of beetle taxa.

Beetles communicate with one another through physical, chemical, or visual means, usually to locate a mate. Although most species engage in sexual reproduction, a few reproduce asexually by cloning themselves, a process known as *parthenogenesis*. Among beetles, limited parental care of the young is the exception, not the rule. The larvae and adults eat a variety of organisms, living and dead, especially plants. Those that prefer leaves, flowers, fruits, needles, cones, and roots can inflict serious damage to food stores, gardens, crops, and managed timber. Some predatory beetles are used as biological control agents against agricultural or forestry pests, while scavenger species provide an essential service to clean study skeletons in natural-history collections around the globe. Recently, the study of beetle structure and function has inspired scientists and engineers

ABOVE **Some beetles** feed on a single plant species; while others feed on a wide range of hosts. Adult Japanese Beetles (*Popillia japonica*) are pests in North America, where they feed on more than 300 plant species.

BELOW **Most beetles** are winged, but some have reduced hind wings and cannot fly, such as species in the African weevil genus *Brachycerus*.

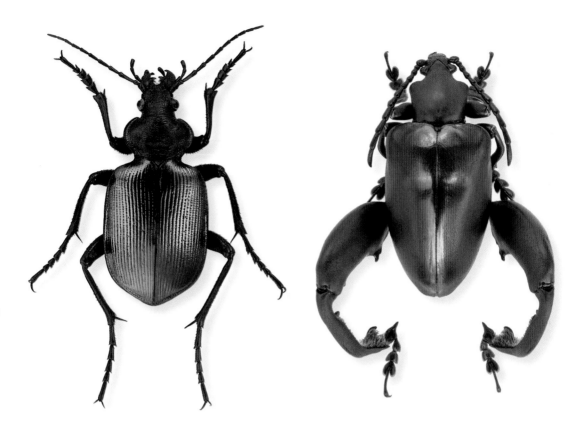

8

ABOVE **One of the most**
challenging tasks
for this project was
to select the 600
candidate beetles
to cover from the
overwhelming
number of species.
Some, such as the
Agreeable Caterpillar
Hunter (*Calosoma
sycophanta*, left), are
visually attractive
and well known
biologically, while
others, such as
the Frog-legged
Leaf Beetle (*Sagra
buqueti*, right),
have noteworthy
adaptations yet
little is known about
their biology.

working in the rapidly growing field of *biomimetics* to develop and design new materials and products ranging from iridescent car paint and reusable adhesive tape to monetary security systems.

*The Book of Beetles* offers a glimpse of this incredible diversity through an overview of 600 beetle species presented within a framework based on their evolutionary relationships. The selected species are divided into four main sections which represent the four Coleoptera suborders. Within each section the arrangement is taxonomic, by family and then subfamily, and then within each subfamily in alphabetical order based on their scientific name (genus, species).

## SELECTION CRITERIA

The species were selected on the basis of several criteria, offering a unique taxonomic survey of the majority of beetle families from around the world:
• *Scientifically compelling* species that are the subjects of focused scientific research, have medicinal uses, or provide inspirations for biomimetic and technological innovation.
• *Curious natural histories* of species that depict unusual adaptations for living in extreme habitats, interesting relationships with other species, or demonstrate other engaging behaviors.
• *Culturally significant* species that appear as mythological and religious symbols, or are used in folk medicine or as food.

• *Economically important* species that are pests, used to control pests and weeds, or provide useful products and services, or provide evidence of medical and legal importance.

• *Rare and threatened* species that are in need of legal protection and conservation.

• *Physically impressive* species that are large, colorful, horned, or have exaggerated or unusually developed legs or mouthparts that are adapted for use in specific behaviors that have evolved through natural selection over millions of years.

Each species is depicted by a razor-sharp life-size photograph and accompanied by a summary of its known distribution, habitat, and feeding habits. The map offers an indication of its global distribution, while the engravings afford readers another point of view. The scientific and common (if any) names are also provided, followed by the species' author and year of description. Concise narratives covering natural history and related species are followed by a brief species diagnosis.

9

BEETLE COLLECTIONS

Beetle collections assembled over decades by dedicated professionals and amateurs provide essential data needed to identify and map sensitive species within a historical context. These scientifically valuable collections also serve as important resources for other scientific and educational endeavors, such as providing the specimens photographed for this book.

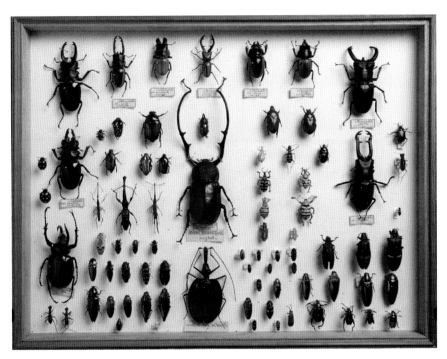

BELOW **Millions of insects**, including beetles, are preserved in natural history collections throughout the world. Specimens are typically pinned, dried, and affixed with a label that records the place and date of capture and the name of the collector. Collections of specimens, such as this one from the Alfred Russel Wallace (1823–1913) collection in the Natural History Museum, London, are stored in boxes and drawers to protect them from museum pests and preserve them for study by future generations of scientists.

# WHAT IS A BEETLE?

The English word "beetle" comes from the Middle English *bityl* or *betyll* and the Old English *bitula*, all of which mean "little biter." Other commonly used names, such as "weevil" and "chafer" derived from Old English and Old High German, also relate to biting. Coleoptera, first coined by Aristotle in the fourth century BCE and later adopted as an order of insects by Carl Linnaeus in 1758, is derived from the Greek words *koleos*, meaning "sheath," and *pteron*, or "winged," and was inspired by the tough elytra of beetles.

## DISTINGUISHING FEATURES

Among other adaptations, beetles are distinguished from other insects by their chewing mouthparts, the conversion of their forewings into hardened elytra, their hind wings that fold lengthwise and across beneath the elytra, and their *holometabolous development*. Holometabolous insects pass through four very distinct life stages: egg, larva, pupa, and adult. The larvae and adults frequently differ in habits and habitat, functioning in the environment as if they were two separate species.

Beetles, like other insects, crustaceans, arachnids, millipedes, centipedes, and their kin with segmented exoskeletons and jointed appendages (antennae, mouthparts, legs), are classified in the phylum Arthropoda. Light and durable, the beetle exoskeleton is incredibly tough and rigid or characteristically soft and pliable, and provides protection and support. It serves as a platform for important tactile and chemosensory structures externally, while providing an internal framework that supports muscles and organs. The exoskeletal surface is smooth and shiny, or dulled by waxy

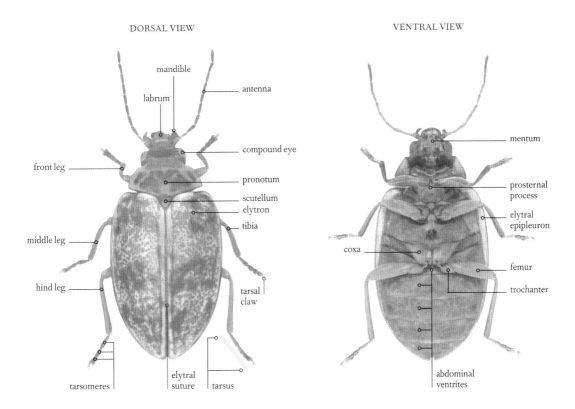

DORSAL VIEW

- mandible
- labrum
- antenna
- compound eye
- front leg
- pronotum
- scutellum
- elytron
- tibia
- middle leg
- hind leg
- tarsal claw
- tarsomeres
- elytral suture
- tarsus

VENTRAL VIEW

- mentum
- prosternal process
- elytral epipleuron
- coxa
- femur
- trochanter
- abdominal ventrites

11

secretions or microscopic networks of cracks (*alutaceous*) resembling that of human skin. The surface is variously festooned with spines, hairlike *setae*, or flattened setae called *scales*, and sculpted with tiny bumps (*tubercles*), pit-like *punctures*, *ridges*, grooves (*striae*), or rows of punctures.

## COLOR

The colors of beetles are derived either from chemical pigments obtained from their food or structural properties of the outer layers of the exoskeleton. Most beetles are black as a result of melanin deposition during *sclerotization*, the chemical hardening process of the exoskeleton that occurs after emergence from the pupa, or *eclosion*. Microscopic surface sculpturing also influences beetle colors, as do patterns of setae, scales, or waxy secretions. Black desert darkling beetles (Tenebrionidae) are sometimes partially or completely covered with a white, yellow, or bluish-gray waxy bloom that reflects light and helps to keep the beetle cool.

The brilliant iridescent and metallic colors of beetles are created by multiple reflective layers in the exoskelton and scales, or a layer of highly complex photonic crystals that reflect light at different wavelengths to create specific metallic colors and shimmering iridescence. These structures are determined genetically, but their final form in individual beetles is determined by conditions experienced during growth and development.

ABOVE **The study** of a hyperdiverse group of organisms such as beetles requires the close examination of a wide range of anatomical structures in order to recognize and distinguish species and correctly classify them into larger groups. The consistent use of precise terms for these structures is essential to clearly communicate the anatomical differences and similarities of beetles among specialists and non-specialists alike.

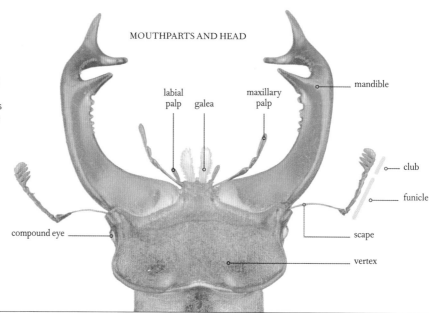

MOUTHPARTS AND HEAD

RIGHT **The head of a beetle** is a rigid structure that supports the compound eyes and the antennae. It also contains the muscles necessary to operate the mouthparts, which can include enlarged mandibles such as in males of *Lucanus cervus*.

labial palp

galea

maxillary palp

mandible

club

funicle

compound eye

scape

vertex

12

BELOW LEFT **The antennae** of most beetles have 11 articles called antennomeres. The spectacular flabellate antennae of the Feather-horned Beetle (*Rhipicera femorata*) and other species in this genus can have up to 40 antennomeres.

BELOW RIGHT **Beetles' mouthparts** project forward or downward, depending on feeding habits. The predatory Peters' Snail-eating Beetle (*Scaphinotus petersi*) uses its elongated mouthparts to extract the soft tissues from inside its prey's shell.

## STRUCTURE

As with other insects, the beetle body is divided into three distinct regions: head, thorax, and abdomen.

### The head

The hardened head capsule is attached to the thorax by a flexible and membranous neck, and is clearly visible from above or partially withdrawn inside the thorax. It bears chewing mouthparts that typically consist of an upper lip (*labrum*), two sets of jaws (*mandibles*, *maxillae*), and a lower lip (*labium*). The usually conspicuous mandibles are modified to cut, grind, or strain various foodstuffs. The maxilla and labium may possess delicate fingerlike structures, or *palps*, that help manipulate food. Beetle mouthparts are directed forward, or *prognathous* (e.g., whirligig beetles [Gyrinidae], ground beetles [Carabidae]), or downward

(*hypognathous*), as in leaf beetles (Chrysomelidae) and weevils. The mouthparts of some beetles, especially those of weevils (Curculionoidea), are borne at the very tip of a snout-like *rostrum*, an adaptation often associated with flower- or seed-feeding habits.

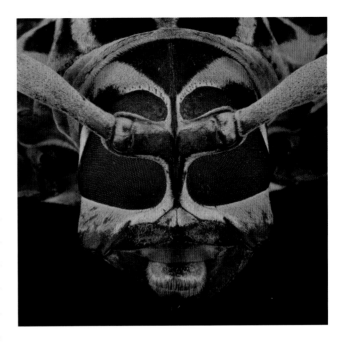

Although usually shorter than the body, the antennae are much longer in many longhorns (Cerambycidae) and brentid weevils (Brentidae). Equipped with incredibly sensitive receptors, these appendages help beetles detect food, locate egg-laying sites, identify vibrations, and assess temperature and humidity. Those of males are sometimes quite elaborate and are packed with chemical receptors for detecting *pheromones*, sexually attractant odors released by females. Each antennal segment is referred to as an *antennomere*. The basic number of antennomeres for beetles is 11, but reductions to as few as seven are common, while 12 or more occur in some species. Antennal modifications are described as *filiform* (threadlike), *moniliform* (bead-like), *serrate* (saw-toothed), *pectinate* (comb-like), *flabellate* (feather-like), *clavate* (gradually clubbed at the tip), *capitate* (abruptly clubbed at tip), *lamellate* (terminal antennomeres flattened or plate-like), or *geniculate* (elbowed).

13

ABOVE **The size, shape, and position** of compound eyes vary greatly among beetles, and these differences are used to distinguish and classify species. For example, some cave-dwelling species have completely lost their compound eyes, while others, such as the Harlequin Beetle (*Acrocinus longimanus*), have eyes that are large and well developed.

The *compound eyes* are entire (rounded or oval in shape), emarginate (kidney-shaped), or are completely divided, as in the whirligigs (Gyrinidae). They are often reduced in flightless species, or absent altogether in cave and litter species that dwell in total darkness. *Ocelli*, simple eyes limited to detecting light and dark, are found only in a few rove beetles (Staphylinidae), some leiodids (Leiodidae) and derodontids (Derodontidae), and in most hide beetles (Dermestidae).

Male heads are sometimes adorned with extraordinary antler- or tusk-like horns that may vary greatly in size depending on overall body size, larval nutrition, and other environmental and genetic factors. Horns enhance the reproductive capabilities of males and are used in battles against rival males to butt, block, pry, or lift them out of the way.

### The thorax

The beetle thorax consists of three segments, each bearing a pair of legs. The clearly visible midsection of a beetle is the *prothorax*, the upper or *dorsal* surface of which is covered by a plate, the *pronotum*. The pronotum may bear horns that work in concert with those of the head, or is scooped out to facilitate burrowing in the soil or rotten wood. The *mesothorax* and *metathorax* bear the elytra and membranous flight wings, respectively. They are broadly connected to one another and are hidden under the elytra. The ventral sclerotized plates for these two thoracic segments are termed the meso- and metaventrite. Dorsally, the elytra usually meet along a straight line down the back called the *elytral suture*. A small triangular plate of the mesothorax called the *scutellum* is often visible between the bases of the elytra.

The legs are modified for burrowing, swimming, crawling, running, or jumping, and usually consists of six distinct segments. The *coxa* is generally short and stout, and firmly anchors the leg into the coxal cavity of the thorax, yet allows for the horizontal to-and-fro movement of the legs. The *trochanter* is usually small and freely movable in relation to the coxa, but fixed to the femur. The *femur* is the largest and most powerful leg segment and is greatly enlarged in species that jump (e.g., Scirtidae). The *tibia* is usually long and slender, but may be modified into a rakelike structure on the front legs of burrowing species, or fringed with long setae to enhance their use as oars by aquatic beetles. The *tarsus* is typically divided into multiple articles called *tarsomeres*, and ends in a claw-bearing segment referred to as the *pretarsus*. Each tarsus consists of up to five tarsomeres (including the pretarsus), the exact number of which may be of diagnostic value and is expressed as a three-digit *tarsal formula* (e.g., 5-5-5 or 3-3-3), which indicates the number of tarsomeres on the front, middle, and hind legs, respectively. The penultimate tarsomere is often difficult to see without examination under high magnification, a fact denoted by the statement "appears 4-4-4, but actually 5-5-5."

14

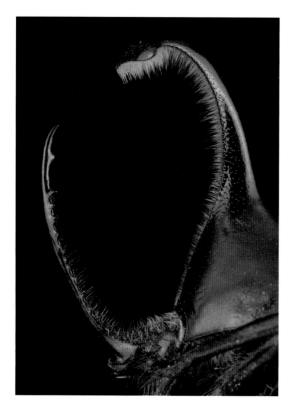

BELOW **Exaggerated structures** are common in some beetle families, including the Scarabaeidae, Lucanidae, and Cerambycidae. In these families, males often have modified and enlarged mandibles and legs, or have projections on the head or prothorax. In several species in the genus *Golofa*, projections are present on both the head and pronotum.

LEFT **The abdomen
of beetles**, contains
the digestive and
reproductive organs
that are typically
protected by a
heavily sclerotized
exoskeleton ventrally
and the elytra
dorsally. However,
several groups
of beetles have
abdominal segments
that extend beyond
the tips of the elytra,
as in the rove beetle
*Actinus imperialis*.

15

## The abdomen

Beetles typically have five visible abdominal segments, although there can
be up to eight. Each segment is comprised of four plates, or *sclerites*: a dorsal
*tergum* or *tergite*, the ventral *sternum*, and two lateral *pleura*. The dorsal
*terga* are thin and flexible in beetles with abdomens completely covered by
the elytra, but are thicker and more rigid in rove beetles (Staphylinidae),
clown beetles (Histeridae), and others with short elytra. The penultimate
and ultimate terga are called the *propygidium* and *pygidium*, respectively.
The lateral *pleura* are usually small, more or less hidden from view, and
have a single breathing pore, or *spiracle*. The ventrally visible abdominal
sterna are called *ventrites*. Ventrites are numbered beginning at the base of
the abdomen and are separated by deep to shallow transversal divisions
called *sutures*, or by narrow membranes. The internal copulatory organs
of males are often of great value in species delimitation and identification.

BELOW **The legs of
beetles** are variously
modified depending
on their function and
the type of substrate
on or in which they
occur. Males of
several species, such
as the Long Arm
Weevil (*Mahakamia
kampmeinerti*), have
legs that differ greatly
from those of females
and are generally
used in battles against
rival males over
limited resources.

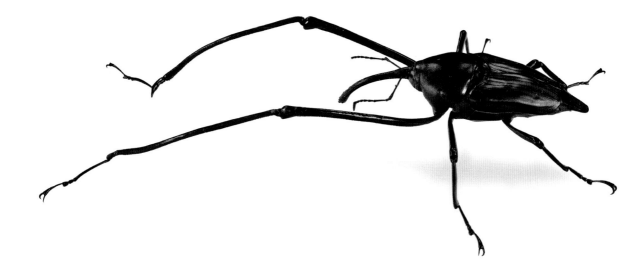

# BEETLE CLASSIFICATION

Our efforts to classify and understand the evolutionary basis for the diversity of beetles and other organisms are called *systematics*. Systematic study involves two narrowly defined, yet highly interdependent fields—*taxonomy* and *phylogenetics*. Taxonomy is the science and practice of recognizing, describing, and naming species, while phylogeny is the study of the relationships of taxa based on their shared evolutionary history to develop a natural, rather than artificial, classification. Overall, beetle species and their genera are currently placed in 1,663 tribes, within 541 subfamilies, nested in 211 families grouped into four suborders (see pages 646–7).

A beetle species is the smallest aggregation of populations that is distinguishable by a unique set of characteristic traits resulting from reproductive and, therefore, genetic isolation. Some species are easily diagnosed on the basis of genital configuration, while others may require the examination of many individuals from different populations to discern traits that are consistently different among closely related species.

## NAMING BEETLES

Linnaeus initiated the naming of organisms using only two words, the genus and species, or *binominal name* (commonly called the scientific name). The binominal is usually italicized and the genus is always capitalized. In scientific documents, the scientific names of beetles are generally followed by the surname of the person who first described the species and the year in which it was described. When a species originally described in one genus is transferred to another subsequently, parentheses

ABOVE **The Swedish physician** Carl Linnaeus (1707–78) described nearly 15,000 species of plants and animals, including 654 species of beetles. He initiated the naming of organisms using only two words, the genus and species, or the binominal name. The tenth edition of the *Systema Naturae*, published in 1758, marks the beginning of the Linnaean system of binominal nomenclature for zoology.

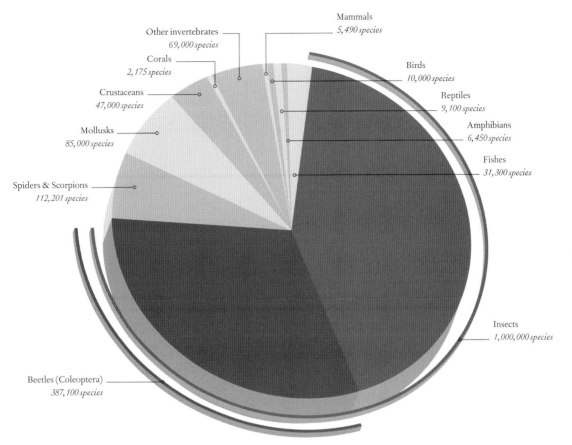

Mammals
*5,490 species*

Other invertebrates
*69,000 species*

Corals
*2,175 species*

Crustaceans
*47,000 species*

Mollusks
*85,000 species*

Spiders & Scorpions
*112,201 species*

Birds
*10,000 species*

Reptiles
*9,100 species*

Amphibians
*6,450 species*

Fishes
*31,300 species*

Insects
*1,000,000 species*

Beetles (Coleoptera)
*387,100 species*

are placed around the author's name and year of description. The year of publication of a name establishes its nomenclatural priority in the event that someone else comes along later and mistakenly describes the same species again under a completely new species name (a *synonym*), or inadvertently uses the same name to describe a totally different species (a *homonym*).

The formation and use of scientific names are codified in the *International Code of Zoological Nomenclature*. When describing a new species of beetle, a coleopterist designates one of the specimens used for the description as the *holotype*. The holotype, placed in the care of a museum or other public institution where it will be accessible to other researchers for examination, will for ever serve as the name bearer and international standard for that species. Beetle *species* are typically grouped into *genera*, *subtribes*, *tribes*, *subfamilies*, *families*, *superfamilies*, and *suborders*, although in some cases (in the less diverse groups) not all ranks are used. Some ranks end in universally accepted suffixes, such as subtribes (-ina), tribes (-ini), subfamilies (-inae), families (-idae), and superfamilies (-oidea).

ABOVE **Approximately** one in four animal species on the planet is a beetle. They are 40 times more diverse than birds, for example.

BELOW **A system** based on hierarchical ranks, from Order down to Species, is used to classify all known beetles.

| | |
|---|---|
| Kingdom | **Animalia** |
| Phylum | **Arthropoda** |
| Class | **Insecta** |
| Order | **Coleoptera** |
| Suborder | **Polyphaga** |
| Superfamily | **Tenebrionoidea** |
| Family | **Tenebrionidae** |
| Subfamily | **Tenebrioninae** |
| Tribe | **Tenebrionini** |
| Genus | ***Tenebrio*** |
| Species with author and year | ***Tenebrio molitor*** **Linnaeus, 1758** |

# EVOLUTION & DIVERSITY

The remains of the ancient beetle-like Protocoleoptera and true beetles are abundant in the fossil record, mostly as impressions in sedimentary rock or entombed in petrified tree sap called *amber*. Fossil Protocoleoptera are known from the Lower Permian rocks of eastern Europe, dating back about 280 million years. The insects were flattened, probably occupied tight spaces under loose bark, resembled the modern insect order of Megaloptera (alderflies, dobsonflies, and fishflies), and likely included precursors to several modern holometabolous insect orders. Protocoleopteran elytra had distinct ribbing and sculpturing resembling that of species in the extant family Cupedidae, but were less regularly sculptured and extended beyond the abdomen. Modern Coleoptera replaced the protocoleopterans by the Late Triassic (240–220 million years ago), when all four of today's beetle suborders were present. Based on fossil evidence from Europe and Central Asia, the evolutionary

lineages of all of the modern Coleoptera were established by the Jurassic (210–145 million years ago).

Amber secreted by conifers during the Jurassic suggests that these ancient trees were already under attack by wood-boring insects similar to modern bark beetles (Curculionidae). At least 60 beetle families have been found preserved in amber, most of which are attributable to tribes and genera that still occur to this day. Amber deposits with fossil intrusions formed in tropical forests and other ancient habitats are poorly represented in the fossil record.

Most fossil beetles from the Quaternary period (1.6–0.5 million years ago) are identical to modern beetles. Their remains are not fossilized, but instead were preserved among permanently frozen detritus, water-lain sediments, prehistoric dung middens, or asphalt seeps.

Mostly small and compact, beetles are well equipped to exploit most terrestrial and freshwater habitats. Beetles owe much of their success to the possession of elytra, allowing the effective concealment of soft membranes that are exposed in other insect groups. Whether beetles live on land or in the water, their elytra protect them from abrasion, desiccation, parasites, and predators. Between the elytra and abdomen is the *subelytral cavity*, an important adaptive feature used by both terrestrial and aquatic beetles. For example, desert species use the subelytral space to insulate the body from sudden changes in temperature and to prevent desiccation, while some aquatic beetles use this space to capture and store oxygen in order to breathe under water. The ability of many beetles to fly also increases their chances to avoid predators, find food, locate mates, and colonize new microhabitats.

ABOVE LEFT **Tough and compact**, many beetles are able to exploit unique microhabitats, including the nests of other animals. Pestiferous Small Hive Beetles (*Aethina tumida*) are scavengers in honeybee colonies, damaging honeycomb as they feed on stores of honey and pollen.

ABOVE RIGHT **Several families** of beetles live in freshwater habitats ranging from small temporary pools and large permanent waterbodies to subterranean aquifers. The Sunburst Diving Beetle (*Thermonectus marmoratus*) thrives in sun-dappled pools.

# COMMUNICATION, REPRODUCTION & DEVELOPMENT

20

Beetles communicate with each other using lights, smells, or sounds. Many fireflies (Lampyridae) are *bioluminescent* and attract mates by producing their own lights, with males and females exchanging species-specific flash patterns. The females of many species emit chemical odors, or *pheromones*, that sexually stimulate conspecific males. Beetles also increase their chances of finding a mate by gathering around odiferous food sources, especially carrion, dung, flowers, or sap flows. Some scarabs (Scarabaeidae), longhorn beetles (Cerambycidae), and bark beetles (Curculionidae), produce sounds by *stridulation*, or rubbing parts of their bodies together. Male deathwatch beetles (Ptinidae) bang their heads against the walls of their wooden galleries to attract the attention of females, while southern African darkling beetles known as tok-tokkies (*Psammodes*) drum their abdomens against rocks and soil to attract mates.

Elaborate courtship behaviors immediately prior to copulation are uncommon among beetles, although the males of some species (e.g., in families Cantharidae, Meloidae, and Cerambycidae) do briefly engage in licking and touching behaviors using their mouthparts, antennae, legs, and genitalia before copulation. In most species, the male simply mounts the female briefly and may remain in contact with her afterward to block the advances of other males and assure his paternity. Females store the male's sperm in a special pouch, or *spermatheca*, until fertilization occurs as the eggs are being laid.

ABOVE **Communication** between male and female beetles of the same species is precise and species-specific to prevent fruitless encounters with the wrong species. The Common Eastern Firefly male (*Photinus pyralis*) signals to females with an illuminated upward swoop.

## DEVELOPMENT AND PARENTAL CARE

Eggs are carefully buried singly or in batches in the soil, or placed in or near the appropriate larval foodstuff. Upon hatching, the larva's mission is simple—to eat and grow. *Larvae* that scavenge carrion and dung or mine plant tissues tend to be grub- or worm-like, while predatory species are generally flattened and leggy. Predatory larvae typically feed on other arthropods, although some prey on small vertebrates. Species with larvae that are *parasitoids* (parasites that eventually kill their host) of other insects (e.g., members of Ripiceridae and Rhipiphoridae) develop by *hypermetamorphosis*, where the first larval *instar* is active and leggy, while the remaining instars are grub-like and relatively inactive.

The mouthparts of larvae are modified for crushing, grinding, or tearing. Most larvae have six legs, although some are legless. The tip of the abdomen may have a pair of fixed or jointed appendages called *urogomphi*. The larva may require several weeks to years before reaching the pupal stage.

The *pupa* is often the life stage best adapted to survive harsh winter conditions in temperate climates. The pupa's abdomen may have functional muscles that allow some movement back and forth. Some species have rows of hardened toothlike structures, or *gin-traps*, on the opposing surfaces of their abdominal segments that are capable of snapping together to protect the soft membranes from attack by small predators and parasites.

At least ten beetle families exhibit various degrees of limited parental care, from tending eggs to provisioning tunnels or nests with food. *Nicrophorus* burying beetles (Silphidae), for example, exhibit advanced parental care. They work in pairs to bury and meticulously prepare a carcass as food for their larvae in an underground chamber and often will remain with their brood until they pupate.

The fairly regular life cycles of beetles generally coincide with changes in temperature and precipitation. Sustained warm weather with the arrival of spring triggers the emergence of temperate species from their pupal chambers, while seasonal rains trigger emergence in consistently hot tropical climates. One or more generations are produced per year, although some species require two or more years to complete their life cycles.

TOP **Male beetles** typically mount females from the back during copulation, as in this pair of Lily Leaf Beetles (*Lilioceris lilii*). Males often have modified structures on their legs and other parts of the body that enable them to grasp females during copulation.

ABOVE **The pupal stage** marks a dramatic transformation from a non-reproductive larva to an adult beetle capable of breeding. In the adult males of *Megasoma mars*, the horns on the head and pronotum, as well as the sexual organs, all develop within the pupa.

RIGHT **When disturbed**, the Spotted Blister Beetle (*Epicauta pardalis*) exudes a potent toxin called cantharidin from its leg joints that causes painful blisters in humans and other animals. In spite of its toxicity, cantharidin was used as an aphrodisiac (see entry for the Spanish Fly, *Lytta vesicatoria*).

# DEFENSE

Large and imposing beetles armed with oversize mandibles or horns, and powerful legs tipped with sharp claws, may intimidate all but the hungriest of predators. Flattened species can slip into tight spaces to avoid attack, while those that are fleet of foot can run away. Some longhorns (Cerambycidae), fungus weevils (Anthribidae), weevils (Curculionidae), and other beetles avoid detection by *crypsis*. They are roughly sculpted or clad in blotchy, somber-colored patchworks of brown, black, and gray scales or markings that render them virtually invisible on a background of fungal-infested or lichen-encrusted bark. Still others can tuck in their legs to resemble small chunks of soil, caterpillar feces, or bird droppings. Even beetles with distinct yet disruptive color patterns or shiny metallic bodies can hide in plain sight by looking less beetle-like against a natural setting.

RIGHT **The Longhorn Beetle** *Macronemus mimus* resembles a dropping as it rests on a leaf, thus possibly avoiding detection by predators. Described in 2013, this species is known only from Brazil and Argentina.

# CHEMICAL AND COLOR DEFENSE

Some beetles defend themselves against predators with chemical arsenals obtained from their diet or synthesized in complex glands, and dispensed through anal turrets, leg joints, or ruptured elytral ridges. In bombardier beetles (Carabidae), hydroquinones, hydrogen peroxide, peroxidases, and catalases are stored separately. When alarmed, these chemicals are injected into a common chamber, resulting in a violent synergistic chemical reaction with an audible "pop" that heralds a boiling, acrid stream from the anus. Soldier beetles (Cantharidae), lady beetles (Coccinellidae), and blister beetles (Meloidae) all store defensive chemicals within their blood and release them through their leg joints when attacked, a process known as *reflex bleeding*. One group of rove beetles (Staphylinidae, subfamily Paederinae) unusually possess symbiotic bacteria in their body that produce a potent defense chemical called paederin. This is more powerful than the venom of black widow spiders (genus *Latrodectus*) and can cause severe dermatitis in humans.

Chemically defended beetles are often distinctively and conspicuously marked with contrasting color patterns, such as red and black or yellow and black, presumably to warn predators of their unpalatability. This phenomenon, known as *aposematism*, is the antithesis to crypsis. In *Müllerian mimicry*, unrelated and unpalatable species that live in the same habitat share similar aposematic patterns and are equally avoided by predators. There are several well-known Müllerian mimicry complexes found in the families Cantharidae, Lampyridae, Lycidae, Meloidae, Tenebrionidae, and Cerambycidae. Harmless species that engage in *Batesian mimicry* resemble other insects that are pugnacious biters and stingers, or are otherwise chemically defended. The shapes and colors of these beetles, often backed up by specific behavioral patterns, are soon associated with the color or behavioral patterns of undesirable modeled prey (e.g., ants, bees, wasps) by experienced predators.

BELOW **The bold and contrasting** color pattern of *Croscherichia sanguinolenta* is an excellent example of aposematic coloration that warns potential predators of a beetle's toxic defenses.

BOTTOM **When disturbed**, darkling beetles such as *Eleodes obscurus* elevate the tip of their abdomen to spray oily and noxious defensive secretions.

23

RIGHT **Green June Beetles** (*Cotinis nitida*) feed on slime flux, which is sap infused with bacteria and other microorganisms that bubbles out through a wound on a tree.

# FEEDING BEHAVIOR

Beetles eat a variety of plant and fungal tissues, living and dead. Some flower-visiting species have tubular mouthparts adapted for sucking up nectar, while those of pollen feeders resemble brushes and are adapted for manipulating fine pollen grains. While hardly in the same class as bees, some beetles do play a significant role in pollination, especially for plants seldom visited by more traditional pollinators. Leaf-mining larvae leave behind them a meandering and ever-widening feeding track filled with feces that traces their growth and development.

## WOOD-FEEDING BEETLES

Wood-borer larvae tunnel into branches, trunks, or roots, and digest cellulose with the aid of symbiotic microorganisms—bacteria and fungi—living in their gut. The egg shells of wood-feeding beetles are inoculated

RIGHT **Although the feeding habits** of larval and adult beetles within the same species often differ, both the larvae and adults of the Multicolored Asian Lady Beetle (*Harmonia axyridis*) prey on aphids. This larva is feeding on the Milkweed Aphid, *Aphis nerii*.

with these gut symbionts as they pass through a residue lining the ovipositor and are consumed by the larva as soon as it hatches.

## DUNG-FEEDING BEETLES

Dung-feeding beetles (Geotrupidae, Scarabaeidae) focus their efforts on feces, especially those voided by large plant-feeding vertebrates, and bury vast amounts of nutrient-rich waste as food for their larvae. For their own nutrition, dung beetles employ their modified mandibles to strain remnants of undigested food, bacteria, yeasts, and molds from dung.

## INSECT-FEEDING BEETLES

Ground and tiger beetles (Carabidae) run down a wide range of insects and invertebrates and tear them into small chunks. Some rove beetles (Staphylinidae) and clown beetles (Histeridae) search through detritus and decaying organic matter for prey, while others are restricted to ant or termite colonies, or live in the fur of small mammals. More specialized predators track their prey using chemical cues. For example, lampyrid larvae track snails down by using their slime trails, while checkered beetles (Cleridae) and bark-gnawing beetles (Trogossitidae) follow plumes of pheromones released by their bark beetle (Curculionidae) prey. Ant-loving scarabs in the genus *Cremastocheilus* also locate the nests of their hosts by tracking ant pheromones. Whirligig beetles (Gyrinidae) identify prey by using waves generated across the surface of the water by struggling insects.

TOP **Canthon imitator**, (Scarabaeidae), shown here on fresh cow dung, rolls balls of dung and buries them as the sole food source for its developing larvae. However, some dung beetles prefer to use carrion, fungi, fruit, millipedes, and the slime tracks of snails.

ABOVE **Adults and larvae** in several beetle families are fungal specialists and consume various fungal structures. *Mycetophagus quadripustulatus* (Mycetophagidae) is commonly found among fungal mycelia under bark, on shelf fungi, in the decaying fruiting bodies of mushrooms and fleshy polypores, as well as in moldy vegetative matter.

## OTHER FEEDING HABITS

Adult and larval carrion and burying beetles (Silphidae), hide beetles (Dermestidae), and others scavenge dead animal tissue, including the remains of other insects, while skin beetles (Trogidae) consume keratin-rich feathers, fur, horns, and hooves. Larvae and adults of the small family Phycosecidae live among sand dunes along coastlines and are scavengers on dead fishes and birds. One of the most highly modified group of beetles (the Leiodidae subfamily Platypsyllinae) contains species that are external parasites of live mammals and leave their hosts only to pupate.

# BEETLE CONSERVATION

The International Union for the Conservation of Nature (IUCN) Red List of Threatened Species™ is a global effort that provides comprehensive data on the conservation status of plants and animals. As of 2014, the IUCN Red List contains 527 species of beetles, primarily from the families Dytiscidae, Carabidae, Lucanidae, Scarabaeidae, and Curculionidae. They are categorized as Least Concern (209), Near Threatened (38), Vulnerable (45), Endangered (44), Critically Endangered (12), and Extinct (16); the remaining species are listed Data Deficient and lack adequate information on their distribution and abundance.

## RARE AND ENDANGERED SPECIES

The Convention on International Trade in Endangered Species of Wild Fauna and Flora (CITES) is an international trade agreement that aims to ensure international trade in species of wild plants and animals does not threaten their survival. The CITES Appendices (I–III) afford different levels of protection from overexploitation; Appendix I lists the most endangered species that are threatened with extinction. For example, all 17 species of the flightless stag beetle *Colophon* (Lucanidae), which are restricted to isolated mountaintops in South Africa, are listed on both the IUCN Red List as endangered and the CITES Appendix I, primarily because of the high prices they command in the marketplace. *Dynastes satanas* (Scarabaeidae), is the only other beetle mentioned by CITES, in Appendix II, which means that it is not necessarily threatened by extinction, but could be if trade is not closely controlled.

Many countries that are signatories of CITES have their own laws that recognize and protect endangered and threatened wildlife, including beetles. For example, the Endangered Species Act 1973 of the United States lists 18 species of beetles, three as threatened and 15 as endangered. Australia's Environment Protection and Biodiversity Conservation Act 1999 lists one beetle, the Wielangta Stag Beetle (*Lissotes latidens*), as endangered. Individual states and provinces of these countries also afford endangered and threatened status to beetles that may or may not be recognized nationally.

Other countries recognize sensitive species of beetles in their Red Data books, which enact ordinances that prohibit the collection, trading, and export of species protected elsewhere by other conventions. Two European organizations actively promote the conservation of beetles on the basis of their ecological roles. The Water Beetle Specialist Group, part of the Species Survival Commission of the IUCN, recognizes the importance of aquatic beetles as bioindicators in wetland management in Europe and Southeast Asia. The Saproxylic Invertebrates Project focuses on selected groups of invertebrates, including beetles, dependent upon standing or fallen trees or wood-inhabiting fungi.

ABOVE **Habitat degradation** and loss are the primary threats to beetles. Inadvertent or purposeful introductions of exotic plants and insect species, electric lights that attract species in unnatural concentrations, and persistent adverse weather also negatively impact beetle populations. These threats are further exacerbated by a steady decline in the number of trained coleopterists who can provide the expertise required for the conservation of beetles and their habitats.

RIGHT **Around the world**, artisans craft pieces of jewelry that incorporate parts of beetle bodies. The elytra of the Giant Metallic Ceiba Borer (*Euchroma gigantea*) are used to make necklaces and other adornments in tropical America.

# BEETLES & SOCIETY

Beetles have long occupied prominent places in our mythologies and in arts and crafts. The Sacred Scarab (*Scarabaeus sacer*) is the best-known beetle of mythology. Images of scarabs commonly appeared in funerary art and hieroglyphs. Scarabs carved in stone bore religious inscriptions from the *Book of the Dead* and were placed in tombs to ensure the immortality of the soul.

## BEETLES IN ART AND DECORATION

Artists have depicted beetles in all manner of media. Fireflies have long appeared in Chinese and Japanese art. One of the most notable examples of beetles in art is the watercolor of the European Stag Beetle (*Lucanus cervus*) by the German Renaissance artist Albrecht Dürer in 1505. In the 1920s, the French artist Eugène Séguy created a famous series of art deco insect portfolios that included many striking beetles.

Craftsmen use the durable body parts of beetles to make jewelry or adorn ornate pieces of furniture and wall coverings. South American indigenous artisans use the elytra of the giant *Euchroma gigantea* (Buprestidae) for necklaces and other decorative pieces. Today in parts of Mexico and Central America, a zopherid beetle popularly known as the Maquech, or Ma'kech (*Zopherus chilensis*), is decorated with brightly colored glass beads, fixed to a short chain tether, and pinned to clothing as a reminder of an ancient Yucatán legend.

ABOVE **Ancient Egyptians** used the Sacred Scarab (*Scarabaeus sacer*) to symbolize their sun god, Ra. This carving is on a temple at Luxor.

## BEETLES AS DELICACIES

Beetles and their grubs are an important part of human diets around the world. In Southeast Asia, grubs of the Red Palm Weevil (*Rhynchophorus ferrugineus*) and Asiatic Rhinoceros Beetle (*Oryctes rhinoceros*) are roasted and eaten as delicacies. The Chinese collect giant water scavengers (Hydrophilidae) and remove the head and appendages before frying them in oil or soaking them in brine. The Aborigines of Australia collect large, nut-flavored longhorn (Cerambycidae) larvae (witchetty grubs) from rotten logs and roast them. In the United States, a line of insect-stuffed lollipops includes the larvae of the Yellow Mealworm, *Tenebrio molitor*.

## BEETLES IN SCIENCE AND TECHNOLOGY

Rather than developing complicated and expensive engineering techniques to develop new products and materials, scientists are mimicking the features of beetles already tested by millions of years of trial and error via evolution. A case in point is the Dew Bank Bottle, a stainless-steel dome microsculpted like the back of the darkling beetle *Onymacris unguicularis* (Tenebrionidae) of the Namib Desert to extract moisture from the air. A similar technology is being developed to collect water for desert-irrigation systems, clear fog from airport runways, and develop fog-free windows and mirrors. Engineers studying the incredibly dense pads of hairlike setae on the feet of some beetles have inspired the development of a reusable and adhesive-free tape that is twice as sticky as other flat tapes.

The shiny and metallic or iridescent colors of beetles, especially of jewel beetles (Buprestidae), scarabs (Scarabaeidae), and weevils (Curculionidae), are of particular interest to physicists. Stacks of reflective layers or honeycomb-like photonic crystals within beetle scales and cuticle simultaneously reflect different wavelengths of light to produce a shimmering effect. The reflective properties of these structures have not only been used to develop iridescent paints, pigments, and cosmetics, but may also prove useful for enhancing monetary security and engineering optical chips for use in ultrafast computers.

29

BELOW **The larvae** of several beetle species, such as those in the genus *Rhychophorus* shown below, are sought after and eaten as delicacies throughout the world. Beetles represent a base for the development of new food products of considerable nutritive value for the future.

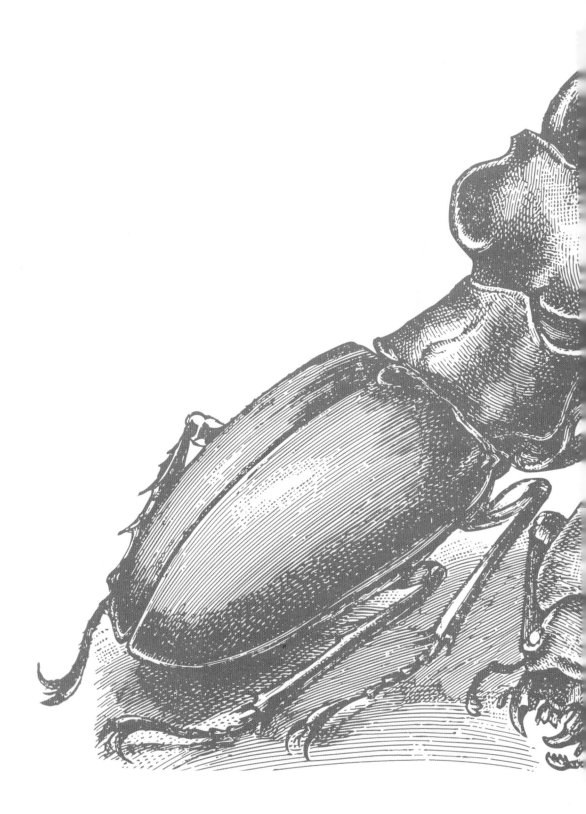

# THE BEETLES

# ARCHOSTEMATA

The suborder Archostemata includes beetles of medium size, ranging from ³⁄₁₆ to 1 in (5–25 mm), with the exception of two species in the genera *Micromalthus* and *Crowsoniella*, which are only approximately ¹⁄₁₆ in (1.5 mm) in length. Most Archostemata differ from all other beetles in having a well-developed, visible hind trochantin (near the hind coxa), although exceptions occur. These beetles typically have scales covering their body and, except in the two small species, the elytra are generally incompletely sclerotized.

Approximately 40 extant species of Archostemata have been described to date from North and South America, Europe, Asia, Australia, and Africa. They are included in the families Crowsoniellidae (one species), Cupedidae (about 30 species), Micromalthidae (one species), Ommatidae (six species), and Jurodidae (one species). Despite intensive searches, some of these species remain exceedingly rarely encountered in nature (for example, *Crowsoniella relicta* is known only from three individuals and *Sikhotealinia zhiltzovae* from a single individual); we hope this book will stimulate the discovery of additional specimens.

The development of Archostemata beetles is poorly understood; larvae of most species are unknown. All known larvae, which are usually elongate and parallel-sided, are associated with fungus-infested wood.

| FAMILY | Crowsoniellidae |
|---|---|
| SUBFAMILY | |
| DISTRIBUTION | Palearctic: Italy |
| MACROHABITAT | Uncertain, probably associated with sweet chestnut (*Castanea sativa*) trees |
| MICROHABITAT | Probably ground- or soil-dwelling |
| FEEDING HABITS | Unknown |
| NOTE | This minute beetle is the only species in the family Crowsoniellidae |

ADULT LENGTH
¹⁄₃₂–²⁄₃₂ in
(1.4–1.6 mm)

34

*CROWSONIELLA RELICTA*
# CROWSONIELLA RELICTA
PACE, 1975

Actual size

Based on the fossil record, the archaic suborder Archostemata was apparently more successful than other groups of beetles in the first half of the Mesozoic, although its diversity subsequently dropped dramatically as it became extinct in Europe (with the exception of *Crowsoniella relicta*). This species is known from only three male specimens collected by washing calcareous soil around the base of an old chestnut tree in the Lepini Mountains of Lazio in central Italy. Although several coleopterists have tried repeatedly, it has been impossible to locate additional individuals at or near the original locality. The modified and reduced mouthparts of *C. relicta* suggest that adults can feed only on liquids or do not feed at all.

## RELATED SPECIES

Although some taxonomists have suggested that the species belongs to the suborder Polyphaga, most recent studies indicate that it is probably closely related to members of Archostemata, which also include the extant families Cupedidae (31 species), Micromalthidae (one species), Ommatidae (six species), and Jurodidae (one species). The smooth elytra of *Crowsoniella relicta* differ from the elytra of typical archostematan beetles, which have window punctures.

**Crowsoniella relicta** is a small, elongate, shiny, smooth, reddish-brown to dark brown wingless beetle. The antenna is seven-segmented with the last segment clavate. The eyes are composed of a small number of ommatidia and the mandibles are atrophied. The prothorax has distinct antennal cavities on each anterior dorsolateral corner, and the meso- and metathorax and first abdominal segment are fused. The larvae are unknown.

| FAMILY | Cupedidae |
|---|---|
| SUBFAMILY | Priacminae |
| DISTRIBUTION | Nearctic: western North America |
| MACROHABITAT | Mixed montane forests |
| MICROHABITAT | Adults found on dead branches or in decaying wood |
| FEEDING HABITS | Larvae probably develop in decaying wood |
| NOTE | Adults are attracted to laundry bleach and lights |

ADULT LENGTH
³⁄₈–⁷⁄₈ in
(10–22 mm)

*PRIACMA SERRATA*

# PRIACMA SERRATA
(LECONTE, 1861)

35

*Priacma serrata* is an uncommonly encountered species that can be locally abundant in late spring and summer. Adults are sometimes found on dead White Fir branches, in old logs and stumps, or flying during the afternoon near fungal-infested logs that are likely home to the developing larvae. Males are strongly attracted to laundry soap containing bleach, and are sometimes attracted in large numbers to laundry hung out of doors, which apparently mimics the pheromone of the female. In captivity, females lay more than 1,000 eggs each.

RELATED SPECIES

*Priacma serrata* is the only species in the genus, and is restricted to western North America. *Priacma* is distinguished from the three other extant genera of cupedid beetles (*Cupes*, *Prolixocupes*, and *Tenomerga*) in the region by having antennae that are barely half as long as the body and the lack of tarsal grooves underneath the prothorax.

**Priacma serrata** is elongate, somewhat convex, parallel-sided, clothed in scales, and reddish brown with variegated gray and black scales. The head has small, bulging eyes, four distinct tubercles on top, and antennae that are scarcely half the length of the entire body. The prothorax has sharp angles in front that project forward; underneath lacks grooves for receiving the tarsi.

Actual size

| FAMILY | Cupedidae |
|---|---|
| SUBFAMILY | Cupedinae |
| DISTRIBUTION | Nearctic: eastern North America |
| MACROHABITAT | Eastern deciduous forest |
| MICROHABITAT | Adults found on bare oak trunks, under bark, and attracted to lights |
| FEEDING HABITS | Unknown |
| NOTE | Nothing is known about the habits of the larvae |

**ADULT LENGTH**
¼–⁷⁄₁₆ in
(7–11 mm)

*CUPES CAPITATUS*
# CUPES CAPITATUS
FABRICIUS, 1801

Adults of *Cupes capitatus* are active in late spring and summer, and are found under bark, on bare trunks of standing dead oaks (*Quercus*), or are attracted to light in wooded habitats. Nothing has been published on larval stages, but they probably bore and develop in firm, fungal-infested wood. The family Cupedidae consists of 31 species in nine genera that are relictual members of a once more diverse lineage of beetles with a fossil record dating back to the Triassic period. The extant species are found in nearly every biogeographical region, but are extinct in Europe.

### RELATED SPECIES

*Cupes capitatus* is the only species in the genus and is restricted to eastern North America. *Cupes* is distinguished from the three other extant genera of cupedids (*Priacma*, *Prolixocupes*, and *Tenomerga*) in the region by having antennae that are longer than half the length of the body and tarsal grooves underneath the prothorax that are separated in front by a pair of low ridges.

Actual size

**Cupes capitatus** is elongate, flat, parallel-sided, clothed in scales, and is grayish black with a reddish or golden head. The head has bulging eyes, four distinct tubercles on top, and long, slender antennae that extend beyond half the body length. The prothorax has distinct grooves underneath to receive the tarsi.

| FAMILY | Cupedidae |
|---|---|
| SUBFAMILY | Cupedinae |
| DISTRIBUTION | Australian: southeastern Australia to Queensland and Tasmania |
| MACROHABITAT | Wooded habitats and, occasionally, structures |
| MICROHABITAT | Adults are found at light, while the larvae live in fungal-infested wood |
| FEEDING HABITS | Larvae feed and develop in fungus-infested wood |
| NOTE | This is one of the few cupedid species with a larva known to science |

ADULT LENGTH
$\frac{3}{8} - \frac{9}{16}$ in
(10–15 mm)

# DISTOCUPES VARIANS

(LEA, 1902)

37

*Distocupes varians* is one of only five of the 31 species of cupedids from around the world for which the larvae are known. The larvae are long, slender, and soft bodied, and are reported to feed and pupate in structural timbers infested with fungi. The adults have been found at lights. Of the four original specimens that Arthur Lea used to describe this species, only one was actually *D. varians*; the remaining three turned out to be two undescribed species, now both in the genus *Adinolepis*.

## RELATED SPECIES

The Australian cupedid fauna consists of six species in two genera, *Adinolepis* and *Distocupes*. *Distocupes* is most easily distinguished from *Adinolepis* by the presence of two pairs of long conical, and forward-projecting tubercles located at the base of the antennae and above the eyes. *Distocupes* contains a single species, *D. varians*.

Actual size

**Distocupes varians** has a head wider than long with two pairs of conical tubercles above the eyes. The pronotum is wider than long, each front angle with two teeth; the underside has moderately deep grooves for receiving the front tarsi. The elytra have large, deep, somewhat squarish windowlike punctures that are lined across the bottom with a thin translucent cuticle.

| FAMILY | Cupedidae |
|---|---|
| SUBFAMILY | Cupedinae |
| DISTRIBUTION | Afrotropical: northern Madagascar |
| MACROHABITAT | Dry forests, savanna |
| MICROHABITAT | Adults and larvae found in rotten logs |
| FEEDING HABITS | Adults and larvae probably eat fungal infested wood |
| NOTE | Very little is known about the natural history of this species |

**ADULT LENGTH**
<sup></sup>11/16–7/8 in
(18–23 mm)

*RHIPSIDEIGMA RAFFRAYI*
# RHIPSIDEIGMA RAFFRAYI
(FAIRMAIRE, 1884)

38

Very little is known about the habits or biology of species of the Cupedidae. Adult and larval *Rhipsideigma raffrayi* are found together in dark, decaying logs. The pale and blind larva is one of only five species known in the entire family. The cylindrical larva has strong mandibles, a wedge-shaped head, and short, weakly developed legs that are adapted for boring through soft, decaying wood. Their exact diet remains unknown, but they probably feed on decaying wood infested with fungi and other microorganisms, as do other cupedid larvae.

RELATED SPECIES

Six species of Cupedidae occur in the Afrotropical realm in the genera *Tenomerga* and *Rhipsideigma*. The elytra of Rhipsideigma are densely covered with scales and have tips extended into a point. Of the five species of *Rhipsideigma*, one is known only from Tanzania, while the other four are restricted to Madagascar. *Rhipsideigma raffrayi* is distinguished by the extensive pattern of creamy-white scales on the sides of the pronotum and elytra.

**Rhipsideigma raffrayi** is elongate, parallel-sided, and flattened. The head has four tubercles, the pair in the rear covered with brown scales. The prothorax has broadly pale sides above and grooves to receive the front tarsi, separated in front by a single ridge underneath. The elytra have dense scales that obscure the surface and create a pattern of light and dark patches.

Actual size

| FAMILY | Micromalthidae |
|---|---|
| SUBFAMILY | Micromalthinae |
| DISTRIBUTION | Nearctic: eastern United States; possibly Belize, introduced elsewhere |
| MACROHABITAT | Eastern hardwood forests |
| MICROHABITAT | Adults and larvae found in moist, decaying logs and stumps |
| FEEDING HABITS | Larvae feed on moist, but not wet, rotten wood |
| NOTE | Adults and larvae capable of reproduction |

ADULT LENGTH
$\frac{1}{32}$–$\frac{1}{8}$ in
(1–3 mm)

*MICROMALTHUS DEBILIS*
# TELEPHONE-POLE BEETLE
LECONTE, 1878

39

Actual size

Telephone-pole Beetles emerge briefly to mate and locate new breeding sites. The larvae develop in logs and stumps in the advanced stages of red-rotten decay. They will attack rotting telephone poles and structural timbers, but are not pests. The highly mobile caraboid larvae may either develop into cerambycoid larva that give birth to more caraboid larvae or develop into adult females, or lay eggs that hatch into curculionoid larvae that develop into adult males. The ability to reproduce asexually as larvae and sexually as adults enables them to multiply quickly and exploit patchy and ephemeral resources.

### RELATED SPECIES
*Micromalthus debilis* is the sole species in the family Micromalthidae and is distinguished from other Archostemata families (Crowsonellidae, Cupedidae, Ommatidae, and Jurodidae) by its bead-like antennomeres, short elytra, and smooth, shiny surface that lacks scales. A second undescribed species, known only from a larva, may occur in China.

**The Telephone-pole Beetle** is small, flat, and shiny brown to black with yellowish antennae and legs. The head is wider than the pronotum and bears antennae, each with 11 short, bead-like antennomeres. The prothorax is widest in front and lacks keeled margins or grooves underneath. The elytra are short, exposing part of five abdominal segments.

| FAMILY | Ommatidae |
|---|---|
| SUBFAMILY | Ommatinae |
| DISTRIBUTION | Australian: central Queensland to Victoria and South Australia |
| MACROHABITAT | Dry eucalyptus woodlands |
| MICROHABITAT | Under bark of dead eucalyptus trees |
| FEEDING HABITS | Unknown |
| NOTE | The genus *Omma* contains mostly fossil species |

**ADULT LENGTH**
½–1 in
(13–25 mm)

*OMMA STANLEYI*
# OMMA STANLEYI
NEWMAN, 1839

Actual size

*Omma stanleyi* is the largest and possibly the most "primitive" species in the genus. The larvae remain unknown, but adults have been collected beneath loose bark on recently dead eucalypt logs. There are three additional species of *Omma* living in Australia, all of which are rarely encountered. At least ten additional fossil species of *Omma* have been described from the lower Jurassic of England, Upper Jurassic of Central Asia and Upper Jurassic and Cretaceous of Siberia and Mongolia. The study of ommids and other Archostemata beetles is helping scientists to understand beetle evolution and their relationships with other insect groups.

### RELATED SPECIES

The Ommatidae consists of six living species in two genera. *Tetraphalerus* occurs in southern South America, while *Omma* is restricted to Australia. *Omma stanleyi* is distinguished by its abruptly narrowed head behind the eyes and the sparse covering of slender, yellowish-brown setae. *Omma mastersi* and *O. sagitta* may be part of a mimicry ring that includes a mutillid wasp and a checkered beetle.

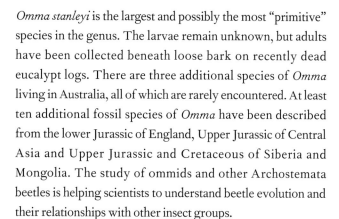

**Omma stanleyi** is elongate, moderately flattened, dull brownish black, and clothed with thick, recumbent, and yellowish-brown setae. The head has small teeth in front, lacks microtubercles on top, and is abruptly narrowed behind the eyes to form a neck. The pronotum and elytra are roughly sculptured with small tubercles. The thorax lacks grooves underneath to receive legs. The flight wings are well developed in both sexes.

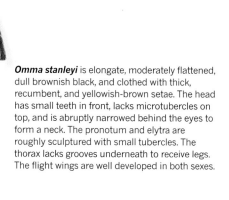

| FAMILY | Jurodidae |
|---|---|
| SUBFAMILY | |
| DISTRIBUTION | Palearctic: Russian Far East, Primorskiy Kray District |
| MACROHABITAT | Unknown |
| MICROHABITAT | Unknown |
| FEEDING HABITS | Unknown |
| NOTE | The only living member of the family is known from one specimen |

ADULT LENGTH
¼ in
(6 mm)

*SIKHOTEALINIA ZHILTZOVAE*
# SIKHOTEALINIA ZHILTZOVAE
LAFER, 1996

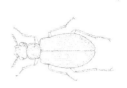

41

*Sikhotealinia zhiltzovae* is known from a single specimen found dead in a forest-cabin window and nothing is known about its natural history. It was originally placed in the family Sikhotealiniidae until it was recognized to resemble the Russian fossil species *Jurodes ignoramus* from the lower middle Jurassic. *Sikhotealinia zhiltzovae* does not have any close living relatives and appears to have affinities with both evolutionarily "primitive" and "advanced" beetles. In spite of the apparent lack of distinct shared advanced characters, this species is tentatively placed among extant beetle families in the suborder Archostemata.

Actual size

RELATED SPECIES
Although the Jurodidae is placed in the suborder Archostemata on the basis of similarities in structures of the thorax, there are several other characters that do not support this relationship. The flight-wing venation and folding pattern, and the mouthparts, especially the large and distinctly shaped clypeus and labrum, do not support a relationship with other archostematans.

**Sikhotealinia zhiltzovae** is slightly flattened and is sparsely clothed with fine, moderately long pubescence. The head is nearly round with slightly protruding eyes that lack any setae; the top of the head, or frons, has one simple eye, or ocellus, in the middle. The elytra each have rows of small and closely set punctures. The abdomen has six ventrites. The flight wings are fully developed.

# MYXOPHAGA

The suborder Myxophaga includes beetles of small to minute size, generally ranging from ⅓₂ to ⅛ in (1.0–2.5 mm). The characteristic adults possess a number of unique morphological characters, such as a maxilla (ventral mouthparts) without a galea, a mobile tooth present on the left mandible, a small number of antennal segments (usually fewer than nine antennomeres), the meso- and metaventrites broadly connected, and hind wings that are rolled apically in resting position.

This suborder currently includes slightly more than 100 described species represented on all continents except Antarctica. The species are grouped into the four families: Lepiceridae (three species), Torridincolidae (about 65 species), Sphaeriusidae (about 20 species), and Hydroscaphidae (about 20 species). Six additional families of Myxophaga (e.g., Tricoleidae and Rhombocoleidae) are known only from the fossil record.

Adults and larvae seem to feed primarily on algae or blue-green algae. Most species are aquatic and live in rivers, hot springs, waterfalls, streams, and seepages, or are found in moist habitats at the edge of water bodies.

| FAMILY | Lepiceridae |
|---|---|
| SUBFAMILY | Lepicerinae |
| DISTRIBUTION | Neotropical: western Mexico to Central America and Venezuela |
| MACROHABITAT | Riparian habitats along rivers |
| MICROHABITAT | Adults live in moist, but not wet, sand |
| FEEDING HABITS | Unknown |
| NOTE | The larvae are unknown although a larva possibly attributable to *Lepicerus inaequalis* was described in 2013 |

ADULT LENGTH
¹⁄₃₂–¹⁄₁₆ in
(1–2 mm)

44

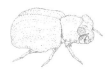

*LEPICERUS INAEQUALIS*
# LEPICERUS INAEQUALIS
MOTSCHULSKY, 1855

Actual size

**Lepicerus inaequalis** is short, broad, and somewhat parallel-sided and convex dorsally. The exoskeleton is hard, distinctly sculpted with ridges, and usually covered with a layer of sand. The large head has bulging eyes and very short antennae with four antennomeres. The pronotum is twice as wide as long and narrower than the elytra. The elytra each have three weak ridges. The tarsomeres are all fused together.

Because of their small size, adults of *Lepicerus inaequalis* are seldom encountered and their larvae are unknown. Adults are found on or in dry sand deposits near streams and rivers in cavities of small rocks, chambers under rocks, buried in moist substrate, or in the galleries of shore-inhabiting rove beetles. They are also attracted to lights. In captivity, they use their broad head and body like bulldozers to move individual sand particles. The other two species, *L. bufo* from Mexico and *L. pichinlingue* from Ecuador, are both found in relatively drier and sandier habitats.

## RELATED SPECIES

There are three species of *Lepicerus* distributed from Mexico to Venezuela and Ecuador. The ridges are strongly raised along the length of the elytra in *L. bufo*, but only slightly so in *L. inaequalis* and *L. pichinlingue*. These last two species are very similar to one another and are best distinguished by their distributions and the male genitalia.

| FAMILY | Torridincolidae |
|---|---|
| SUBFAMILY | Deleveinae |
| DISTRIBUTION | Palearctic: China, Yunnan Province |
| MACROHABITAT | Spray zones and seepage areas near waterfalls in forests |
| MICROHABITAT | On rocks covered with algae and a thin (up to $\frac{1}{16}$ in / 2 mm) film of water |
| FEEDING HABITS | Unknown |
| NOTE | Very little is known about this species |

ADULT LENGTH
$\frac{1}{16}$–$\frac{1}{8}$ in
(2–3 mm)

*SATONIUS STYSI*

# SATONIUS STYSI

HÁJEK & FIKÁČEK, 2008

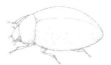

*Satonius stysi* is a small and easily overlooked beetle that lives on wet, algae-covered rocks in the spray zones of waterfalls and seeps. These moist environments, known as hygropetric habitats, are continually covered with a thin film of water that is about $\frac{1}{16}$ in (2 mm) thick. Little else is known about the natural history of this species, which is known only from two different localities in Yunnan Province, China. It was named in honor of Professor Pavel Štys of Charles University, Prague, Czechoslovakia, a specialist of true bugs.

**Actual size**

### RELATED SPECIES

There are six species of *Satonius*. Five are found in China and one is restricted to Japan. *Satonius stysi* is distinguished from the others by its relatively large size, more elongate body outline, narrowly bordered pronotum, and the deflexed lateral edges of the elytra that are visible from directly above only briefly along their bases. The flight wings are fully developed.

**Satonius stysi** is egg-shaped in outline, black, and somewhat lighter brown underneath. The head has large, coarsely faceted eyes. The prothorax is broadest at the base. The elytra are broadest near the base, with surfaces that lack any grooves or rows of punctures. The legs are short and flattened. The abdomen has five ventrites, with the first ventrite depressed along the sides to receive the hind femora.

| FAMILY | Hydroscaphidae |
|---|---|
| SUBFAMILY | |
| DISTRIBUTION | Palearctic: southern Europe and Asia, from France to Iran |
| MACROHABITAT | Seeps, springs, streams, and rivers |
| MICROHABITAT | On rocks covered with algae, sandy or gravelly banks, and wet mud |
| FEEDING HABITS | Adults and larvae feed on algae |
| NOTE | *Hydroscapha* species resemble small rove beetles (Staphylinidae) |

**ADULT LENGTH**
¹⁄₃₂–¹⁄₁₆ in
(1–2 mm)

46

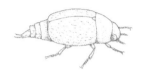

*HYDROSCAPHA GRANULUM*
# HYDROSCAPHA GRANULUM
(MOTSCHULSKY, 1855)

Actual size

*Hydroscapha granulum* lives in moist sand, gravel, mud or on wet algae-covered rocks along the edges of small to large moving bodies of water. Females produce and deposit only one smooth, dark, oval egg at a time that is very large in relation to her abdomen. The elongate larvae are dark gray and strictly aquatic. Both adults and larvae are found in large numbers together in suitable shallows along streams where they feed on algae. Adults breathe under water by capturing an air bubble under their elytra.

## RELATED SPECIES

There are 15 species of *Hydroscapha* found in western North America, Mexico, South America, Eurasia, North Africa, Southeast Asia, and Madagascar. They resemble small rove beetles with their short elytra and exposed abdomens. However, they are distinguished by possessing a distinct notopleural suture and their aquatic way of life. *Hydroscapha granulum* is best distinguished from the other two Western Palearctic *Hydroscapha* species by the male genitalia.

**Hydroscapha granulum** is elongate, broadest anteriorly, uniformly dark brown, with short elytra and an exposed abdomen. The head is narrower than the pronotum. The pronotum is widest at the posterior angles. The elytra are short, each cut off or truncated at the tips, exposing four abdominal segments. The abdomen narrows posteriorly. The hind femora are partially covered by hind coxal plates and the tarsal formula is 3–3–3.

| | |
|---|---|
| FAMILY | Sphaeriusidae |
| SUBFAMILY | |
| DISTRIBUTION | Palearctic: Europe |
| MACROHABITAT | Near water bodies such as streams, rivers, and ponds |
| MICROHABITAT | Ground-dwelling |
| FEEDING HABITS | Probably feeds on algae |
| NOTE | One of the smallest beetles |

ADULT LENGTH
¹⁄₃₂ in
(0.6–0.7 mm)

*SPHAERIUS ACAROIDES*

# SPHAERIUS ACAROIDES

WALTL, 1838

47

•
Actual size

Probably as a result of their minute size, very little is known about the feeding habits of members of the genus *Sphaerius*, although it has been suggested that at least some species feed on algae. *Sphaerius acaroides* is endemic to Europe and found in sun-exposed, moist, sandy or gravelly substrates at river edges, where it burrows. Adult individuals are quick to emerge from their holes when the substrate becomes wet. The aquatic *Sphaerius* larvae possess air-filled, balloon-shaped sacs associated with the spiracles (breathing pores) on their abdomen. This species is frequently collected in association with individuals of the beetle families Hydraenidae, Hydrophilidae, and Limnichidae.

**Sphaerius acaroides** is a very small, hemispherical, smooth, shiny black beetle. The antennae are relatively long, with 11 segments and a three-segmented club. The elytra are markedly convex and cover the abdomen completely. The abdomen has only three visible abdominal segments. The tarsi have three segments. The hind wings are fully developed and fringed with proportionally long setae.

RELATED SPECIES

The genus *Sphaerius*, containing about 20 species, is represented on all continents except Antarctica. It is the only member of the family Sphaeriusidae, which is part of the suborder Myxophaga. There are two other species of *Sphaerius* in Europe: *S. hispanicus*, which can be found in France and Spain; and *S. spississimus*, from France and Italy. The form of the pronotal and elytral microsculpture is the main point of difference between all three of the European species.

# ADEPHAGA

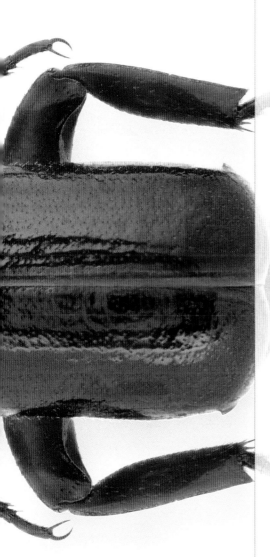

The suborder Adephaga is a diverse group of highly specialized beetles. The adults are primarily characterized by the two-segmented palp-like galea of the maxilla, the antennae that usually have 11 antennomeres, the enlarged hind coxae that completely divide the first abdominal ventrite, the first three abdominal ventrites that are connate, and the presence of abdominal defensive glands. Their size ranges broadly from about from $\frac{1}{32}$ to $3\frac{5}{16}$ in (1 to 85 mm).

The suborder includes approximately 40,000 extant species currently placed in the families Gyrinidae (about 875 species), Haliplidae (about 220 species), Noteridae (about 250 species), Amphizoidae (five species), Hygrobiidae (six species), Dytiscidae (about 3,750 species), Aspidytidae (two species), Meruidae (one species), Trachypachidae (six species), and Carabidae (about 40,000 species). Conventionally these families are grouped into two major groups, the Hydradephaga for the aquatic groups (the first eight families listed above) and the Geadephaga for the terrestrial groups (the last two families listed above).

Members of Adephaga are found in almost all imaginable terrestrial and aquatic habitats, except salt water. Adults and larvae of most species are predacious.

| FAMILY | Gyrinidae |
|---|---|
| SUBFAMILY | Gyrininae |
| DISTRIBUTION | Nearctic, Neotropical: Southern Arizona to Nicaragua |
| MACROHABITAT | Ponds and streams |
| MICROHABITAT | Adults swim on surfaces of quiet pools with graveled bottoms |
| FEEDING HABITS | Adults scavenge floating dead or dying insects |
| NOTE | Gyrinids are supremely adapted for living on the water's surface |

ADULT LENGTH
⁹⁄₁₆ in
(14–15 mm)

50

# DINEUTUS SUBLINEATUS

(CHEVROLAT, 1833)

Actual size

Lone or small groups of adult *Dineutus sublineatus* gyrate over the water's surface with amazing speed and dive for brief periods when threatened. Members of the family are hence commonly called "whirligig beetles." Their heads are equipped with two separate pairs of compound eyes. Each pair is dedicated to seeing above or below the water's surface. Recent neurobiological research reveals that the visual information received through the upper pair helps them to maintain their orientation to their surroundings and other whirligig beetles. *Dineutus* species produce a distasteful, anal milky secretion that repels predators and possibly helps to propel them across the water.

## RELATED SPECIES

The genus *Dineutus* includes 84 species that are distributed through most regions of the world, with about 15 species occurring in the Americas. They are distinguished from other gyrinids in the region by their large size, lack of markings, and presence of a depressed area underneath for receiving the front legs. *Dineutus sublineatus* is distinguished by its color, large size, and its distribution.

**Dineutus sublineatus** is streamlined, broadly oval, somewhat convex, and very dark olive above and black underneath. The antennae have six antennomeres and the scutellum is hidden from view. The sides of the pronotum and elytra lack any pubescence. The elytra have sinuate side margins and rounded tips in both sexes. The front legs are raptorial and adapted for grabbing prey, while the middle and hind legs are short and paddle-like.

| FAMILY | Trachypachidae |
|---|---|
| SUBFAMILY | Trachypachinae |
| DISTRIBUTION | Nearctic: western North America to Saskatchewan, south to southern Colorado and Utah, and coastal ranges of California |
| MACROHABITAT | Lowland and montane deciduous and coniferous forests |
| MICROHABITAT | Ground-dwelling adults live under leaf and needle litter, and in gardens |
| FEEDING HABITS | Adults prey on insects |
| NOTE | Trachypachid beetles resemble ground beetles (Carabidae) |

ADULT LENGTH
⅛ – ¼ in
(3–6 mm)

*TRACHYPACHUS INERMIS*
# UNARMED TEMPORAL FALSE GROUND BEETLE
MOTSCHULSKY, 1850

51

Adult *Trachypachus inermis* (formerly known as *T. holmbergi*) are active on sunny days from spring through fall. They prefer dry, open or slightly shaded habitats that are sparsely covered with mosses and vascular vegetation, especially among leaf or coniferous litter, but also occur in urban flower gardens. When threatened, they will dive down into litter to escape. *Trachypachus* species resemble carabid beetles, but are distinguished by the smooth antennomeres lacking setae and by the large hind coxae that extend to the side of the body.

RELATED SPECIES

The Trachypachidae consists of two genera: the South American *Systolosoma* (two species), and Nearctic and Palearctic *Trachypachus* (four species). One species of *Trachypachus* is restricted to the Palearctic, while the other three are found in western North America. The Unarmed Temporal False Ground Beetle is distinguished from these species by the narrowed outline of its pronotum, fine elytral punctation, and broad distribution.

Actual size

**The Unarmed Temporal False Ground Beetle** is uniformly dark with a bronze luster. The pronotum is distinctly narrower at the base than middle with a deep, transverse depression across the base. The elytra each have 3–9 rows of fine punctures that become very faint at the tips; the flight wings underneath are fully developed.

| FAMILY | Carabidae |
|---|---|
| SUBFAMILY | Nebriinae |
| DISTRIBUTION | Nearctic: eastern North America |
| MACROHABITAT | Lowlands and mountains |
| MICROHABITAT | Adults live along graveled brook, stream, and river banks with shade |
| FEEDING HABITS | Adults prey on insects |
| NOTE | Adults with fully developed or reduced wings |

**ADULT LENGTH**
⅜–½ in
(10–12 mm)

52

*NEBRIA PALLIPES*
# PALE-LEGGED GAZELLE BEETLE
SAY, 1823

Adult Pale-legged Gazelle Beetles are dark, shiny nocturnal insects that inhabit wet, stony gravel bars, especially those under trees or shrubs. During the day they are commonly found under rocks, leaves, and other debris along swift, clear streams and other flowing waters, as well as those of lakeshores and cave streams. They are most active in spring and summer. Those with fully developed wings are not known to be capable of flight, while those with reduced wings are definitely flightless. Both the adults and larvae probably overwinter.

### RELATED SPECIES

*Nebria* consists of about 380 species distributed throughout the Northern Hemisphere. Of these 52 occur in the Nearctic, including *N. pallipes*. *Nebria pallipes* is distinguished from many species of *Nebria* in the region by the pale appendages, red spots on head, broad pronotal side margins and single seta on hind coxa, and abdominal segments 3–5.

**Pale-legged Gazelle Beetles** are shiny black with pale reddish-brown antennae and legs. The head has two reddish spots between the eyes, and antennomeres 1–4 of the long antennae lack any setae. The oval elytra are wider than the somewhat heart-shaped pronotum. Each elytron has a row of five punctures. The middle coxae each have two setae. The last two abdominal segments each have a pair of setae.

Actual size

| | |
|---|---|
| FAMILY | Carabidae |
| SUBFAMILY | Carabinae |
| DISTRIBUTION | Nearctic: eastern North America and Arizona |
| MACROHABITAT | Deciduous and mixed forests |
| MICROHABITAT | Ground-dwelling |
| FEEDING HABITS | Predator |
| NOTE | A relatively common species |

ADULT LENGTH
³⁄₁₆–¼ in
(5–6 mm)

*NOTIOPHILUS AENEUS*

# BRASSY BIG-EYED BEETLE

(HERBST, 1806)

53

This small beetle apparently reproduces in the spring and early summer, and spends the winter in the adult stage. The adults live in moss and leaf litter in damp places in deciduous and mixed forests; they are also occasionally found in forest clearings and roadsides. They are challenging to catch by hand because of their small size and swiftness. Like other members of the genus *Notiophilus*, larvae and adults of *N. aeneus* probably prey on small arthropods including collembolans. Adults are macropterous and are sometimes attracted to artificial lights at night.

### RELATED SPECIES

The genus *Notiophilus* contains about 55 species in the world of which 15 are found in North America, north of Mexico. *Notiophilus aeneus* occurs in eastern North America and is easily distinguished from the other species of the genus in the area by the entirely pale reddish coloration of the antennae and legs.

**The Brassy Big-eyed Beetle** is a relatively small shiny carabid; the upper surface is black with brassy luster. The head is much broader than the pronotum, the frons has multiple carinae, and the eyes are voluminous. The males are distinguished from the females by having the first three tarsomeres of the front legs and the first tarsomere of the middle legs slightly expanded and with spongy pubescence ventrally.

Actual size

| FAMILY | Carabidae |
|---|---|
| SUBFAMILY | Cicindinae |
| DISTRIBUTION | Neotropical: north-central Argentina |
| MACROHABITAT | Lowland salt flats |
| MICROHABITAT | On dried, cracked, salt-laden clay surrounding brackish pools |
| FEEDING HABITS | Adults prey on fairy shrimps |
| NOTE | Adults swim on the surface of pools with 17 percent salinity and dive for their prey |

**ADULT LENGTH**
⅛–⁷⁄₁₆ in
(10–11 mm)

*CICINDIS HORNI*
# HORN'S FAIRY SHRIMP
# HUNTING BEETLE
BRUCH, 1908

54

*Cicindis horni* lives along the margins of brackish vernal pools on large salt flats. This nocturnal species flies to light and spends the day resting in burrows under tiled soil polygons away from the water's edge. Beetles emerge from their burrows at dusk to search for food and mates. They are unusual among ground beetles in that they swim across the surface of these brackish pools, propelling themselves with their middle legs, and dive to search for their prey, fairy shrimp. Mating takes place on the muddy shore or on the surface of the water. The larvae are unknown.

## RELATED SPECIES

The subfamily Cicindinae consists of two species in two genera. *Archaeocindis johnbeckeri* is restricted to the northern Persian Gulf, while *C. horni* occurs only in the Córdoba Province of Argentina. The pronotal and elytral apical margins of the former species are saw-toothed, while those of *C. horni* are smooth. Further, the head of *A. johnbeckeri* bears a single setal-bearing puncture above each eye, while *C. horni* lacks this feature.

**The Horn's Fairy Shrimp Hunting Beetle** is shiny, and mostly pale yellowish tan, except for the blackish eyes and darker tips and middle margins of the mandibles. The eyes lack any seta-bearing punctures above them. The pronotal and elytral margins are smooth. The elytra have a very pale pattern along the sides. The middle tibiae are each fringed with long setae.

Actual size

| FAMILY | Carabidae |
|---|---|
| SUBFAMILY | Cicindelinae |
| DISTRIBUTION | Nearctic: central United States |
| MACROHABITAT | Grasslands and prairies |
| MICROHABITAT | Ground-dwelling adults live in well-drained, sparsely vegetated habitats |
| FEEDING HABITS | Adults prey on beetles, grasshoppers, and caterpillars |
| NOTE | The second largest tiger beetle in the New World |

ADULT LENGTH
1⅛–1⅜ in
(29–35 mm)

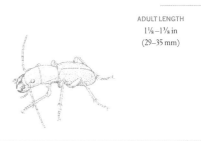

*AMBLYCHEILA CYLINDRIFORMIS*
# GIANT GREAT PLAINS TIGER BEETLE
(SAY, 1823)

55

The Giant Great Plains Tiger Beetle is a nocturnal predator that is active from spring through late summer and is sometimes encountered on warm, overcast days running across roads or sparsely vegetated grasslands. Rather than dig their own burrows for shelter, they spend their days occupying the burrows of other animals, such as prairie dogs, badgers, and gophers. The larvae may reach 2½ in (62 mm) in length. Small clusters of larvae are found in burrows dug in barren clay banks near streams and ravines, or in vertical clay banks on the flanks of bluffs, the D-shaped entrances of which are ¼–⁵⁄₁₆ in (6–8 mm) in diameter.

### RELATED SPECIES

The genus *Amblycheila* consists of seven species from the western United States and northern Mexico. It is distinguished from the North American *Omus* by its larger size (greater than ¾ in / 20 mm) and the South American *Picnochile fallaciosa* by its broad head. *Amblycheila cylindriformis* is found east of the Rockies and its elytra have multiple rows of coarse punctures; *A. hoversoni* from southern Texas is larger (1¼–1⁷⁄₁₆ in / 32–36 mm) and has fewer rows of elytral punctures.

**The Giant Great Plains Tiger Beetle** is large, shiny black, and often has brownish elytra. The sides of the large, prominent mandibles have seta-bearing punctures. The pronotum has front corners that are prominent and project forward. The elytra are fused down the middle, each with three raised ridges with multiple rows of large punctures in between.

Actual size

| FAMILY | Carabidae |
|---|---|
| SUBFAMILY | Cicindelinae |
| DISTRIBUTION | Nearctic: eastern North America |
| MACROHABITAT | Deciduous hardwood forest and mixed woodland |
| MICROHABITAT | Sunny, open forest floors, roadways, and trails |
| FEEDING HABITS | Preys on ground-dwelling insects |
| NOTE | This species has a two-year life cycle |

ADULT LENGTH
⅜–⁹⁄₁₆ in
(10–14 mm)

*CICINDELA SEXGUTTATA*
# SIX-SPOTTED TIGER BEETLE
FABRICIUS, 1775

56

Actual size

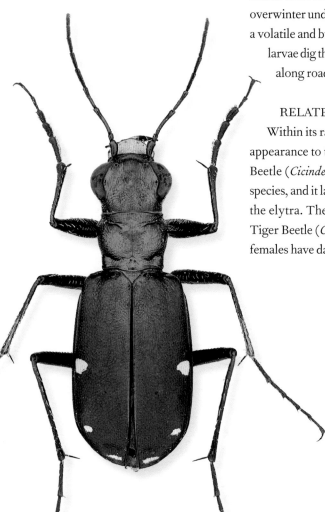

This normally solitary and familiar beetle is active in spring and early summer; individuals and small groups are encountered only rarely in the fall. They occupy the forest floor early in the season, but as the trees leaf out, they move to sunlit areas along roads, trails, and woodland edges to hunt for insects and find mates. Individuals seek shelter during inclement weather and overwinter under loose tree bark. When captured, they secrete a volatile and burning fluid from the tip of their abdomen. The larvae dig their vertical burrows in sandy, clay, or loamy soils along roads and dry creek beds.

## RELATED SPECIES

Within its range, the Six-spotted Tiger Beetle has a similar appearance to the green form of the Northern Barrens Tiger Beetle (*Cicindela patruela*), but it is a brighter green than that species, and it lacks a complete middle line across the middle of the elytra. There are several green subspecies of the Festive Tiger Beetle (*C. scutellaris*), but they are duller overall and the females have darker labra.

**The Six-spotted Tiger Beetle** is brilliant metallic green, with or without a bluish tinge on both the dorsal and ventral surfaces, with six white spots on the apical half of the elytra; some individuals or populations have four, two, or no spots. Sculpting of the upper surface consists of small, flat bumps. The labrum is almost white. The underside and legs are bristling with scattered long white setae.

| FAMILY | Carabidae |
|---|---|
| SUBFAMILY | Cicindelinae |
| DISTRIBUTION | Neotropical: Mexico, Belize, Guatemala, Nicaragua, Costa Rica, Panama, Colombia |
| MACROHABITAT | Lowland rainforests, up to an altitude of approximately 3,300 ft (1,000 m) |
| MICROHABITAT | Forest canopy, usually more than 100 ft (30 m) above ground |
| FEEDING HABITS | Both adults and larvae are predatory on insects |
| NOTE | *Ctenostoma* adults apparently prefer to prey on ants |

ADULT LENGTH
⅜–¾ in
(9.5–19 mm)

*CTENOSTOMA MACULICORNE*
# SPOTTED-HORN
# COMB-MOUTHED BEETLE
(CHAUDOIR, 1860)

57

This relatively common species ranges from Oaxaca and Veracruz in Mexico to Colombia. The adults are arboreal and found on twigs and foliage in the canopy and understory of rainforests and cloud forests. Adults of the Spotted-horn Comb-mouthed Beetle have been found from April to July and in October and November. They have fully developed wings and are capable of flight; they are attracted to lights at night. The larvae apparently use holes in rotting twigs to wait for their prey.

Actual size

## RELATED SPECIES
The genus *Ctenostoma* includes approximately 110 Neotropical species that collectively range from Mexico to Paraguay and Bolivia. The species are grouped into eight subgenera. *Ctenostoma maculicorne* is closely related to *C. davidsoni* from Costa Rica, *C. guatemalensis* from Guatemala, and *C. laeticolor* from Nicaragua, Costa Rica, and Panama; all three belong to the subgenus *Neoprocephalus*.

**The Spotted-horn Comb-mouthed Beetle** is an elongate, parallel-sided, long-legged, glabrous reddish-brown tiger beetle; the elytra have on each side a long, narrow, usually sigmoid, yellow median band and a small, elongate spot on the anterior third near the suture. The eyes are rather small, the vertex smooth, and the labrum has seven teeth. The second segment of the maxillary palpus is broad and notched. The pronotum is subspheric in shape and the elytra are covered with small foveae, decreasing in size from base to apex.

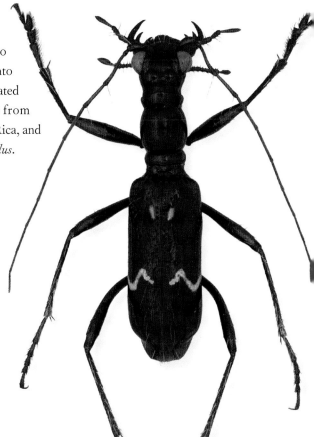

| FAMILY | Carabidae |
|---|---|
| SUBFAMILY | Cicindelinae |
| DISTRIBUTION | Nearctic: coastal eastern United States |
| MACROHABITAT | Coastal beaches |
| MICROHABITAT | Open sandy beaches at and just above tide line |
| FEEDING HABITS | Adults prey on insects and amphipods |
| NOTE | Larvae take up to two years to fully develop; this species is federally listed as endangered in the United States |

ADULT LENGTH
½–⁹⁄₁₆ in
(13–15 mm)

58

*HABROSCELIMORPHA DORSALIS*
# NORTHEASTERN BEACH TIGER BEETLE
(SAY, 1817)

Adult Northeastern Beach Tiger Beetles hunt for amphipods and insects around the clock from June through August. The larvae dig their vertical burrows in the sand just above the high-tide line. Once distributed along the Atlantic coast from Massachusetts to Virginia, this species is now restricted to a few sites along the coast of Massachusetts and the western and eastern shores of the Chesapeake Bay in Maryland and Virginia. The dramatic decline of this species was due largely to habitat degradation from human and vehicular activity. It was declared endangered in 1990. Efforts are under way to re-establish populations within their historical range.

## RELATED SPECIES

There are five distinct subspecies of *Habroscelimorpha dorsalis* based on body size, color pattern, and differences in molecular DNA. The other subspecies, which are smaller and darker, are found along coastal beaches in southern Atlantic and Gulf Coast states, and also in Cuba.

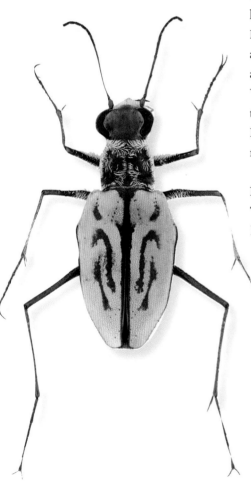

Actual size

**The Northeastern Beach Tiger Beetle** is mostly white with variable bronze markings. The tips of the elytra are rounded (male) or broadly notched (female). The underside is dark bronze to blackish green with dense white setae on the thorax. The legs have long claws and the hind femora are long, extending well beyond the body.

| FAMILY | Carabidae |
|---|---|
| SUBFAMILY | Cicindelinae |
| DISTRIBUTION | Afrotropical: Mozambique, South Africa, Tanzania, Malawi, Zimbabwe, Zambia, and Botswana |
| MACROHABITAT | Savanna |
| MICROHABITAT | Open sandy patches among shrubby trees and bushes |
| FEEDING HABITS | Adults and larvae prey on insects |
| NOTE | The scientific name *Manticora* means "one who devours men" |

ADULT LENGTH
1⁵⁄₈–2³⁄₁₆ in
(42–57 mm)

*MANTICORA LATIPENNIS*
# MANTICORA LATIPENNIS
WATERHOUSE, 1837

59

These large, flightless beetles live in scrub-covered sandy savannas, and run erratically on long legs with their heads and mandibles held high as they hunt for large caterpillars, crickets, termites, beetles, and other arthropods. Males also use their long, curved mandibles to grasp a female's prothorax during copulation. The flat-headed larvae live in vertical burrows from which they will lunge at prey that venture close to the entrance. Larval development may take several years depending upon the availability of food. The name *Manticora* is derived from an ancient Persian legend and means "one who devours men."

Actual size

### RELATED SPECIES
*Manticora* includes 13 African species, all of which have wide elytra with distinct "shoulders" or humeri, a large head and mandibles, and a labrum with six teeth. *Manticora latipennis* has very broad, heart-shaped elytra that are curved along the sides and have distinct ridges along their length and a tuberculate surface. The African genus *Mantica* is similar, but has narrow elytra, a small head and mandibles, and a labrum with only four teeth.

**Manticora latipennis** is very hard bodied, shiny, and uniformly black or sometimes reddish brown. The male's left mandible is slightly shorter and distinctly bent over its longer right mandible, while the female's mandibles are shorter and similar in shape. The very broad and fused elytra are heart-shaped, with a surface distinctly ridged and densely covered with tubercles.

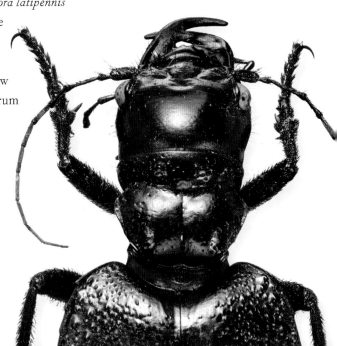

| FAMILY | Carabidae |
|---|---|
| SUBFAMILY | Cicindelinae |
| DISTRIBUTION | Neotropical: Argentina (Río Negro, Salta), Bolivia (Chapare), Brazil (Goiás), Colombia, Ecuador, French Guiana, Guyana (Demerara), Peru, Venezuela |
| MACROHABITAT | Lowland to midland river edges and nearby vegetation |
| MICROHABITAT | Ground-dwelling |
| FEEDING HABITS | Predator |
| NOTE | Adults are nocturnal; larvae are diurnal |

ADULT LENGTH
⁹⁄₁₆–¹¹⁄₁₆ in
(15–18 mm)

*PHAEOXANTHA AEQUINOCTIALIS*
# LESSER AND GIRDLED XANTHINE TIGER BEETLE
DEJEAN, 1825

Adults of this South American species are nocturnal and found running quickly across open sandy beaches, river or stream sandbars, and in nearby vegetated fields. During the day they take cover in burrows dug 1¹⁵⁄₁₆–5¾ in (50–150 mm) into dry sand on the upper reaches of beaches. The fast-running adults have fully developed flight wings but apparently are not capable of flight. The larvae are diurnal and found in burrows on bare sand; their life stage is about 7–10 months, including a dormancy in the third instar. The species shows a univoltine life cycle triggered by the annual flood pulse.

## RELATED SPECIES

The genus *Phaeoxantha* includes 12 species restricted to South America. It is related to the genera *Tetracha* (with about 55 species) and *Aniara* (with one species). *Phaeoxantha cruciata* is most similar to *P. aequinoctialis* but it is smaller and has fine, short setae covering the elytra. Two subspecies are considered as valid by some authors: *P. a. aequinoctialis* and *P. aequinoctialis bifasciata*.

**Phaeoxantha aequinoctialis** is a tiger beetle whose body is mainly pale yellow, like the sand upon which it is found, except for a characteristic dark spot on the elytra. The labrum is transverse, not extended anteriorly at the middle, and has four submarginal setae and the clypeus has a pair of setae. The elytra lack short, fine setae.

Actual size

| FAMILY | Carabidae |
| --- | --- |
| SUBFAMILY | Cicindelinae |
| DISTRIBUTION | Neotropical: southern Argentina and Chile |
| MACROHABITAT | Southern temperate forests and grasslands in lowlands at 16–2,620 ft (5–800 m) |
| MICROHABITAT | Under fallen trunks and leaf litter |
| FEEDING HABITS | Adults and larvae prey primarily on insects and other arthropods |
| NOTE | Adults are fast runners |

ADULT LENGTH
⅛–¹¹⁄₁₆ in
(16–17 mm)

*PICNOCHILE FALLACIOSA*
# NOTHOFAGUS TIGER BEETLE
(CHEVROLAT, 1854)

61

Flightless adults of the Nothofagus Tiger Beetle run rapidly on barren ground and grassy or mossy substrates. They pause frequently as they hunt for insects on long summer days that are typical of the higher southern latitudes from November through February. They take shelter at night and during thunderstorms under fallen logs and other debris on the forest floor. The larval burrows are often clustered in barren ground, especially with clay substrates associated with southern beeches (*Nothofagus* spp.). The larvae live in vertical burrows and prey on small insects that walk within striking distance of a burrow's entrance. Adults are found in open grassy areas and forested habitats.

## RELATED SPECIES

The genus *Picnochile* is one of ten genera of tiger beetles in the tribe Megacephalini that live in the New World. This genus is distinguished from other flightless genera in the region by having a pronotum that is much broader than the head. *Picnochile fallaciosa* is the sole species in the genus *Picnochile*.

**The Nothofagus Tiger Beetle** is predominantly dull black with appendages that are mostly reddish brown. The pronotum is broadly expanded just behind the front margin and abruptly narrowed at the middle toward the elytra. The elytra are elliptical in outline, each with a broad ridge running down its length. The front legs of the male have somewhat expanded tarsomeres.

Actual size

| FAMILY | Carabidae |
|---|---|
| SUBFAMILY | Cicindelinae |
| DISTRIBUTION | Nearctic, Neotropical: southern United States to Nicaragua |
| MACROHABITAT | Wetlands, grassy upland habitats, irrigated farms, warm deserts |
| MICROHABITAT | Ground-dwelling adults live on shorelines of lakes and rivers, and adjacent moist grassy areas |
| FEEDING HABITS | Adults and larvae prey on insects |
| NOTE | This species possibly acts as a natural control of pest insects |

**ADULT LENGTH**
½–¾ in
(12–20 mm)

62

*TETRACHA CAROLINA*
# PAN AMERICAN
# BIG-HEADED TIGER BEETLE
(LINNAEUS, 1767)

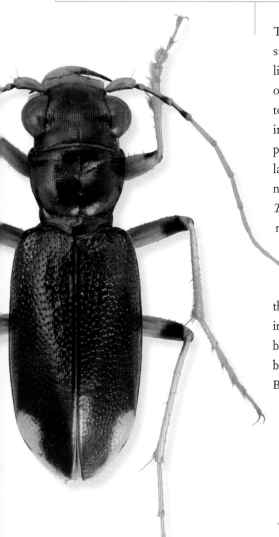

The adults of this beetle are often seen in groups on warm summer nights, and are frequently attracted to permanent lights near water. During the day, they hide either under rocks or in cracks in mud. Although fully winged, they are reluctant to fly and do so only when danger is imminent. They may be important predators of crop pests in cotton fields, and their presence may be an indicator of agro-system health. The larvae establish their vertical burrows in various substrates near or away from water. The various subspecies of *Tetracha carolina* in the Caribbean and South America are now considered valid species.

## RELATED SPECIES

There are 58 species of *Tetracha* distributed throughout the Western Hemisphere. They differ from other tiger beetles in the region by their pale appendages and upper surfaces with bright metallic colors that are usually dominated by copper, blue, and green hues. The Pan American Big-headed Tiger Beetle is distinguished by its colors and the shape and extent of the pale markings on the elytra.

**The Pan American Big-headed Tiger Beetle** is metallic purple and green with pale yellowish-brown appendages. The head is broad with prominent eyes and distinct mandibles. The front angles of the pronotum extend forward. The bright reddish-purple elytra are shiny green on the sides with large, pale curved markings on the tips. Males have broad front tarsi with setose brushes underneath.

Actual size

| FAMILY | Carabidae |
|---|---|
| SUBFAMILY | Cicindelinae |
| DISTRIBUTION | Oriental and Australian: from the Malay Archipelago to northern Australia |
| MACROHABITAT | Tropical forests |
| MICROHABITAT | Primarily on branches, foliage, and tree trunks |
| FEEDING HABITS | Probably feeds mostly ants |
| NOTE | One of the most widely distributed species in the genus |

**ADULT LENGTH**
⅝–1 in
(16–25 mm)

*TRICONDYLA APTERA*
# TRICONDYLA APTERA
(OLIVIER, 1790)

63

Very little is known about the life cycle and biology of *Tricondyla aptera*, or for that matter of any species of the genus. The adults are usually found alone, randomly, on tree trunks, on foliage, running from branch to branch, on or under piles of wood, and sometimes on the soil. They move quickly and are difficult to catch. By their body shape, they look very much like large ants and, although not yet confirmed, it seems that they feed mostly on ants.

## RELATED SPECIES

About 45 species are included in the genus *Tricondyla*, which is divided into five subgenera according to the most recent taxonomic revision. Four distinct subspecies of *T. aptera* are currently recognized and separated by minor differences, including size, coloration, and sculpture on the surface of elytra. Adults of these subspecies are difficult to differentiate since morphologically intermediate specimens are found between them.

Actual size

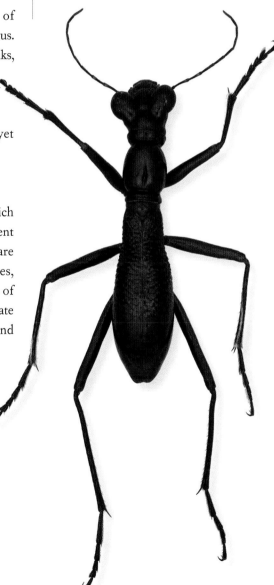

***Tricondyla aptera*** is a robust species, black or dark brown without elytral pattern, rather brilliant, sometimes with blue reflection. As with the other members of the genus, the body is elongate and the elytra narrow at the base and dilated in the apical half, clearly gibbous in lateral view. As the species name suggests, it lacks flight wings.

| FAMILY | Carabidae |
|---|---|
| SUBFAMILY | Carabinae |
| DISTRIBUTION | Palearctic and Nearctic: widespread native in the Palearctic; naturalized introduction in eastern United States |
| MACROHABITAT | Deciduous forests |
| MICROHABITAT | On the ground or on tree trunks |
| FEEDING HABITS | Preys on Lepidoptera larvae and pupae |
| NOTE | Intentionally introduced to North America for the biological control of two introduced moth pests |

**ADULT LENGTH**
⅞–1⅜ in
(21–35 mm)

64

*CALOSOMA SYCOPHANTA*
# AGREEABLE CATERPILLAR HUNTER
(LINNAEUS, 1758)

*Calosoma sycophanta* is native to the Palearctic, where it is broadly distributed, and has been intentionally introduced as early as 1906 to various parts of North America for the biological control of the Gypsy Moth (*Lymantria dispar*) and Brown-tail Moth (*Euproctis chrysorrhoea*). It is now established in the eastern United States. The adults and larvae are found on the ground or climbing on trees of various species in deciduous forests in search of caterpillars. Adults are fully winged and excellent fliers, and can live up to four years in captivity.

## RELATED SPECIES

*Calosoma sycophanta* belongs to a group containing six species, five of which occur in the Palearctic (including the Himalayas), and *C. frigidum*, which is native to North America and found over most of the temperate region. *Calosoma sycophanta* is superficially similar to *C. scrutator*, based on its size and coloration, but differs in that the head and pronotum are black as opposed to metallic.

**The Agreeable Caterpillar Hunter** is a handsome large beetle that has brilliantly green elytra, usually with golden or cupreous reflections. The males are easily distinguished from the females in that the first three tarsomeres of the front legs are dilated and there are spongy, adhesive setae underneath; in addition, males have a brush of stout setae on the apical half of the middle tibia (this is lacking in the females).

Actual size

| FAMILY | Carabidae |
|---|---|
| SUBFAMILY | Carabinae |
| DISTRIBUTION | Neotropical: Argentina and Chile |
| MACROHABITAT | Forested and woodlot areas |
| MICROHABITAT | Ground-dwelling |
| FEEDING HABITS | Predator on earthworms, gastropods, and small insects |
| NOTE | Many subspecies have been described in the literature based on slight color variations |

ADULT LENGTH
⅞–1³⁄₁₆ in
(22–30 mm)

*CEROGLOSSUS CHILENSIS*
# CHILEAN MAGNIFICENT BEETLE
(ESCHSCHOLTZ, 1829)

65

This beautiful polymorphic *Ceroglossus* species is found in central Chile and the western Argentine provinces of Neuquén, Río Negro, and Chubut. This species lives in forests, forest edges, thickets, coppices, and occasionally clearings, from sea-level to approximately 6,500 ft (2,000 m) in altitude. The adults hide during the day under fallen decaying trees, leaf litter, or stones. They feed on earthworms, gastropods, and probably also small insects, and are known to be attracted to fruits. Like many forest carabids they have short flight wings and are thus incapable of flight.

## RELATED SPECIES

Eight species of *Ceroglossus* are currently recognized, all of them restricted to Chile and western Argentina. They are highly prized by amateur entomologists and collectors. Many color forms and several subspecies have been described. In the last taxonomic treatment of the genus, 19 subspecies were listed for *C. chilensis* alone. The subspecies differ slightly in color and have minor morphological variations.

Actual size

**The Chilean Magnificent Beetle** is a handsome, elongate, brilliantly colored carabid. In most specimens, the color of the head and pronotum differs from that of the elytra, which may be blue, green, or reddish purple, often with the lateral margins in a contrasting color. The antennae and legs are black. The main characteristic of the species is the presence in the male of carinae underneath antennal segments 6, 7, and 8.

| FAMILY | Carabidae |
|---|---|
| SUBFAMILY | Carabinae |
| DISTRIBUTION | Palearctic: Europe |
| MACROHABITAT | Usually in deciduous and mixed forests |
| MICROHABITAT | Under surfaces such as rotten logs. |
| FEEDING HABITS | Adults and larvae feed on snails in their shells. |
| NOTE | Stridulations produced by adults are thought to act as an acoustic warning against potential vertebrate predators |

ADULT LENGTH
½–¾ in
(12–19 mm)

66

*CYCHRUS CARABOIDES*
# CYCHRUS CARABOIDES
LINNAEUS, 1758

This species, which is endemic to the boreal and temperate regions of Europe, is typically found under moss and rotten logs, as well as under the bark of old stumps, in deciduous and mixed forests with considerable soil moisture. In some parts of Europe *Cychrus caraboides* also occurs in heather moors. Hibernation takes place in the adult and larval stages. Adults of both sexes produce a loud stridulation by rubbing the elytra and abdomen together, which probably acts as an acoustic warning to potential predators.

## RELATED SPECIES

The genus *Cychrus* includes more than 120 species living in the Nearctic and Palearctic realms. It is closely related to the genus *Cychropsis*, which is considered by some authors as a subgenus of *Cychrus*. *Cychrus cordicollis*, from Italy and Switzerland, differs from *C. caraboides* in having posteriorly sinuate sides to the pronotum. In *C. attenuatus*, which is also endemic to Europe, the tibiae are reddish instead of black.

**Cychrus caraboides** is entirely black. The head is elongate and narrow, with long mandibles that allow the insect to reach inside snail shells to eat the flesh. The labrum is deeply bilobed and the penultimate article of the maxillary palp has long apical setae. The pronotum is short, with sides that are not sinuate posteriorly and rounded posterior angles. The elytra are relatively short, oval, very convex, and granulate.

Actual size

| FAMILY | Carabidae |
|---|---|
| SUBFAMILY | Carabinae |
| DISTRIBUTION | Palearctic: Honshu, Kyushu, Shikoku, Sado, and Awashima islands, Japan; Kuril Islands, Russia |
| MACROHABITAT | Deciduous and mixed forests |
| MICROHABITAT | Hides under or in rotten logs during the day |
| FEEDING HABITS | Adults and larvae feed on snails |
| NOTE | The long, narrow head and prothorax of the adult enable it to prey on snails |

ADULT LENGTH
1³⁄₁₆–2½ in
(30–65 mm)

*DAMASTER BLAPTOIDES*

# DAMASTER BLAPTOIDES

KOLLAR, 1836

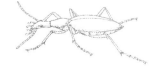

67

The genus *Damaster* includes flightless species that are restricted to Japan and the surrounding islands. *D. blaptoides* reproduces in the spring and early summer, and the new adults emerge later in the year. Hibernation occurs only in the adult stage. The species has been released on the Hawaiian Islands as a potential biological control agent against land snail pests but the introduction was unsuccessful as populations of *D. blaptoides* did not survive in their new environment. The nocturnal beetle usually attacks snails with a thick shell and large aperture by reaching into the prey with their head, and those with a thin shell and small aperture by crushing the shell.

## RELATED SPECIES

Taxonomists have different views regarding the number of species in the genus *Damaster*. Some have recognized four distinct species while others consider as valid a single species with seven or eight subspecies. Members of *Damaster* are closely related to those of *Acoptolabrus* and *Coptolabrus*, which inhabit Asia, and they are sometimes considered to belong to a single genus.

**Damaster blaptoides** is a handsome, elongate, narrow, flightless beetle with long antennae and legs. Some specimens are uniformly reddish brown to black, but in others the head and pronotum, and sometimes also the elytra, have a greenish, bluish, violaceous, or cupreous luster. Variation has also been observed in the size of the head, which may be relatively narrow or stout. The apex of each elytron ends in a spiniform projection that varies greatly in length among individuals.

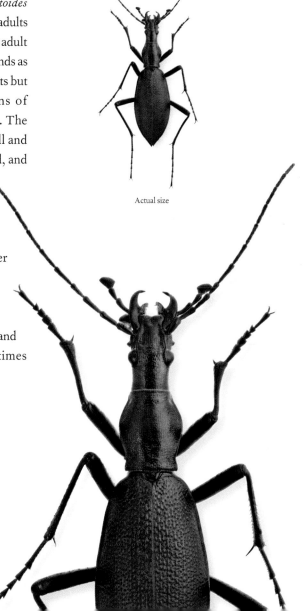

Actual size

| FAMILY | Carabidae |
|---|---|
| SUBFAMILY | Hiletinae |
| DISTRIBUTION | Neotropical: Brazil and Peru |
| MACROHABITAT | Tropical rainforests |
| MICROHABITAT | Ground-dwelling |
| FEEDING HABITS | Predator |
| NOTE | Seldom encountered but can be abundant under favorable conditions |

**ADULT LENGTH**
⅜–½ in
(9–12 mm)

68

*EUCAMARAGNATHUS BATESI*
# EUCAMARAGNATHUS BATESI
(CHAUDOIR, 1861)

Actual size

Adults of *Eucamaragnathus batesi* live near small forest streams and swamps on open fine silt, wandering about near the water's edge at night and hiding in leaf litter or beneath branches on the forest floor during the day. They have also been observed walking beneath the water surface. Adults have very small flight wing remnants underneath their elytra, hence they are flightless. This species was found abundantly at one locality in southeastern Peru during the rainy season. Since coleopterists usually avoid visiting tropical rainforests during the rainy season, it could explain why the species has been rarely encountered.

RELATED SPECIES

The genus *Eucamaragnathus* is pantropical and includes 14 species in Southeast Asia, Africa, and South America; it is related to the genus *Hiletus*, whose members are confined to tropical Africa. *Eucamaragnathus batesi* occurs in southeastern Peru and western Brazil, and is closely related to the other three South American species of the genus, *E. amapa*, *E. brasiliensis*, and *E. jaws*.

**Eucamaragnathus batesi** is a medium-size, markedly iridescent, black carabid. The medial edge of the mandible is markedly serrate. The pronotum is cordate, its base narrower than the apex across the front angles, and its anterior impression is smooth, and the first five elytral striae do not extend to the apex. The male has a tooth on the ventral surface of the front femur.

| FAMILY | Carabidae |
|---|---|
| SUBFAMILY | Scaritinae |
| DISTRIBUTION | Nearctic: northern Pacific Coast of United States |
| MACROHABITAT | Open sea beaches |
| MICROHABITAT | Ground-dwelling adults live on exposed, moist, sandy beaches |
| FEEDING HABITS | Adults eat small crustaceans |
| NOTE | Their slender, almost mole-like bodies are adapted for burrowing |

ADULT LENGTH
¼ in
(6–7 mm)

*AKEPHORUS OBESUS*
# OBESE POINT-BEARING BEETLE
LECONTE, 1866

69

Actual size

The flightless adults of the Obese Point-bearing Beetle come out during spring and summer nights to hunt for small crustaceans on wet, sandy beaches. They are slow runners, but strong burrowers and take shelter during the day in the sand, or under logs and other debris washed up on the beach. The "point-bearing" portion of their common name is derived directly from the Greek words *ake* ("point") and *phoro* ("to bear or carry"), and is likely in reference to the single apical spur found on the tip of the adult's front tibia.

## RELATED SPECIES

The genus *Akephorus* was once included as a subgenus of *Dyschirius*. Two species are distributed along the Pacific Coast from Washington to Baja California: *A. obesus* is distinctly bicolored and found north of San Francisco, while the Marine Point-bearing Beetle (*A. marinus*) is yellowish brown with a dark line down the middle of the pronotum and a broad elytral patch, and has a southern distribution.

**The Obese Point-bearing Beetle** is elongate, narrowly constricted between the pronotum and elytra, and bicolored. The mandibles, appendages, and pronotum are reddish brown, while the head, "waist," and somewhat iridescent elytra are darker. The "shoulders" of the short and oval elytra, or humeri, are rounded, a character typically indicative of winglessness.

| FAMILY | Carabidae |
|---|---|
| SUBFAMILY | Scaritinae |
| DISTRIBUTION | Nearctic: eastern North America and Cuba |
| MACROHABITAT | Mixed deciduous forests |
| MICROHABITAT | Adults and larvae live and develop in dead tree limbs, snags, and logs |
| FEEDING HABITS | Adults stab and feed on the amoeboid stage of slime molds |
| NOTE | Wrinkle beetles were once in their own family, the Rhysodidae |

ADULT LENGTH
¼–⁵⁄₁₆ in
(6–8 mm)

*OMOGLYMMIUS AMERICANUS*
# AMERICAN CRUDELY CARVED WRINKLE BEETLE
(LAPORTE, 1836)

Adults and larvae of the American Crudely Carved Wrinkle Beetle live in fungus-infested deciduous trees, especially elm (*Ulmus* spp.), maple (*Acer* spp.), and oak (*Quercus* spp.). Adults are also found in tree holes and woodpiles. This species belongs to a group known as wrinkled bark beetles. Adults do not tunnel into wood, but use their wedge-like heads to force their way between layers as they search for food. They are unique among beetles in that their mandibles are not used for chewing, but are instead modified to protect highly modified mouthparts that pierce the amoeboid stages of slime molds upon which they prey.

## RELATED SPECIES

Most of the 150 species of *Omoglymmius* are from the Oriental Realm, with only two occurring in the Nearctic, *O. americanus* and *O. hamatus*. *Omoglymmius hamatus* has lobes on the head that almost meet along a short, nearly parallel line along the top with margins that are not sinuate behind, and is restricted to western North America.

Actual size

**American Crudely Carved Wrinkle Beetles** are elongate, slender, hard bodied, and shiny reddish to dark brown. The head has a distinct groove in the back, with lobes on top nearly touching at a single point and margins strongly sinuate behind. The pronotum has three deep grooves, while the elytra have distinct rows of punctures. Males have calcars, spine-like processes, at the apex of the tibiae.

| FAMILY | Carabidae |
|---|---|
| SUBFAMILY | Scaritinae |
| DISTRIBUTION | Neotropical: central-east and west Mexico |
| MACROHABITAT | From 500 to 5,900 ft (150–1,800 m) |
| MICROHABITAT | Adults are ground-dwelling |
| FEEDING HABITS | Adults prey on insects; larval habits unknown |
| NOTE | This is the most colorful species of *Pasimachus* |

ADULT LENGTH
¾–1⅛ in
(20–28 mm)

*PASIMACHUS SUBANGULATUS*

# SUBANGULATE WARRIOR BEETLE

(CHAUDOIR, 1862)

71

The flightless adults of the Subangulate Warrior Beetle are typically nocturnal predators of ground-dwelling insects and are moderately fast runners. They are mostly active from May through August, and in October. They spend their days hidden in burrows and under rocks and debris. Adults will also burrow into the soil to estivate during the dry season. The larvae are unknown. *Pasimachus* beetles have large mandibles and resemble stag beetles (Lucanidae), but they are easily distinguished by their slender, rather than lamellate, antennae.

## RELATED SPECIES

There are 32 species in the genus *Pasimachus* that are distributed across the southern United States and into Central America. They are generally large, broad, and black, with some species having metallic blue, purple, or green borders or surfaces. The mostly green coloration of the Subangulate Warrior Beetle is distinctive among species in the genus.

**The Subangulate Warrior Beetle** is black with the side margins and base of the prothorax, and the elytra green or, rarely, blue-green. The head and thorax typically have a green luster. The sides of the pronotum are not sinuate and the posterior angles are rounded. The elytra are convex and the sides are strongly rounded behind the humeri.

Actual size

| FAMILY | Carabidae |
|---|---|
| SUBFAMILY | Scaritinae |
| DISTRIBUTION | Neotropical: Brazil |
| MACROHABITAT | Lowland tropical forest |
| MICROHABITAT | Adults live on ground among accumulations of flood debris |
| FEEDING HABITS | The feeding habits of this species are unknown |
| NOTE | This species is thought to live among ants |

**ADULT LENGTH**
¼–⅜ in
(7–9 mm)

*SOLENOGENYS FUNKEI*
# FUNKE'S CHANNEL-JAW BEETLE
ADIS, 1981

Nothing is known about the biology and ecology of this beetle. Although found on the ground among flood debris, this may not be its preferred habitat. Adults are caked in a grayish-brown mixture of sand and clay, but it is not known if this is because they are burrowers or if this is an adaptation for remaining undetected in ant nests, or both. Its possible association with ants is suggested by the tough exoskeleton, grooves underneath the head for receiving the antennae, and retractable mouthparts. All of these adaptations are found in other beetles that are known to live with ants.

### RELATED SPECIES
*Solenogenys* contains three species, all restricted to the Amazon Basin. It differs from other small, elongate carabid genera in the region with loosely attached forebodies by the eyes that are visible from above, antennal grooves under the head, eight elytral ridges, and a scaly surface caked in mud. Funke's Channel-jaw Beetle is distinguished by its larger size, pair of tubercles on the back of the head, and mandibles with a distinct dorsal protuberance.

Actual size

**Funke's Channel-jaw Beetle** is elongate, coarsely punctate, with smooth appendages. The broad, ant-like head, pronotum, and elytra are covered with small white scales, and coated with mud. The pronotum is octagonal in outline and slightly wider than the head. The elytra are parallel-sided and gradually and evenly taper to the tips.

| FAMILY | Carabidae |
|---|---|
| SUBFAMILY | Loricerinae |
| DISTRIBUTION | Palearctic and Nearctic: Europe, Asia, and North America |
| MACROHABITAT | Wet, often muddy environments |
| MICROHABITAT | Ground-dwelling |
| FEEDING HABITS | Predator |
| NOTE | Possesses long setae on the antennae and under the head that act as a trap to capture prey |

ADULT LENGTH
¼–⅜ in
(7–9 mm)

*LORICERA PILICORNIS*
# HAIRY-HORNED SPRINGTAIL-HUNTER
(FABRICIUS, 1775)

73

The specific name for *Loricera pilicornis* derives from the Latin *pili* ("hairs") and *cornus* ("horn"), and refers to the presence of stiff setae on the basal segments of the antennae. These setae, which are oriented in different directions, act as a specialized trap for the capture of springtails (Collembola), their favorite prey. This species lives in wet, often muddy, places along marshes, ponds, pools, lakes, and irrigation ditches. It reproduces in the spring and early summer, and overwinters in the adult stage. This species is an excellent flier and is attracted to light at night.

## RELATED SPECIES

*Loricera pilicornis* belongs to a genus comprising 13 species in the subarctic, boreal, and temperate regions of the world. Five species occur in North and Central America, including two in mountains of Mexico and Guatemala, and nine can be found in Asia and Europe. Taxonomists recognize two subspecies of *L. pilicornis*: one is restricted to Russia's Kuril Islands and to the Aleutian Islands and Kenai Peninsula in Alaska, while the other ranges over a large part of Europe, Asia, and North America.

Actual size

**The Hairy-horned Springtail-hunter** is shiny and black, usually with a greenish or bluish luster, the tibiae paler than the femora. The sides of the pronotum are not, or hardly, sinuate in the basal half, the elytra have 12 regular striae, there is no humeral carina, and the seventh interval normally lacks foveae. As with many carabids, in the males the first three tarsomeres are broadened.

| FAMILY | Carabidae |
|---|---|
| SUBFAMILY | Omophroninae |
| DISTRIBUTION | Nearctic: northeastern North America to southwest United States |
| MACROHABITAT | Sandy shores of wetlands |
| MICROHABITAT | Ground-dwelling adults run and burrow in wet sand |
| FEEDING HABITS | Adults prey on insects |
| NOTE | These distinctive carabids were once considered in a separate family |

**ADULT LENGTH**
³⁄₁₆–¼ in
(5–7 mm)

74

*OMOPHRON TESSELLATUM*
# MOSAIC ROUND SAND BEETLE

SAY, 1823

Actual size

**The Mosaic Round Sand Beetle** is broadly oval, convex, and has metallic green markings on a pale brown background. The dark head is marked with a pale "M." The pronotum has a central dark patch, and sides that do not form a continuous arc with those of the elytra. The elytra have 15 grooves and the proportion of light to dark areas is about even.

Adults of the Mosaic Round Sand Beetle are mostly nocturnal, gregarious, and are found year round on wet sand or clay along the shores of lakes, rivers, and streams, even ocean beaches, and are occasionally attracted to light. Their days are typically spent in burrows dug in the soil, but they will sometimes come out on bright, sunny days. Overwintering adults emerge to feed and mate in spring and remain active throughout the summer. This species is distributed from the Maritime Provinces to Virginia, west to Alberta and southwestern Arizona.

RELATED SPECIES

The genus *Omophron* includes about 70 species found in most biogeographic realms, except Australia and the Pacific. These very distinctive carabids are round, very convex, and lack a visible scutellum. *Omophron tesselatum* is distinguished from the other ten species in the Nearctic Realm by the M-shaped pattern on its head, 15 elytral grooves, and the male genitalia.

| FAMILY | Carabidae |
|---|---|
| SUBFAMILY | Elaphrinae |
| DISTRIBUTION | Nearctic: northern California |
| MACROHABITAT | Margins of vernal pools |
| MICROHABITAT | Ground-dwelling adults live on clay mud among rushes |
| FEEDING HABITS | Adults prey on insects |
| NOTE | This species is listed as "threatened" by federal and state governments |

ADULT LENGTH
³⁄₁₆–¼ in
(5–6 mm)

*ELAPHRUS VIRIDIS*

# DELTA GREEN GROUND BEETLE

HORN, 1878

75

The Delta Green Ground Beetle is active in spring along the edges of naturally occurring rain-filled depressions, or vernal pools that are filled by winter rains. They hunt for springtails in open patches or among the bases of rushes on warm, sunny, and windless days. This species is known only from southern Solano County, California, where it occurs in the Jepson Prairie area. Its historical range is unknown, but it is likely to have been much broader than today. The known population is highly restricted, encompasses less than 7,000 acres (2,800 ha), and continues to be threatened by agricultural development.

## RELATED SPECIES

There are 39 species of *Elaphrus* widely distributed in the Northern Hemisphere, of which 19 occur in the Nearctic. These big-eyed beetles resemble small tiger beetles. The elytra lack grooves along their length, but do have alternating rows of seta-bearing punctures. The Delta Green Ground Beetle is distinguished from other North American species in the genus by its brilliant green color and lack of pits on the elytra.

Actual size

**The Delta Green Ground Beetle** is brilliant green with large eyes and dark coppery patterns on the head and pronotum. Underneath the abdomen, the last visible abdominal segment is brownish. The tibiae of all legs are mostly brown with metallic tips. The smooth elytra are spotless or, more commonly, have raised and highly polished spots.

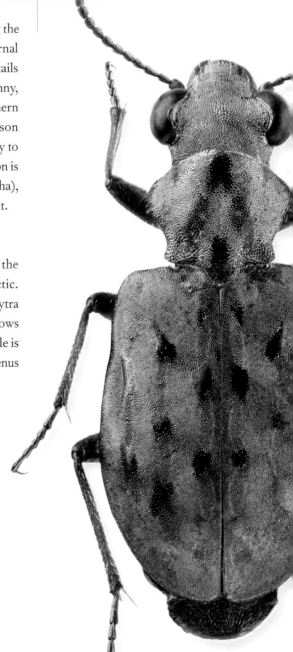

| FAMILY | Carabidae |
|---|---|
| SUBFAMILY | Broscinae |
| DISTRIBUTION | Palearctic and Nearctic: native to most of temperate Europe and western Siberia; introduced to, and established in, Prince Edward Island and Cape Breton Island, Canada |
| MACROHABITAT | Sparsely vegetated sandy areas |
| MICROHABITAT | Ground-dwelling |
| FEEDING HABITS | Predator |
| NOTE | More than 50 non-native Carabidae species are established in Canada, most of which originate from the Palearctic |

ADULT LENGTH
⅝ – ⅞ in
(16–23 mm)

*BROSCUS CEPHALOTES*
# BROSCUS CEPHALOTES
(LINNAEUS, 1758)

*Broscus cephalotes* occurs in the temperate regions of most of Europe and western Siberia, although it has been introduced accidentally to eastern Canada. Adults are active at night, while during the day they hide under stones, logs, and carcasses on sand dunes and beaches. This species reproduces during the summer and early fall. The larvae hibernate and the newly emerged adults appear in late spring and summer. The flight wings are fully developed in this species but it is uncertain whether the adults are capable of flight.

RELATED SPECIES

*Broscus nobilis*, from Bulgaria, Greece, and the Middle East, has a metallic dorsal surface and pale yellowish antennae and legs. *Broscus insularis*, endemic to the Balearic Islands, and *B. politus*, from Sicily and northern Africa, have a paler first antennal segment and reddish remaining ones. Overall, the genus *Broscus* includes 23 species, all in the Palearctic except for the adventive species in Canada.

**Broscus cephalotes** is a relatively large, pedunculate, glabrous, entirely black beetle without metallic luster. The head is almost as wide as the pronotum. The mandibles are markedly large. The eyes are rather small and the temples swollen. The pronotum is convex, constructed basally, with two lateral setae. The elytra have rows of very fine punctures. In the male the first three tarsomeres of the front leg are expanded and there are adhesive setae underneath.

Actual size

| FAMILY | Carabidae |
|---|---|
| SUBFAMILY | Apotominae |
| DISTRIBUTION | Neotropical: Brazil |
| MACROHABITAT | In the upper reaches of the Xingu River, Amazon Basin |
| MICROHABITAT | Ground-dwelling |
| FEEDING HABITS | Predator |
| NOTE | This is the only representative of the genus *Apotomus* in the Neotropical Realm. All other known species occur in the Palearctic, Oriental, Afrotropical, and Australian realms |

ADULT LENGTH
³⁄₁₆ in
(4–5 mm)

*APOTOMUS REICHARDTI*

# APOTOMUS REICHARDTI

ERWIN, 1980

77

Actual size

Only four specimens of *Apotomus reichardti* are known, and all were attracted to light at night in November at one locality at the northern edge of the Mato Grosso Plateau in the interior of Brazil. Apart from the fact that the species can fly, little is known about its biology. However, its habits are probably similar to those of other species of the genus, which have been collected on mudflats adjacent to rivers. *Apotomus reichardti* is geographically isolated—all the other known members of the genus are found in the Old World or Australia.

RELATED SPECIES

The genus *Apotomus* contains 22 species in the southern Palearctic, Oriental, Afrotropical, and Australian realms, as well as Brazil. The genus has not been revised in modern times and relationships between the species are poorly understood. *Apotomus reichardti* differs from other members of the genus by the greatly enlarged prothorax and the absence of lateral prothoracic setae.

**Apotomus reichardti** is a relatively small beetle with a pedunculate body, a globose prothorax that is nearly twice the width of the head, and markedly long maxillary palpi. The body is dark reddish brown with slightly paler legs, and the pronotum and elytra are pubescent. The species also has a stout spur above the antennal comb on the front tibia.

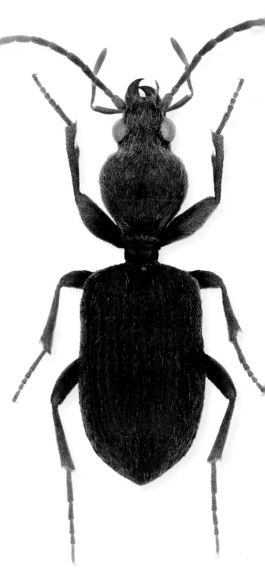

| FAMILY | Carabidae |
|---|---|
| SUBFAMILY | Siagoninae |
| DISTRIBUTION | Palearctic: southern Europe, northern Africa, and western Asia |
| MACROHABITAT | Open areas |
| MICROHABITAT | Ground-dwelling |
| FEEDING HABITS | Myrmecophagous, feeding on species of ants |
| NOTE | The recently discovered larva, which occurs in soil crevices, has been referred to as a "blind running ant killer" |

ADULT LENGTH
⅜–½ in
(9–13 mm)

# SIAGONA EUROPAEA
DEJEAN, 1826

*Siagona europaea* is a widely distributed species usually encountered in open areas such as pastures and abandoned croplands with scattered trees, on sandy-clay soils that become deeply fissured in the late spring and summer. The adults are almost exclusively myrmecophagous, preying on adults and immature stages of several species of ants. The wings are fully developed and the insect, which is active strictly at night, is attracted to lights.

## RELATED SPECIES

Two other species of *Siagona* are found in Europe. *Siagona jenissoni*, from Spain and Morocco, has a stridulatory organ on the prothorax; it also has short flight wings and is thus unable to fly. *Siagona dejeani*, from Spain and Morocco, is also flightless and much larger than *S. europaea* (adults are ⅞–1 in, or 21–25 mm, long). Overall, the genus *Siagona* includes about 80 species in Europe, Asia, and Africa.

Actual size

**Siagona europaea** is a flat beetle covered dorsally with relatively dense setae and with a stalk-like constriction between the pro- and mesothorax. The eyes are large and the mandibles strong with large retinaculum (toothlike process). The pronotum is narrowed posteriorly and the proepisternum has no stridulatory file. The blind larva is characteristic in having long antennae, legs, and urogomphi.

| FAMILY | Carabidae |
|---|---|
| SUBFAMILY | Melaeninae |
| DISTRIBUTION | Neotropical: northern South America |
| MACROHABITAT | Tropical rainforest |
| MICROHABITAT | Unknown |
| FEEDING HABITS | Unknown |
| NOTE | All known individuals of this species were collected from a single locality in northern Colombia |

ADULT LENGTH
³⁄₁₆ in
(4–5 mm)

*CYMBIONOTUM FERNANDEZI*

# CYMBIONOTUM FERNANDEZI

BALL & SHPELEY, 2005

79

*Cymbionotum fernandeʒi* is known from 38 specimens that were collected in May at one locality in the Magdalena River valley, Bolívar, northern Colombia. These specimens were collected at an ultraviolet light within a plantation of exotic trees native to the Oriental Realm and southern China, and therefore the species' native microhabitat associations are unknown. One specimen of a closely related species, *C. negrei*, from the Apure River basin of Venezuela, was found under the bark of a tree. Whether adults of these two species favor subcortical habitats in tropical rainforests needs to be confirmed.

## RELATED SPECIES

This species belongs to the subgenus *Procoscinia*, which also includes *Cymbionotum negrei*, a rarely collected species known from Venezuela. These two species are the only members of the genus *Cymbionotum* found in the Western Hemisphere. All the other 18 species occur in the Eastern Hemisphere, in southern Europe, Africa (north of the Tropic of Capricorn), and southwestern Asia.

**Cymbionotum fernandezi** is a small, broad, depressed, pedunculate beetle. The dorsal surface is uniformly rufous and densely setose. The posteriolateral dentiform projections on the pronotum are distinctly anteriad of the posterior margin and the proepipleuron is not visible in dorsal view. In addition, the posterior margin of the pronotum is not beaded.

Actual size

| FAMILY | Carabidae |
|---|---|
| SUBFAMILY | Trechinae |
| DISTRIBUTION | Nearctic: North America |
| MACROHABITAT | Lowland deciduous forests |
| MICROHABITAT | Adults found under loose bark of dead and dying trees |
| FEEDING HABITS | Adults prey on springtails and mites |
| NOTE | A very small, but easily recognized species |

ADULT LENGTH
¹⁄₃₂–¹⁄₁₆ in
(1–2 mm)

80

*MIOPTACHYS FLAVICAUDA*
# MIOPTACHYS FLAVICAUDA
(SAY, 1823)

Actual size

Adult *Mioptachys flavicauda* are found year round under the loose bark of dead or dying trees and logs. In eastern North America this species is especially common on hardwoods, such as oak (*Quercus* spp.), maple (*Acer* spp.), walnut (*Juglans* spp.), and cottonwood (*Populus* spp.), while in California it occurs on Ponderosa Pine (*Pinus ponderosa*). They are capable of flight and are occasionally attracted to light on spring and summer nights. Adults feed on small arthropods and, probably, their eggs. The specific epithet *flavicauda*, derived from the Latin words *flavus* ("yellow") and *caudus* ("tail"), is a specific reference to the pale tips of the elytra.

RELATED SPECIES

The genus *Mioptachys* contains 13 species distributed in the Western Hemisphere, of which 12 occur in the Neotropical Realm. Only one species, *M. flavicauda*, lives in the Nearctic. This species is immediately distinguished from other species of Carabidae in the region by its small size, dull yellowish apical third of the elytra, and pale appendages.

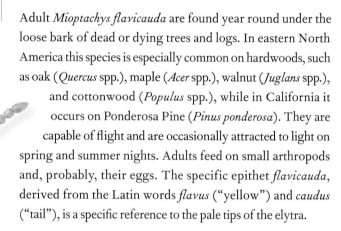

**Mioptachys flavicauda** is weakly convex, blackish to nearly black, with the apical third of elytra dull yellowish; the antennae and legs are yellowish brown. The eyes each have two setae below. The elytra have side margins that are broad, pale, and somewhat translucent. The underside of the abdomen has two setae on the last segment. Males have first two tarsomeres on the front legs expanded with pads of setae underneath.

| FAMILY | Carabidae |
|---|---|
| SUBFAMILY | Psydrinae |
| DISTRIBUTION | Nearctic, Palearctic: North America, southern Europe, and Middle East |
| MACROHABITAT | Mostly in coniferous forests |
| MICROHABITAT | Adults found under bark and debris |
| FEEDING HABITS | Unknown |
| NOTE | Adults defend themselves by producing a fetid odor |

ADULT LENGTH
¼–⁵⁄₁₆ in
(6–8 mm)

*NOMIUS PYGMAEUS*
# STINKING BEETLE
(DEJEAN, 1831)

81

Actual size

Stinking Beetle adults are most often found under loose bark, logs, rocks, and in leaf litter. When alarmed or experiencing a life-threatening event, such as becoming trapped in spider web, adults emit a noxious odor that resembles overripe cheese or a dead mouse that persists from just a few seconds to 30 minutes or more. It has been reported that an entire village was evacuated because of the smell. Fully winged adults are attracted to lights and smoke of forest fires, and sometimes find their way into homes. It is broadly distributed in Canada, the United States, Mexico, southern Europe, Cyprus, Morocco, and Iran.

### RELATED SPECIES
The three species of *Nomius* are distributed in the Northern Hemisphere and Afrotropical Realm. The Stinking Beetle is most easily distinguished from its nearest relatives by its northern distribution. In comparison with its nearest generic relative, the North American *Psydrus piceus* that lives under the bark of pine trees, only *Nomius* produces an odor.

**The Stinking Beetle** is reddish to black without a metallic luster. The first two antennomeres of the bead-like antennae are thickly clothed with short setae. The pronotum is almost twice as wide as it is long, with three or four setae along each side. The elytral surface is grooved and lacks any setae. The front tarsomeres of males are not expanded with setose pads underneath.

| FAMILY | Carabidae |
|---|---|
| SUBFAMILY | Paussinae |
| DISTRIBUTION | Australian: Australia (New South Wales, South Australia) |
| MACROHABITAT | Dry areas |
| MICROHABITAT | Adults live under surfaces (logs, bark); larvae are associated with ants |
| FEEDING HABITS | Presumed predators as adults; presumed predator of ants as larvae |
| NOTE | The potent antipredator chemical defenses of *Arthropterus* adults can cause lesions in humans |

ADULT LENGTH
⁹/₁₆–⅝ in
(15–16 mm)

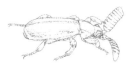

*ARTHROPTERUS WILSONI*
# ARTHROPTERUS WILSONI
(WESTWOOD, 1850)

Actual size

***Arthropterus wilsoni*** adults are reddish brown and rather flattened dorsoventrally, and the body is covered with small punctures dorsally. The antennae, which are flat, have segments 3–11 broadly expanded, about three times as broad as long, forming an oval structure. The head bears large, protruding eyes. The pronotum is slightly wider than long, with its sides sinuated posteriorly. The tibiae are wide and flat.

Based on field observations and morphological studies of species in the tribe Paussini, to which *Arthropterus wilsoni* belongs, it is assumed that these peculiar-looking beetles are obligate guests of ants (myrmecophile) for at least part of their life cycle. *Arthropterus* adults rarely occur with ants in nature and have predator-type mouthparts rather than the reduced and highly modified mouthparts of other Paussini that are associated with ants in the adult stage. These observations have led experts to hypothesize that the larval stage must be myrmecophile. Recent studies have shown that indeed the first-instar larva of an unknown species of *Arthropoterus* possesses unique structural features (such as a broad circular disk at the apex of the abdomen with extremely modified setae) that are consistent with habits in close association with ants.

## RELATED SPECIES
*Arthropterus* is closely related to *Megalopaussus* and *Mesarthropterus* (with one species each), as well as *Cerapterus* (with approximately 30 species). The genus *Arthropterus* contains about 65 species present in Australia, New Guinea, and New Caledonia. *Arthropterus wilsoni* belongs to the *A. macleayi* species group along with *A. wasmanni*, *A. macleayi*, *A. westwoodi*, and *A. angulatus*. This genus has been poorly studied and several species are known only from the specimens used in the original descriptions.

| FAMILY | Carabidae |
|---|---|
| SUBFAMILY | Brachininae |
| DISTRIBUTION | Neotropical: from Mexico (Yucatán) to Peru, Bolivia, Uruguay, and Argentina (Catamarca, Jujuy) |
| MACROHABITAT | Tropical ecosystems |
| MICROHABITAT | Sandy trails or riverine beaches |
| FEEDING HABITS | Adults are predators and scavengers; larvae feed on the eggs of mole crickets |
| NOTE | This is the most widespread species in the genus. Adults make a crackling sound when they discharge quinones from their abdominal defense glands |

ADULT LENGTH
⁹⁄₁₆–¾ in
(15–20 mm)

*PHEROPSOPHUS AEQUINOCTIALIS*

# PHEROPSOPHUS AEQUINOCTIALIS
(LINNAEUS, 1763)

83

Adults of this species are nocturnal, and usually found at night running along sandy trails or riverine beaches. During the day, they often hide in groups under stones, logs, or clumps of grass. They are generalist predators and scavengers on animal and plant materials. The larvae feed on the eggs of mole crickets, particularly those of the genus *Scapteriscus*, which are pests of turf and pasture grasses and vegetable seedlings. The species has been considered a potential biological control agent against mole crickets in the southeastern United States.

## RELATED SPECIES

The genus *Pheropsophus* belongs to the subtribe Pheropsophina in the tribe Brachinini. *Pheropsophus* includes approximately 125 species, which are grouped into three subgenera: *Pheropsophus*, with seven species endemic to the Neotropical Realm; *Aptinomorphus*, with two species from Madagascar; and *Stenaptinus*, with about 115 species present in the Eastern Hemisphere. The relationships between the numerous species have not been investigated.

**Pheropsophus aequinoctialis** is a robust species with a yellow to reddish-yellow head, antennae, pronotum, and legs, and yellow to reddish-yellow elytra with two large black spots on each side united along the suture. The mandibular scrobe has a single long seta. The elytra have well-defined, but low and rounded, costae. The front coxal cavities are closed behind and the propleural suture is absent.

Actual size

| FAMILY | Carabidae |
|---|---|
| SUBFAMILY | Harpalinae |
| DISTRIBUTION | Afrotropical: Africa (known at least from Botswana, Mozambique, Namibia, Tanzania, South Africa, and Zimbabwe) |
| MACROHABITAT | In open habitats, often with sparse trees such as the Silver Cluster-leaf (*Terminalia sericea*) |
| MICROHABITAT | On the ground surface |
| FEEDING HABITS | Predator |
| NOTE | *Anthia thoracica* and the sympatric carabid species *Thermophilum homoplatum* share similar color patterns, including large round or ovate "eyespots," and both possess chemical defense against predators |

ADULT LENGTH
1⅞–2⅛ in
(47–53 mm)

*ANTHIA THORACICA*
# ANTHIA THORACICA
(THUNBERG, 1784)

84

Adults of this species are mostly active from October to March, with a peak of activity in the months of November and December. They are usually found singly, walking rapidly on sand or gravel roads, or in open areas such as grasslands with scattered shrubs or trees. Although diurnal, they can also be encountered in the twilight or at night after a series of days without rain. The adults can eject defense secretions from their abdominal glands over a distance of 3 ft (1 m) or more, often directed at the head and eyes of a potential attacker.

RELATED SPECIES
*Anthia* includes about 20 species and is closely related to *Thermophilum*, which is considered as a subgenus of *Anthia* by some taxonomists. *Anthia maxillosa*, which lives in the same regions as *A. thoracica*, is similar but differs in the lack of setal patches on the pronotum and the lack of a band of white setae along the lateral margins of the elytra.

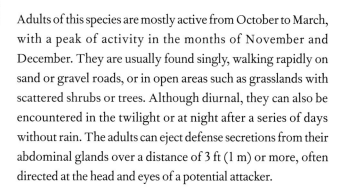

**Anthia thoracica** is a large black carabid conspicuous for the presence of large round patches of yellow or brown setae on the sides of the pronotum. The sexes are easily distinguished. The mandibles are markedly long and sickle-shaped in the male, and short and stout in the female. The pronotum has two large basal flanges projecting over the base of the elytra in the male, as opposed to two basal tubercles in the female.

Actual size

| FAMILY | Carabidae |
|---|---|
| SUBFAMILY | Harpalinae |
| DISTRIBUTION | Neotropical: Paraguay (Concepción, Alto Paraguay), Brazil (Mato Grosso) |
| MACROHABITAT | Forests |
| MICROHABITAT | Adults are usually found under logs |
| FEEDING HABITS | Feeding habits of both larvae and adults uncertain, probably predatory |
| NOTE | A colorful but rarely encountered ground beetle |

ADULT LENGTH
1–1³⁄₁₆ in
(25–30 mm)

*BRACHYGNATHUS ANGUSTICOLLIS*
# BRACHYGNATHUS ANGUSTICOLLIS
BURMEISTER, 1885

85

Despite the relatively large size and very attractive color of *Brachygnathus angusticollis*, almost nothing is known of the natural history of this beetle, or for that matter of any species of *Brachygnathus*. They are slow-moving insects, likely nocturnal, and are usually found hiding under logs in forests during the day. Although the feeding habits of the *Brachygnathus* species are uncertain, it is thought that they may feed on snails or millipedes, which are often found with them in abundance.

RELATED SPECIES

The genus *Brachygnathus* includes seven species that have various metallic colors dorsally and are all endemic to the Neotropical Realm. Its affinities to other genera are not well established and different taxonomic positions have been proposed to date. *Brachygnathus oxygonus* is superficially similar to *B. angusticollis* but has a proportionally shorter pronotum and more convex elytra, and the membranous small foveae on the sternites 4–6 are not semicircular but transversely stretched.

Actual size

**Brachygnathus angusticollis** is a beautifully colored beetle: The head, pronotum, and sides of the elytra are green and the disk of the elytra is metallic red. As its specific name implies, the pronotum is narrow and elongate, its posterior angles projected posteriorly as sharp spines, the anterior angles somewhat lobed, and the anterior margin not bordered. The elytral striae have coarse punctures on the basal half of the elytra and the base of each abdominal sternite 4–6 has a pair of semicircular foveae of membranous appearance.

| FAMILY | Carabidae |
| --- | --- |
| SUBFAMILY | Harpalinae |
| DISTRIBUTION | Neotropical: Guatemala, Nicaragua, Costa Rica, Panama, Colombia, Ecuador |
| MACROHABITAT | Tropical forests |
| MICROHABITAT | On vegetation, in rolled leaves |
| FEEDING HABITS | Probably herbivorous |
| NOTE | Possesses morphological adaptations typical of arboreal beetles |

ADULT LENGTH
$^{7}/_{16}$–½ in
(11–13 mm)

86

*CALOPHAENA BICINCTA LIGATA*
# CALOPHAENA BICINCTA LIGATA
BATES, 1883

*Calophaena bicincta ligata* adults are commonly found in daytime in rolled leaves of plants in the family Marantaceae (primarily on *Calathea lutea*), often with hispine beetles of the genus *Cephaloleia* (family Chrysomelidae). There seems to be no apparent aggressive interaction between individual carabid and chrysomelid beetles that occur within the same leaf roll. Several adaptations such as specialized adhesive setae on their tarsi, bilobed tarsomeres, pectinate (comb-like) tarsal claws, and an elongate prothorax are characteristic of beetle species associated with vegetation. It has been speculated that individuals of *Calophaena bicincta ligata* take up chemicals from their host plants (flavonoids produced for defense against herbivores) and use them for their own chemical defense.

RELATED SPECIES

The genus *Calophaena*, which belongs to the tribe Calophaenini, contains nearly 50 described species in the Neotropical Realm. *Calophaenoidea*, which includes a single Neotropical species (*C. arrowi*), differs from *Calophaena* in having markedly expanded sides to its pronotum and distinct lobes at the anterior angles of the pronotum (especially prominent in males). Species of *Calophaena* can be separated, in part, by differences in their color patterns.

**Calophaena bicincta ligata** is an elongate, flattened ground beetle with a long, narrow pronotum, long legs, and long antennae. The body is pale yellowish brown except for the prominent black hemispherical compound eyes and the two black transverse bands on the elytra. Tarsomere 4 is deeply bilobed.

Actual size

| FAMILY | Carabidae |
|---|---|
| SUBFAMILY | Harpalinae |
| DISTRIBUTION | Palearctic: southern Europe, North Africa, and Canary Islands east to Iran |
| MACROHABITAT | Wetlands |
| MICROHABITAT | Near water bodies such as pools, ponds, and streams |
| FEEDING HABITS | Predator |
| NOTE | The larva feeds upon amphibians |

ADULT LENGTH
$^{11}/_{16}$–$^{15}/_{16}$ in
(18–24 mm)

*CHLAENIUS CIRCUMSCRIPTUS*

# CHLAENIUS CIRCUMSCRIPTUS
(DUFTSCHMID, 1812)

87

The adults of *Chlaenius circumscriptus* feed on a variety of food items, including frogs and salamanders, but the larvae prey exclusively on live amphibians. The larva waits and lures the amphibian by unique movements of its antennae and mandibles, which draw the attention of the vertebrate to a potential prey. When the amphibian approaches the movement, the larva almost always succeeds to avoid the predator's tongue and takes the opportunity to attach itself to the amphibian with its specialized hooked mandibles. This is a rare case where a small invertebrate preys on a larger vertebrate. Extinction of several populations has been reported in parts of its range.

RELATED SPECIES

This species belongs to the subgenus *Epomis*, which is considered by some taxonomists as a distinct genus. The group contains about 30 species in Eurasia and Africa. *Chlaenius dejeanii*, from the eastern Mediterranean region, differs in that it is slightly smaller (⅝–¾ in, or 16–19 mm), the shape of the pronotum differs slightly, and the lateral intervals of the elytra are more punctate.

Actual size

**Chlaenius circumscriptus** is a black carabid with a greenish or bluish metallic luster and contrastingly paler, yellowish lateral margins of the elytra. The antennae and legs are pale reddish yellow or brownish yellow. The coarsely punctate pronotum is slightly larger than long, its maximum width at the middle or slightly before, and the posterior angles rounded. The sides of the elytra are nearly parallel and the elytral striae are conspicuous.

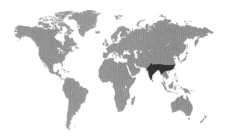

| FAMILY | Carabidae |
|---|---|
| SUBFAMILY | Harpalinae |
| DISTRIBUTION | Oriental and Palearctic: India, Bangladesh, Burma, southern China |
| MACROHABITAT | Open forests |
| MICROHABITAT | Under rocks and logs |
| FEEDING HABITS | Predator |
| NOTE | The distinct color pattern on these beetles, which can release potent chemical secretions from their abdomen, acts as a warning system to potential predators |

ADULT LENGTH
11/16–1 in
(18–25 mm)

88

CRASPEDOPHORUS ANGULATUS
# CRASPEDOPHORUS ANGULATUS
(FABRICIUS, 1781)

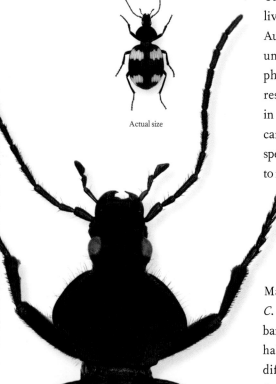

Actual size

There are about 150 species in the genus *Craspedophorus*, which live in southern Asia, sub-Saharan Africa, Madagascar, and Australia. Adults of *Craspedophorus*, which are typically found under rocks and logs, secrete a strong repellent (mostly phenols) produced by specialized abdominal glands. The reservoirs that hold the defense secretions are rather large in species of *Craspedophorus* compared with those of other carabids. Last-instar nymphs of an unidentified cockroach species from Vietnam, also black with four yellow spots, appear to mimic adults of *C. sublaevis*, with which they cohabit in a case of Batesian mimicry. *Craspedophorus angulatus* is very similar to *C. sublaevis* in shape and coloration, but it is uncertain whether it is also part of a mimicry complex.

### RELATED SPECIES

Many species of *Craspedophorus* are externally similar to *C. angulatus*, having black elytra with two yellow transverse bands, one in the anterior half and the other in the posterior half. The genus has not been revised and the structural differences between the species are not well established. Approximately ten species have been reported from India and Sri Lanka, including *C. hexagonus* and *C. pubiger*.

**Craspedophorus angulatus** is a large carabid with conspicuous, dense, suberect setae over the pronotum, elytra, and part of the head. The upper surface is black with two yellow bands on each side of the elytra, the posterior one half-moon-shaped. The last segment of each palp is strongly securiform (triangular and compressed) and the pronotum densely punctate. The metepisternum is very short and transverse.

| FAMILY | Carabidae |
|---|---|
| SUBFAMILY | Harpalinae |
| DISTRIBUTION | Oriental: Vietnam, Laos, southern India, Sri Lanka |
| MACROHABITAT | Near water bodies |
| MICROHABITAT | On the surface of, or in, sand |
| FEEDING HABITS | Predators |
| NOTE | The body shape and modified front legs of this species enable individuals to dig efficiently in sand |

*CYCLOSOMUS FLEXUOSUS*

# CYCLOSOMUS FLEXUOSUS

(FABRICIUS, 1775)

89

Adults of this genus superficially resemble those of the carabid genus *Omophron*, however the two genera are not closely related and belong to different subfamilies. Both *Cyclosomus* and *Omophron* share a number of morphological similarities such as an oval body form, expansion and prolongation of the prosternal process, and a similar color pattern. *Cyclosomus* species are associated with sandy microhabitats and use their modified front legs to burrow in the substrate. *Cyclosomus flexuosus*, a fast runner and digger, is one of 13 species currently recognized in this genus.

### RELATED SPECIES

*Cyclosomus suturalis*, which shares the same distribution as *C. flexuosus*, is smaller and more oval, with the lateral margins of the pronotum clearly paler than the disk and the diskal band of the elytra less expanded laterally. *Cyclosomus inustus*, described from specimens collected in Hong Kong, is said to have slightly shorter elytra, shallower elytral striae, and a narrower diskal band of the elytra than *C. flexuosus*.

Actual size

**Cyclosomus flexuosus** is an oval carabid with a uniformly reddish-brown head, reddish-brown pronotum with slightly paler lateral margins, and orange elytra with a characteristic black pattern. The sides of the pronotum are more or less parallel in the basal half and the anterior angles protrude; there is one mid-lateral seta on each side. The first three tarsomeres of the front and middle legs in the male have adhesive setae underneath.

| FAMILY | Carabidae |
|---|---|
| SUBFAMILY | Harpalinae |
| DISTRIBUTION | Nearctic: eastern United States |
| MACROHABITAT | Eastern lowland and montane deciduous forests |
| MICROHABITAT | Ground-dwelling adults live in open habitats |
| FEEDING HABITS | Adults prey on snails, grubs, earthworms, and other invertebrates |
| NOTE | The most colorful of all *Dicaelus* species |

ADULT LENGTH
¾–1 in
(20–25 mm)

*DICAELUS PURPURATUS*
# DICAELUS PURPURATUS
BONELLI, 1813

Adult *Dicaelus purpuratus* are flightless and defend themselves by emitting smoke-like or dark-colored defensive fluid from their anus that consists mostly of formic acid. They inhabit upland and floodplain deciduous forests, old fields, and pastures, and are active during the evening from spring through fall. They spend their days under loose bark of fallen trees, or under logs and rocks. When preying on snails, they use their powerful mandibles to bite through the shell. The active larvae inhabit rotten logs or live under stones and, like the adults, will defend themselves by ejecting a dark fluid from their anus.

### RELATED SPECIES
Sixteen species of *Dicaelus* are restricted to the temperate and tropical zones of Canada, the United States, and Mexico. *Dicaelus purpuratus* is distinguished from other species in the genus by its purple or violet color, sculpturing of the elytral surface, and an abdominal patch of setae. The subspecies *D. p. splendidus* is coppery-red or green, and ranges from Minnesota and Louisiana to North Dakota and Arizona.

**Dicaelus purpuratus** is purplish or violet with a broad head with two seta-bearing punctures over each eye. The pronotum is wider than the head. The elytra are fused down the middle and the spaces in between the elytral grooves are evenly raised and convex. The last abdominal segment has a patch of punctures underneath bearing short setae near the tip.

Actual size

| FAMILY | Carabidae |
|---|---|
| SUBFAMILY | Harpalinae |
| DISTRIBUTION | Nearctic: eastern North America to Idaho, Nevada, and Arizona |
| MACROHABITAT | Sparsely vegetated, well-drained soils, especially near water |
| MICROHABITAT | At night adults are found slowly walking on ground |
| FEEDING HABITS | Adults feed on seedlings and prey on caterpillars |
| NOTE | Sometimes considered a minor economic pest |

ADULT LENGTH
½–¹¹⁄₁₆ in
(13–17 mm)

*GEOPINUS INCRASSATUS*

# GEOPINUS INCRASSATUS

(DEJEAN, 1829)

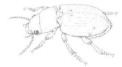

91

*Geopinus incrassatus* are relatively large and clumsy-looking beetles. Their pale yellowish-brown body helps to camouflage them against pale, sandy substrates. The rakelike front legs are adapted for burrowing and the beetles are capable of digging deep into damp, sandy soils. They are sometimes found under well-embedded logs, pieces of wood, and rocks. The fully-winged adults are sometimes encountered swarming around lights on summer nights. This species is sometimes a minor pest when they eat seedlings in seed beds in agricultural systems, especially in wheat, cabbage, flax, corn, and oat fields.

## RELATED SPECIES

*Geopinus incrassatus* is the sole species in the genus. The robust body and legs, well adapted for digging, are distinctive. The morphological characteristics of both adults and larvae suggest that it is an aberrant species of *Anisodactylus*, a genus that requires further study and may eventually be broken up into several different genera.

**Geopinus incrassatus** is robust, convex, and pale reddish yellow-brown with diffuse darker areas on the pronotum and elytra. The short, broad head has grooves in front of the eyes to receive the first antennomere and strongly curved mandibles. The elytra lack distinct seta-bearing punctures. Males have tarsomeres 2–4 of the front legs moderately expanded with sparsely spongy setose pads underneath.

Actual size

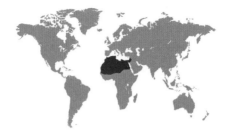

| FAMILY | Carabidae |
|---|---|
| SUBFAMILY | Harpalinae |
| DISTRIBUTION | Palearctic and Afrotropical: northern Africa (from western Mauritania to the Sinai Peninsula), Israel, and Jordan |
| MACROHABITAT | Savannas and semidesert areas |
| MICROHABITAT | Ground-dwelling |
| FEEDING HABITS | Predator |
| NOTE | The only species of *Graphipterus* that is able to stridulate, making a screeching sound by rubbing its femora against the elytra |

ADULT LENGTH
⅜–¾ in
(10–19 mm)

92

*GRAPHIPTERUS SERRATOR*
# GRAPHIPTERUS SERRATOR
(FORSKÅL, 1775)

*Graphipterus serrator* is a characteristic species in savannas and semidesert areas of northern Africa, Israel, and Jordan. The adults are fast-running and active during the day. They avoid the highest temperatures by hiding under vegetation or burrowing in the soil. The three larval stages of this beetle live in association with nests of several species of ants, usually in a burrow near the ants' brood chambers (where the ants keep their eggs and larvae). The unique channeled mandibles in the first and second larval stages of *G. serrator* are specialized for feeding on the ants' brood.

## RELATED SPECIES

The genus *Graphipterus* contains about 140 species, the vast majority living on the African continent. *Graphipterus minutus*, which occurs in northern Saudi Arabia, Jordan, Syria, Iraq, and Iran, is the species most closely related to *G. serrator* based on structural characters of the adult but it has no stridulatory apparatus. The six known subspecies of *G. serrator* differ mainly by details of the elytral pattern.

**Graphipterus serrator** is a medium-size carabid whose upper surface is covered with black and white scales, producing an attractive coloration pattern. This is the only species of the genus with a stridulatory apparatus consisting of fine serration along the epipleuron and lateral side of the abdomen and of a smooth longitudinal ridge along the medial side of the hind femur. The rubbing of the femora against the serrate sides of the elytra and abdomen produces a peculiar screeching sound.

Actual size

| FAMILY | Carabidae |
|---|---|
| SUBFAMILY | Harpalinae |
| DISTRIBUTION | Nearctic: eastern North America (New Hampshire to southeastern Wyoming and northern Colorado, south to Oklahoma, Arkansas and northeastern Georgia) |
| MACROHABITAT | Forests |
| MICROHABITAT | Under stones and logs |
| FEEDING HABITS | Predators |
| NOTE | The characteristic first-instar larva of this species possesses stout, dorsally fixed urogomphi near the apex of the abdomen, which bears numerous long setae |

ADULT LENGTH
½–¹¹⁄₁₆ in
(12–17 mm)

HELLUOMORPHOIDES PRAEUSTUS BICOLOR
# HELLUOMORPHOIDES PRAEUSTUS BICOLOR
(HARRIS, 1828)

93

Adults of some species of *Helluomorphoides* (e.g., *H. latitarsis* and *H. ferrugineus*) have been observed plundering foraging and migrating columns of army ants of the genus *Neivamyrmex* and running away with their prey and broods. This behavior probably occurs in *H. praeustus bicolor* also, but this remains to be documented. The chemical secretions produced by abdominal glands of adults enable them to repel the ants. The flight wings of adult *H. p. bicolor* are fully developed but their ability to fly has not yet been confirmed.

## RELATED SPECIES
*Helluomorphoides ferrugineus*, ranging from New Jersey to South Carolina and west to Arizona and Utah, is probably the species most closely related to *H. praeustus*. Adults differ mainly in the shape of the male genitalia. Three subspecies of *H. praeustus* are currently recognized and separated from each other by their coloration and by the relative length of antennal segments 5–10.

Actual size

**Helluomorphoides praeustus bicolor** is a medium-size, flattened carabid with a reddish-brown head and pronotum and black elytra, except usually near the base. Antennal segments 5–10 are broadened. The pronotum is slightly constricted posteriorly and coarsely but somewhat sparsely punctate, except for two narrow longitudinal areas near the middle. The elytral striae are densely and confusedly punctate.

| FAMILY | Carabidae |
|---|---|
| SUBFAMILY | Harpalinae |
| DISTRIBUTION | Australian: New South Wales, Victoria, and South Australia |
| MACROHABITAT | Dry forests |
| MICROHABITAT | Associated with decomposing logs |
| FEEDING HABITS | Predator |
| NOTE | One of the longest species in the diverse family Carabidae |

ADULT LENGTH
1⁹⁄₁₆–2¹⁵⁄₁₆ in
(40–75 mm)

94

*HYPERION SCHROETTERI*
# HYPERION SCHROETTERI
(SCHREIBERS, 1802)

*Hyperion schroetteri* is one of the longest species of Carabidae of the world, reaching nearly 3 in (80 mm) in length. It is endemic to southern Australia, where it is usually found in dry areas. The species is rarely collected but specimens have been found in and under rotten logs and in decaying debris in tree hollows. Some individuals are also attracted to light at night. It probably feeds on scarabaeoid beetle larvae and other invertebrates.

RELATED SPECIES

The genus *Hyperion* comprises a single species. It belongs to the tribe Morionini and is believed to be closely related to the genera *Morion* (with about 40 species worldwide), *Megamorio* (with six species in Africa), and *Platynodes* (with one species in Africa). Overall, about 85 species are currently recognized in the tribe Morionini.

**Hyperion schroetteri** is a parallel-sided, elongate black beetle of great size. It has powerful jaws capable of nipping quite severely. The antennal segments are bead-like, the head has large eyes, prominent temples, and deeply impressed frontal impressions, and the pronotum is broadest anteriorly, without setae along the lateral margins, and with deep, linear basal impressions.

Actual size

| FAMILY | Carabidae |
|---|---|
| SUBFAMILY | Harpalinae |
| DISTRIBUTION | Oriental: Malay Archipelago (Borneo, Java, Malaysia, Sumatra) |
| MACROHABITAT | Rainforest |
| MICROHABITAT | Ground-dwelling |
| FEEDING HABITS | Adult feeding habits are uncertain; larvae feed on fungi |
| NOTE | Species of *Mormolyce*, commonly referred to as fiddle, violin, or banjo beetles, are prized by collectors |

ADULT LENGTH
2⅜–3½ in
(60–90 mm)

*MORMOLYCE PHYLLODES*

# JAVAN FIDDLE BEETLE

HAGENBACH, 1825

95

This was the first species described in the genus *Mormolyce* and was named *phyllodes* ("leaflike") because of its resemblance to a dead leaf. It lives in rainforests, where the adults are usually found under tree trunks lying on the ground. The larvae develop for eight to nine months in chambers they dig in *Polyporus* fungi growing on dead trees. The female apparently lays a single egg in suitable fungi. This beetle was included on the International Union for Conservation of Nature's Red List of Threatened Species in 1990 but was removed in 1996.

## RELATED SPECIES

The genus *Mormolyce* includes five species occurring in the Malay Archipelago. Because of the spectacular body form of the species, the genus was isolated in its own tribe in the past, but many taxonomists now agree that it belongs to the diverse and widespread subtribe Pericalina of the tribe Lebiini. *Mormolyce* species differ mostly by the shape of the pronotum and basal edge of the elytra.

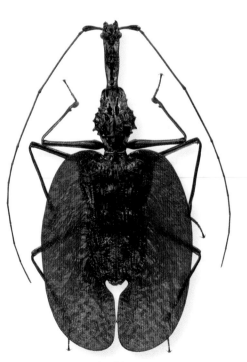

**The Javan Fiddle Beetle** is very distinctive, with a large, flat, leaf-shaped body and expanded translucent sides to the elytra. The antennae are long, reaching behind the middle of the elytra, and the legs are slender. The pronotum is slightly elongate, widest in the basal two-thirds, and its sides are denticulate.

Actual size

| FAMILY | Carabidae |
| --- | --- |
| SUBFAMILY | Harpalinae |
| DISTRIBUTION | Oriental: southern and southeastern Asia from India to China and Japan, including Sri Lanka and the Maluku Islands (Moluccas) |
| MACROHABITAT | Open fields |
| MICROHABITAT | On vegetation |
| FEEDING HABITS | Predator |
| NOTE | An important predator of several arthropod pest species |

ADULT LENGTH
¼–⁵⁄₁₆ in
(6.5–8 mm)

96

*OPHIONEA INDICA*
# OPHIONEA INDICA
(THUNBERG, 1784)

With its distinctive coloration, *Ophionea indica* is a characteristic element of southern Asia. The species is commonly found in rice paddies, where the adults can be observed on leaves. It is an important predator of nymphs and adults of the Brown Planthopper (*Nilaparvata lugens*) and other rice pests in Asia such as the Asian Rice Gall Midge (*Orseolia oryzae*), the Asiatic Rice Borer (*Chilo suppressalis*), and the Pink Stemborer (*Sesamia inferens*). *Ophionea indica* can also be found in fields of other crops.

## RELATED SPECIES

*Ophionea* includes approximately 20 species in the Oriental and Australian realms. *Ophionea nigrofasciata*, from southeastern Asia, is similar but the base of the elytra is reddish brown, not black. *Ophionea interstitialis*, also from southeastern Asia, has a pair of lateral setae on the pronotum and only two white spots on the elytra.

Actual size

**Ophionea indica** is a relatively small and narrow carabid. The head is black with a metallic luster, the pronotum is reddish brown, and the elytra are reddish brown with the base and a wide band just behind the middle black with a metallic luster and four small white spots. The legs are yellowish brown except that the apex of each femur is darker. The pronotum is elongate, convex, and nearly cylindrical, and lacks lateral setae.

| FAMILY | Carabidae |
|---|---|
| SUBFAMILY | Harpalinae |
| DISTRIBUTION | Nearctic: eastern United States |
| MACROHABITAT | Lowlands |
| MICROHABITAT | On the ground surface, often on wet soil consisting of wet sand |
| FEEDING HABITS | Predators |
| NOTE | Adults of this species are strong burrowers |

*PANAGAEUS CRUCIGER*
# PANAGAEUS CRUCIGER
SAY, 1823

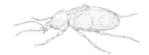

97

Many individuals of the nocturnal *Panagaeus cruciger* in natural-history collections have been found either at night near artificial lights or obtained from drift material along the seashore. Dead adults along the seashore were probably carried into the water by the wind during their flight. Individuals are known to occur along the edge of saline marshes or in meadows near the sea, where they hide at the base of plants, or under pieces of wood and stones. Published reports suggest that this species overwinters in ant nests.

RELATED SPECIES

*Panagaeus* includes 14 species in North America and Eurasia. Two other species (*P. fasciatus* and *P. sallei*) also occur in the United States. *Panagaeus fasciatus* is smaller with a reddish or reddish-brown head and pronotum, and a black transverse median elytral band that does not extend along the midline anteriorly to the base or posteriorly to the apex of the elytra. *Panagaeus sallei* has a longer pronotal sinuation near the base and the black transverse median elytral band does not reach the middle of the elytra.

Actual size

**Panagaeus cruciger** is a broad carabid, covered dorsally with relatively dense, quite long, erect setae. The body is black with two orange spots on the elytra. The black transverse median band on the elytra reaches the midline, where it narrowly extends anteriorly to the base and posteriorly to the apex of the elytra. The eyes are protruding and the last segment of the maxillary and labial palps are compressed and triangular.

| FAMILY | Carabidae |
|---|---|
| SUBFAMILY | Harpalinae |
| DISTRIBUTION | Afrotropical: from Liberia east to Uganda, and south at least to southeastern Democratic Republic of the Congo |
| MACROHABITAT | Forests |
| MICROHABITAT | Probably under bark |
| FEEDING HABITS | Predator |
| NOTE | Has an unusually flat body |

ADULT LENGTH
1¹⁄₁₆–1³⁄₁₆ in
(27–30 mm)

98

*PLATYNODES WESTERMANNI*

# PLATYNODES WESTERMANNI

WESTWOOD, 1847

The genus *Platynodes* includes a single African species. Although little is known about its habits, it is likely that the adults occur under the bark of dead trees or logs based on their markedly flat body shape. As for other members of the tribe Morionini for which information is available, *P. westermanni* is probably nocturnal and carnivorous, feeding on small and medium-size arthropods. The males have broadened front tarsi that bear setae on their ventral surface that are longer than those in females. The specific function of these longer setae is not known.

## RELATED SPECIES

*Platynodes* is closely related to *Megamorio*, an African genus with six species. Members of *Megamorio* differ in having much less developed temples and a more convex body. Two subspecies of *P. westermanni* are currently recognized: *P. w. westermanni* and *P. w. peregrinus*, in which the middle and last segments of the antennae are slightly shorter and the seventh interval of the elytron is less carinate than in *P. w. westermanni*.

**Platynodes westermanni** is a medium-size, markedly flat black carabid. The eyes are relatively small but protruding. The temples are large and prominent, and the frontal furrows are broad, deep, and sharply defined. The pronotum is markedly constricted posteriorly and has lateral setae. The apex of the prosternal process is broadly expanded. The seventh elytral interval is more or less carinate over its entire length.

Actual size

| FAMILY | Carabidae |
|---|---|
| SUBFAMILY | Harpalinae |
| DISTRIBUTION | Australian: Australian Capital Territory, New South Wales, Queensland, South Australia, Victoria |
| MACROHABITAT | Forests with *Eucalyptus* trees |
| MICROHABITAT | Adults are arboreal; larvae dig in holes in the ground |
| FEEDING HABITS | Predator on ants (especially the Meat Ant, *Iridomyrmex purpureus*) |
| NOTE | The short, retractable legs and antennae of adults in this genus are thought to be adaptations for living with ants |

ADULT LENGTH
⅛–⁷⁄₁₆ in
(8.5–11 mm)

*SPHALLOMORPHA NITIDULOIDES*
# SPHALLOMORPHA NITIDULOIDES
GUÉRIN-MÉNEVILLE, 1844

99

This commonly collected species, which belongs to the tribe Pseudomorphini, is nocturnal, although adults have been collected during daytime under the bark of *Eucalyptus* trees. Known larvae of *Sphallomorpha*, including those of *S. nitiduloides*, dig holes in the ground around ant nests, where they capture and feed on passing ants. This behavior is very similar to that observed in tiger beetle larvae of the carabid subfamily Cicindelinae. Some species in this tribe are ovoviviparous (the females produce eggs that hatch within their body), but this has not been confirmed in *Sphallomorpha*.

### RELATED SPECIES
*Sphallomorpha* is a large genus of more than 135 species, most found in Australia and a few in New Guinea. *Sphallomorpha nitiduloides* belongs to a group of nine fairly similar species distributed over the majority of mainland Australia, though most are found in the northern tropical region. This species is externally very similar to *S. picta*; the two can be differentiated with confidence only by the structures of the internal sac of the male genitalia.

Actual size

**Sphallomorpha nitiduloides** is a wide, flattened carabid with the characteristic habitus of all species of Pseudomorphini. The pronotum is reddish with wide yellow lateral margins. The elytra are reddish-black to black, with a neat anchor-shaped yellow band along the middle. The labrum has four setae and the elytra lack a fringe of elongate setae.

| FAMILY | Carabidae |
|---|---|
| SUBFAMILY | Harpalinae |
| DISTRIBUTION | Neotropical: east of, or on the lower eastern slopes of, the Andes in Venezuela, Brazil, Colombia, Peru, Bolivia, Paraguay, and Argentina |
| MACROHABITAT | Along streams and rivers in lowland areas |
| MICROHABITAT | Sandy riverbanks |
| FEEDING HABITS | Predator, probably on other small arthropods |
| NOTE | Adults and larvae can sometimes be found together in large numbers after sunset |

**ADULT LENGTH**
⅝ – ¾ in
(16–19 mm)

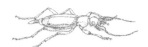

100

*TRICHOGNATHUS MARGINIPENNIS*
# TRICHOGNATHUS MARGINIPENNIS
LATREILLE, 1829

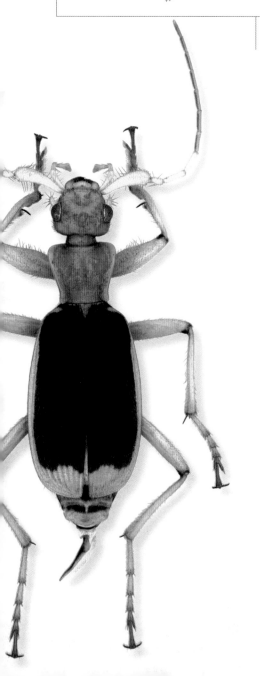

Both adults and the long-legged larvae of *Trichognathus marginipennis* are fast-running, nocturnal predators and are known to search for their prey, sometimes together, on sandy beaches along streams and rivers. The adults can be found hiding during the day under rocks and debris along river edges covered with vegetation. The flight wings of adults are fully developed and they can therefore probably fly. The recently described pupa has five pairs of long, stalk-like abdominal projections that extend laterally, the specific function of which remains uncertain.

RELATED SPECIES

The genus *Trichognathus*, which belongs to the tribe Galeritini, includes a single variable species. It appears to be closely related to the African genus *Eunostus*, which includes 14 species. *Trichognathus marginipennis* differs from the other Galeritini species in South America by the first antennal segment, which bears two rows of setae underneath, and the presence of a large tubercle with spine-like setae at the base of each maxilla.

Actual size

**Trichognathus marginipennis** is a medium-size carabid with a light reddish-brown head and pronotum, bluish-green elytra that usually have yellow lateral and apical margins, and yellow antennae and legs, although the femora are often partly darker. The surface is covered with fine, sparse pubescence. The head is almost as wide as the pronotum and the eyes are relatively small but prominent. The pronotum is constricted basally and the elytra are convex, with their maximum width behind the middle.

| FAMILY | Haliplidae |
|---|---|
| SUBFAMILY | |
| DISTRIBUTION | Nearctic: eastern North America to Wisconsin and Louisiana |
| MACROHABITAT | Margins of ditches, woodland pools, swamps, ponds, and lakes |
| MICROHABITAT | Weedy margins among dense mats of vegetation and algae |
| FEEDING HABITS | Adults are omnivorous; larvae feed on algae |
| NOTE | Adults can remain submerged under water for long periods by storing a bubble of air between their elytra and abdomen |

ADULT LENGTH
³⁄₁₆ in
(4–5 mm)

*HALIPLUS LEOPARDUS*

# HALIPLUS LEOPARDUS

ROBERTS, 1913

101

Actual size

Underwater, *Haliplus leopardus* and other haliplids move their legs alternately, which is more suggestive of crawling than swimming, hence the common name for the family, crawling water beetles. Adults are typically found at the water's edge in dense mats of algae growing among aquatic vegetation. They must periodically rise to the water's surface to replenish the supply of air that is stored underneath the elytra and greatly expanded hind coxal plates. *Haliplus* larvae are also aquatic and respire via short microtrichial gills. Although this species was originally described from Massachusetts, it is widely distributed in eastern North America.

## RELATED SPECIES

The genus *Haliplus* is distributed worldwide and is likely not monophyletic. It includes 56 species in the New World, of which 43 are recorded in North America. *Haliplus leopardus* is placed in the subgenus *Paraliaphlus*. It is distinguished from other species in the region by its relatively large size, lack of anterior pronotal margin at the sides, and the coarse surface sculpturing of the middle trochanters.

**Haliplus leopardus** has a large medial spot in front of the pronotum. The elytra are broadly oval, broadest just before their bases, each has seven large, uneven spots, and the base and suture are broadly black. The elytral tips are obtuse, not sinuate, and slightly oblique. The elongate middle trochanter has several deep, coarse punctures. In males the front and middle tarsi are thickened.

| FAMILY | Meruidae |
|---|---|
| SUBFAMILY | |
| DISTRIBUTION | Neotropical: Venezuela |
| MACROHABITAT | Tropical rainforest |
| MICROHABITAT | Whitewater waterfall flowing over a broad expanse of bedrock and rock seepages |
| FEEDING HABITS | Not yet determined |
| NOTE | This is the only species of Meruidae; larvae were described for the first time in 2011 |

**ADULT LENGTH**
¹⁄₃₂ in
(0.8–0.9 mm)

*MERU PHYLLISAE*
# COMB-CLAWED CASCADE BEETLE
SPANGLER & STEINER, 2005

Actual size

The Comb-clawed Cascade Beetle is known from a single locality in the Amazonas district of Venezuela, where most of the beetles observed were found crawling on the broad, shallow surface and margins of a whitewater cascade flowing over exposed granite bedrock. Beetles in the laboratory spend most of their time crawling over submerged dead leaves but sometimes float to the surface, where they walk upside down underneath the surface film in a manner similar to that of hydraenid and very small hydrophilid beetles. While underwater, it appears they draw their oxygen supply from air bubbles trapped under their elytra. Those kept in captivity lived just over six months.

## RELATED SPECIES

*Meru phyllisae* is the only species in the family Meruidae, a family of beetles that is most closely related to the aquatic Adephaga, especially the burrowing water beetles (Noteridae), as well as the amphizoid beetles (Amphizoidae), cliff water beetles (Aspidytidae), crawling water beetles (Haliplidae), hygrobiid beetles (Hygrobiidae), and predacious diving beetles (Dytiscidae). It is distinguished from those families by having hind coxae extensively fused to the abdomen and by microscopic internal features.

**The Comb-clawed Cascade Beetle** is egg-shaped, light to dark brown, and has large, shallow punctures bearing soft, flat, wrinkled setae. The conspicuous eyes are coarsely faceted. The convex pronotum is narrower than the base of the elytra. The scutellum is not visible. The convex elytra are widest behind the base and have rows of large deep punctures. The tarsal formula is 5-5-5, and the claws are large and pectinate. The first three of the five abdominal ventrites are fused.

| FAMILY | Noteridae |
|---|---|
| SUBFAMILY | Noterinae |
| DISTRIBUTION | Oriental and Palearctic: Andaman Islands, Sri Lanka, India, Bangladesh, Burma, Vietnam, Malaysia, Indonesia, Japan, China, Nepal, Pakistan, Iraq |
| MACROHABITAT | Shallow water bodies |
| MICROHABITAT | On debris, submerged plants, or the substrate |
| FEEDING HABITS | Predator and occasional scavenger |
| NOTE | Species in this family are commonly referred to as burrowing water beetles because the adults tend to burrow through the substrate of small freshwater bodies |

ADULT LENGTH
¹⁄₁₆ in
(1.8–2.2 mm)

*NEOHYDROCOPTUS SUBVITTULUS*

# NEOHYDROCOPTUS SUBVITTULUS
(MOTSCHULSKY, 1859)

103

Actual size

This small aquatic species is widely distributed in Asia. It lives primarily in ponds, swamps, and irrigation ditches in shallow, muddy water rich in aquatic vascular plants. Pupation takes place underwater in an airtight pupal cell prepared by the larva and attached to the roots of aquatic plants. Larvae and adults are primarily carnivorous, feeding on wide variety of small aquatic invertebrates, including fly larvae (primarily in the family Chironomidae) and insect eggs, though they may also scavenge on dead insects. The adults have fully developed flight wings and are attracted to artificial lights at night.

## RELATED SPECIES

The genus *Neohydrocoptus* is placed in its own tribe Neohydrocoptini, and includes 28 Asian and African species. Two subspecies are recognized as valid: the typical form *N. subvittulus subvittulus*, widely distributed in Asia; and *N. s. seychellensis* from the Seychelles. Adults of the latter form differ in having a narrower body, more superficial punctation, and a slightly differently colored longitudinal band on the elytral disk.

**Neohydrocoptus subvittulus** is a small oblong, convex beetle. The head and pronotum are rather pale reddish brown and the elytra are dark brown with a short, paler longitudinal band in the middle. The two apical spurs of the front tibiae are straight and subequal in length (or almost so). The pronotum does not have depressions near the posterior angles—a few punctures are present in that area at most. The posterior edge of the hind coxal process is distinctly notched in the center.

| FAMILY | Amphizoidae |
|---|---|
| SUBFAMILY | Amphizoinae |
| DISTRIBUTION | Nearctic: western North America |
| MACROHABITAT | Cool and cold mountain streams |
| MICROHABITAT | Semiaquatic adults and larvae found among rocks, roots, and debris |
| FEEDING HABITS | Adults and larvae scavenge dead terrestrial and aquatic insects |
| NOTE | Threatened adults secrete a yellowish anal fluid that smells of rotten wood |

**ADULT LENGTH**
$^{7}/_{16}$–$^{9}/_{16}$ in
(11–15 mm)

104

*AMPHIZOA INSOLENS*
# AMPHIZOA INSOLENS
LECONTE, 1853

Adults and larvae of *Amphizoa insolens* are poor swimmers, and yet are found in cool or cold, slow- or fast-flowing streams at the bases of waterfalls, under rocks, on coarse gravel along the shore, clinging to exposed roots beneath undercut banks, or on floating debris in backwater eddies. They are especially common along stretches of slow-moving waters and streams that do not drop steeply. Mature larvae pupate well away from water. This species ranges from southeastern Alaska and southern Yukon to the San Gabriel, San Bernardino, and San Jacinto mountains of southern California, and east of the Rocky Mountains south to northeast Nevada and northwest Wyoming.

RELATED SPECIES

*Amphizoa* is the sole genus in the family Amphizoidae and consists of five species, including two from central and eastern China and North Korea, and three from western North America. *Amphizoa insolens* is distinguished from these species by the convex and oval elytra and the finely notched side margins of the pronotum.

Actual size

**Amphizoa insolens** is elongate-oval, broad, and dull dark brown to black. The pronotum has finely notched sides with the middle as broad as the base. The elytra are somewhat egg-shaped in outline, slightly narrowed at the base and slightly broader just before the apex, with a convex surface, and without ridges along the sides. The legs are slender and not modified for swimming.

| FAMILY | Aspidytidae |
| --- | --- |
| SUBFAMILY | |
| DISTRIBUTION | Afrotropical: Western Cape of South Africa |
| MACROHABITAT | Northwest fynbos |
| MICROHABITAT | Wet rock faces of permanent seeps |
| FEEDING HABITS | Adult and larval feeding habits are unknown |
| NOTE | Named after Niobe, Queen of Thebes, who still shed tears after turning to stone |

ADULT LENGTH
³⁄₁₆–¹⁄₄ in
(5–7 mm)

*ASPIDYTES NIOBE*
# CLIFF WATER BEETLE
RIBERA, BEUTEL, BALKE & VOGLER, 2002

The Cliff Water Beetle is known from only two sites in the Western Cape province of South Africa. Both adults and larvae are found together on wet rock faces in permanent water seeps about ¹⁄₃₂–¹⁄₁₆ in (1–2 mm) deep. Adults live in crevices and small depressions in the rock that are partially obscured by algae. When disturbed, they are capable of moving quite quickly over the rock face until taking cover under algal filaments. The larvae are found in similar microhabitats and also creep over the exposed, yet shaded, rock surfaces. They apparently develop through three stages, or instars, before pupating.

RELATED SPECIES

*Aspidytes* is the only genus in the family Aspidytidae and contains two widely disjunct species, the South African *A. niobe* and *A. wrasei* (Chinese Cliff Beetle) from China. The discovery of two species of *Aspidytes* from widely different parts of the world highlights our ignorance of the biodiversity in rare and extreme habitats.

Actual size

**The Cliff Water Beetle** is small, oval, and is not adapted for swimming, but for crawling within thin sheets of water flowing from seeps over rock. The second antennal segment is partly contained within the first. The tarsi of males have numerous adhesive setae on the ventral side. The flight wings of this beetle are well developed.

| FAMILY | Hygrobiidae |
|---|---|
| SUBFAMILY | |
| DISTRIBUTION | Palearctic and Afrotropical: Europe, northern Africa, Turkey, Israel |
| MACROHABITAT | Small water bodies (usually with stagnant water) in lowland areas |
| MICROHABITAT | At the bottom of water bodies |
| FEEDING HABITS | Both larvae and adults are predators |
| NOTE | Adults are referred to as Squeak Beetles because they produce audible stridulations by rubbing the apex of their abdomen against a file on the ventral surface of their elytra |

ADULT LENGTH
³⁄₈–⁷⁄₁₆ in
(8.5–10.5 mm)

*HYGROBIA HERMANNI*
# SQUEAK BEETLE
(FABRICIUS, 1775)

Actual size

The small number of species in this family live in the mud, silt, and detritus at the bottom of small water bodies such as pools, ponds, small lakes, ditches, and canals. The adults can remain underwater for approximately 30 minutes before they have to go back to the surface to breathe and store another air bubble under their elytra. Both adults and larvae are good swimmers and are known to feed on small worms (Oligochaeta, Tubificidae) and aquatic fly larvae (Diptera, Chironomidae). The adults swim using alternate leg movements. The eggs of this species are deposited on the surface of submerged plants and typically hatch after two to three weeks.

RELATED SPECIES

*Hygrobia* is the only known genus in this species-poor family of beetles. In addition to the Palearctic *H. hermanni*, there are five described species in the genus: four from Australia (*H. australasiae* and *H. nigra* occur mainly in the southeastern part of the continent, *H. maculata* in northern Queensland and the Northern Territory, and *H. wattsi* in Western Australia); and one from southwestern China (*H. davidi*). All species other than *H. hermanni* are considered rare.

**The Squeak Beetle** is an oval-shaped brown to reddish-brown beetle with large, protuberant eyes. It has a broad pronotum with a transverse black band near the anterior and posterior margins. The head is noticeably narrower than the pronotum. The legs are fringed with long swimming setae. The ventral surface of the body is strongly convex.

| FAMILY | Dytiscidae |
|---|---|
| SUBFAMILY | Dytiscinae |
| DISTRIBUTION | Palearctic: Eurasia |
| MACROHABITAT | Boreal and temperate ecosystems |
| MICROHABITAT | In freshwater bodies |
| FEEDING HABITS | Predator |
| NOTE | Individuals of these aquatic insects are sold at local markets and used as an aphrodisiac in Asia |

ADULT LENGTH
1⅛–1⅜ in
(28–35 mm)

*DYTISCUS MARGINALIS*
# GREAT DIVING BEETLE
LINNAEUS, 1758

107

*Dytiscus marginalis* is a common aquatic beetle species that occupies a broad geographic range throughout the boreal and temperate areas of the Palearctic Realm, ranging from Ireland east to Japan. It lives mainly in ponds, less frequently in running water, and is an important predator of small fish, both as adults and larvae. Individuals also feed on small aquatic invertebrates such as mosquito larvae. Adults have fully developed flight wings and regularly fly between ponds. They can fly for more than three hours at a time at a speed of approximately 8 ft/sec (2.5 m/sec).

## RELATED SPECIES

The genus *Dytiscus* contains 26 species in Europe, Asia, and North America as far south as Guatemala. *Dytiscus marginalis* is closely related to two species, *D. persicus*, which is found in Afghanistan, Iran, and the region around the Black Sea, and *D. delictus* from the Russian Far East. Currently, two subspecies are recognized within this species, one widespread in the western and central parts of the Palearctic Realm and the other in the eastern parts.

Actual size

**The Great Diving Beetle** is a large, ovate, dark greenish beetle with the sides of the pronotum and the lateral edges of the elytra bearing a yellowish band. The female is easily distinguished in having one tuft of long setae at the base of the front femur (there are two in the male), the first three tarsomeres of the front and middle legs narrow (they are distinctly broader in the male), and conspicuous longitudinal grooves on the basal half of the elytra (which are smooth in the male).

| FAMILY | Dytiscidae |
|---|---|
| SUBFAMILY | Dytiscinae |
| DISTRIBUTION | Nearctic, Neotropical, Afrotropical, and Palearctic realms |
| MACROHABITAT | Deserts and other dry habitats |
| MICROHABITAT | Temporary pools |
| FEEDING HABITS | Adults and larvae prey on small aquatic animals |
| NOTE | This species has the most rapid development in the Dytiscidae |

**ADULT LENGTH**
½–¹¹⁄₁₆ in
(12–17 mm)

108

*ERETES STICTICUS*
# ERETES STICTICUS
(LINNAEUS, 1767)

*Eretes sticticus* is a denizen of pools, cattle tanks, and temporary ponds in mostly dry regions. Adults are quick to colonize newly formed pools and will just as quickly abandon them before they dry up. They eat the larvae of mosquitoes and midges, and will scavenge dead fish. Development from egg to pupa is rapid and occurs in about two weeks. In captivity, the larvae will prey on clam and fairy shrimp. Its broad distribution is unusual among Dytiscidae. This species was previously known as *E. occidentalis* in North America.

## RELATED SPECIES

There are four species of *Eretes* found on all continents, except Antarctica. *Eretes sticticus* is best distinguished from the other species by the male genitalia. It is also generally larger than other *Eretes*, except *E. explicitus*, and has a fragmented and indistinct black band across the elytra. In south-central North America, it occurs with *E. explicitus* and can only be distinguished by the male genitalia.

**Eretes sticticus** is pale yellow or brown with variable spots. The head has a black, bilobed spot. The pronotum may or may not have a black bar or series of spots across the middle. The elytra have scattered fine dark spots, sometimes coalescing into a poorly developed band just before the tips and with three spots along each side.

Actual size

| FAMILY | Dytiscidae |
|---|---|
| SUBFAMILY | Dytiscinae |
| DISTRIBUTION | Nearctic, Neotropical: southwestern California and southern Utah, to western Texas, Mexico, and northern Central America |
| MACROHABITAT | Montane pine, pine-oak forests and lower transition areas from 2,500 to 6,000 ft (750–1,800 m) |
| MICROHABITAT | Clear, shallow, slow-moving streams or stream pools at the base of mountains, with open sandy or gravelly bottoms |
| FEEDING HABITS | Adults and larvae prey on insects at night |
| NOTE | The bright yellow markings make them difficult to see against a sun-dappled background |

ADULT LENGTH
$^7\!/_{16}$–$^9\!/_{16}$ in
(11–15 mm)

*THERMONECTUS MARMORATUS*
# SUNBURST DIVING BEETLE
HOPE, 1832

109

The Sunburst Diving Beetle is a montane species that is restricted to altitudes above 2,500 ft (750 m) in the southwestern United States, Mexico, and northern Central America. In southwestern North America they often occur in pools of intermittent desert, chaparral, or upland streams. Individuals from populations in the mountains of southern California and Baja California are generally larger and more elongate than the rest of the population. They also appear darker and have a greater number of smaller yellow spots.

RELATED SPECIES

Of the 19 species of *Thermonectus* that have been described, only two, *T. marmoratus* and *T. ʒimmermani* are strikingly patterned with bright yellow markings. *Thermonectus ʒimmermani* is the smaller of the two ($^3\!/_8$–$^7\!/_{16}$ in / 9–11 mm), has a bright yellow head with an incomplete M-shaped black mark, a mostly bright yellow pronotum, and irregular yellow stripes and spots on the elytra.

Actual size

**The Sunburst Diving Beetle** has a yellow head with a variable black M-shaped mark and a mostly black pronotum. The black elytra are widest behind the middle, and have two dominant and numerous (14–22) other bright yellow spots. The underside is bright orange to reddish orange. The male's front tarsi are expanded with three large and many (15–19) smaller adhesive disks, used to grip the female during mating.

| | |
|---|---|
| FAMILY | Dytiscidae |
| SUBFAMILY | Hydroporinae |
| DISTRIBUTION | Palearctic and Afrotropical: from Egypt southward through the eastern part of the continent to South Africa; it is also found on Madagascar and recently reported from Cameroon |
| MACROHABITAT | Fresh and alkaline water bodies |
| MICROHABITAT | Springs, marshes, swamps, streams; adults are attracted to lights at night |
| FEEDING HABITS | Predaceous |
| NOTE | One of the smallest species in the family Dytiscidae |

ADULT LENGTH
$^{1}/_{32}$–$^{1}/_{16}$ in
(1.4–2 mm)

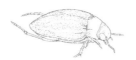

*BIDESSUS OVOIDEUS*

# BIDESSUS OVOIDEUS

RÉGIMBART, 1895

Actual size

Although the feeding habits of adults and larvae of the small *Bidessus ovoideus* remain unknown, based on observations from related species it is thought that they feed on minute aquatic invertebrates (dead or live). Like other dytiscids, the adults use air that is trapped beneath their elytra to respire, which enables them to stay submerged for prolonged periods. They come to the surface periodically to renew the air bubble. This African aquatic beetle lives in marshes, swamps, and springs with dense vegetation and is occasionally found on muddy soil near the edge of permanent pools.

RELATED SPECIES

The genus *Bidessus* contains approximately 50 species, distributed in Africa, Europe, and western Asia, with one species (*B. unistriatus*) extending into eastern Asia. *Bidessus ovoideus* belongs to an assemblage of 33 species (the *B. sharpi* species group) that is restricted to the African continent and whose members are characterized by an impunctate ventral surface and elytra with sparse and indistinct punctation. Species that closely resemble *B. ovoideus* (e.g., *B. seydeli*) can be separated by features of the male genitalia.

**Bidessus ovoideus** is a small ovoid beetle with a usually pale to dark brown upper surface. The elytra and the head are finely punctured. The pronotum, legs, and antennae are pale brown. The elytra each have three vaguely defined, broken, longitudinal, pale brown lines on each side. The tarsal segments on the hind legs decrease in width toward the apex.

| FAMILY | Dytiscidae |
|---|---|
| SUBFAMILY | Laccophilinae |
| DISTRIBUTION | Nearctic: southwestern USA (Arizona, New Mexico, Texas), northern Mexico (Baja California, Chihuahua, Durango, Jalisco, Nayarit, Sinaloa, Sonora) |
| MACROHABITAT | Occurs mostly at 1,000–4,000 ft (300–1,200 m) |
| MICROHABITAT | In pools and ponds |
| FEEDING HABITS | Predator and scavenger |
| NOTE | A colorful predaceous diving beetle |

ADULT LENGTH
³⁄₁₆–¼ in
(4.2–5.5 mm)

*LACCOPHILUS PICTUS COCCINELLOIDES*

# LACCOPHILUS PICTUS COCCINELLOIDES
RÉGIMBART, 1889

111

Actual size

Species in *Laccophilus*, which typically occur in relatively open pools and ponds in forested and grassland areas, have some of the more distinct color patterns of all dytiscids. Some authors have argued that brightly colored water beetles in the arid ecosystems of the southwestern United States and northern Mexico have evolved to help them blend in at the bottom of gravelly, sandy, or silty water bodies. *Laccophilus pictus coccinelloides* is usually found in pools of mountain streams with gravelly bottoms in the pine–oak woodland vegetation zone. Although generally inconspicuous, the adults are readily obtained by sweeping through the water at a depth of 12–25 cm (5–10 in) with a metal sieve or strainer.

RELATED SPECIES

*Laccophilus* belongs to the subfamily Laccophilinae, which is characterized in part by the absence of a visible scutellum. It is a large genus occurring on all continents except Antarctica and comprises about 150 species. There are two subspecies currently recognized in addition to *L. pictus coccinelloides*: *L. p. insignis*, ranging from southern Kansas south to central Veracruz; and *L. p. pictus*, ranging from central Veracruz to Jalisco and south to Honduras.

*Laccophilus pictus coccinelloides* is a brightly colored water beetle with a strongly contrasting yellow and black pattern. The elytra have four isolated yellow spots along the midline as well as other spots laterally. The front and middle legs are narrow, while the hind legs are broadened and have emarginated apical spurs at the tip of their tibia. There are no marked differences between the sexes, although females tend to be slightly larger than males.

# POLYPHAGA

Adults in this suborder are characterized by several morphological structures, such as the presence of cervical sclerites (in the membrane between the head and the prothorax, although this structure is reduced in several groups), the entire first abdominal ventrite (i.e., not divided by the hind coxae), and peculiarities of the flight wings. The larvae have five-segmented legs (their tibia and tarsus are fused) and a single tarsal claw.

Polyphaga is the largest suborder of Coleoptera, with an estimated 325,000 extant species representing about 90 percent of all beetles described to date. These species are currently placed in about 160 families, which are grouped into 16 superfamilies. The families Staphylinidae, Scarabaeidae, Buprestidae, Elateridae, Tenebrionidae, Cerambycidae, Chrysomelidae, and Curculionidae each contain at least 10,000 described species.

The feeding habits of the Polyphaga are extremely varied, some species being predaceous but many developing in various plant tissues or decaying organic matter. They are found in most aquatic and terrestrial habitats.

| FAMILY | Hydrophilidae |
|---|---|
| SUBFAMILY | Helophorinae |
| DISTRIBUTION | Palearctic and Nearctic: Northern Eurasia and Alaska |
| MACROHABITAT | Taiga and tundra wetlands |
| MICROHABITAT | Sandy river edges and snowmelt ponds |
| FEEDING HABITS | Adults are detritivores; larvae are presumably predaceous |
| NOTE | A widely distributed northern water beetle species, also known from Neogene and Quaternary fossils |

**ADULT LENGTH**
³/₁₆–¼ in
(5–7 mm)

114

*HELOPHORUS SIBIRICUS*
# HELOPHORUS SIBIRICUS
(MOTSCHULSKY, 1860)

Actual size

This cold-adapted water scavenger beetle is known from boreal and sub-boreal habitats across northern Europe, Siberian Asia, and Alaska, but not farther east in North America. Adults are known to be detritivores. Larvae of this species are unknown but presumed to be semiterrestrial predators, as are other members of the subfamily. The species is apparently remarkably conserved through geological time based on the discovery of Miocene through Pleistocene fossils.

These ancient specimens suggest a previously much more widespread distribution into western Europe and the Great Lakes region of the United States.

## RELATED SPECIES

The subfamily Helophorinae contains more than 180 species, all within the genus *Helophorus*. This is broken into numerous subgenera, with *H. sibiricus* placed in the subgenus *Gephelophorus*. Only one other species, *H. auriculatus*, in this subgenus overlaps the distribution of *H. sibiricus*. The two species are larger than most other members of the genus, and differ from each other in the shapes of the pronotal margins and other external details.

**Helophorus sibiricus** is a heavily costate and punctate beetle with a metallic opalescent luster that is typical of many members of the subfamily Helophorinae. Several important characters that allow well-preserved Miocene fossils to be assigned to this species include the large size, distinctive granules of the pronotum, and details of the striae and sutures on various parts of the body.

| FAMILY | Hydrophilidae |
|---|---|
| SUBFAMILY | Epimetopinae |
| DISTRIBUTION | Neotropical: Mato Grosso, Brazil |
| MACROHABITAT | Pantanal floodplains |
| MICROHABITAT | Unknown |
| FEEDING HABITS | Presumed microphagous in gravel interstices |
| NOTE | Smooth, parallel ridges under the pronotal hood may function as sliders to facilitate pushing through grainy substrates |

ADULT LENGTH
³⁄₁₆ in
(3.6 mm)

*EPIMETOPUS LANCEOLATUS*

# EPIMETOPUS LANCEOLATUS

PERKINS, 2012

115

The detailed biologies, including feeding habits, of these beetles are largely unknown, but their external morphologies are extraordinary. Hooded shore beetles are known from semi-aquatic sandy habitats, and the unique structure of the pronotal hood is speculated to assist in pushing through the grains by exerting downward pressure on the head. Based on the habitat and size of the beetles, they probably feed on microorganisms or plant matter in the interstices of this habitat, but this has not been directly documented. This species is known from only two specimens from the great South American wetland known as the Pantanal.

RELATED SPECIES

The hooded shore beetles comprise a very limited diversity of genera within the subfamily, but species diversity is extensive in *Epimetopus*, with 56 described species. The majority were only recently (2012) described based on extensive specimen records from North, Central, and South America. Classification of the group has varied—it has been considered both a distinct family, the Epimetopidae, and a subfamily of Hydrophilidae.

Actual size

**Epimetopus lanceolatus** is extensively sculptured dorsally, with the surface dominated by the prominent pronotal hood that covers the head. The morphology of the hood varies widely among various species groups in the genus. Despite the obvious and highly variable surface sculpturing, identification to species level mostly depends on examination of the male genitalia.

| FAMILY | Hydrophilidae |
|---|---|
| SUBFAMILY | Georissinae |
| DISTRIBUTION | Nearctic: western North America |
| MACROHABITAT | Near streams |
| MICROHABITAT | Coarse sand or mud near water |
| FEEDING HABITS | Adults are herbivores and saprophages; larvae are predators |
| NOTE | Although most species of *Georissus* occur near permanent water bodies, new species were recently discovered in wet leaf litter in high elevation cloud forests. |

ADULT LENGTH
¹⁄₁₆ in
(1.9–2.1 mm)

116

*GEORISSUS CALIFORNICUS*
# GEORISSUS CALIFORNICUS
LECONTE, 1874

●
Actual size

These knobby beetles occur along streams in a zone that is neither dry nor saturated with water. The strongly armored surface of the beetle is well equipped for pushing through the substrate and typically covered with a crusty layer of cemented mud. The adults feed on bits of vegetation or organic debris carried in the water current and washed up on the banks, and the recently described larvae are predators of other small invertebrates. Larvae pass through two instars during development. This species is sensitive to human-induced habitat modification due to its specific preferences in the riparian profile and is uncommon in collections.

## RELATED SPECIES

About 75 species of *Georissus* are described worldwide, all more or less similar but with subtle differences in features of surface sculpturing and the shapes of the pronota. The genus was once considered distinct enough to be included in its own family, Georissidae (also Georyssidae), and in older literature can be located under these names.

**Georissus californicus** is characteristic of other members of the genus worldwide in possessing a knobby, heavily armored dorsal surface that is typically coated with debris. The ventral parts of the prothorax are greatly reduced, allowing the head to be deeply tucked downward and contributing to the tank-like form.

| FAMILY | Hydrophilidae |
| --- | --- |
| SUBFAMILY | Spercheinae |
| DISTRIBUTION | Palearctic: western Europe to north-central Asia |
| MACROHABITAT | Aquatic |
| MICROHABITAT | Still bodies of water with aquatic vegetation |
| FEEDING HABITS | Adults are filter-feeders; larvae are predaceous or saprophagous |
| NOTE | Adults of species in this genus are the only known filter-feeding Coleoptera |

ADULT LENGTH
¼ in
(5.5–7 mm)

*SPERCHEUS EMARGINATUS*
# SPERCHEUS EMARGINATUS
SCHALLER, 1783

117

Actual size

*Spercheus emarginatus* is a widespread species within a group of water beetles that represent the only known Coleoptera that filter-feed as adults. They inhabit quiet, nutrient-rich bodies of water and hang upside down just below the water surface. They filter microorganisms from the subsurface using mouthparts that are morphologically adapted to this feeding strategy. Larvae feed either above or below the water surface as scavengers or opportunistic predators. Phylogenetic placement of the group is controversial and its members are viewed either as a derived group of water scavenger beetles or as a separate family and sister group to other Hydrophiloidea.

## RELATED SPECIES

The genus *Spercheus* contains 20 described species with representatives in various parts of world, particularly tropical Africa. *Spercheus emarginatus* is the only species that occurs across its extensive Palearctic distribution.

**Spercheus emarginatus** is dorsally convex, oval, and lacks obvious swimming adaptations. The head and mouthparts are adapted for filter-feeding below the water-surface film. The head is broad and constricted behind the eyes, and the clypeus and ventral mouthparts are broad, allowing maximum contact with the water undersurface. The clypeus is strongly emarginate in males, less so in females.

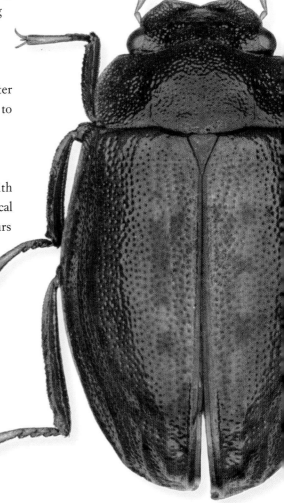

| FAMILY | Hydrophilidae |
|---|---|
| SUBFAMILY | Chaetarthriinae |
| DISTRIBUTION | Australian: New Zealand (South Island) |
| MACROHABITAT | South temperate forests |
| MICROHABITAT | Moss-covered rocks along streams |
| FEEDING HABITS | Adults are presumed detritivores; larva feeding habits are unknown |
| NOTE | A phylogenetically important species recently rediscovered at several localities in New Zealand |

**ADULT LENGTH**
¹⁄₁₆–¹⁄₈ in
(2.1–3.1 mm)

*HORELOPHUS WALKERI*
# HORELOPHUS WALKERI
ORCHYMONT, 1913

Actual size

This endemic New Zealand water scavenger beetle was known from only a few specimens for more than 100 years following its description. However, populations were rediscovered in South Island in 2010, allowing detailed study. Adult beetles inhabit southern beech (*Nothofagus* spp.) forests on moss-covered rocks along small streams and in the spray of small waterfalls. Despite extensive effort, no larvae have been collected, so knowledge of the life history of the species remains incomplete. Adults are presumed to be detritivores. A phylogenetic study published in 2013 suggests this species should be placed in the tribe Anacaenini with members of the subfamily Chaetarthriinae rather than in its own isolated subfamily Herelophinae as was done previously.

## RELATED SPECIES
*Horelophus walkeri* is the only member of the genus and is unique both taxonomically and in external appearance among other New Zealand members of the Hydrophilidae.

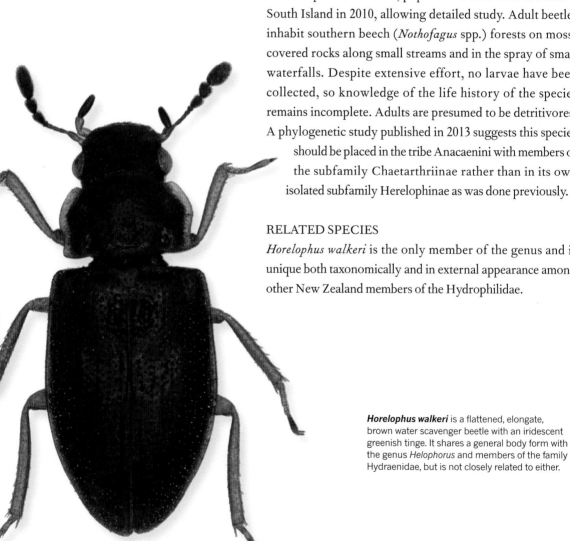

**Horelophus walkeri** is a flattened, elongate, brown water scavenger beetle with an iridescent greenish tinge. It shares a general body form with the genus *Helophorus* and members of the family Hydraenidae, but is not closely related to either.

| FAMILY | Hydrophilidae |
|---|---|
| SUBFAMILY | Hydrophilinae |
| DISTRIBUTION | Palearctic: Europe and northeastern Asia |
| MACROHABITAT | Aquatic |
| MICROHABITAT | Ponds, small lakes, backwaters |
| FEEDING HABITS | Adults are omnivorous, larvae are predatory |
| NOTE | These large beetles do well in small aquariums containing some plant material for shelter |

ADULT LENGTH
1½–1⅝ in
(38–42 mm)

*HYDROPHILUS PICEUS*
# GIANT SILVER WATER BEETLE
LINNAEUS, 1758

119

The Giant Silver Water Beetle inhabits ponds, lakes, and other bodies of water where vegetative cover is available. Adults feed on vegetation and other kinds of organic matter and are opportunistically predatory. They accept fish food in captivity. Adults fly and are attracted to lights at night during warm weather, but otherwise are fully aquatic. Eggs are enclosed in silken "cocoons." Larvae are predatory on other small animals and possess sharp mandibles that can inflict painful bites. Prey items are masticated and digested externally using the elongate sickle-like mandibles.

### RELATED SPECIES
About 25 species in the genus *Hydrophilus* are described in temperate and tropical regions of the Eastern Hemisphere. *Hydrophilus piceus* has a distinct median longitudinal ridge along the abdominal ventrites, which is not present in *H. aterrimus*, a species with a similar distribution.

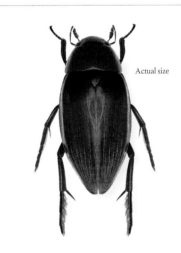

Actual size

**The Giant Silver Water Beetle** is a streamlined black beetle with clubbed reddish antennae. The legs function like oars when the beetle swims. The antennae possess specialized hydrofuge setae that provide a pathway for fresh air to be routed to plastron surfaces on other parts of the body while most of the beetle is submerged.

| FAMILY | Hydrophilidae |
| --- | --- |
| SUBFAMILY | Hydrophilinae |
| DISTRIBUTION | Nearctic and Neotropical: North America, South America, Caribbean islands |
| MACROHABITAT | Aquatic |
| MICROHABITAT | Slow-moving streams and ponds |
| FEEDING HABITS | Adults are detritivores; larvae are predaceous |
| NOTE | Adults communicate by stridulation, producing "chirping" calls underwater |

ADULT LENGTH
⁵⁄₁₆–½ in
(8–12 mm)

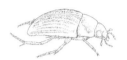

*TROPISTERNUS COLLARIS*
# TROPISTERNUS COLLARIS
(FABRICIUS, 1775)

This widely distributed water scavenger beetle is locally common in weedy ponds and quiet backwater areas of streams. Adults are typical among other water scavenger beetles as grazers of plant tissues or small animal carcasses. They will take flake fish food in captivity. Larvae are predators and consume prey by extraoral digestion, typically with the head above the water surface. Adults communicate by a series of "chirps" produced by stridulation of the abdomen against a file on each elytron. Males tap the heads of females during copulation using their maxillary palpi, and females attach the silken egg case to objects underwater.

RELATED SPECIES

*Tropisternus* is a large genus containing 58 species in the Nearctic and Neotropical realms. Species taxonomy is not well resolved. The situation is further complicated by extensive variations in color patterns in many species, including *T. collaris*. At least some currently recognized subgenera are not corroborated in recent phylogenetic studies.

Actual size

**Tropisternus collaris** is a widely distributed species that exhibits extensive variation in the relative coverage of dark and light colors, especially the elytral stripes. Individuals may be dark brown with a narrow margin of tan, or predominantly tan with dark stripes and a median pronotal black spot. The sharply pointed ventral keel occurs in a number of aquatic water scavenger beetles.

| FAMILY | Hydrophilidae |
| --- | --- |
| SUBFAMILY | Sphaeridiinae |
| DISTRIBUTION | Holarctic: North America, Europe, northern Asia |
| MACROHABITAT | Various |
| MICROHABITAT | Wet ungulate dung |
| FEEDING HABITS | Saprophagous |
| NOTE | Introduced to North America from Europe in the late-eighteenth or early-nineteenth centuries |

ADULT LENGTH
³/₁₆–¼ in
(4–7 mm)

*SPHAERIDIUM SCARABAEOIDES*

# SPHAERIDIUM SCARABAEOIDES
(LINNAEUS, 1758)

Actual size

*Sphaeridium scarabaeoides* is part of a large subfamily of semiterrestrial or terrestrial beetles from an otherwise mostly aquatic family. The terrestrial habitat of the group is regarded as a secondary evolutionary development from an aquatic common ancestor. This species was first recorded in North America in the early nineteenth century and its spread throughout the continent as far south as Mexico City has been documented through museum records. Adults and larvae burrow through wet livestock and wild herbivore dung, feeding on the nutrient-rich broth of decomposition.

### RELATED SPECIES

There are about 40 species of *Sphaeridium*; they all have native ranges in the Old World, and are particularly diverse in the Old World tropics. All three species in North America were introduced from Europe. Four European endemic and one introduced Asian species overlap with *S. scarabaeoides*. They are distinguished by size, color, different-shaped pronota, and details of the male genitalia.

**Sphaeridium scarabaeoides** is a shiny oval beetle with short, clubbed antennae and relatively elongate maxillary palpi. The dorsal outline is strongly convex, while the ventral surface is flat and somewhat inflexed around the margin and leg bases. The orange elytral marking is shared with several other species but differs in relative coverage and shape.

| FAMILY | Sphaeritidae |
|---|---|
| SUBFAMILY | |
| DISTRIBUTION | Palearctic: Europe, northern Asia |
| MACROHABITAT | Forests |
| MICROHABITAT | Wet, fermenting substrates |
| FEEDING HABITS | Saprophagous |
| NOTE | Found at tree wounds feeding on fermenting sap |

**ADULT LENGTH**
³/₁₆–¼ in
(5–7 mm)

122

*SPHAERITES GLABRATUS*
# FALSE CLOWN BEETLE
(FABRICIUS, 1792)

This species is the most widespread and commonly encountered member of a very small family. Adults and larvae are saprophagous and appear to feed mostly on bacteria- and yeast-rich exudates of damaged trees, tree stumps, and other organic substrates in the process of rotting and fermenting. Adults have been reported feeding and mating at decaying birch stumps in coniferous forests, but larval feeding has never been directly documented. Larval development is apparently rapid, with adults appearing within a month. Rapid larval development and a number of larval and adult characters suggest a close phylogenetic relationship to Histeridae.

## RELATED SPECIES

Only five species of Sphaeritidae are described, all but one from Europe and Asia. *Sphaerites glabratus* is the only species that occurs across its range, with other, similar species in China. A single North American species, *S. politus*, is similar enough to *S. glabratus* that some controversy exists over whether they represent separate species, and some records indicate that the two may overlap in extreme northeast Asia.

Actual size

**The False Clown Beetle** has the general appearance of a robust, shiny black beetle similar in overall appearance to many Histeridae. The elytra possess rows of punctures, not the strial lines of most hister beetles, and only a small portion of the last abdominal segment is exposed, as compared with the greater pygidial exposure in hister beetles.

| FAMILY | Synteliidae |
|---|---|
| SUBFAMILY | |
| DISTRIBUTION | Neotropical: central mountains of Mexico |
| MACROHABITAT | Semiarid shrublands |
| MICROHABITAT | Rotting cacti |
| FEEDING HABITS | Predatory |
| NOTE | Inhabits dead and dying cacti, where it feeds on fly larvae |

ADULT LENGTH
⁷/₈–1³/₈ in
(22–35 mm)

*SYNTELIA WESTWOODI*
# SYNTELIA WESTWOODI
SALLÉ, 1873

123

*Syntelia westwoodi* is the largest described member of the small and poorly known family Synteliidae. It lives in high-altitude (5,500–9,800 ft / 1,700–3,000 m) desert and semiarid shrub habitats in the central Mexican mountains. Larvae and adults have been found feeding on fly larvae associated with succulent necrosis of large columnar cacti, and are members of a rapidly changing community of beetles that take advantage of the hoards of maggots that immediately colonize and consume the rotting plant tissue. The family is phylogenetically closely related to the Histeridae, a relationship supported by shared morphological characters and results of molecular studies.

## RELATED SPECIES

Nine species of Synteliidae are described worldwide, all from the genus *Syntelia*, and with a peculiar split distribution between south and southeast Asia and Mesoamerica. *Syntelia westwoodi* is one of the largest members of the family. Additional undescribed species occur in Central America, and more can be expected given the patchy distribution and apparent rarity of species.

Actual size

**Syntelia westwoodi** is an elongate, heavy-bodied beetle with a slightly narrowed and flattened forebody, short, stout legs, and large, projecting mandibles. The form of the body is well adapted to pushing through fibrous or semifluid interiors of rotting succulent plant tissues, and grasping and holding squirming maggots, which are the primary prey items.

| FAMILY | Histeridae |
|---|---|
| SUBFAMILY | Niponiinae |
| DISTRIBUTION | Palearctic: east Asia |
| MACROHABITAT | Forests |
| MICROHABITAT | Under bark and in borings of coniferous trees |
| FEEDING HABITS | Predatory on bark beetles |
| NOTE | An important predator of forest-pest bark beetles |

ADULT LENGTH
³⁄₁₆ in
(3.5–4.5 mm)

124

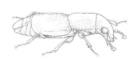

*NIPONIUS OSORIOCEPS*

# NIPONIUS OSORIOCEPS

LEWIS, 1885

Actual size

This hister beetle is a specialist predator of bark beetle larvae. In particular, it is an important natural control organism for the scolytine species *Phloeosinus perlatus*, a pest of valuable timber trees within the genus *Cunninghamia* throughout east and southeast Asia. *Niponius osorioceps* larvae and adults live within subcortical bark beetle tunnel systems, where they feed on bark beetle larvae. The impact on bark beetle populations by individual species such as *N. osorioceps* is difficult to assess, but it is only part of a large community of bark beetle predators that undoubtedly has an impact on bark beetle numbers.

### RELATED SPECIES

At least 23 additional species of *Niponius* inhabit the eastern Palearctic and Oriental realms. This is the only genus within the subfamily, so recognition at that level is not difficult. However, members of some other subfamilies of Histeridae share the elongate adult body shape of *N. osorioceps* and also occupy scolytine beetle galleries and subcortical habitats.

**Niponius osorioceps** is typical of other species predatory on bark beetles in possessing an elongate, cylindrical body and forward-projecting mandibles that are suited to capture prey within the narrow confines of bark beetle galleries. The projections on the anterior part of the head and the pattern of punctures on the last visible abdominal segment are characteristic of this species.

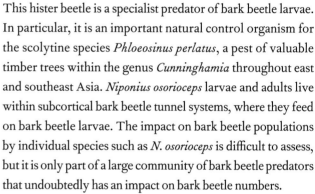

| FAMILY | Histeridae |
|---|---|
| SUBFAMILY | Abraeinae |
| DISTRIBUTION | Palearctic and Afrotropical: North Africa, Asia Minor |
| MACROHABITAT | Wooded savannas |
| MICROHABITAT | Galleries of wood-boring beetles |
| FEEDING HABITS | Predaceous |
| NOTE | A known predatory of powder post beetles that infest acacias in African savannas |

ADULT LENGTH
¹⁄₁₆ in
(1.8–2.2 mm)

*TERETRIUS PULEX*
# TERETRIUS PULEX
(FAIRMAIRE, 1877)

125

Actual size

*Teretrius pulex* has been recorded inhabiting the galleries of bostrichid powder post beetles infesting acacias in savanna and semidesert regions including *Lyctus hipposideros*, *Acantholyctus corinifrons*, *Enneadesmus forficula*, *E. trispinosus*, *Xylopertha picea*, and *Sinoxylon senegalense*, but apparently prefers the galleries of species in the subfamily Lyctinae. A related member of the genus (*T. nigrescens*) is reported as an important natural control agent of the Lesser Grain Borer (*Rhyẕopertha dominica*), a damaging pest of stored products in equatorial Africa and other regions where it has been introduced.

## RELATED SPECIES
The genus *Teretrius* belongs to the tribe Teretriini along with *Pleuroleptus* from the Palearctic Realm, the Nearctic and Neotropical *Teretriosoma* and *Xyphonotus* from South Africa and Madagascar. It comprises at least 72 named species distributed in all major faunistic regions. The species are similar and the species-level taxonomy is poorly resolved.

**Teretrius pulex** is a small quadrate histerid. The small size of most members of the genus compensates for the blocky body shape in permitting movement through wood-boring beetle galleries, particularly those of bostrichid powder post beetles, as it searches for prey.

| FAMILY | Histeridae |
|---|---|
| SUBFAMILY | Trypeticinae |
| DISTRIBUTION | Oriental and Australian: Pacific islands of Southeast Asia |
| MACROHABITAT | Tropical forests |
| MICROHABITAT | Galleries of wood-boring curculionid beetles |
| FEEDING HABITS | Predaceous |
| NOTE | Individuals travel deep into logs via wood-boring beetle galleries in search of prey |

ADULT LENGTH
⅛ in
(2.5–3.2 mm)

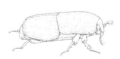

*TRYPETICUS CINCTIPYGUS*
# TRYPETICUS CINCTIPYGUS
(MARSEUL, 1864)

Actual size

This species and other members of the large genus *Trypeticus* for which information is available are obligate predators of platypodine and scolytine weevils, and possibly other wood-boring beetles. They are able to travel extensively in the gallery systems in search of prey and possess the ability to walk forward and backward, though they cannot turn around. Specimens can also be collected using flight-intercept traps or by beating vegetation. Collectors may monitor several gallery entrance holes and capture *Trypeticus* specimens when they are en route from one gallery system to another.

## RELATED SPECIES

The genus *Trypeticus* contains 100 described species. Species taxonomy is relatively well known thanks to a 2003 comprehensive revision. Species determinations are complicated by sexual dimorphism involving several morphological characters in many species. This necessitates keying male and female specimens separately. The male genitalia are not as useful for species identification as they are for most hister beetle genera due their poorly sclerotized structure and the difficulty of extracting them from specimens.

**Trypeticus cinctipygus** is an elongate, tubular hister beetle with a rectangular pronotum that is longer than wide, and elongate, tapering elytra and pygidium. Females and males differ in the shapes of the frontal region and vertex of the head, and possess subtle differences in length and width ratios of some body regions.

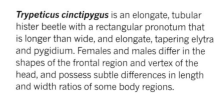

| FAMILY | Histeridae |
|---|---|
| SUBFAMILY | Trypanaeinae |
| DISTRIBUTION | Neotropical: South America |
| MACROHABITAT | Tropical forests |
| MICROHABITAT | Subcortical; associated with wood-boring beetles |
| FEEDING HABITS | Predaceous |
| NOTE | These elongate hister beetles are able to enter the galleries of pinhole borers, which are their main prey |

ADULT LENGTH
⅛–³⁄₁₆ in
(3.2–3.6 mm)

*TRYPANAEUS BIPUSTULATUS*

# TRYPANAEUS BIPUSTULATUS

(FABRICIUS, 1801)

127

*Trypanaeus bipustulatus* and other members of the genus are specialized predators of pinhole borers in the curculionid subfamily Platypodinae. The adults patrol the limbs of recently dead trees and follow the equally cylindrical borers into their galleries. They are able to go forward or backward in the galleries as a result of their specialized leg morphology. The male genitalia are elongate and flexible, possibly an adaptation to copulation in the cylindrical confines of prey galleries. The larvae presumably feed on pinhole borer larvae and undergo only two larval instars, as is typical for the family.

## RELATED SPECIES

*Trypanaeus* includes 46 described species, but species taxonomy is poorly resolved and the actual number of valid species is unknown. Species present a consistent cylindrical body form and all may be specialist predators of pinhole borers.

Actual size

**Trypanaeus bipustulatus** exhibits an elongate, cylindrical body form that is typical of predatory beetles associated with the galleries of wood-boring beetles that form their primary diets. Forward-projecting mandibles and short legs with flexible body-wall articulations are all typical adaptations to this lifestyle.

| FAMILY | Histeridae |
|---|---|
| SUBFAMILY | Saprininae |
| DISTRIBUTION | Palearctic, Oriental, and Australian: east and southeast Asia, Australia |
| MACROHABITAT | Various |
| MICROHABITAT | Carrion |
| FEEDING HABITS | Predator of fly larvae |
| NOTE | A ubiquitous element of the carrion fauna throughout Asia and Australia |

**ADULT LENGTH**
³/₁₆–¹/₄ in
(4–6.2 mm)

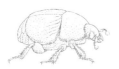

128

*SAPRINUS CYANEUS*
# SAPRINUS CYANEUS
(FABRICIUS, 1775)

Actual size

This spectacularly colored, widely distributed hister beetle is common on decomposing animal carcasses. Saprophagous fly larvae (maggots) are the primary diet of both adult and larval beetles, though some Asian *Saprinus* reportedly are capable of capturing adult flies. Adult beetles are good fliers and are attracted to carrion and similar smelly substrates by following odor plumes. Adult beetles feed, mate, and deposit eggs on or near the carcass. The larvae develop rapidly on this ephemeral resource and undergo only two instars before pupating.

### RELATED SPECIES

At least 159 species of the genus *Saprinus* are described from many parts of the world. Most or all prey on fly larvae, with varying preferences for mainly dung or carrion substrates. Numerous species are bright iridescent blue or green in color. Species discrimination is based on details of male genitalia, in addition to more obvious external differences in color, size, surface patterns, and leg structure.

**Saprinus cyaneus** is typical of many, but not all, species of *Saprinus* in being bright metallic blue in color. Numerous other members of the subfamily Saprininae share the same general body shape and diet of fly maggots on rotting organic matter.

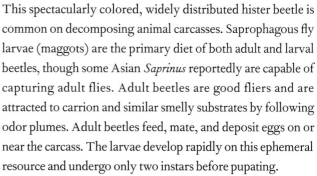

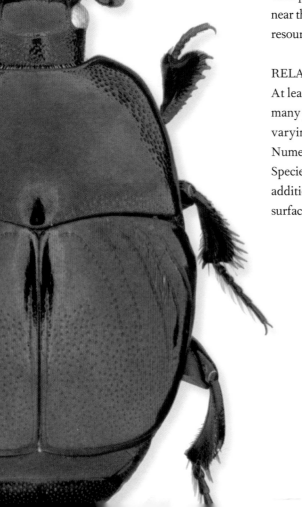

| FAMILY | Histeridae |
|---|---|
| SUBFAMILY | Dendrophilinae |
| DISTRIBUTION | Nearctic: eastern North America |
| MACROHABITAT | Forests |
| MICROHABITAT | Layered bark |
| FEEDING HABITS | Predatory |
| NOTE | Common under the layered bark of cottonwood and other poplars |

ADULT LENGTH
⅛–³⁄₁₆ in
(2.5–3.6 mm)

*PLATYLOMALUS AEQUALIS*

# PLATYLOMALUS AEQUALIS

(SAY, 1825)

129

Actual size

*Platylomalus aequalis* is one of the most common subcortical (living under bark) histerid beetles in eastern parts of North America. It is particularly common in the multiple-layered bark of cottonwood trees, which extends the range of the species into riparian forest habitats of the Great Plains. Adults and larvae both feed mainly on fly larvae, particular those within the family Xylophagidae, which are common in the same bark habitats. The front tibiae of males are enlarged relative to those of females and are presumably used to restrain the female during mating.

## RELATED SPECIES

*Platylomalus* can be separated from the other North American genera in the tribe Paromalini (*Xestipyge*, *Carcinops*, and *Paromalus*) by the elytra which lack complete striae and by its broad, dorsoventrally flattened body. The species is the only member of the genus in North America, although at least 58 additional species of the genus are described from other parts of the world.

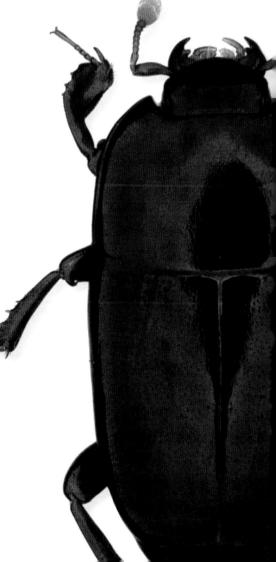

**Platylomalus aequalis** adults present an excellent example of an extremely flat body shape that is an obvious adaptation to living in the narrow dimensions of the subcortical habitat. Many other beetles and insects share this habitat and most exhibit some degree of dorsoventral flattening (compare this with the elongate-cylindrical shapes of beetles, such as *Niponius osorioceps*, that inhabit the nearby galleries of borers).

| FAMILY | Histeridae |
|---|---|
| SUBFAMILY | Onthophilinae |
| DISTRIBUTION | Palearctic: northern Europe |
| MACROHABITAT | Subterranean habitats, organic litter |
| MICROHABITAT | Mole burrows, litter habitats, carrion |
| FEEDING HABITS | Predatory, possibly saprophagous |
| NOTE | Known to undergo its entire life cycle in mole tunnels |

**ADULT LENGTH**
⅛–³⁄₁₆ in
(2.5–3.5 mm)

*ONTHOPHILUS PUNCTATUS*
# ONTHOPHILUS PUNCTATUS
(MÜLLER, 1776)

Actual size

Detailed biological information on this species is limited, but both larvae and adults have been recorded from mole runs. Adults have also been collected from forest litter, carrion, and other decomposing organic substrates. Members of this genus are known to prey on fly eggs or fly larvae, but some are also suspected of grazing on bacteria- and fungus-rich, moist substrates on decomposing substances. Members of *Onthophilus* possess specialized brushes on their mouthparts consistent with filtering microbial food particles from such habitats (microphagous). Larvae are presumed to undergo only two larval instars, as with other hister beetles.

## RELATED SPECIES

The genus *Onthophilus* includes at least 38 species, mainly in North America, Europe, and Asia. Biologies are poorly known but apparently diverse. The genus is distinct and easily recognized, and dominates species diversity within the Onthophilinae fauna of the Holarctic Realm. Species are distinguished mainly by differences in the patterns of ridges, punctures, and other elaborations of the external surfaces of the body, and details of the male genitalia.

**Onthophilus punctatus** is dramatically costate and punctate, characters that it shares with other members of the genus. The surface topography of the beetle is often obscured by a layer of dried organic crust that coats the beetle as it burrows through moist, fermenting organic matter and soil.

| FAMILY | Histeridae |
|---|---|
| SUBFAMILY | Histerinae |
| DISTRIBUTION | Palearctic: Europe and northwestern Asia |
| MACROHABITAT | Various |
| MICROHABITAT | Vertebrate carcasses, dung, and other decaying organic substances |
| FEEDING HABITS | Predatory on fly maggots |
| NOTE | Develop rapidly as larvae and are long-lived as adults |

ADULT LENGTH
¼ in
(6–6.5 mm)

*HISTER QUADRINOTATUS QUADRINOTATUS*

# HISTER QUADRINOTATUS QUADRINOTATUS

SCRIBA, 1790

131

This colorful hister beetle is common on decaying animal substrates such as carrion or dung. Adults and larvae are predators of fly maggots and eggs. The beetles colonize vertebrate carcasses in various stages of decomposition and the larvae complete development rapidly, with complete generation times of about 30 days from egg to adult. Rapid larval development and long adult life is typical of many hister beetle species. The beetles may be encountered across a wide range of habitats, from beaches to forests, and this may account for the species' wide distribution and abundance.

RELATED SPECIES

At least 15 species of the worldwide genus *Hister* share the range and habitat preferences of *H. quadrinotatus quadrinotatus*, including at least one, *H. quadrimaculatus*, that also possesses the prominent orange markings on the elytra. As least four *Hister* species have been recorded at single localities in certain areas.

Actual size

**Hister quadrinotatus quadrinotatus** is one of the more brightly colored members of the family, though the orange markings on the elytra also occur in other species of the genus *Hister* and in a few other Histerinae genera. Hister beetles are universally extremely hard-bodied beetles and most are capable of contracting their appendages into protective grooves for protection.

| FAMILY | Histeridae |
|---|---|
| SUBFAMILY | Histerinae |
| DISTRIBUTION | Palearctic: Europe, northwestern Asia |
| MACROHABITAT | Forests |
| MICROHABITAT | Under bark of dead trees |
| FEEDING HABITS | Predatory |
| NOTE | Profoundly flattened and adapted to life in the narrow spaces beneath bark |

ADULT LENGTH
⁵⁄₁₆–³⁄₈ in
(8–10 mm)

*HOLOLEPTA PLANA*
# FLAT CLOWN BEETLE
(SULZER, 1776)

The Flat Clown Beetle lives under bark of dead or dying trees, particularly *Populus*. The large mandibles are used to capture fly larvae and other arthropods and hold them during preoral processing. The predatory larvae occur in the same habitat and are less flattened, but have soft bodies suitable for squeezing through narrow spaces. The beetles prefer moist areas and during dry conditions may migrate to the narrowest parts of the habitat where residual moisture occurs. The species is host to the phoretic mite *Lobogynioides andreinii*. The mite larvae eat nematodes, but adults steal food from the beetle as it feeds.

RELATED SPECIES

Seventy-seven species of *Hololepta* are described worldwide, all of which are very similar. *Hololepta plana* is the only species in Europe and the only widespread northern Eurasian species. Several other species are known from scattered localities in northern Asia.

Actual size

**The Flat Clown Beetle** is profoundly flattened—the depth of the body is approximately one-tenth its total length. The legs are pressed against the body for effective pushing, and the mandibles extend far forward to allow the beetle to capture prey in narrow spaces. The entire body is strongly armored, a feature shared by other members of the Histeridae.

| FAMILY | Histeridae |
|---|---|
| SUBFAMILY | Histerinae |
| DISTRIBUTION | Neotropical: Central America, South America, Caribbean |
| MACROHABITAT | Forests, palm groves |
| MICROHABITAT | Palm trees |
| FEEDING HABITS | Predatory on wood-boring beetles |
| NOTE | An important predator of palm weevils, destructive pests of palm trees |

ADULT MALE LENGTH
¾–1¼ in
(20–32 mm)

ADULT FEMALE LENGTH
¹¹⁄₁₆–1 in
(17–25 mm)

*OXYSTERNUS MAXIMUS*

# OXYSTERNUS MAXIMUS

(LINNAEUS, 1767)

133

This large hister beetle feeds on palm weevils, which include several species in the genus *Rhynchophorus* that attack palms in tropical regions of the world. Across tropical America the most important prey species for *Oxysternus maximus* is the South American Palm Weevil, *R. palmarum*. The beetle pushes its way through galleries and tissue damaged by the weevil larvae and feeds on the fat, 2–3 in-long (50–75 mm) grubs. Larvae and adults both feed on the weevils, and the species is considered an important natural control for these pests in palm plantations. Males possess relatively longer mandibles than females, resulting in pronounced sexual dimorphism.

## RELATED SPECIES

*Oxysternus maximus* is the only species in the genus. It shares its saproxylic habitat with other, somewhat similar, members of the tribe Hololeptini that are also predatory on wood-boring or subcortical insects, but is less dorsoventrally flattened.

Actual size

**Oxysternus maximus** is a heavily armored, large, black tropical hister beetle with elongate, forward-projecting mandibles. The stocky build of the adults is well suited to pushing through the dense, fibrous tissue of damaged palm trunks in search of weevil grubs. Prey are secured by the enlarged, asymmetrical mandibles and consumed via extraoral digestion.

| FAMILY | Histeridae |
|---|---|
| SUBFAMILY | Histerinae |
| DISTRIBUTION | Palearctic: Europe, northwest Asia |
| MACROHABITAT | Rotting organic matter, dung |
| MICROHABITAT | Vertebrate dung |
| FEEDING HABITS | Predatory on fly larvae |
| NOTE | A maggot predator capable of substantially reducing filth fly populations |

*PACHYLISTER INAEQUALIS*
# PACHYLISTER INAEQUALIS
(OLIVIER, 1789)

This common European hister beetle is associated primarily with livestock dung, and cattle dung in particular. It can be found under, or burrowing through, moist dung heaps. Adults and larvae are important predators of feces-infesting maggots, and may occur in other situations where organic decomposition supports populations of maggots. The heavily armored adults are long-lived relative to the rapidly developing larvae, a common pattern within the family. Larvae undergo only two instars.

### RELATED SPECIES

*Pachylister inaequalis* is the only commonly encountered member of the genus across Europe and northwest Asia. The genus includes 20 additional species distributed in Asia and Africa, and several have been widely introduced to other regions for fly biocontrol. Species are separated based on external differences in the surfaces of the body and legs, and details of the male genitalia. A number of genera within the subfamily share a similar overall body form.

**Pachylister inaequalis** adults are robust, heavily armored, oval beetles with short, flattened legs, and large, forward-projecting, asymmetrical mandibles. The body shape and short legs are adapted to pushing through dense, moist dung or rotting organic matter and carrion in search of fly larvae.

Actual size

| FAMILY | Histeridae |
|---|---|
| SUBFAMILY | Haeteriinae |
| DISTRIBUTION | Nearctic: western and northern United States, southern Canada |
| MACROHABITAT | Forests |
| MICROHABITAT | Nests of ants in the subfamily Formicinae |
| FEEDING HABITS | Presumed predatory or feeds on host regurgitation |
| NOTE | Lives only in association with ant colonies |

ADULT LENGTH
⅛ in
(3.1–3.4 mm)

*HAETERIUS TRISTRIATUS*
# HAETERIUS TRISTRIATUS
HORN, 1874

135

Actual size

Most hister beetles are active predators of other insects, especially fly larvae and wood-boring beetles. But members of this species and others in the subfamily are specialized "guests" of social insect colonies (inquilines), mainly ants. *Haeterius tristriatus* occurs with formicine ants in the genera *Formica* and *Lasius*. The beetle possesses special appeasement glands that secrete substances attractive to the ants, thereby forming a chemically mediated symbiosis between guest and hosts. The beetle's feeding habits are poorly known but it may prey on ant broods or eggs, and some members of the genus have been observed engaging in trophallaxis, soliciting host regurgitation.

## RELATED SPECIES

At least 30 species of *Haeterius* have been described, with approximately 25 known from the regions occupied by this species. California has the richest fauna, but the actual number across the region is unknown due to the probability that undescribed species may exist in addition to the named species, especially in southwestern deserts. Distributional patterns among known species are poorly documented.

**Haeterius tristriatus** possesses specialized setae, glandular elaborations of the body, and short, stubby legs that are typical characteristics of beetles morphologically adapted to life with social insects. The pattern of setae and surface sculpturing is species-specific in *Haeterius* and other members of the Haeteriinae subfamily.

| FAMILY | Histeridae |
|---|---|
| SUBFAMILY | Chlamydopsinae |
| DISTRIBUTION | Australian: South Australia |
| MACROHABITAT | Eucalyptus forests |
| MICROHABITAT | Termite nests |
| FEEDING HABITS | Unknown, presumably predatory |
| NOTE | Termite hosts obtain an appeasement substance from the strange trichomes on this beetle's elytra |

ADULT LENGTH
³⁄₁₆ in
(3.9–4.1 mm)

136

*EUCURTIA COMATA*
# EUCURTIA COMATA
(BLACKBURN, 1901)

Actual size

*Eucurtia comata* is representative of the subfamily Chlamydopsinae in possessing modified morphological structures associated with integration into the nests of social insects. Presumably most members of the subfamily occur with ants, but *E. comata* occurs with termites, based on observations of a single living specimen. *Eutermes* termites were observed surrounding the beetle and licking a substance from the prominent trichomes extending from protrusions at the base of the elytra. This intriguing but scanty bit of biology is more than is available for most species in the subfamily, many of which are known from only single specimens without host associations.

### RELATED SPECIES

Only this single species is included in the genus *Eucurtia*. However, approximately 180 species within the subfamily occur across tropical Asia, the Pacific islands, and Australia. Many are similar in possessing modifications of the body associated with the evolution of an inquilinous lifestyle.

**Eucurtia comata** is typical of many chlamydopsine hister beetles in possessing trichomes extending from specialized glandular structures on the elytra. These elongate clusters of setae carry secretions from the glands that are much sought after by their termite hosts and result in the complete acceptance of the beetles into the termite colony.

| FAMILY | Histeridae |
|---|---|
| SUBFAMILY | Chlamydopsinae |
| DISTRIBUTION | Australian: northern Queensland |
| MACROHABITAT | Subtropical forests |
| MICROHABITAT | *Pheidole* ant colonies |
| FEEDING HABITS | Predaceous |
| NOTE | Available evidence suggests that members of this genus are fully integrated inquilines of *Pheidole* ant colonies |

ADULT LENGTH
¹⁄₁₆—¹⁄₈ in
(2.2–2.7 mm)

*PHEIDOLIPHILA MAGNA*
# PHEIDOLIPHILA MAGNA
DÉGALLIER & CATERINO, 2005

137

Actual size

Species of the genus *Pheidoliphila* that are represented by specimens with relevant collecting data live among ants of the genus *Pheidole*. However, many species are known only from specimens collected using flight-intercept traps, so host information is not available and the association with *Pheidole* is presumptive. *Pheidoliphila magna* is typical among many chlamydopsine hister beetles in possessing secretory trichomes at the bases of the elytra that produce appeasement chemicals attractive to host ants. Adults and larval beetles probably function as nest parasites, feeding on ant larvae or scavenging on dead or dying ants, but bionomic details are unknown.

### RELATED SPECIES

The genus *Pheidoliphila* includes 25 species from Australia and one from New Guinea. External morphological diversity within the genus is extensive, and species may be grouped according to the patterns of punctation and setae, the presence of horns, knobs, and / or deep depressions on the pronotum, and other obvious differences. Despite these differences in appearance, 21 of the 26 species remained unknown to science prior to their descriptions in 2005.

**Pheidoliphila magna** is one of the larger species within the genus, and one of the few that exceed ¹⁄₁₆ in (2 mm) in length. Adults possess a pair of rounded, inwardly curved processes on the front of the pronotum that are separated by a deep excavation. These processes may serve as handles, allowing the ants to carry the beetles around.

| FAMILY | Hydraenidae |
|---|---|
| SUBFAMILY | Hydraeninae |
| DISTRIBUTION | Neotropical: South America, Colombia |
| MACROHABITAT | Aquatic |
| MICROHABITAT | Margins of ponds |
| FEEDING HABITS | Grazers of organic matter and algae-covered surfaces |
| NOTE | The body of the beetle is covered with an envelope of air that makes it float when it is dislodged |

ADULT LENGTH
¹⁄₁₆ in
(1.9–2 mm)

*HYDRAENA ANISONYCHA*
# HYDRAENA ANISONYCHA
PERKINS, 1980

Actual size

This is a relatively large member of a family containing minute (¹⁄₁₆ in, or 1.8 mm) aquatic or semi-aquatic beetles. The majority of other species in the genus are found in wet substrates along streams, but this species occurs around ponds. Members of the family whose feeding habits are known scrape algae and other organic matter from wet surfaces. Specialized glands on the body produce secretions that assist in holding an envelope of air around much of the body while the beetle is submerged. Hydraenid collectors can use this to their advantage because it causes the beetles to float whenever their habitats are agitated.

### RELATED SPECIES

The family Hydraenidae contains approximately 1,200 species, but many additional species remain undescribed, especially in South America. Among described South American species *Hydraena anisonycha* is unique in being relatively large and possessing a pair of elongate ridges on the ventral thorax (metaventrite). Most species within the genus require dissection and examination of male sex organs for correct identification.

**Hydraena anisonycha** has an overall shape that is typical of most members of the genus, but it is larger and the elytral punctures are not arranged in rows. Males of this species differ from females in possessing unevenly developed claws on the middle legs and asymmetrically enlarged hind legs.

| FAMILY | Hydraenidae |
|---|---|
| SUBFAMILY | Ochthebiinae |
| DISTRIBUTION | Nearctic and Neotropical: western North America, south to central Mexico |
| MACROHABITAT | Small bodies of water |
| MICROHABITAT | Margins of ponds and runoff areas, including alkaline hot springs |
| FEEDING HABITS | Microphagous grazers |
| NOTE | Shows an affinity to alkaline hot springs, but not limited to that habitat |

ADULT LENGTH
¹⁄₁₆ in
(1.8–2.4 mm)

*OCHTHEBIUS AZTECUS*

# OCHTHEBIUS AZTECUS

SHARP, 1887

139

Actual size

This species was described from the vicinity of Mexico City, but has been found as far north as North Dakota. The majority of documented records are from hot, often alkaline, springs, but others are from cold freshwater habitats. Hydraenids feed on the microscopic flora and fauna in the interstitial spaces of sand and soil along the edges of ponds and streams. Adults of *Ochthebius* possess glands on the head that produce secretions that are spread over the body by the legs. This creates zones that capture a layer of air that is used for respiration while the beetle is submerged.

## RELATED SPECIES

Forty-three species of *Ochthebius* are described from America north of Mexico, with many more from Mesoamerica and South America. Species are very similar, and detailed study—including dissection to examine male sex organs—is required to separate them. *Hydraena*, *Ochthebius*, and *Limnebius* comprise the largest genera in the family, and several species may occur at the same localities, separated by microhabitat preferences.

**Ochthebius aztecus** is typical among members of the genus in possessing subtle, but often complex, sculpturing of the dorsal body surface, especially on the disk of the pronotum, which in this species comprises a tapering median groove and two shorter adjacent grooves. This species also possesses distinctive hydrofuge pubescence on the sixth ventrite of the abdomen.

| FAMILY | Ptiliidae |
|---|---|
| SUBFAMILY | Ptiliinae |
| DISTRIBUTION | Afrotropical: Cameroon |
| MACROHABITAT | Tropical forests |
| MICROHABITAT | Presumably on fungi |
| FEEDING HABITS | Fungivorous |
| NOTE | Members of this genus include some of the smallest known non-parasitoid insects |

ADULT LENGTH
¹⁄₃₂ in
(0.61–0.67 mm)

*DISCHERAMOCEPHALUS BRUCEI*
# DISCHERAMOCEPHALUS BRUCEI
GREBENNIKOV, 2008

Actual size

**Discheramocephalus brucei** is a medium-size member of a genus that includes some of the smallest free-living insects. They are characterized by the distinct grooves on the pronotum and top of the head near the eyes. The general body shape is similar to that of many other species of ptiliid beetles.

*Discheramocephalus brucei* is one of seven species in a genus that includes some of the smallest known beetles, with *D. minutissimus* approaching the smallest size of any non-parasitoid insect, at ¹⁄₆₄ in (0.4 mm) in total length. Only some egg parasitoid Hymenoptera are smaller. Presumably, egg and brain size are the factors limiting miniaturization in insects. Ptiliid beetles are exclusively fungivores, though the feeding habits and other details of biology are unknown for species of *Discheramocephalus*. Other minute members of the family are specialists on fungal spores, and this is likely the feeding substrate of these tiny beetles as well.

## RELATED SPECIES
At least 550 species of Ptiliidae are currently described, including many that are less than ¹⁄₃₂ in (1 mm) in length. Six similar species in addition to *D. brucei* are included in this genus. They must be examined using compound microscopy to separate them based on subtle differences in sculpturing and other features of the body surface, and internal sex organs. Additional species within the genus are likely to be discovered in appropriate habitats.

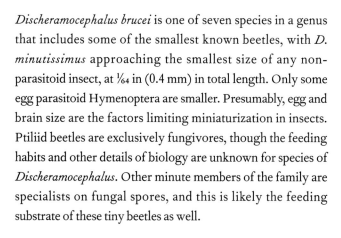

| FAMILY | Ptiliidae |
| --- | --- |
| SUBFAMILY | Ptiliinae |
| DISTRIBUTION | Nearctic and Neotropical: Pacific coast of North America and Baja California |
| MACROHABITAT | Ocean beaches |
| MICROHABITAT | Under seaweed and other organic debris |
| FEEDING HABITS | Presumed fungivorous |
| NOTE | One of the few beetles living in intertidal zones on ocean beaches |

ADULT LENGTH
$\frac{1}{32}$ in
(0.8 mm)

*MOTSCHULSKIUM SINUATICOLLE*

# MOTSCHULSKIUM SINUATICOLLE

MATTHEWS, 1872

141

Actual size

Few beetles are adapted to life in the intertidal zone of beaches. This species is found under seaweed and other organic matter on Pacific beaches from British Columbia to Baja California. Details of its habits are unknown, but presumably it feeds on fungus growing in these habitats. Possibly, it is a spore-feeder, a specialization shared by other minute members of the family. Locality data for *Motschulskium sinuaticolle* are incomplete along the length of the known range. Additional collecting targeting minute Coleoptera in intertidal habitats will likely reveal that the species is more common than current records indicate.

## RELATED SPECIES

Approximately 550 species of the family are described, but many more are undescribed. No other species of Ptiliidae are known to be adapted to the intertidal zones in the area of occurrence of this species, and only the single species is included within the genus *Motschulskium*.

**Motschulskium sinuaticolle** is typical of small ptiliids in overall body form. The combination of its small size, golden pubescence, gray or black color, and the association with intertidal organic debris are unique attributes that can be used to identify specimens.

| FAMILY | Ptiliidae |
|---|---|
| SUBFAMILY | Cephaloplectinae |
| DISTRIBUTION | Neotropical: western Amazon |
| MACROHABITAT | Tropical rainforest |
| MICROHABITAT | Army ant nests and emigration columns |
| FEEDING HABITS | Adults feed on secretions of host ants; larval feeding habits are unknown |
| NOTE | This species is reliant on the army ants with which they live |

ADULT LENGTH
¹⁄₁₆ in
(2.2–2.5 mm)

*CEPHALOPLECTUS MUS*
# CEPHALOPLECTUS MUS
(MANN, 1926)

•

Actual size

**Cephaloplectus mus** are distinct among beetles by their limuloid (horseshoe crab-shaped) bodies, absence of wings and eyes, unusually developed prosternal process, and obligate symbiotic association with ant colonies. Observed body length in preserved specimens is often shorter than that of living specimens due to postmortem contraction.

All members of the subfamily Cephaloplectinae are referred to as horseshoe crab beetles and are reliant on ant colonies (inquilines). Members of *Cephaloplectus mus* have been documented as associates of the army ant species *Eciton vagans* and generally are collected through interceptions during periodic emigration events when the ants relocate their nests. Other species within the same subfamily have been recorded from *Formica*, *Lasius*, *Neivamyrmex*, and *Pheidole*. Biologies are poorly understood, but the ants tolerate the beetles' presence and allow them to "graze" on the surfaces of their bodies. The larvae and their biological role in the inquiline/host system are unknown.

RELATED SPECIES

*Cephaloplectus mus* is one of seven described species in the genus. *Cephaloplectus* species overlap with members of the other widespread genus of the subfamily, *Limulodes*, in tropical America and both may be found in army any nests and emigration columns. Thirty-seven species of horseshoe crab beetles are described worldwide. The species level taxonomy of *Cephaloplectus* is poorly resolved.

| FAMILY | Agyrtidae |
|---|---|
| SUBFAMILY | Agyrtinae |
| DISTRIBUTION | Holarctic: Russia (Kuril Islands, Kamchatka, Commander Islands); United States (Aleutian, Pribilofs, Kodiak, Afognak, and Chirikof Islands) |
| MACROHABITAT | Island beaches |
| MICROHABITAT | Organic debris on seashores |
| FEEDING HABITS | Saprophagous |
| NOTE | Breeding populations survived a 2008 volcanic eruption that killed all other beetles on Kasatochi Island, Alaska |

ADULT LENGTH
¼–⁵⁄₁₆ in
(6–8 mm)

*LYROSOMA OPACUM*

# LYROSOMA OPACUM

MANNERHEIM, 1853

143

Actual size

*Lyrosoma opacum* inhabits seashores on the Aleutian and Kuril islands in the north Pacific. Adults occur in organic debris such as seaweed and abandoned birds' nests, where they are scavengers, and have been observed feeding on dead fish and other carrion. Larval feeding habits are presumed to be similar, but bionomics of immature stages are poorly known. *Lyrosoma opacum* was the only beetle species that survived a 2008 volcanic eruption that wiped out most of the terrestrial fauna on Kasatochi Island. The family Agyrtidae is phylogenetically important as a possible sister taxon to all other members of the enormous superfamily Staphylinoidea.

## RELATED SPECIES

*Lyrosoma opacum* is one of two species in the genus, with the second, *L. pallidum*, occurring farther west along seashores as far south as South Korea. The two species overlap at a single locality on the Kamchatka Peninsula, Russia. *Lyrosoma opacum* is the larger of the two species and differs in having reticulate elytra (smooth in *L. pallidum*).

**Lyrosoma opacum** is a medium-size generalized brown beetle with rounded pronotal margins and ovate elytra. Adults of the species bear an uncanny resemblance to ground beetles in the family Carabidae, though the two families are not related. The unique seashore habitat is a great clue to its identity.

| FAMILY | Agyrtidae |
| --- | --- |
| SUBFAMILY | Necrophilinae |
| DISTRIBUTION | Palearctic: Europe |
| MACROHABITAT | Forests |
| MICROHABITAT | Decaying organic matter, leaf litter |
| FEEDING HABITS | Saprophagous |
| NOTE | A cold-adapted species that is often active during fall, winter, and early spring |

ADULT LENGTH
¼–³⁄₈ in
(7–9 mm)

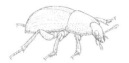

NECROPHILUS SUBTERRANEUS
# NECROPHILUS SUBTERRANEUS
(DAHL, 1807)

These beetles are unusual due to their tendency to be more active during cool seasons of the year than in the warmer months. They are found in moist forest habitats, at high elevations, and in the entrances and twilight zones of caves. Larvae and adults feed on decaying organic matter, including carrion and rotting mushrooms, and may be collected by baiting pitfalls with these substances. Larvae are considered to be among the most generalized within the staphylinoid group of families, and representatives of the family are known from Early Jurassic fossils, suggesting great antiquity.

## RELATED SPECIES

*Necrophilus subterraneus* is the only member of the genus in Europe, but several similar genera of agyrtid beetles overlap in distribution and additional species of *Necrophilus* occur in Asia and North America. *Necrophilus* may be distinguished from other genera by the broader, more oval body form, the numerous but relatively weak costae of the elytra, and details of the mandibles.

Actual size

**Necrophilus subterraneus** is a medium-size, oval brown beetle, with broadly margined and punctate pronotum and elytra. It is generally more ovate than other agyrtids. The species looks like a small silphid and was included in that family until relatively recently.

| FAMILY | Leiodidae |
|---|---|
| SUBFAMILY | Camiarinae |
| DISTRIBUTION | Australian: New Zealand (North Island) |
| MACROHABITAT | Southern temperate forests |
| MICROHABITAT | Moist forest litter |
| FEEDING HABITS | Presumed mycophagous |
| NOTE | This and other members of the tribe Camiarini share a convergent morphology with members of the rove beetle subfamily Scydmaeninae |

ADULT LENGTH
⅛–³⁄₁₆ in
(3.4–3.6 mm)

*CAMIARUS THORACICUS*
# CAMIARUS THORACICUS
(SHARP, 1876)

145

The original describer of this species, Thomas Broun, erroneously considered that it might form a link between the Scydmaeninae and Silphidae, where the species was originally placed. This is representative of the taxonomic ambiguity that has plagued this south temperate assemblage within the Leiodidae. The species occurs in moist forest litter on the North Island of New Zealand, and was included in a study of Coleoptera inhabiting forested habitats of suburban Auckland. However, very little is known of the biology of the species or of other members of the subfamily.

## RELATED SPECIES
The genus contains two species, both occurring in New Zealand. They are members of the southern temperate subfamily Camiarinae, which includes 27 genera and about 90 species, six genera and 16 species of which are included in the tribe Camiarini. The subfamily presents a broad range of morphological diversity considering its relatively small size, and probably does not form a natural grouping based on the results of several phylogenetic studies.

**Camiarus thoracicus** possesses a body form convergent with that of many members of the rove beetle subfamily Scydmaeninae. The rounded head, ovate pronotum, and elongate-oval elytra caused the original describer confusion about the species' phylogenetic affinities.

Actual size

| FAMILY | Leiodidae |
|---|---|
| SUBFAMILY | Leiodinae |
| DISTRIBUTION | Nearctic: scattered localities throughout the western United States and transcontinental in the northern United States and southern Canada |
| MACROHABITAT | Forests |
| MICROHABITAT | Coarse woody debris, under bark and moist surfaces |
| FEEDING HABITS | Grazes on slime molds |
| NOTE | Conglobulate (rolls into a ball) when disturbed |

ADULT LENGTH
1/16–1/8 in
(2.3–2.7 mm)

*AGATHIDIUM PULCHRUM*
# AGATHIDIUM PULCHRUM
LECONTE, 1853

Actual size

*Agathidium pulchrum* is one of the most widespread and commonly collected members of the large genus *Agathidium*. Adults and larvae of this species and other members of the genus graze on slime molds and fungi. They occur in forests under the bark of dead wood or on other moist organic substrates that support growths of slime molds and basidiomycete fungi. They seek shelter or drop when disturbed, and the highly convex body shape allows them to conglobate, or roll into a ball. The genus gained some notoriety in the popular press in 2005 when three species were named after members of the George W. Bush presidency, *A. bushi*, *A. cheneyi*, and *A. rumsfeldi*.

RELATED SPECIES

Currently, 98 species of the genus are described for North and Central America, and this number is likely to rise as additional material becomes available from less well-collected areas. A large number of species also occur in the Palearctic and Oriental realms. A similar genus, *Gelae*, shares external features with *Agathidium*. Dissections to examine male sex organs are required for positive identification of many species.

**Agathidium pulchrum** is strongly convex dorsally and concave ventrally. It is unusual among most North American members of the genus in possessing orange-yellow markings dorsally instead of being uniformly black. The asymmetrical tusk of the left male mandible is variable in degree of development.

| FAMILY | Leiodidae |
| --- | --- |
| SUBFAMILY | Coloninae |
| DISTRIBUTION | Palearctic: Bosnia and Herzegovina, Serbia, Montenegro |
| MACROHABITAT | Karst landscapes |
| MICROHABITAT | Caves |
| FEEDING HABITS | Microphagous rock-scraper |
| NOTE | Walks sideways or backwards against the flow of water while feeding |

ADULT LENGTH
¼–⁵⁄₁₆ in
(7–7.6 mm)

*HADESIA VASICEKI*
# HADESIA VASICEKI
MÜLLER, 1911

147

This troglobitic beetle is known from a single cave in Bosnia. It presents morphological adaptations typical of beetles that live in caves but exhibits an unusual feeding strategy associated with water flowing along cave walls. The beetles position themselves with the posterior end pointing upward, against the flow of water. They then either walk sideways or climb backward against the current. Presumably this allows the accumulation of food particles in the ventral mouthparts, which are lined with dense setae. When not in the stream of water, the beetles progress in typical fashion, one tarsus in front of the other.

## RELATED SPECIES

Until recently, the genus contained only a single species with two subspecies. Two additional species have been described and one subspecies was elevated to species, resulting in a current total of four. Species identification requires study of the genitalia and elytral epipleuron. Numerous similar species in genera of the subtribe Anthroherponina also occur in caves of the Balkan region.

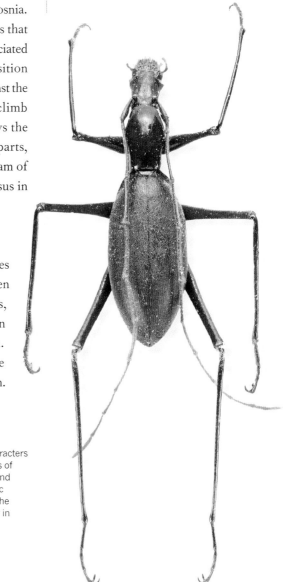

Actual size

**Hadesia vasiceki** presents a suite of morphological characters that are typical of true troglobitic, cave-adapted, species of beetles. The narrow, elongate body, long appendages, and complete absence of eyes are similar to other troglobitic leiodids in eastern Europe. *Glacicavicola bathyscioides*, the North American lava-tube leiodid, is remarkably similar in appearance, presumably as a result of convergence.

| FAMILY | Leiodidae |
|---|---|
| SUBFAMILY | Cholevinae |
| DISTRIBUTION | Palearctic: Slovenia |
| MACROHABITAT | Karst landscapes |
| MICROHABITAT | Caves |
| FEEDING HABITS | Saprophagous |
| NOTE | The first true troglobitic beetle described in the world |

ADULT LENGTH
⁵⁄₁₆–⁷⁄₁₆ in
(8–11 mm)

148

*LEPTODIRUS HOCHENWARTII HOCHENWARTII*
# LEPTODIRUS HOCHENWARTII HOCHENWARTII

SCHMIDT, 1832

This species has the distinction of being the first troglobitic beetle described in the world based on specimens collected by an early explorer of caves in one of the European karst regions. Populations occur deep within caves, where individuals may be numerous and have been observed scavenging on carrion and other organic matter. This species reportedly undergoes metamorphosis that differs from most holometabolous insects. Large eggs hatch into non-feeding larvae that immediately pupate and emerge as adults, effectively skipping a feeding larval stage. The species is considered threatened and is protected.

### RELATED SPECIES

*Leptodirus hochenwartii* is the only member of the genus and is divided into six subspecies distributed among various cave systems in Europe as far west as eastern Italy. It may be confused with a number of other troglobitic leiodid beetles that are similarly modified to life deep within caves.

**Leptodirus hochenwartii hochenwartii** is an example of a highly modified troglobite lacking eyes and wings, and possessing inflated elytra, a narrow, elongate forebody, and long, spindly legs and antennae. This body form is found in other eastern European troglobitic leiodids and in the North American species *Glacicavicola bathyscioides*.

Actual size

| FAMILY | Leiodidae |
|---|---|
| SUBFAMILY | Cholevinae |
| DISTRIBUTION | Nearctic: Kentucky, USA |
| MACROHABITAT | Caves |
| MICROHABITAT | Twilight zone |
| FEEDING HABITS | Saprophagous |
| NOTE | Adult captive specimens maintained under simulated cave conditions have lived up to 2.5 years |

ADULT LENGTH
¹⁄₁₆–⅛ in
(2–2.8 mm)

*PTOMAPHAGUS HIRTUS*
# KENTUCKY CAVE BEETLE
(TELLKAMPF, 1844)

149

Actual size

The Kentucky Cave Beetle is restricted to the cave system in and around Mammoth Cave National Park in Kentucky, USA. Specimens held under cool, moisture-laden conditions similar to their caves of origin thrived on a diet of dried yeast, but required samples of native cave soil to complete development and reproduce. Adults held under these conditions survived for up to 2.5 years, which is considered long-lived among adult insects. The beetles are apparently eyeless and blind, but transcriptome studies have documented the existence of light-processing proteins and circadian-rhythm genes. Indeed, in behavioral experiments, the beetles showed sensitivity to light in light/dark choice tests.

**The Kentucky Cave Beetle** is an eyeless, teardrop-shaped beetle. The overall shape, size, and color are typical of many other members of this and several related genera. Despite the apparent absence of eyes, the beetles are capable of responding to light by using a small lens patch where the compound eye is in other species.

## RELATED SPECIES

The genus *Ptomaphagus* includes over 50 species in the United States and southern Canada. Separating species requires detailed study and dissections of male sex organs, though distributional information can also be useful. Many additional species and several similar genera are known from other parts of the world, excluding African and Pacific regions.

| FAMILY | Leiodidae |
|---|---|
| SUBFAMILY | Platypsyllinae |
| DISTRIBUTION | Nearctic and Palearctic: North America, Europe |
| MACROHABITAT | Wetland areas |
| MICROHABITAT | Beavers and beaver lodges/burrows |
| FEEDING HABITS | Parasitic on beaver dandruff and skin secretions |
| NOTE | This oddly flattened beetle was once classified as a flea |

**ADULT LENGTH**
¹⁄₁₆–⅛ in
(2–3 mm)

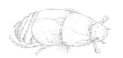

*PLATYPSYLLUS CASTORIS*
# BEAVER BEETLE
RITSEMA, 1869

150

Actual size

**The Beaver Beetle** has a dorsoventrally flattened body (fleas are laterally flattened) and the legs are short and spined, adaptations that allow the beetle to push its way through the thick fur of its host. The elytra are short, and wings are absent. The antennae are stubby and clubbed, and the mandibles are flattened and plate-like.

The Beaver Beetle is profoundly adapted to life as an external parasite of American Beavers (*Castor canadensis*) and Eurasian Beavers (*C. fiber*). Both adults and larvae occur on the animals, where they feed on dandruff, and skin and wound secretions. Pupation occurs in organic litter in beaver lodges and burrows. Up to 60 percent of beavers yielded beetles in one survey; the presence of the beetles does not seem to disturb the mammals. Isolated records from other hosts exist, but these may be incidental. Beetles may be collected from recently killed beavers by combing the fur or capturing the insects as they leave the cooling body.

### RELATED SPECIES

Members of the subfamily Platypsyllinae exhibit a gradient in morphological adaptations to life associated with mammals, from the flattened, but otherwise beetle-like *Leptinus* (mammal nest beetles) and *Leptinillus* (*Aplodontia* and *Castor* beaver nest beetles) to the highly modified Beaver Beetle. *Leptinillus validus* sometimes occurs on beavers with the Beaver Beetle, but can be distinguished by its much more beetle-like appearance, including longer elytra and relatively unmodified mouthparts.

| FAMILY | Silphidae |
|---|---|
| SUBFAMILY | Silphinae |
| DISTRIBUTION | Oriental and Australian: Southeast Asia, New Guinea |
| MACROHABITAT | Tropical forests |
| MICROHABITAT | Rotting organic matter, especially carrion |
| FEEDING HABITS | Saprophagous or possibly predatory on fly maggots |
| NOTE | May pollinate the gigantic flowers of *Amorphophallus gigas* |

ADULT LENGTH
½–¹¹⁄₁₆ in
(13–17 mm)

*NECROPHILA FORMOSA*

# NECROPHILA FORMOSA

(LAPORTE, 1832)

151

Species of the *Chrysosilpha* subgenus of *Necrophila*, including *N. formosa*, have been collected using traps baited with rotting fish and from decaying vegetation. Members of the genus elsewhere are associated with carrion habitats but are primarily predators of fly maggots. Feeding habits of this species have apparently not been documented directly, so they may also be maggot predators. The beetles have been recorded at the giant inflorescence of the aroid *Amorphophallus gigas*, which smells like rotting fish as a result of trimethylamine production. Possibly the species plays a role in fertilization of these remarkable flowers.

RELATED SPECIES

This species is one of three within the subgenus *Chrysosilpha*. All occur in tropical Asia, but *Necrophila formosa* is the only one with an orange pronotum.

Actual size

**Necrophila formosa** and the other two members of the subgenus *Chrysosilpha* are unusual among silphid beetles in possessing bright, iridescent green to purple elytra. Adults of all three species may be collected on rotting fish or other kinds of carrion.

| FAMILY | Silphidae |
|---|---|
| SUBFAMILY | Nicrophorinae |
| DISTRIBUTION | Nearctic: eastern North America |
| MACROHABITAT | Forests and open prairies |
| MICROHABITAT | Animal carcasses |
| FEEDING HABITS | Saprophagous |
| NOTE | The sexes share parental care of young larvae on buried carcasses |

ADULT LENGTH
1³⁄₁₆–1¾ in
(30–45 mm)

*NICROPHORUS AMERICANUS*
# AMERICAN BURYING BEETLE
OLIVIER, 1790

Based on museum specimen records, the legally protected American Burying Beetle once occupied practically every eastern US state and southeastern Canadian province in North America. It now occurs only on islands off the northeastern United States coast and scattered areas of the eastern Great Plains. For reproduction, mated pairs locate and bury a fresh bird or mammal carcass, prepare it by coating it in special antibiotic saliva, then the female lays her eggs on it. Both sexes remain with the newly hatched larvae for a period of time, feeding them by regurgitation until they are able to feed independently and complete development.

## RELATED SPECIES

At least ten additional species of the genus *Nicrophorus* may be found within the current or historical range of the American Burying Beetle. None is as large, nor do they possess the striking orange thorax of this species. Other species typically occupy smaller carrion food sources and none appears to have suffered the obvious decline experienced by the American Burying Beetle.

**The American Burying** Beetle is the largest North American beetle within the staphylinoid group of families. Males and females differ in the shape of the orange patch on the top of the head. The cooperative burial of food sources and advanced parental care exhibited by these and other members of the genus is unique among beetles.

Actual size

| FAMILY | Staphylinidae |
|---|---|
| SUBFAMILY | Glypholomatinae |
| DISTRIBUTION | Australian: southeastern Australia |
| MACROHABITAT | Temperate forests |
| MICROHABITAT | Carrion, fungi, leaf litter, grass tussocks |
| FEEDING HABITS | Presumed fungivorous |
| NOTE | A cold-adapted species, with most collections made during the southern hemisphere fall or winter |

ADULT LENGTH
¹⁄₁₆–¹⁄₈ in
(2.3–2.7 mm)

*GLYPHOLOMA ROTUNDULUM*
# GLYPHOLOMA ROTUNDULUM
THAYER & NEWTON, 1979

153

Actual size

*Glypholoma rotundulum* is a member of the enigmatic rove beetle subfamily Glypholomatinae. The subfamily is one of several phylogenetically important members of the omaliine group found in south temperate regions of the world. This species is confined to temperate forests in southeastern Australia and has been collected from traps that required the insects to travel across snow, suggesting unusual cold tolerance. Species from the northern parts of the range are fully winged, but most from the south possess reduced wings and are incapable of flight. Based on gut content analyses, the beetles are believed to feed on fungi.

## RELATED SPECIES

*Glypholoma rotundulum* is the only species within the subfamily that occurs in Australia, though several species within the genus are known from temperate forests in Argentina and Chile. The possibility exists that additional species may be discovered in Australia.

The species are similar in general body form to members of the subfamily Omaliinae, and were included as a tribe within that subfamily for many years.

**Glypholoma rotundulum** is a convex, ovate, dark brown rove beetle with strongly costate elytra. Only the last abdominal segment is typically exposed behind the elytra. The paired ocelli on the head suggest a close affinity with members of the subfamily Omaliinae. Phylogenetic studies have placed it near that group, but not within it.

| FAMILY | Staphylinidae |
|---|---|
| SUBFAMILY | Microsilphinae |
| DISTRIBUTION | Neotropical: southern Chile |
| MACROHABITAT | Southern temperate forests |
| MICROHABITAT | Organic forest litter |
| FEEDING HABITS | Unknown, but thought to be mycophagous or saprophagous |
| NOTE | A member of one of the least-known and most enigmatic groups of rove beetles |

ADULT LENGTH
⅛ in
(3–3.2 mm)

*MICROSILPHA OCELLIGERA*
# MICROSILPHA OCELLIGERA
(CHAMPION, 1918)

Actual size

Members of the Microsilphinae are among the least-studied groups of the enormous family Staphylinidae. Nothing is known of this species beyond the morphology of adult specimens and their occurrence in organic litter of southern temperate forests. Feeding habits are deduced to be mycophagous or saprophagous on fungal- and microbe-rich organic substrates based on the known feeding habits of members of the related subfamily Omaliinae, but this has yet to be confirmed. Details of the larvae and other life stages are unknown. Members of the subfamily have been previously included in several other families, including Silphidae and Leiodidae.

## RELATED SPECIES

Two other described species of this genus occur in South America, in southern Argentina, and an additional species is described from New Zealand. Many undescribed species have been noted by staphylinid specialists, and their existence complicates correct species identifications.

**Microsilpha ocelligera** is a somber brown-colored rove beetle that presents an unusual combination of characters, including clubbed antennae, paired dorsal ocelli, and elongate elytra. These features led to the placement of various members of the genus in other families, until detailed study revealed their close relationship to the rove beetle subfamily Omaliinae.

| FAMILY | Staphylinidae |
| SUBFAMILY | Omaliinae |
| DISTRIBUTION | Oriental: Southeast Asia |
| MACROHABITAT | Tropical forests |
| MICROHABITAT | Wet forest litter |
| FEEDING HABITS | Presumed mycophagous |
| NOTE | As with numerous other rove beetles that have complete elytra, this species was previously erroneously placed in Silphidae |

ADULT LENGTH
³⁄₁₆ in
(4.6–4.8 mm)

*DEINOPTEROLOMA SPECTABILE*
# DEINOPTEROLOMA SPECTABILE
SMETANA, 1985

155

Actual size

This species is an Asian member of a genus with a broadly disjunct distribution. Most species occur in montane forests in eastern Asia (Himalaya, China) and in tropical forests of southeast Asia, and two are known from western North America. This distribution pattern is thought to be a remnant of the connection between northeast Asia and northwestern North America during the Cenozoic Era. The bionomics of this species are unknown, but adults and larvae presumably feed on fungi associated with decaying organic matter. The deep pits of the dorsal surface may be the openings of glands that secrete protective hydrophobic compounds that coat the body surface.

RELATED SPECIES

*Deinopteroloma* comprises seven species in Southeast Asia in addition to *D. spectabile*, and two species in the Pacific Northwest of North America. The genus is distinctive in appearance, but species are quite similar to one another and must be separated on the basis of subtle differences in surface ornamentation and internal male genitalia morphologies.

**Deinopteroloma spectabile** is one of many rove beetle species that have uncharacteristically complete, strongly convex elytra covering the abdomen. The concave margins of the pronotum and deep glandular pits of the dorsal surface may be adaptations to life in saturated decaying organic matter.

| FAMILY | Staphylinidae |
|---|---|
| SUBFAMILY | Omaliinae |
| DISTRIBUTION | Nearctic: northwest North America, from California to Alaska |
| MACROHABITAT | Temperate rainforests |
| MICROHABITAT | Fungi, moss, and forest organic litter |
| FEEDING HABITS | Fungivorous |
| NOTE | This rare snout-bearing rove beetle is endemic to the cool, wet forests of the Pacific Northwest |

ADULT LENGTH
³⁄₁₆ in
(4.2–5.4 mm)

156

*TANYRHINUS SINGULARIS*
# TANYRHINUS SINGULARIS
MANNERHEIM, 1852

Actual size

This unusual snouted rove beetle inhabits temperate rainforests throughout much of the Pacific Northwest. Specimens for which collection data are available were usually taken in mushrooms associated with logs and other decaying organic matter on the forest floor or suspended in the canopy. A few have been collected under bark. *Tanyrhinus singularis* is considered rare and possibly at risk from conversion of old-growth forest to managed timber plantations. Little is known of the bionomics of the species except that it is likely a fungivore; larvae are undescribed.

## RELATED SPECIES

No other species of rove beetle in the region has a snout that is as elongate as that of *Tanyrhinus singularis*, though adults of a related genus, *Trigonodemus*, have a slightly elongate frons and similar body shape. The species may be mistaken for weevils or members of a few other beetle families with snouts, but the pair of ocelli excludes all groups except Omaliinae.

**Tanyrhinus singularis** adults are unusual among most rove beetles and other non-curculionoid beetles in possessing mouthparts that are located on an elongate, narrow snout superficially resembling that of weevils. The body is typical of many other members of the subfamily Omaliinae in having elytra that largely or completely cover the abdomen.

| | |
|---|---|
| FAMILY | Staphylinidae |
| SUBFAMILY | Empelinae |
| DISTRIBUTION | Nearctic: from southern Alaska to California |
| MACROHABITAT | Pacific coast rainforest |
| MICROHABITAT | Wet forest litter |
| FEEDING HABITS | Unknown |
| NOTE | This oddly shaped rove beetle was described originally in the family Phalacridae |

ADULT LENGTH
¹⁄₁₆ in
(1.5–1.7 mm)

*EMPELUS BRUNNIPENNIS*

# EMPELUS BRUNNIPENNIS

(MANNERHEIM, 1852)

157

Actual size

This obscure beetle was originally described as a member of the genus *Litochrus* within the Phalacridae. It was subsequently moved to Clambidae, where it remained for many years, and relatively recently was placed in its own family (Empelidae) or included within the subfamily Omaliinae. Finally, it has been recognized as a distinct member of the omaliine group of subfamilies within its one subfamily. Other than circumstances surrounding the collection of specimens, nothing is known of its life history. It has been collected from Douglas-fir (*Pseudotsuga menziesii*) habitat in both old-growth and clear-cut situations.

RELATED SPECIES

*Empelus brunnipennis* is the only described member of the subfamily. Difficulties with family placement are the main issues confronting correct identification of this enigmatic rove beetle. It is characterized by the hind coxae being expanded posteriorly as plates partly covering the femora (when seen in ventral view).

**Empelus brunnipennis** shares a superficial resemblance to many other small, convex, oval brown beetles, most notably, but not limited to, members of Phalacridae, Clambidae, and certain Leiodidae. The long elytra and the antennae with the apical three antennomeres forming an abrupt club are characteristic of this species.

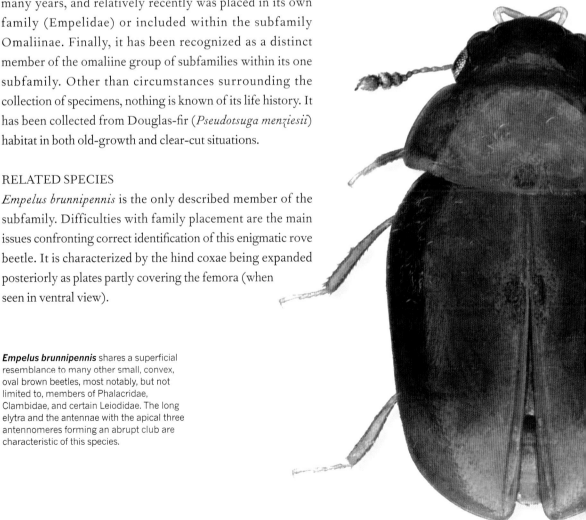

| FAMILY | Staphylinidae |
|---|---|
| SUBFAMILY | Proteininae |
| DISTRIBUTION | Palearctic and Afrotropical: Europe, northwestern Africa |
| MACROHABITAT | Forests |
| MICROHABITAT | Forest litter, mossy substrates |
| FEEDING HABITS | Presumed saprophagous |
| NOTE | This species was identified from Roman-era sediments in Great Britain that are almost 2,000 years old |

ADULT LENGTH
⅛ in
(2.5–3 mm)

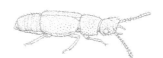

*METOPSIA CLYPEATA*
# METOPSIA CLYPEATA
P. MÜLLER, 1821

Actual size

Little is known about this widespread species of small rove beetle. It is a member of a relatively small subfamily, the diversity of which is dominated by the large genus *Megarthrus*. *Metopsia clypeata* seems to occur across a wide variety of landscape types, where it likely subsists on decaying organic matter in pockets of moist litter. Other members of the subfamily engage in a behavior called water loading. Water is channeled to the dorsal surface through capillary action and accumulates in a droplet on top of the beetle before collapsing. Whether *M. clypeata* engages in this behavior is unknown.

## RELATED SPECIES

Eleven species in addition to *Metopsia clypeata* are included in the genus. All but one, *M. similis*, are much more limited in their distributions. The two widespread species are quite similar in external appearance and dissections to examine male genitalia are required to separate them reliably. Other members of the subfamily and a few omaliine rove beetles bear a superficial resemblance to members of *Metopsia*.

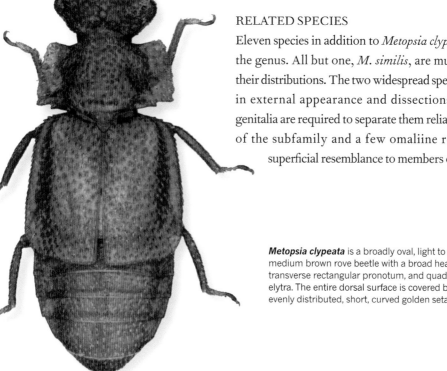

**Metopsia clypeata** is a broadly oval, light to medium brown rove beetle with a broad head, transverse rectangular pronotum, and quadrate elytra. The entire dorsal surface is covered by evenly distributed, short, curved golden setae.

| FAMILY | Staphylinidae |
|---|---|
| SUBFAMILY | Micropeplinae |
| DISTRIBUTION | Neotropical: southern Mexico |
| MACROHABITAT | Forests |
| MICROHABITAT | Forest leaf litter |
| FEEDING HABITS | Unknown, probably saprophagous |
| NOTE | Known only from a single locality in Chiapas, Mexico |

ADULT LENGTH
¹⁄₁₆ in
(1.8–1.9 mm)

*PEPLOMICRUS MEXICANUS*
# PEPLOMICRUS MEXICANUS
CAMPBELL, 1978

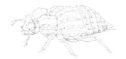

159

Actual size

This species and others within the subfamily were considered a distinct family, the Micropeplidae, for many years owing to their unusual morphologies. They are now known to be members of one of three major lineages of rove beetles that also includes Omaliinae and Pselaphinae. This species was described from a series of five specimens collected at a single locality in Chiapas, Mexico. They were collected by sifting forest litter, but other details of the life history are unknown. Members of Micropeplinae are believed to be saprophagous on decaying organic matter and/or fungi.

## RELATED SPECIES

Seven species within the genus *Peplomicrus* occur in the New World tropics and two more occur in China. Species within the genus are distinguished by minor differences in the arrangements of the dorsal ridges, punctures, and other, sometimes subtle, variations in external features. Members of the similar genus *Micropeplus* can be separated by features of the head and presence of fewer abdominal ridges.

**Peplomicrus mexicanus** is a stout, heavily sculptured rove beetle. The strong ridges of the dorsal surface and deep punctures on the elytra are typical features of members of the subfamily Micropeplinae that allow them to be immediately distinguished from most other rove beetle subfamilies. The large number of abdominal ridges are characteristic of *Peplomicrus* species.

| FAMILY | Staphylinidae |
|---|---|
| SUBFAMILY | Neophoninae |
| DISTRIBUTION | Neotropical: southern South America |
| MACROHABITAT | South temperate forests |
| MICROHABITAT | Forest understory foliage |
| FEEDING HABITS | Fungivorous; grazes on fungi growing on leaves |
| NOTE | Unusual among rove beetles in being active on exposed leaf surfaces during daytime |

ADULT LENGTH
⅛–³⁄₁₆ in
(3.3–3.7 mm)

*NEOPHONUS BRUCHI*
# NEOPHONUS BRUCHI
FAUVEL, 1905

Actual size

Members of this single species in the subfamily Neophoninae are important phylogenetically in resolving relationships within the large omaliine lineage of rove beetle subfamilies. They occur on understory leaf surfaces in south temperate forests, and gut-content analyses indicate that they graze on various kinds of fungi. Adults possess modified setae on their tarsi that assist with gripping leaf surfaces, and specialized brushes on their mouthparts for scraping fungi growing on leaf surfaces. They are unusual among most rove beetles in being exposed on leaves during daytime, and can be collecting by beating vegetation over a white sheet.

## RELATED SPECIES

No other species of this subfamily are known. Specimens may be mistaken for members of the subfamily Omaliinae owing to the presence of ocelli and superficially similar body form. But the distinctive dorsal habitus, bulging eyes, and many unique details of anatomy set them apart from all other rove beetles.

**Neophonus bruchi** is a medium-size rove beetle with large, bulging eyes, a broad, shiny reddish-brown to black forebody, and large dorsal punctures that are arranged in rows on the elytra. The abdomen tapers evenly from the broad base of the elytra. Females are slightly more reddish in coloration than males.

| FAMILY | Staphylinidae |
|---|---|
| SUBFAMILY | Dasycerinae |
| DISTRIBUTION | Nearctic: Appalachian Mountains, southeastern United States |
| MACROHABITAT | Montane forests |
| MICROHABITAT | Fungus-covered logs and standing dead trees |
| FEEDING HABITS | Fungivorous: grazes on polypore mushrooms and crusting fungi |
| NOTE | Nearctic species of *Dasycerus* are flightless |

ADULT LENGTH
¹⁄₁₆ in
(1.8–2 mm)

*DASYCERUS CAROLINENSIS*

# DASYCERUS CAROLINENSIS

HORN, 1882

161

Actual size

*Dasycerus carolinensis* adults can be found on the surfaces of shelf and encrusting fungi on large dead logs and standing dead trees in moist mountain forests at middle to high elevations of the southern Appalachian Mountains. The larvae also occur in these habitats but are much less commonly encountered. In addition, adults may occasionally be taken in leaf-litter samples. Members of the genus probably feed on the fungi on which they are found, but this has not been confirmed with certainty. These unusual rove beetles are phylogenetically important in resolving relationships among a number of other rove beetle subfamilies that are members of the same evolutionary branch of the family, including Omaliinae, Micropeplinae, Pselaphinae, and others.

## RELATED SPECIES

*Dasycerus carolinensis* occurs with a second species at the same localities, *D. bicolor*. The latter species differs in possessing a black spot on each elytron. The possibility exists that additional undescribed species occur in the same region. Further *Dasycerus* species occur in California, Europe, and Asia, and share the same general appearance of the body, but they differ in fine details of sculpturing and male genitalia.

**Dasycerus carolinensis** adults are unusual among rove beetles in possessing complete elytra, a heavily sculptured surface of the head and body, and delicate bead-like antennal segments. These features are typical of all members of the subfamily Dasycerinae, and are unique among rove beetles worldwide.

| FAMILY | Staphylinidae |
|---|---|
| SUBFAMILY | Pselaphinae |
| DISTRIBUTION | Nearctic: eastern North America |
| MACROHABITAT | Eastern deciduous forests |
| MICROHABITAT | Colonies of ants of the genus *Lasius* |
| FEEDING HABITS | Fed by host ants via regurgitation; also possibly predatory or saprophagous on dead ants |
| NOTE | Lives only in association with ant nests |

ADULT LENGTH
¹⁄₁₆ in
(1.8–2 mm)

162

Actual size

*ADRANES LECONTEI*

# ADRANES LECONTEI

BRENDEL, 1865

This beetle belongs to the supertribe Clavigeritae, whose members all share unique behavioral and morphological characters associated with integration into social insect colonies (inquilinism). The main host ants of this species are members of the genus *Lasius*. Details of the biology of *Adranes lecontei* are poorly known, but adult beetles possess modified trichomes at the base of the abdomen that produce secretions attractive to the ants. The ants probably feed the beetles through regurgitative trophallaxis, as documented in related species. Adults are seldom collected, but targeting host ant nests yields them with some regularity. The larvae are unknown but may prey on host larvae.

## RELATED SPECIES

The range of at least one other species of the genus *Adranes*, *A. coecus*, overlaps that of this species, but it may be differentiated by characters of the legs and male genital structures. Three additional species of the genus occur elsewhere in North America. Similar members of the clavigerite genus *Fustiger* differ in possessing small eyes, whereas *Adranes* is eyeless.

**Adranes lecontei** possesses antennae comprising only three antennomeres, with only the enlarged third segment obvious. The antennae, abdomen, and other body parts show a pattern of reduction and consolidation typical of morphologically specialized ant guests. The clusters of glandular trichomes at the base of the abdomen are typical of beetles at the highest order of integration as ant guests.

| FAMILY | Staphylinidae |
|---|---|
| SUBFAMILY | Pselaphinae |
| DISTRIBUTION | Palearctic: Europe |
| MACROHABITAT | Temperate forests |
| MICROHABITAT | Organic forest litter |
| FEEDING HABITS | Predatory |
| NOTE | The barrel-shaped abdomen is typical of members of the diverse tribe Batrisini |

ADULT LENGTH
⅛ in
(2.8–3.2 mm)

*BATRISUS FORMICARIUS*

# BATRISUS FORMICARIUS

AUBÉ, 1833

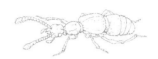

163

Actual size

*Batrisus formicarius* is a widespread European inhabitant of forest litter, sometimes associated with formicine ants, but also free-living in leaf litter and coarse woody debris. Feeding habits of this and most other pselaphine rove beetles are exclusively predatory. Mites and springtails are favored prey items. The beetles locate and approach prey using highly tuned sensory organs on their antennae and palpi, then lunge on prey when in close proximity. Prey items are masticated and digested externally, and the resulting slurry is ingested by the beetle. The larvae are unique in possessing eversible sticky processes to capture and immobilize prey.

## RELATED SPECIES

*Batrisus formicarius* is a member of a large group of very similar species in the tribe Batrisini. They may be distinguished from other members of the subfamily by the barrel-shaped abdomen, which is nearly circular in cross section. Within the Batrisini, structural differences on the male head and antennae, and male genital structures, are used to separate species, including the three other species of *Batrisus* that occur in Europe and temperate Asia.

**Batrisus formicarius** is a robust, brown pselaphine rove beetle typical of the batrisine group of genera. Adult anatomy of pselaphines is characterized by rigid construction and prominent circular cavities (foveae) that extend internally and provide further rigidity and strength.

| FAMILY | Staphylinidae |
|---|---|
| SUBFAMILY | Phloeocharinae |
| DISTRIBUTION | Nearctic: northwest North America |
| MACROHABITAT | Temperate rainforests |
| MICROHABITAT | Forest litter |
| FEEDING HABITS | Unknown, presumed predatory |
| NOTE | A rare rove beetle of unknown habits from Pacific coast rainforests |

ADULT LENGTH
³⁄₁₆ in
(4–4.5 mm)

164

*VICELVA VANDYKEI*
# VICELVA VANDYKEI
(HATCH, 1957)

This rarely collected species is endemic to coastal rainforests from Oregon to southern Alaska. Other than the collecting localities and habitats, nothing is known of its life history. Most members of the subfamily Phloeocharinae are similarly poorly known, but predatory feeding habits in both adults and larvae are suspected based on the morphology of the mouthparts. The few known specimens have been collected from leaf litter and riparian debris. Discovery of the bionomic attributes of this species and availability of fresh material for molecular analysis would contribute to a better understanding of phylogenetic relationships within Phloeocharinae.

## RELATED SPECIES

This genus may be easily separated from other members of the subfamily by the presence of a tridentate, beak-like clypeus. Only two species of this distinctive genus of rove beetles are known, with the second reported from northwestern Russia.

Actual size

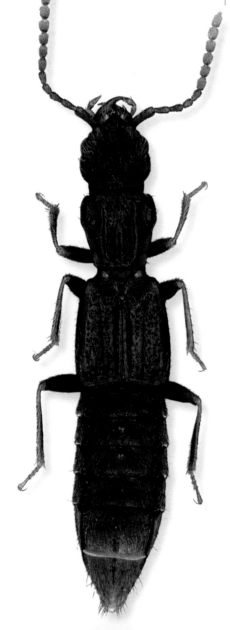

**Vicelva vandykei** is a medium-size elongate, parallel-sided rove beetle. The dorsal surface is dark brown and shiny, with distinct longitudinal grooves separated by raised areas bearing short, erect setae. The pronotum is broadest just behind the head and has recurved margins.

| FAMILY | Staphylinidae |
| --- | --- |
| SUBFAMILY | Tachyporinae |
| DISTRIBUTION | Palearctic: Europe and northern Asia |
| MACROHABITAT | Forests |
| MICROHABITAT | Mushrooms and bracket fungi |
| FEEDING HABITS | Predatory |
| NOTE | A common fungus-associated rove beetle that feeds on fly larvae |

ADULT LENGTH
³⁄₁₆–¼ in
(5–6 mm)

*LORDITHON LUNULATUS*
# LORDITHON LUNULATUS
(LINNAEUS, 1760)

165

Adults and larvae of this rove beetle species are common
associates of gilled and polypore mushrooms in forests across
northern Eurasia. Adults have been observed to feed on
fungus gnat larvae and small Housefly (*Musca domestica*)
maggots under laboratory conditions, and larvae are presumed
to be predatory as well. Otherwise, the life cycle and habits of
this and other species in the genus are poorly known. Adults
fly readily and apparently find fungal substrates by
following odor plumes produced by volatiles
emanating from the fungi.

## RELATED SPECIES

At least ten other species of *Lordithon* overlap the distribution
of this species, and approximately 140 species are described in
the genus worldwide, mainly from northern temperate zones.
This species appears under *Bolitobius* in older literature,
a genus name with an extremely convoluted nomenclatural
history. It is now properly included as a species of the
subgenus *Bolitobus* (note the slightly different spelling)
within *Lordithon*.

Actual size

**Lordithon lunulatus** is a brightly colored rove beetle with a striking,
alternating black–orange–black–orange–black dorsal color sequence.
Yellow spots highlight the base of the elytra and a yellow ring is present
on the abdomen. The narrow, tapering head is characteristic of this
genus within the tachyporine subfamily of rove beetles.

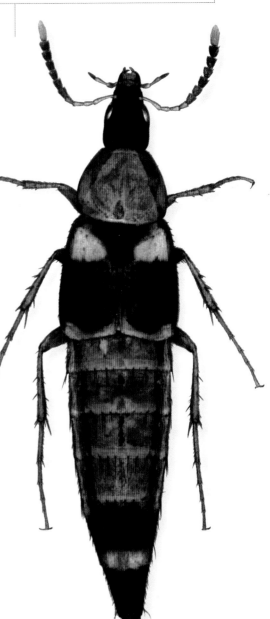

| FAMILY | Staphylinidae |
|---|---|
| SUBFAMILY | Aleocharinae |
| DISTRIBUTION | Nearctic: North America, north of Mexico |
| MACROHABITAT | Forests |
| MICROHABITAT | Nests of formicine ants |
| FEEDING HABITS | Adults and larvae are fed by hosts through trophallaxis |
| NOTE | A specialized nest parasite of formicine ants |

ADULT LENGTH
Adult length: ³⁄₁₆–¼ in
(5.3–6.4 mm)

*XENODUSA REFLEXA*
# XENODUSA REFLEXA
(WALKER, 1866)

Actual size

Adults and larvae of *Xenodusa reflexa* are adapted to an obligate association with formicine ants and spend most of their lives in ant nests. Specialized glandular setae on the adult abdomen produce appeasement chemicals that are attractive to host ants. Both adults and larvae are fed by regurgitation by the ants (trophallaxis). They are considered nest parasites because beetle larvae compete with ant larvae for care and feeding by the ants. Ants in the genus *Camponotus* are the most frequently documented hosts for this species, but other species breed in *Formica* nests and overwinter in *Camponotus* nests.

## RELATED SPECIES

Four species of the genus *Xenodusa* occur in the United States and southern Canada, and an additional species occurs in Mexico. *Xenodusa reflexa* is the most widely distributed species. It differs from species that overlap in ranges by its relatively larger size (³⁄₁₆–¼ in, or 5.3–6.4 mm) and setose ventral surface. A widespread eastern species, *X. cava*, is similar, but lacks long setae on the ventral surface of the body.

**Xenodusa reflexa** is a comparatively large, mahogany-brown member of the rove beetle tribe Lomechusini. The broad, reflexed pronotum and unusual trichome bundles along the abdomen are characteristic of the genus. Similar glandular trichomes are found on various parts of the bodies of other myrmecophilous beetles, and presumably also function in producing and distributing glandular appeasement chemicals.

| FAMILY | Staphylinidae |
|---|---|
| SUBFAMILY | Scaphidiinae |
| DISTRIBUTION | Oriental: Sumatra and Sulawesi, Indonesia; Sarawak, Malaysia |
| MACROHABITAT | Tropical forests |
| MICROHABITAT | Fungus on logs and standing dead trees |
| FEEDING HABITS | Fungivorous |
| NOTE | The neck may be twice the body length |

ADULT LENGTH
½–¾ in
(13–20 mm)

*DIATELIUM WALLACEI*
# LONG-NECKED SHINING FUNGUS BEETLE
PASCOE, 1863

167

From the head back, this remarkable insect looks like a typical member of the tribe Scaphidiini of the subfamily Scaphidiinae, but the extremely elongate neck in both sexes render it unique among rove beetles. The biology of the species is poorly known, but other members of the subfamily graze on fleshy or encrusting fungi on dead wood or other organic substrates in forest habitats as both adults and larvae. Adults may be encountered on exposed fungal surfaces day or night. They are wary and prone to flight or dropping, requiring a slow, stealthy approach if observations or photographic efforts are to be successful.

## RELATED SPECIES

This species is placed in the same tribe as the enormous genus *Scaphidium* based on recent phylogenetic studies and general appearance, exclusive of the outsize neck. It is not likely to be confused with any other animal within its range, but some African brentid weevils have elongate forebodies comprising parts of the thorax and neck that are superficially similar.

Actual size

**The Long-necked Shining Fungus Beetle** is unique among rove beetles and perhaps all beetles in possessing an extremely long neck that may be twice the length of the body in some male specimens. The neck is longer on average in males but its length is variable in both sexes.

| FAMILY | Staphylinidae |
|---|---|
| SUBFAMILY | Piestinae |
| DISTRIBUTION | Neotropical: South America |
| MACROHABITAT | Tropical rainforest |
| MICROHABITAT | Coarse woody debris |
| FEEDING HABITS | Mycophagous/saprophagous |
| NOTE | Found under bark of coarse woody debris in Amazonian forests of South America |

**ADULT LENGTH**
⁵⁄₁₆–⁷⁄₁₆ in
(8–10.5 mm)

*PIESTUS SPINOSUS*
# PIESTUS SPINOSUS
(FABRICIUS, 1801)

*Piestus* is the most speciose genus in the subfamily Piestinae, which includes approximately 110 described species worldwide. *Piestus spinosus* is a widespread species in the Amazonian region of South America. It is found under the bark of logs and other coarse woody debris, or in organic litter in the vicinity of woody debris. This species is probably saprophagous on fungus and microorganism-rich decaying organic matter in the moist interstices of subcortical spaces, but feeding habits have not been directly documented for this species.

## RELATED SPECIES

The subfamily Piestinae currently includes seven extant genera (e.g., *Eupiestus* from the eastern Palearctic and Oriental realms; *Hypotelus* from the Nearctic and Neotropical realms) plus *Abolescus*, known from only one fossil from Kazakhstan. Approximately 50 species of *Piestus* are known from Neotropical forests, including a large number of recently described species. They differ in size, shape, presence and development of the head horns, color, and details of the male genitalia.

Actual size

**Piestus spinosus** is one of the most striking members of this large South American genus. The long, broadly spaced frontal horns and contrasting orange-brown forebody and black abdomen are useful characters for separating the species from other members of the genus.

| FAMILY | Staphylinidae |
|---|---|
| SUBFAMILY | Osoriinae |
| DISTRIBUTION | Oriental: Indonesia, Philippines |
| MACROHABITAT | Tropical forests |
| MICROHABITAT | Dead wood |
| FEEDING HABITS | Unknown, probably fungivorous or saprophagous |
| NOTE | The life history of this species is unknown |

ADULT LENGTH
⁹⁄₁₆–⁵⁄₈ in
(14–16 mm)

*BOROLINUS JAVANICUS*

# BOROLINUS JAVANICUS
(LAPORTE, 1835)

169

*Borolinus javanicus* is a member of the unusual rove beetle tribe Leptochirini. Specimens of *Borolinus* species have been collected from dead-wood habitats but their bionomics are otherwise unknown. Some other species of Leptochirini have been reported to occur with termites, both as adults and larvae, but the nature of this association is unknown. Other members of the subfamily have been reported to feed on fungi or rotting vegetation. In the latter case they may receive most of their nutrition from bacteria within these substrates.

## RELATED SPECIES

Members of *Borolinus* share a character with other osoriine rove beetles in the form of long, cylindrical abdominal segments that are less flexible than in most rove beetles. *Borolinus* species possess strongly projecting mandibles and a pair of prominent horns on the front of the head. *Borolinus javanicus* can be separated from the other 13 species in the genus by the combination of horns on the head, and the arrangement of teeth on the mandibles.

Actual size

**Borolinus javanicus** shares features with other leptochirine rove beetles that include the comparatively large forebody and small, tubular abdomen. The shape of the enlarged mandibles and frontal horns are characteristic of this species.

| FAMILY | Staphylinidae |
|---|---|
| SUBFAMILY | Oxytelinae |
| DISTRIBUTION | Australian: southwestern Australia |
| MACROHABITAT | Wet sclerophyll forest |
| MICROHABITAT | Forest leaf litter |
| FEEDING HABITS | Saprophagous |
| NOTE | Apparently restricted to a small area of *Eucalyptus* forests in extreme southwestern Australia |

ADULT LENGTH
³⁄₁₆–¼ in
(4.5–6 mm)

*OXYPIUS PECKORUM*
# OXYPIUS PECKORUM
NEWTON, 1982

Actual size

*Oxypius peckorum* was described from approximately 50 specimens collected from wet sclerophyll forest in a 60-mile-long (100 km) area in southwestern Australia. Specimens were collected from forest leaf and coarse woody debris litter. Although the feeding habits of *O. peckorum* have not been directly confirmed, gut-content analysis of both adults and larvae suggest a mixed diet of decaying plant matter, fungal spores and hyphae, and bits of mites. Larvae collected prior to adults were placed in a different subfamily, the Piestinae. Subsequent collections of adults allowed correct association and reassessment of characters of the Oxytelinae.

RELATED SPECIES
*Oxypius peckorum* is the only representative of the genus. No other beetle is likely to be confused with this unusual species. Based on analysis of morphological characters, *Oxypius* appears to be most closely related to the enigmatic genus *Euphanias*. The latter includes five rare species from various parts of the world, but not from Australia.

**Oxypius peckorum** is an elongate, flattened rove beetle with a uniquely shield-like, irregularly sculptured pronotum. The unusually widened abdomen beyond the elytra is considered an important character, among several others, linking the genus with the putative sister taxon *Euphanias*.

| FAMILY | Staphylinidae |
|---|---|
| SUBFAMILY | Oxyporinae |
| DISTRIBUTION | Palearctic: Europe |
| MACROHABITAT | Forests |
| MICROHABITAT | Fleshy fungi and adjacent organic matter |
| FEEDING HABITS | Fungivorous |
| NOTE | Larvae and adults feed on fungus, especially fleshy mushrooms |

ADULT LENGTH
¼–⅜ in
(7–10 mm)

*OXYPORUS RUFUS*

# RED ROVE BEETLE

(LINNAEUS, 1758)

171

The large sickle-shaped mandibles give the Red Rove Beetle a predatory appearance, but adults and larvae of this species and others of the subfamily feed on fleshy fungi—another common name for this beetle is Red Mushroom Hunter. They can be found on mushrooms growing on dead wood in forests. Adults are wary beetles that fly readily when approached or drop into the leaf litter, where they are surprisingly difficult to track. Certain adaptations of the mouthparts, particularly the dramatically expanded labial palpi, presumably are equipped with special sensory organs used to select fungal hosts. Development is rapid, with generation times of less than three weeks under optimal conditions.

RELATED SPECIES

Approximately ten additional species of *Oxyporus* may overlap in distribution with the Red Rove Beetle, the most common of which is *O. maxillosus*, a predominantly yellow species except for its black head and pronotum. In addition to color, other species differ in host preferences and details of the male sex organs. Approximately 100 species of Oxyporinae are described worldwide, all in the genera *Oxyporus* and *Pseudoxyporus*.

Actual size

**The Red Rove Beetle** is a brightly patterned orange and black insect with a glossy integument. The size of the mandibles and width of the head vary among individuals.

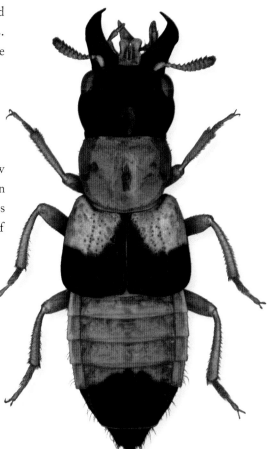

| FAMILY | Staphylinidae |
|---|---|
| SUBFAMILY | Megalopsidiinae |
| DISTRIBUTION | Neotropical: Veracruz, Mexico |
| MACROHABITAT | Forests |
| MICROHABITAT | Rotting wood, forest litter |
| FEEDING HABITS | Predatory |
| NOTE | Small invertebrates are sheared apart via a rotary mill formed by the mouthparts |

ADULT LENGTH
³⁄₁₆ in
(3.5–3.8 mm)

*MEGALOPINUS CRUCIGER*
# MEGALOPINUS CRUCIGER
(SHARP, 1886)

Actual size

*Megalopinus cruciger*, as with other members of the subfamily, occurs under bark and in rotting logs or leaf litter. It is uncharacteristically slow-moving for a rove beetle. Predation has been confirmed through laboratory studies of a related North American species that accepted small fly larvae. Larvae were pinned down and manipulated by the mouthparts into a rounded mass that was held aloft and rotated while being sheared apart by the mandibles. This food-processing method was referred to as a rotary mill. The resulting slurry was then filtered through specialized setae and spines while being sucked into the mouth opening.

## RELATED SPECIES

*Megalopinus cruciger* is one of several members of this genus from southern Mexico and adjacent areas of Central America, all very similar in appearance. *Megalopinus* is the only genus within the subfamily. Species diversity is poorly documented and additional undescribed species are likely to be discovered. Some 100 species of *Megalopinus* are described from tropical and subtropical regions of the world, with a few in temperate areas.

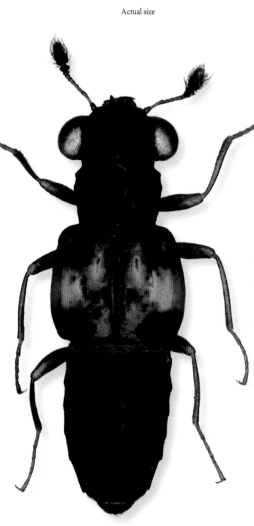

**Megalopinus cruciger** is distinct among rove beetles in possessing large bulbous eyes, short antennae, and unique bifurcate processes of the labrum. The polished dorsal surface is typical of most species in the genus and species identification is based on subtle differences in overall appearance and structural features of the male genitalia.

| FAMILY | Staphylinidae |
|---|---|
| SUBFAMILY | Scydmaeninae |
| DISTRIBUTION | Palearctic: Europe |
| MACROHABITAT | Forests |
| MICROHABITAT | Organic forest litter |
| FEEDING HABITS | Predatory |
| NOTE | Uses tiny suction cups to hold mites while feeding on them |

ADULT LENGTH
¹⁄₃₂ in
(0.8–1 mm)

*CEPHENNIUM THORACICUM*

# CEPHENNIUM THORACICUM

(MÜLLER & KUNZE, 1822)

173

Actual size

This European scydmaenine rove beetle is a specialized predator of oribatid mites, a feeding strategy it shares with other members of the subfamily. This species and some of its relatives employ a specialized array of disks on the lower mouthparts to attach to heavily armored prey. These disks function as suction cups to attach to the smooth surface of mites. The beetle scrapes a hole in the body of the mite while it is held in place and injects digestive juices into the victim. The beetle then sucks the liquefied body fluids from the prey. Larvae have similar structures.

## RELATED SPECIES

More than 100 species and many subspecies of *Cephennium* occur in Europe and northern Asia. They are similar and must be separated based on detailed study of external characters and internal genital structures. A single species also occurs in California, the United States. *Cephennium* and *Chelonoidum* are the two largest members of the tribe Cephenniini.

**Cephennium thoracicum** is a short, robust rove beetle with complete elytra (in contrast to most other rove beetles) and a pair of prominent openings (foveae) on the base of the elytra. The body forms within the tribe Cephenniini are similar and are unique within the subfamily Scydmaeninae, most of which are more elongate and ant-shaped.

| FAMILY | Staphylinidae |
|---|---|
| SUBFAMILY | Scydmaeninae |
| DISTRIBUTION | Nearctic: eastern North America |
| MACROHABITAT | Forests |
| MICROHABITAT | Organic forest litter |
| FEEDING HABITS | Predatory |
| NOTE | Specialized predator of oribatid mites |

**ADULT LENGTH**
¹⁄₁₆ in
(1.7–2 mm)

*CHEVROLATIA AMOENA*
# CHEVROLATIA AMOENA
LECONTE, 1866

Actual size

*Chevrolatia amoena* is a distinctive member of the rove beetle subfamily Scydmaeninae. It is not commonly collected throughout its range but is widely distributed and flies to lights or is taken in leaf-litter samples in forests. This species is assumed to be a specialist predator of oribatid mites, as documented for other scydmaenines, but its feeding habits have not been directly confirmed. Members of the related genus *Euconnus* coat heavily armored mite prey with a layer of paralysis-inducing salivary "venom" and wait for them to relax so that soft tissues can be accessed and consumed.

### RELATED SPECIES
*Chevrolatia* is the only genus within the tribe Chevrolatiini. Of the 11 species worldwide, only one other species, *C. occidentalis*, overlaps with *C. amoena* in eastern North America. The two species may be distinguished by differences in the lengths of the pronotal ridges and by details of the male genitalia.

**Chevrolatia amoena** shares a general body form typical of other members of the subfamily but somewhat atypical for most rove beetles in that the elytra almost completely cover the abdomen. It is more elongate than most scydmaenines, and possesses a dense beard of golden setae around the neck and a sharp ridge at the middle base of the pronotum.

| FAMILY | Staphylinidae |
|---|---|
| SUBFAMILY | Steninae |
| DISTRIBUTION | Australian: New Guinea |
| MACROHABITAT | Tropical forests |
| MICROHABITAT | Moist forest litter |
| FEEDING HABITS | Predatory |
| NOTE | Adults of this species use a unique prey-capture method involving the extensible labium. |

ADULT LENGTH
¼–⁵⁄₁₆ in
(7–8 mm)

*STENUS CRIBRICOLLIS*

# STENUS CRIBRICOLLIS

LEA, 1931

175

This species is a member of a large, globally distributed genus. Adults employ a unique prey-capture technique involving the elongate, protrusible labium. The paired lobes at the tip of this structure are equipped with specialized setae covered with sticky proteins and other compounds. The beetles use these organs to capture prey such as springtails in the same way frogs and chameleons use their sticky tongues. *Stenus* beetles also possess glands at the tip of the abdomen that produce surfactants that cause the beetle to be rapidly propelled across the surface of water until a solid surface can be reached.

## RELATED SPECIES

*Stenus cribricollis* is a member of an enormous genus comprising well over 2,000 species worldwide, including many that are currently undescribed. Species are divided into subgenera and species groups, with *S. cribricollis* included within the subgenus *Hypostenus* along with about 60 other species in New Guinea alone. Many species are quite similar and detailed study of surface punctuation and male genitalia is required for identification.

Actual size

**Stenus cribricollis** is one of a group of New Guinea species that exhibit purple or bluish iridescence. The overall body form is quite consistent with other members of the subfamily, in particular the elongate, tubular abdomen and relatively heavy, sclerotized, elongate body, specialized ventral mouthparts, and bulbous eyes. Variation among species is expressed by differences in internal sex organs, color, and surface sculpturing.

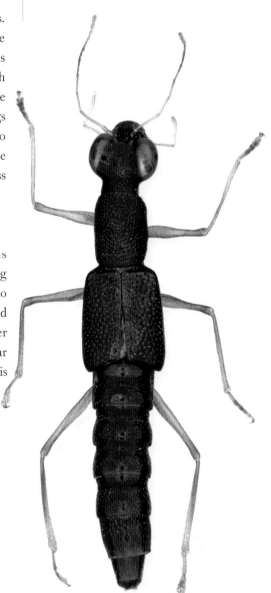

| FAMILY | Staphylinidae |
|---|---|
| SUBFAMILY | Euaesthetinae |
| DISTRIBUTION | Neotropical: Chile |
| MACROHABITAT | Coastal rainforests |
| MICROHABITAT | Deep forest litter |
| FEEDING HABITS | Predatory |
| NOTE | Other than its habitat, little is known about this species |

**ADULT LENGTH**
⅛ in
(3 mm)

176

*ALZADAESTHETUS FURCILLATUS*
# ALZADAESTHETUS FURCILLATUS
SÁIZ, 1972

|
Actual size

This small rove beetle is known only from a limited area of rainforest in the provinces of Valdivia and Osorno, Chile. Specimens of this and other members of the subfamily can be collected by sifting moist forest litter and extracting using Berlese, Tullgren, or similar devices. Specimens are rarely seen alive, and few details are known of the biology of the species. Based on its relationships and mouthpart morphology, the beetle is likely to be a micropredator of other arthropods living deep in the forest litter. Fossils of members of the subfamily that are similar to living species have been found in early Cretaceous Lebanese amber.

RELATED SPECIES

One other member of the genus is known. It and members of similar genera in the subfamily Euaesthetinae occur in the same areas of coastal rainforest as *Alzadaesthetus furcillatus*. Separating them requires researching original species descriptions and dissections to examine male sex organs.

**Alzadaesthetus furcillatus** is an elongate, parallel-bodied, moderately sclerotized staphylinid. The mandibles are elongate, curved, and extremely sharp. This general body form is typical of most members of the subfamily Euaesthetinae, though most others are a more somber brown or yellowish color.

| FAMILY | Staphylinidae |
|---|---|
| SUBFAMILY | Solieriinae |
| DISTRIBUTION | Neotropical: southern South America |
| MACROHABITAT | Temperate forest |
| MICROHABITAT | Organic forest litter |
| FEEDING HABITS | Unknown |
| NOTE | Close relatives of this obscure species were recently discovered in Cretaceous amber from Burma |

ADULT LENGTH
³⁄₁₆ in
(4.5 mm)

*SOLIERIUS OBSCURUS*

# SOLIERIUS OBSCURUS

(SOLIER, 1849)

177

Actual size

This morphologically generalized rove beetle is known from a few specimens from southern Chile and Argentina. The subfamily was thought to be a south temperate endemic taxon with a single species. However, discoveries in 2012 in Burmese amber revealed that the subfamily had a much broader distribution during the mid- to late Cretaceous (approximately 100 million years ago). These fossils (species described in the new genus *Prosolierius*) very closely resemble the south temperate species in both general appearance and detailed morphological characters. *Solierius obscurus* is placed in the staphylinine subfamily group, but the absence of larval characters makes its exact position uncertain within the group. Nothing is known about the species' bionomics.

## RELATED SPECIES

Only a single extant species is known in the subfamily. The discovery of related beetles preserved in Cretaceous amber (*Prosolierius tenuicornis*, *P. crassicornis*, and *P. mixticornis*) leaves open the possibility that additional species may be discovered in understudied habitats or fossil faunas.

**Solierius obscurus** is a relatively generalized rove beetle of unremarkable external appearance. The combination of character states has led to the removal of the species from the omaliine group to the staphylinine group of rove beetles.

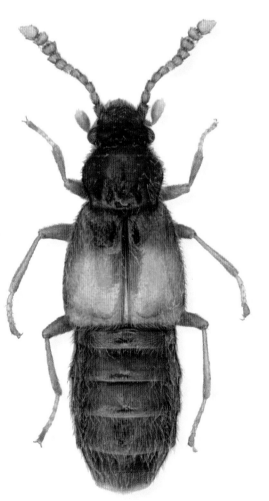

| | |
|---|---|
| FAMILY | Staphylinidae |
| SUBFAMILY | Leptotyphlinae |
| DISTRIBUTION | Nearctic: Alaska, United States |
| MACROHABITAT | Coniferous woodland |
| MICROHABITAT | Soil |
| FEEDING HABITS | Unknown |
| NOTE | The discovery of this species challenged views about insect distributions in northern North America |

ADULT LENGTH
¹⁄₃₂ in
(1–1.4 mm)

178

CHIONOTYPHLUS ALASKENSIS
# CHIONOTYPHLUS ALASKENSIS
SMETANA, 1986

Actual size

Members of the subfamily Leptotyphlinae are minute, soil-dwelling rove beetles that are rarely collected using standard methods of litter-sifting. The use of soil flotation techniques has revealed a wider distribution and diversity during recent years. Discovery of this relict species in an area previously not covered by glaciers of Fairbanks, Alaska, challenged the view that these minute, wingless beetles were unable to survive the extreme cold of the subarctic, especially during past glacial maxima. Although feeding habits in the group are unknown, based on mouthpart morphology, they are probably micropredators of other minute invertebrates that co-occur in deep soil.

## RELATED SPECIES

No similar species of leptotyphlines are known to occur within the distribution of this species, though use of appropriate sampling techniques may turn up additional undescribed species. This and other leptotyphlines share superficial similarity to members of the genus *Mayetia*, within another rove beetle subfamily, the Pselaphinae. They also occur in deep soil habitats, and may co-occur in other areas of the Northern Hemisphere.

**Chionotyphlus alaskensis** is an extremely elongate, wingless and eyeless, pale brown rove beetle. The elongate, almost worm-like shape of the body is well equipped to life transiting interstitial spaces of soil particles.

| FAMILY | Staphylinidae |
|---|---|
| SUBFAMILY | Pseudopsinae |
| DISTRIBUTION | Nearctic: British Columbia, Canada; Washington and California, United States |
| MACROHABITAT | Temperate rainforest |
| MICROHABITAT | Wet forest litter |
| FEEDING HABITS | Unknown |
| NOTE | The largest known specimen series of this species was collected from a log jam in a river |

ADULT LENGTH
³⁄₁₆ in
(4.5–5.2 mm)

*ASEMOBIUS CAELATUS*

# ASEMOBIUS CAELATUS

HORN, 1895

179

Actual size

Only a few individuals of this enigmatic species were collected in British Columbia, Canada, and Washington State, the United States, until it was taken in large numbers from flood debris in a British Columbia river. The biology of this species is unknown, but other members of the subfamily are associated with wet forest substrates and have been collected on fungi and near small mammal nests. Nothing is known of feeding habits or other aspects of its life history. The type locality is "California" with no further information provided.

## RELATED SPECIES

In the region where this species is known to occur, only members of the pseudopsine genera *Nanobius* and *Zalobius* are likely to be confused with *Asemobius caelatus*. They differ in details of dorsal body sculpturing features of the underside of the head.

**Asemobius caelatus** is a brown rove beetle with unusual armored sculpturing and distinct punctures on the dorsal body surface. Most members of the subfamily share the heavy sculpturing. Their biologies are poorly known.

| | |
|---|---|
| FAMILY | Staphylinidae |
| SUBFAMILY | Paederinae |
| DISTRIBUTION | Neotropical: South America |
| MACROHABITAT | Amazonian forests |
| MICROHABITAT | Forest litter |
| FEEDING HABITS | Predatory |
| NOTE | The elongate mandibles and habits of related rove beetles suggest predatory feeding habits |

**ADULT LENGTH**
³⁄₁₆–¹⁄₄ in
(5–6 mm)

180

*ECHIASTER SIGNATUS*
# ECHIASTER SIGNATUS
SHARP, 1876

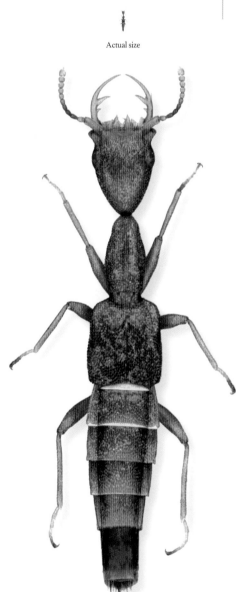

Actual size

This medium-size rove beetle was described from 11 specimens by the great nineteenth-century naturalist and beetle-taxonomist David Sharp from the east-central Amazon of Brazil. The habits of members of the genus are almost certainly predatory, consistent with most other members of the subfamily, but no direct evidence is available about this species' habits. The very elongate mandibles definitely suggest a predatory lifestyle in the interstitial spaces of tropical forest litter. Specimens of *Echiaster* species are typically common in sifted leaf-litter samples.

### RELATED SPECIES
Sharp described ten species in the genus *Echiaster* from the central Amazon in the same publication. At least 23 additional species are known from Brazil, all similar in appearance. Many more species are described from temperate and tropical forests worldwide. A related and similar genus, *Myrmecosaurus*, includes species that are myrmecophilous with New World fire ants (*Solenopsis*).

**Echiaster signatus** shares a similar body form with other *Echiaster* species, specifically a dull, sandpaper-like body surface, large oval head, narrow tapering body, and narrow neck. The length of the mandibles varies among members of the genus and reaches an extreme in *E. signatus*. The sharp teeth of the labrum are also a distinctive feature of many species.

| FAMILY | Staphylinidae |
|---|---|
| SUBFAMILY | Paederinae |
| DISTRIBUTION | Palearctic: northern Europe and northwestern Asia; the reported presence of this species in North America needs confirmation |
| MACROHABITAT | Various |
| MICROHABITAT | Wet meadows, irrigated farmland, riparian zones along streams, and around lakes |
| FEEDING HABITS | Predatory |
| NOTE | This and related species within the genus are among the very few beetles that pose a legitimate risk to human health |

ADULT LENGTH
¼–⁵⁄₁₆ in
(6–8 mm)

*PAEDERUS RIPARIUS*
# PAEDERUS RIPARIUS
(LINNAEUS, 1758)

181

The biology of these beetles is typical of the subfamily, which are general predators of small arthropods. However, they pose a serious public-health threat because of a substance, paederin, that occurs within their body fluids. Paederin is a dermatitis-inducing toxin capable of producing blistering lesions on contact with skin that can last several weeks, and is synthesized by endosymbiotic bacteria living within the beetles. Large populations of the beetles may occur near farmlands, and their attraction to lights may cause serious problems for nearby residents.

### RELATED SPECIES
*Paederus* is a large genus comprising about 150 species and has a worldwide distribution. About 20 species, including *P. riparius*, have been documented to contain enough pederin to cause dermatitis, with the amount of the toxin varying between species.

Actual size

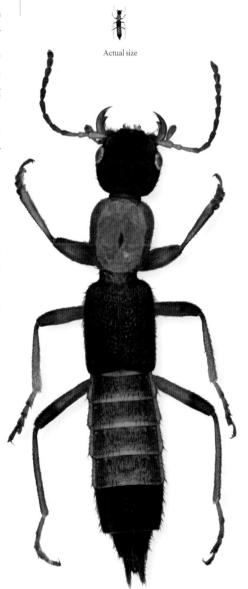

**Paederus riparius** is a strikingly colored, orange and black rove beetle, with an iridescent purplish luster to the elytra. This color pattern is widely distributed among various *Paederus* species, but is not universal. Crushing these insects on human skin may result in a long-lasting blister that can potentially spread through additional contact.

| FAMILY | Staphylinidae |
|---|---|
| SUBFAMILY | Staphylininae |
| DISTRIBUTION | Australian: New Guinea and extreme northern Australia |
| MACROHABITAT | Tropical forests |
| MICROHABITAT | Leaf litter, dung, carrion |
| FEEDING HABITS | Predatory on flies |
| NOTE | Preys on flies associated with animal carcasses |

ADULT LENGTH
⅝–⅞ in
(16–22 mm)

182

*ACTINUS IMPERIALIS*
# ACTINUS IMPERIALIS
FAUVEL, 1878

Adults of this unusually large and gaudily colored rove beetle frequent smelly substrates such as carrion and dung that are likely to attract flies. Adults actively seek out and destroy predators that feed on maggots and opportunistically capture adult flies. The immature stages presumably share the predatory habits of the adults but details of their biology are not well documented. One source mentions an association with cardamom (plants in the ginger family Zingiberaceae), without giving additional details. Adults exhibit strong sexual dimorphism of the mandibles and head, with males often having larger heads and longer mandibles than females.

### RELATED SPECIES

Two similar species are known from the genus, with *Actinus macleayi* from northern Australia differing mainly in having a less strongly punctured head and pronotum, in addition to other minor differences. In other respects *A. imperialis* superficially resembles other large members of the staphylinid subtribe Philonthina, but few are as brightly colored.

Actual size

**Actinus imperialis** is unusually large for a staphylinid beetle, with a metallic green head and pronotum and brilliant metallic purple elytra. The abdomen possesses a triangular orange spot at the posterior end. The punctures on the head are diagnostic for this species.

| FAMILY | Staphylinidae |
|---|---|
| SUBFAMILY | Staphylininae |
| DISTRIBUTION | Neotropical: central South America |
| MACROHABITAT | Forests near rivers and streams |
| MICROHABITAT | The body and nests of South American Water Rats (*Nectomys squamipes*) |
| FEEDING HABITS | Predatory on fleas |
| NOTE | Phoretic on small mammals and found in their nests feeding on fleas |

ADULT LENGTH
¼–⁵⁄₁₆ in
(6.5–7.5 mm)

*AMBLYOPINODES PICEUS*
# AMBLYOPINODES PICEUS
(BRÈTHES, 1926)

183

Members of this species and others in the tribe Staphylinini, subtribe Amblyopinina are unique among rove beetles in their adaptations to life on the bodies and in the nests of small mammals, mainly rodents. Adults of this species grasp the hair and skin between the ears of South American Water Rats (*Nectomys squamipes*) and travel with the animal, and the larvae occur in water rat nests. Early entomologists thought these beetles were parasitic on the animals, but later researchers revealed that they are predators of fleas and serve a beneficial function for the rats by reducing flea populations in their nests. The flattened morphology of the beetle's head is similar to that of other unrelated species that live on mammals.

RELATED SPECIES

At least five other species of the genus occur in the same region. Identification of species is based on examination of internal male sex structures and, to a lesser extent, the arrangement of specialized setae on the body. Other genera of the tribe are similar and may be distinguished using available keys and by mammal host associations.

Actual size

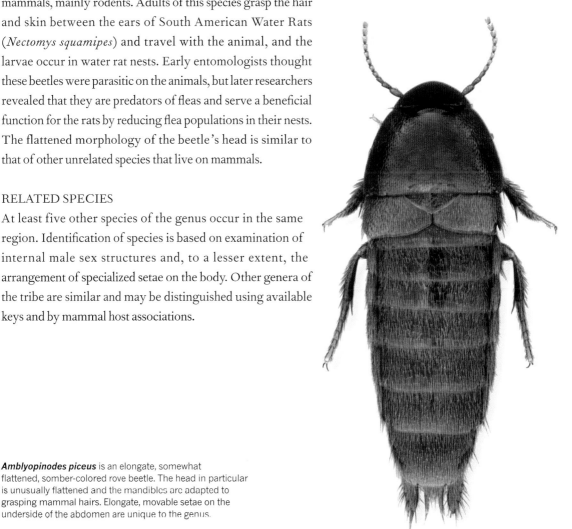

**Amblyopinodes piceus** is an elongate, somewhat flattened, somber-colored rove beetle. The head in particular is unusually flattened and the mandibles are adapted to grasping mammal hairs. Elongate, movable setae on the underside of the abdomen are unique to the genus.

| FAMILY | Staphylinidae |
|---|---|
| SUBFAMILY | Staphylininae |
| DISTRIBUTION | Afrotropical: South Africa |
| MACROHABITAT | Mountain forests |
| MICROHABITAT | Forest litter |
| FEEDING HABITS | Predatory |
| NOTE | The species is unusual within the subfamily in being flightless due to the reduced size of its wings |

ADULT LENGTH
$^{11}/_{16}$–$1^3/_8$ in
(17–33 mm)

184

# ARROWINUS PHAENOMENALIS
(BERNHAUER, 1935)

Members of this genus constitute the tribe Arrowinini. The group is of particular interest to specialists of rove beetles on account of their importance in understanding evolutionary relationships among various branches of the subfamily Staphylininae. Specimens of the species have been collected using pitfall traps and by sifting organic litter in mountain forests. *Arrowinus* belongs to a group of staphylinids in which the adults and larvae of most species are active predators. The flight wings are reduced to small vestiges, rendering the beetles flightless. Based on the morphology of adult and larval mouthparts, and analysis of gut contents, they are predators.

## RELATED SPECIES

Four species of *Arrowinus* occur in different areas of South Africa. They are all black or dark brown in color, but may be distinguished by differences in the distribution of elongate setae on the head and shapes of ridges on the abdomen. The external appearance of these species is similar to other large rove beetles in the same subfamily, although the small vestigial flight wings are a useful clue to their identity.

**Arrowinus phaenomenalis** is a large black predatory rove beetle endemic to South Africa. Size of adults is highly variable in this species, with the smallest specimens only half the body length of the largest. The hind wings are reduced in all members of the genus, rendering them flightless and likely contributing to their restricted distributions.

Actual size

| FAMILY | Staphylinidae |
|---|---|
| SUBFAMILY | Staphylininae |
| DISTRIBUTION | Australian: Australia |
| MACROHABITAT | Various—anywhere carrion sources occur |
| MICROHABITAT | Carrion at various stages of decomposition |
| FEEDING HABITS | Predatory |
| NOTE | An agile predator of maggots on dead animals |

ADULT LENGTH
$^{11}/_{16}$–$^{7}/_{8}$ in
(18–22 mm)

*CREOPHILUS ERYTHROCEPHALUS*
# DEVIL'S COACH HORSE
(FABRICIUS, 1775)

185

The Devil's Coach Horse is one of the largest rove beetles in Australia. It is commonly encountered on vertebrate carcasses, where it is a predator of carrion-infesting flies. Adults find the carcass and deposit eggs. Upon hatching, the larvae feed on fly eggs, larvae, and pupae, and develop rapidly, with three larval stages. Adults are strong fliers, and may repeat the cycle on the same carcass if it is still in active decomposition or disperse to another carrion source. Researchers have found a nosematid microsporidian parasite occupying the pigment cells of the compound eyes of this species.

## RELATED SPECIES

This distinctive species is not likely to be confused with any other rove beetles in the region. The common name of the species is shared by *Ocypus olens*, another large predatory rove beetle that is European in origin but has been introduced to Australia. That species is dull black in color.

**The Devil's Coach Horse** is a strikingly marked rove beetle with an orange head, large mandibles, a glossy black thorax, and a dull black abdomen. The large wings are folded in a very specific pattern beneath the short elytra when not deployed. Males have proportionately larger heads than females.

Actual size

| FAMILY | Staphylinidae |
|---|---|
| SUBFAMILY | Staphylininae |
| DISTRIBUTION | Palearctic: Europe and Asia |
| MACROHABITAT | Pastures |
| MICROHABITAT | Herbivore dung |
| FEEDING HABITS | Predatory |
| NOTE | This species is considered endangered throughout much of its range due to changes in pasture management |

**ADULT LENGTH**
$^{11}/_{16}$–$1^{1}/_{16}$ in
(18–27 mm)

*EMUS HIRTUS*
# MAID OF KENT BEETLE
(LINNAEUS, 1758)

The Maid of Kent Beetle is a well-known member of the insect fauna of cattle pastures in Europe, although the conversion to intensively managed pastures and use of parasite prophylactic treatments in livestock has rendered it much less common across its former range. The species enjoyed attention in the popular press when it was rediscovered in Kent in 1997 after being considered locally extinct. The adults and larvae inhabit cattle and other livestock dung, where they feed mainly on fly maggots. Writings from the nineteenth century also mention other beetle larvae as possible prey.

### RELATED SPECIES
*Emus hirtus* is the only member of the genus in western Europe and is unlikely to be mistaken for any other rove beetles that overlap in distribution. A second species in the genus, *E. griseosericans*, is restricted to Xizang (Tibet). Several other large (>1 in/25 mm) staphylinine rove beetles coexist and compete for prey with this species, but none shares its fuzzy, yellow and black appearance.

Actual size

**The Maid of Kent Beetle** is a large, fuzzy, yellow and black rove beetle with large mandibles well adapted to preying on fly larvae. Some speculate that the strikingly bicolored pattern mimics bumblebees.

| FAMILY | Staphylinidae |
|---|---|
| SUBFAMILY | Staphylininae |
| DISTRIBUTION | Neotropical: Mexico to Argentina |
| MACROHABITAT | Tropical and subtropical forests |
| MICROHABITAT | Carrion and dung |
| FEEDING HABITS | Predaceous |
| NOTE | Small males mimic females to avoid aggressive larger males and mate successfully with females |

ADULT MALE LENGTH
$^{11}/_{16}$–$1^{1}/_{16}$ in
(17–27 mm)

ADULT FEMALE LENGTH
$^{9}/_{16}$–$^{3}/_{4}$ in
(15–20 mm)

*LEISTOTROPHUS VERSICOLOR*
# TRANSVESTITE ROVE BEETLE
(GRAVENHORST, 1806)

187

Unlike many other member of the subfamily, Transvestite Rove Beetles do not feed on maggots but on adult flies and other insects. The beetles are agile, and prey is captured at carrion or dung feeding sites, which they guard. Abdominal secretions from the beetles lure flies to the area. Disputes over mating privileges are settled by male–male combat, but small males mimic females and mate with females without resorting to aggression. Small males may even mate successfully with females while being mistakenly courted by large males.

## RELATED SPECIES
*Leistotrophus versicolor* is the only extant member of the genus, though a fossil species is described from Oligocene sediments from the western USA. Other large staphylinine rove beetles share similar habitats, but confusion with this species is unlikely.

Actual size

**The Transvestite Rove Beetle** is a large, fuzzy, mottled brown rove beetle. Adults are agile day-active predators of flies. Males vary tremendously in size, head width, and mandible length; on average, these features are all larger than those of females. The large mandibles of males are used in male–male combat during competition for mates.

| FAMILY | Staphylinidae |
|---|---|
| SUBFAMILY | Staphylininae |
| DISTRIBUTION | Nearctic: western North America |
| MACROHABITAT | Pacific Ocean beaches |
| MICROHABITAT | Intertidal zone of sandy beaches |
| FEEDING HABITS | Predatory |
| NOTE | A specialized inhabitant of ocean beaches that preys on crustaceans |

ADULT LENGTH
⅝–¾ in
(16–20 mm)

*THINOPINUS PICTUS*
# PICTURED ROVE BEETLE
LECONTE, 1852

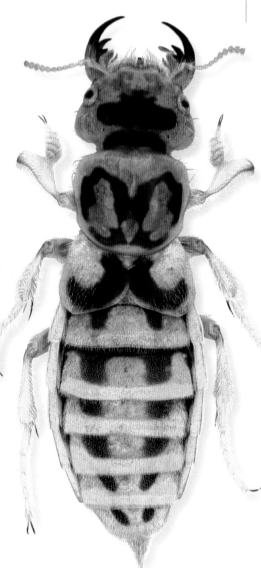

The Pictured Rove Beetle is one of the few species of beetle that is adapted to life in the salty habitat of ocean beaches. It spends the day burrowed in loose sand above the high-tide line and at night travels to just above the spray zone and forages or waits for passing prey. The main prey items for both adult and larvae are beach hoppers (amphipods) and other small beach invertebrates. As with most predatory beetles, prey is masticated and mixed with saliva using the mandibles and maxillae, and the semiliquid slurry is swallowed as it is produced.

## RELATED SPECIES

Only a single species of *Thinopinus* is known and *T. pictus* is not likely to be confused with any other large predatory rove beetle owing to its distinctive appearance and unusual habitat. An equivalent niche is occupied by a completely unrelated group of beetles, Phycosecidae, which occur on beaches of southern hemisphere Pacific islands and Australia.

**The Pictured Rove Beetle** is a boldly patterned species with circular black markings on the thorax and horizontal markings on the abdomen against a light tan background. The black and tan pattern predominates across much of the range of this species but populations on dark-sand beaches in Oregon are darker in coloration, presumably in response to selection pressure from nocturnal predators.

Actual size

| FAMILY | Pleocomidae |
|---|---|
| SUBFAMILY | Pleocominae |
| DISTRIBUTION | Nearctic: Transverse and Peninsular ranges of southern California |
| MACROHABITAT | Pine forests |
| MICROHABITAT | Males attracted to lights; females and larvae live in burrows |
| FEEDING HABITS | Adults do not feed; larvae eat roots |
| NOTE | Males fly in the rain searching for flightless females |

*PLEOCOMA AUSTRALIS*
# SOUTHERN RAIN BEETLE
FALL, 1911

ADULT MALE LENGTH
$^{15}\!/_{16}$–1$^{1}\!/_{8}$ in
(24–28 mm)

ADULT FEMALE LENGTH
up to 1$^{3}\!/_{4}$ in
(44 mm)

189

Male Southern Rain Beetles emerge from their burrows after the first fall rains at dusk, after dark, or just before dawn, and are frequently attracted to lights and pools of water. They fly low over the ground in search of females releasing pheromones from their burrows. Males die soon after mating, but females may live several more months in their burrows before laying eggs deep below the surface. The larvae feed on the roots of Canyon Live Oak (*Quercus chrysolepis*), molt seven or more times, and may take up to ten or more years to reach maturity.

RELATED SPECIES
*Pleocoma* consists of about 33 species with distributions restricted by the fact that females are flightless. Species in this genus occur in regions that have never been subjected to glaciation or inundation by seas over the past two or three million years. The presence of populations along coastal areas subject to inundation by water suggests that the beetles migrated here. Male *P. australis* are distinguished by their color and distribution.

Actual size

**The Southern Rain Beetle** male has a dark reddish-brown forebody with a V-shaped scoop on the head, black elytra, fully developed hind wings, and reddish-brown setae. The flightless female is much larger, heavier-bodied, uniformly reddish brown, and lacks adornments on the head and functional hind wings. Both sexes have 11 antennomeres, rakelike front tibiae, and lack functional chewing mouthparts.

| FAMILY | Geotrupidae |
|---|---|
| SUBFAMILY | Taurocerastinae |
| DISTRIBUTION | Neotropical: southern Chile and Argentina |
| MACROHABITAT | Patagonian steppe |
| MICROHABITAT | Open scrub and grassland |
| FEEDING HABITS | Adults eat dung |
| NOTE | The only species in the genus *Taurocerastes* |

ADULT LENGTH
$^{15}/_{16}$–1$^{1}/_{32}$ in
(24–26 mm)

*TAUROCERASTES PATAGONICUS*
# TAUROCERASTES PATAGONICUS
PHILIPPI, 1866

The flightless adults of *Taurocerastes patagonicus* are diurnal. They drag dung pellets of sheep, rabbits, and guanacos with their front legs into irregular and unbranched burrows that are dug at an angle of about 70 degrees and are supplied with a dung mass 2–2¾ in (50–70 mm) long and ¾–1¼ in (20–30 mm) in diameter at the end. It is not clear if the provisions are for the adults or their brood. Burrow entrances are sealed with stones, dung pellets, or plugs of soil. Larvae have been found buried in sandy or gravelly soils in areas of adult activity, but not in association with burrows or dung.

## RELATED SPECIES

*Taurocerastes* contains just this one species. Its nearest relative is *Frickius*, which includes two species that also occur in Chile and Argentina. *Taurocerastes* is distinguished from both species of *Frickius* by the lack of flight wings in both sexes, relatively smooth surface sculpturing, and the pronotal armature of the male.

**Taurocerastes patagonicus** is broadly oval, convex, and somewhat shiny black. Males have a pair of long, curved, forward-projecting pronotal horns, while females have two relatively small tubercles just behind the head. The convex elytra are faintly grooved and fused along the elytral suture, while the flight wings underneath are not developed.

Actual size

| FAMILY | Geotrupidae |
|---|---|
| SUBFAMILY | Bolboceratinae |
| DISTRIBUTION | Australian: eastern and southern Australia, including north Tasmania |
| MACROHABITAT | Coastal plains and adjacent tablelands |
| MICROHABITAT | Adults and probably larvae burrow in the soil |
| FEEDING HABITS | Adults and probably larvae eat humus and fungi |
| NOTE | The male's elongated forward projection on the clypeus is unique within the Geotrupidae |

ADULT MALE LENGTH
¾–⅞ in
(19–21 mm)

ADULT FEMALE LENGTH
⁹⁄₁₆–¾ in
(15–19 mm)

*ELEPHASTOMUS PROBOSCIDEUS*
# ELEPHASTOMUS PROBOSCIDEUS
(SCHREIBERS, 1802)

191

Little is known of the biology or habits of *Elephastomus proboscideus*. The adults are nocturnal and are attracted to light. They are also strong burrowers and are known to feed on pieces of fungi at the bottom of their burrows. The entrances to their usually vertical burrows are marked by a "push-up" of soil that has a "ropey" appearance when fresh. The larvae are unknown, but they, like other species of Bolboceratinae, develop in deep burrows where they feed on bits of fungi and other plant material provided by adults.

## RELATED SPECIES

The nine species of *Elephastomus* are restricted to eastern Australia and Tasmania, and are distinguished from other geotrupids by the male's greatly elongated forward projection on the clypeus. *Elephastomus proboscideus* is distinguished by its two blunt "teeth" on the clypeal tip. Males of the coastal subspecies *E. p. proboscideus* have a ridge in front of their eyes consisting of two conjoined tubercles, while males of the inland *E. p. kirbyi* have a blunt ridge.

Actual size

**Elephastomus proboscideus** is light to dark reddish brown. The forward projection on the male's clypeus is greatly produced and tipped with two "teeth"; the clypeus is short and rounded in females. The mouth is located far back in males. Both sexes lack any armature on the pronotum, although the surface is more sculptured in the male. The middle legs are nearly in contact at their bases.

| FAMILY | Geotrupidae |
|---|---|
| SUBFAMILY | Geotrupinae |
| DISTRIBUTION | Nearctic: eastern North America |
| MACROHABITAT | Temperate hardwood forests and mixed woods |
| MICROHABITAT | Adults found around fungi and animal waste on forest floor |
| FEEDING HABITS | Adults eat fungus, feces, and other materials |
| NOTE | Adults attracted to light and provision their larvae with dead leaves |

**ADULT LENGTH**
½–⅞ in
(13–21 mm)

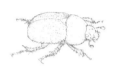

192

*GEOTRUPES SPLENDIDUS*
# SPLENDID EARTH-BORING BEETLE
(FABRICIUS, 1775)

The Splendid Earth-boring Beetle is one of the most common and widely distributed *Geotrupes* beetles in eastern North America. Adults emerge in the fall and prefer to eat fungi, but are also attracted to feces, carrion, and feathers. Males dig burrows beneath fungi where they wait for the arrival of females. Mated pairs overwinter in these burrows and emerge in spring to continue feeding and lay their eggs. The female digs a burrow 6–7 in (150–180 mm) deep before taking a sharp, right-angled turn. She then provisions the end of each burrow with bits of dead leaves or lawn clippings that serve as food for the developing larva that pupates in summer.

## RELATED SPECIES

There are 11 species of *Geotrupes* in North America, from which *G. splendidus* is distinguished by its bright green or coppery green color, its strongly impressed elytral grooves with punctures that are the same color as the surrounding surfaces, and the expanded and inwardly projecting front tooth on the front tibiae of the male. The genus *Geotrupes* includes 18 species in the Palearctic Realm, one of which, *G. spiniger*, has been introduced to southeastern parts of Australia.

**The Splendid Earth-boring Beetle** is bright metallic green or coppery green, or occasionally light blue or rarely purplish black. The antennae are dark reddish brown with lighter clubs. The punctures of the deeply impressed elytral grooves are the same color as the surrounding elytral surface. Further, the grooves along each side of the scutellum do not reach the base of the elytra.

Actual size

| FAMILY | Geotrupidae |
|---|---|
| SUBFAMILY | Geotrupinae |
| DISTRIBUTION | Palearctic: eastern Europe |
| MACROHABITAT | Steppe zone, open fields, pastures, plains, roadsides |
| MICROHABITAT | Adults live on the ground or in tunnels, in sandy areas; larvae develop in tunnels |
| FEEDING HABITS | Adults and larvae feed on leaves |
| NOTE | A protected species in Poland. Unlike other members of the family, it feeds on leaves rather than dung |

| ADULT LENGTH |
|---|
| $^9/_{16}$–$^{15}/_{16}$ in (15–24 mm) |

*LETHRUS APTERUS*
# LETHRUS APTERUS
(LAXMANN, 1770)

193

Males of *Lethrus apterus* are very unusual-looking because they have two large teeth on each mandible that resemble fangs. In spring, the overwintering adults of both sexes emerge and dig a burrow in the ground. Males soon begin searching for burrows occupied by females and will aggressively defend them from rival males. Mated pairs expand the tunnel further into several chambers that they line with leaves to serve as food for the developing larvae. These tunnels may reach down to 3 ft (1 m) in depth. This species can cause serious damage to vines and many other crops by cutting and eating leaves, and was once considered a major pest of Sunflowers (*Helianthus annuus*) in Bulgaria.

### RELATED SPECIES

The genus *Lethrus* contains about 120 species, all of which are flightless, similar in morphology, and typically restricted to small areas. In his 1871 book *The Descent of Man*, Charles Darwin wrote, "In *Lethrus*, a beetle belonging to the great division of lamellicorns, the males are known to fight, but are not provided with horns, though their mandibles are much larger than those of the females."

**Lethrus apterus** is a flightless black beetle with a short body, a large head, and a broad prothorax. The elytra are short and fused together along the midline. The head of males is larger than that of females. The spectacular male mandibles bear two large teeth each, the ventral teeth on the left and right mandibles being symmetrical.

Actual size

| FAMILY | Passalidae |
|---|---|
| SUBFAMILY | Passalinae |
| DISTRIBUTION | Neotropical: Mexico, Guatemala |
| MACROHABITAT | Moist tropical forests at high elevations |
| MICROHABITAT | Logs, rotting logs, wooded areas |
| FEEDING HABITS | Adults and larvae feed on decaying wood, and larvae also feed on adults' feces |
| NOTE | A rare and localized species of subsocial beetle |

**ADULT LENGTH**
2⅝–2¹⁵⁄₁₆ in
(68–75 mm)

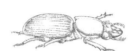

194

*PROCULUS GORYI*
# PROCULUS GORYI
(MELLY, 1833)

Actual size

**Proculus goryi** is a very large beetle. The frontal structure has a small horn and the beetle has a large, elongate prothorax. The elytra are shiny, black, and ovate, with some setae, mainly around the edges. The elytral striae are marked with strong punctation. The antennae are curved, with a club that includes different numbers of flat plates. The legs are black.

One of the largest bess beetles (Passalidae) in the world, the flightless *Proculus goryi* occurs in Mexico and Guatemala at elevations of 2,600–4,100 ft (800–1,250 m). Both adults and larvae live together in decaying logs where they feed on rotting wood. They communicate with one another by producing sounds by stridulation. Eggs are placed in a "nest" of chewed wood mixed with feces. Both adults and larvae feed on decaying wood and must consume adult feces laced with microorganisms to help them digest wood. Adults provide their larvae with chewed wood to eat.

### RELATED SPECIES

The genus *Proculus* includes the world's largest Passalidae and is distinguished from other passalid genera by the oval elytra and reduced eyes. The five additional species of *Proculus*, including *P. burmeisteri*, *P. jicaquei*, *P. mniszechi*, *P. opacipennis*, and *P. opacus*, live mostly in high-elevation mountains and range from Mexico to Colombia.

| FAMILY | Trogidae |
|---|---|
| SUBFAMILY | Troginae |
| DISTRIBUTION | Nearctic, Neotropical: Western Hemisphere; introduced elsewhere |
| MACROHABITAT | Drier habitats in temperate and subtropical habitats |
| MICROHABITAT | Adults and larvae found with animal carcasses in final stages of dry decay |
| FEEDING HABITS | Adults and larvae feed on keratin |
| NOTE | When disturbed, adults feign death and look like small clods of soil |

ADULT LENGTH
³⁄₈–⁹⁄₁₆ in
(9–15 mm)

*OMORGUS SUBEROSUS*

# OMORGUS SUBEROSUS

(FABRCIUS, 1775)

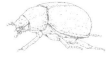

195

Actual size

Adult and larval *Omorgus suberosus* feed on keratin and are among the last insects to visit the remains of a vertebrate, where they feed on the skin, horns, hooves, hair, and feathers. Larvae feed and develop in shallow vertical burrows beneath the carcass. Adults are sometimes found under old cow chips and are one of the most common species of *Omorgus* to fly to light. A South American native, this species now occurs throughout the Western Hemisphere, Australia, and several islands in the Pacific Ocean. They were likely introduced to central Europe in wool shipments from Argentina.

## RELATED SPECIES

*Omorgus* comprises 114 species that are widely distributed mostly in the drier regions of the Southern Hemisphere. *Omorgus suberosus* is distinguished from other species in the genus by the tubercles on the head, relatively smooth pronotum and elytra, small, shiny areas on the elytra giving a checkered appearance, fully developed flight wings, and the male genitalia.

**Omorgus suberosus** is elongate-oval, slightly flattened, with a somewhat smooth pronotum and elytra, and clothed with short, woolly setae. The head has two distinct tubercles. The scutellum is constricted at the base and appears shaped like an arrowhead. The elytra have distinct humeri and ridges with irregular shiny areas alternating with low tubercles. Both the legs and tarsi have short, sparse setae.

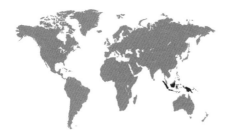

| FAMILY | Lucanidae |
| --- | --- |
| SUBFAMILY | Lampriminae |
| DISTRIBUTION | Australian and Oriental: Papua New Guinea, Indonesia |
| MACROHABITAT | Bush and forests |
| MICROHABITAT | Adults are found in the bush; larvae tunnel in decaying wood |
| FEEDING HABITS | Adults have been found feeding on tree sap and rotting fruits; larvae feed on decaying wood |
| NOTE | The attractive species in this genus can vary in color from metallic green or bronze to blue, red, or violet |

ADULT MALE LENGTH
¹⁵⁄₁₆–2 in
(23.7–50.7 mm)

ADULT FEMALE LENGTH
¾–1¹⁄₃₂ in
(18.9–26 mm)

*LAMPRIMA ADOLPHINAE*
# LAMPRIMA ADOLPHINAE
(GESTRO, 1875)

*Lamprima adolphinae* is a distinctly sexual dimorphic species. The males have mandibles that are much larger and more strongly curved than those of the females. Females lay their eggs in the decaying logs of gum trees (*Eucalyptus*) and sheaok (*Casuarina*). The C-shaped larvae are sometimes extracted from logs and eaten by women and girls of the Eipo tribe living in the highlands of west New Guinea.

## RELATED SPECIES

*Lamprima adolphinae* is the most common species in the genus but is restricted to Papua New Guinea and Indonesia. The other known species are found in different regions: *L. aenea* from Norfolk Island, *L. insularis* from Lord Howe Island, *L. aurata* from Tasmania and Australia, and *L. latreillii*, *L. micardi*, and *L. varians* from Australia.

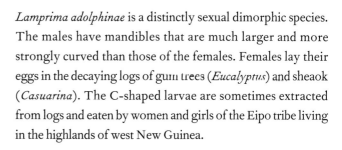

**Lamprima adolphinae** shows an important sexual dimorphism. The male has long, curved, parallel-sided, upturned mandibles. The head is small. The surface of the body is green or metallic bright green, but green, bronze, blue, red, and brownish color variations also occur. The toothed mandibles have very dense yellow setae.

Actual size

| FAMILY | Lucanidae |
|---|---|
| SUBFAMILY | Lampriminae |
| DISTRIBUTION | Australian: northeastern Queensland |
| MACROHABITAT | Rainforest and wet sclerophyll forests |
| MICROHABITAT | Adults found in logs, stumps, and on sapping tree trunks |
| FEEDING HABITS | Adults eat rotten wood, sap, and fruit |
| NOTE | Males use their mandibles in grappling matches with other males |

*PHALACROGNATHUS MUELLERI*
# MUELLER'S STAG BEETLE
(MACLEAY, 1885)

| ADULT MALE LENGTH |
|---|
| $^{15}/_{16}$–$2^{7}/_8$ in |
| (24–72 mm) |

| ADULT FEMALE LENGTH |
|---|
| $^{7}/_8$–$1^{13}/_{16}$ in |
| (23–46 mm) |

197

Mueller's Stag Beetle, also known as the Rainbow, Magnificent, or King Stag Beetle, is the largest stag beetle in Australia, and was named after the botanist Baron Ferdinand von Mueller. It breeds in dry or saturated rotting wood of fallen logs and standing living or dead trees that are infected with white rot fungus. The larvae may take up to three years to reach maturity, and molt within cells constructed from their own feces. Adults fly at dusk from April through September, and are attracted to light. They eat rotting wood, plant sap, and fruits.

RELATED SPECIES
The subfamily Lampriminae includes *Streptocerus* from Chile and Argentina, *Dendroblax* from New Zealand, *Hololamprina* from eastern Australia, and *Lamprima* (see opposite) and *Phalacrognathus* from Australia and New Guinea.

Actual size

**The Mueller's Stag Beetle** is bronzy green with an iridescent coppery shine. Males have long, parallel mandibles that extend forward before curving upward and ending in broad and flattened divergent points. The convex prothorax is wider than long and has a dull brassy hue. The shiny elytra are smooth in the male and punctured in the female.

| FAMILY | Lucanidae |
|---|---|
| SUBFAMILY | Lucaninae |
| DISTRIBUTION | Neotropical: southern South America |
| MACROHABITAT | Broadleaf evergreen forest |
| MICROHABITAT | Flowers, sapping wounds on trees, at light |
| FEEDING HABITS | Adults feed on tree sap |
| NOTE | The only species of *Chiasognathus* capable of producing sound |

**ADULT LENGTH**
¹⁵/₁₆–3½ in
(24–88 mm)

*CHIASOGNATHUS GRANTII*
# CHILEAN STAG BEETLE
STEPHENS, 1831

Male Chilean Stag Beetles stand guard over their females with their long, arched mandibles and legs, ready to repel other males. Rival males use their mandibles to grab a competitor's prothorax to lift him. Males are capable of drawing blood with their sharp mandibles, but the shorter mouthparts of the female can deliver an even more painful pinch. Adults are found on trees or among Canelilla (*Hydrangea serratifolia*) flowers. They fly during the day or dusk, and can produce sound by rubbing their hind femora against a ridge on the sides of the elytra. The larvae develop in the soil.

## RELATED SPECIES

*Chiasognathus* includes seven species, all of which are endemic to souther South America. They are distinguished from all other genera of New World stag beetles by their antennal club composed of six antennomeres. Both sexes of the Chilean Stag Beetle are distinguished by their large size, spinose elytral tips, large tooth, ridge, or tubercle located underneath each mandible, apparently shiny elytra, and their ability to stridulate.

Actual size

**The Chilean Stag Beetle** is light to dark reddish brown with green, gold, or purple reflections. Each of the male's major saw-toothed mandibles has a large tooth underneath, and is two to six times longer than the head. The female's mandibles are shorter with a ridge or large tubercle underneath. The shiny, densely punctate, and setose elytra are each tipped with a small spine.

| | |
|---|---|
| FAMILY | Lucanidae |
| SUBFAMILY | Lucaninae |
| DISTRIBUTION | Afrotropical: South Africa, Western Cape Province |
| MACROHABITAT | Mountains, high elevations |
| MICROHABITAT | Under stones |
| FEEDING HABITS | Adults feed on various detritus in the soil |
| NOTE | One of the rarest stag beetles in the world |

ADULT MALE LENGTH
¾–1¹⁄₁₆ in
(20 to 26.5 mm)

ADULT FEMALE LENGTH
¹¹⁄₁₆–¹⁵⁄₁₆ in
(17.1 –24 mm)

*COLOPHON HAUGHTONI*
# CAPE STAG BEETLE
BARNARD, 1929

199

Species of *Colophon* are endemic to remote mountain-top habitats and are the only stag beetles found at higher elevations in the Western and Southern Cape. The larvae likely feed on woody roots and plant detritus. Adults are typically active early in the morning. All *Colophon* species are cold-adapted species and may be vulnerable to the effects of climate change. The establishment of repeater stations for cell-phone service in remote areas and supporting infrastructure may facilitate access to remote populations by unauthorized collectors. As a result, all species in the genus *Colophon* are listed on Appendix II of CITES (Convention on the International Trade in Endangered Species of Wild Fauna and Flora).

RELATED SPECIES

There are 17 species described in *Colophon* including *C. primosi*, which has long and slender yellow-orange mandibles and *C. izardi*, which shows orange spots on the prothorax in some specimens.

Actual size

**The Cape Stag Beetle** is medium-size, with a heavily sclerotized body. They are generally black or dark brown, and have teeth at the apex of their tibia that are adapted for digging. This species is flightless but short vestigial wings are found under their elytra. Mandibles in males are enlarged and are used for combat to obtain the favor of females.

| FAMILY | Lucanidae |
|---|---|
| SUBFAMILY | Lucaninae |
| DISTRIBUTION | Oriental: western Indonesia (Sumatra) |
| MACROHABITAT | Tropical forests |
| MICROHABITAT | On or in tree trunks |
| FEEDING HABITS | Adults feed on overripened fruit and tree sap; larvae feed in decaying logs |
| NOTE | Individuals in this species show many metallic color variations |

**ADULT MALE LENGTH**
1¹⁵⁄₁₆–4¼ in
(49–109 mm)

**ADULT FEMALE LENGTH**
1³⁄₁₆–1⁷⁄₁₆ in
(30–36 mm)

*CYCLOMMATUS ELAPHUS*
# DEER STAG BEETLE
GESTRO, 1881

The male Deer Stag Beetle uses its enlarged antler-like mandibles in intraspecific battles with other males, usually in defense of oviposition sites for the females. While grappling their opponents with their mandibles, males use their long front legs to pitch their body upward in order to throw their adversaries backward. Both sexes are encountered on flowers or on tree trunks, and often fly to lights at night. The C-shaped larvae feed and develop in decaying logs. The nutritional quality of the wood consumed by larvae greatly influences their development, as evidenced by the considerable size variation observed in the adults.

## RELATED SPECIES

The genus *Cyclommatus* contains more than 85 described species, mostly distributed in the Oriental Realm. One species, *C. albersii*, reaches as far north as China. *Cyclommatus metallifer*, another large-mandibled species also found in Indonesia, is shiny and metallic, with a series of smaller teeth behind each median mandibular tooth.

Actual size

**The Deer Stag Beetle** is a large stag beetle displaying clear sexual dimorphism. The male has very long (often as long as the body), slightly curved mandibles, sometimes with a strong basal tooth. The numbers of teeth on the mandibles vary. The body color ranges from metallic green to bronze and brown, and some females are black or brownish red.

| FAMILY | Lucanidae |
|---|---|
| SUBFAMILY | Lucaninae |
| DISTRIBUTION | Afrotropical: West and Central Africa |
| MACROHABITAT | Tropical forests |
| MICROHABITAT | Adults are found on tree trunks and flowers; larvae live in decaying wood |
| FEEDING HABITS | Adults feed on old fruits and tree sap; larvae feed on decaying wood |
| NOTE | The smaller females have a black head and almost entirely black elytra |

ADULT MALE LENGTH
1¹/₃₂–2³/₁₆ in
(26–55 mm)

ADULT FEMALE LENGTH
¾–1¼ in
(20.2–31.8 mm)

*HOMODERUS MELLYI*
# HOMODERUS MELLYI
PARRY, 1862

201

Actual size

*Homoderus mellyi* is a large African stag beetle. The species has numerous small teeth in its mandibles, which are nearly or totally absent in other members of the genus. Adults feed on old fruits and tree sap, and have been collected at light traps and sometimes in banana traps. Entomologists have recently succeeded in rearing them in captivity. The larvae are C-shaped and seem to feed in the decaying wood of logs.

## RELATED SPECIES

*Homoderus mellyi* is the most common member of the genus, and is found in Central and West Africa. The other known species in *Homoderus* are *H. gladiator*, *H. johnstoni*, and *H. taverniersi*. *Homoderus gladiator*, which measures 1⁹/₁₆–2³/₈ in (40–60 mm), is locally rare in parts of its range and threatened from habitat destruction and exploitation of adults for the insect trade. The genus *Homoderinus* is closely related.

**Homoderus mellyi** is a large stag beetle displaying sexual dimorphism. In the male, the frontal ridge is well developed and the mandibles are large. The color varies from brown to brownish red, with black spots on the thorax in most specimens. The mandibles show various numbers of teeth.

| FAMILY | Lucanidae |
|---|---|
| SUBFAMILY | Lucaninae |
| DISTRIBUTION | Nearctic: eastern United States |
| MACROHABITAT | Eastern deciduous hardwood forests |
| MICROHABITAT | Adults found on stumps, under logs, and are attracted to lights |
| FEEDING HABITS | Adults drink sap; larvae eat decayed wood |
| NOTE | The largest stag beetle in North America |

ADULT LENGTH
¹⁵⁄₁₆–1⁹⁄₁₆ in
(24–39 mm)

202

*LUCANUS ELAPHUS*
# GIANT STAG BEETLE
FABRICIUS, 1775

The Giant Stag Beetle is a "giant" among North American lucanids, but is moderately sized compared with several tropical species. Its specific epithet is derived from the Greek *elaphos* meaning "deer" or "stag." Adults feed on sapping tree wounds, and are attracted to light in summer, especially June and July. Females lay eggs in the crevices of stumps and logs. The larvae tunnel and develop in moist, decaying wood and may take several years to reach adulthood. This species may occur as far north as Minnesota, Michigan, and Quebec.

## RELATED SPECIES

*Lucanus* is represented by four species in North America, and are distinguished from other lucanids in the region by their elongate form, elbowed (geniculate) antennae, divided compound eyes, rounded side margins of the pronotum, and nearly smooth elytra. Major males of the Giant Stag Beetle are distinguished by their long, forked mandibles.

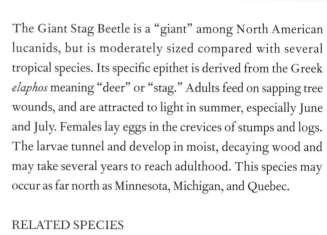

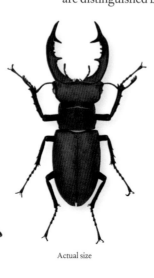

**The Giant Stag Beetle** is dark reddish brown. Major males have heads broader than the pronotum. Their mandibles are forked at the tips and exceed the combined length of the head and pronotum. The labrum is somewhat triangular and narrowly rounded in both sexes. Males and females have uniformly colored legs that match the rest of the body.

Actual size

| FAMILY | Lucanidae |
|---|---|
| SUBFAMILY | Lucaninae |
| DISTRIBUTION | Oriental: south, east, and southeastern Asia |
| MACROHABITAT | Tropical wet forest |
| MICROHABITAT | Adults are found on tree trunks; larvae develop in decaying logs |
| FEEDING HABITS | Adults occasionally feed on decaying fruits and tree sap; larvae feed on decaying wood |
| NOTE | Various color forms of this species have been proposed as subspecies |

ADULT MALE LENGTH
1⁵⁄₁₆–3⅛ in
(33–80 mm)

ADULT FEMALE LENGTH
1⁵⁄₁₆–1⅝ in
(34–42 mm)

*ODONTOLABIS CUVERA*

# ODONTOLABIS CUVERA

HOPE, 1842

203

*Odontolabis cuvera* is a large, common, and conspicuous stag beetle that ranges from Nepal and northeastern India, to northwestern Burma, northern Thailand, central Laos, northern Vietnam, and southern China. The C-shaped larvae feed and develop in decaying logs. Adults occasionally feed on rotting fruit, especially bananas, and tree sap, and can be attracted to lights. Males have three distinct forms based on the extent of mandibular development, ranging from relatively long and curved to somewhat short and straight. Mandibles are polymorphic and in some males are large and curved. The females are smaller, with a short head and short mandibles.

## RELATED SPECIES

The Asian genus *Odontolabis* includes 36 species and about as many subspecies. They are typically shiny chestnut-brown or black, while the mostly yellow or brown elytra are sometimes distinctly bicolored. The species are best distinguished by features of the male's mandibles and genitalia. *Odontolabis mouhoti* is similar to *O. cuvera*, but it has elytra that are duller and the male's elytra are mostly yellow with a dark narrow sutural stripe.

**Odontolabis cuvera** is oblong, convex, and mostly shiny chestnut-brown to black. The large rectangular head of the male is flattened, with a distinct process behind each eye, while that of the female is short and broadly angled at the eye. The elytra are distinctly bicolored with broad yellowish-brown sides and a narrow to broad, dark triangle down the center.

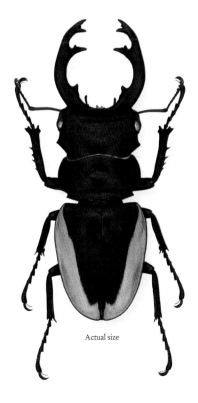

Actual size

| FAMILY | Scarabaeidae |
|---|---|
| SUBFAMILY | Scarabaeinae |
| DISTRIBUTION | Neotropical: Argentina |
| MACROHABITAT | Thorn desert habitat |
| MICROHABITAT | Sandy and clay soils |
| FEEDING HABITS | Feeds on dry dung |
| NOTE | Small populations of these flightless beetles are thought to be at risk of local extinction |

ADULT LENGTH
½–1³⁄₁₆ in
(13–30 mm)

204

# EUCRANIUM ARACHNOIDES

BRULLÉ, 1834

Actual size

*Eucranium arachnoides* is the commonest and most widespread species in the genus. The small, patchily distributed populations of this flightless beetle are susceptible to extirpation as a result of habit modification and loss. Adults live in dry desert habitat and are most active from November through January. Unusual among dung beetles, *Eucranium* species excavate burrows first, then go out during the day in search of the dry dung pellets of Goats (*Capra aegagrus*), Guanaco (*Lama guanicoe*), Horses (*Equus ferus caballus*), and Cattle (*Bos primigenius*). They carry the dung pellet in their front legs while walking forward with their middle and hind legs. At night, these beetles walk about randomly, apparently in search of mates.

## RELATED SPECIES

The small South American tribe Eucraniini contains four genera: *Anomiopsoides*, *Ennearabdus*, *Eucranium*, and *Glyphoderus*. *Eucranium* is endemic to the Monte and Chacoan biogeographic provinces of Argentina, and consists of six flightless species that are distinguished by microscopic peculiarities of their elytra: *E. arachnoides*, *E. belenae*, *E. cyclosoma*, *E. dentifrons*, *E. planicolle*, and *E. simplicifrons*. All its members are flightless.

**Eucranium arachnoides** is a flightless, relatively large dung beetle with a black body. The broad pronotum, which has no horns, is wider than the elytra. The adults have a pair of anteriorly produced fingerlike projections on their clypeus. The tarsi on the middle legs are longer than the spur at the apex of the middle tibia. Significant variation (e.g., body size, elytral punctures) can occur between individuals.

| FAMILY | Scarabaeidae |
|---|---|
| SUBFAMILY | Scarabaeinae |
| DISTRIBUTION | Afrotropical, Palearctic: Arabian Peninsula and northeastern Africa |
| MACROHABITAT | Arid regions with large mammals |
| MICROHABITAT | Adults burrow under dung piles and are attracted to lights |
| FEEDING HABITS | Adults and larvae eat dung |
| NOTE | More common on Arabian Peninsula than African continent |

ADULT LENGTH
1⁷⁄₁₆–2³⁄₈ in
(37–60 mm)

*HELIOCOPRIS GIGAS*
# HELIOCOPRIS GIGAS
(LINNAEUS, 1758)

205

Once thought to be solely dependent upon elephant dung, *Heliocopris gigas* appears well adapted to utilizing the waste of wild and domesticated ruminants as well. They are nocturnal animals and are attracted to light. The female digs beneath a dung pile, rapidly hauls dung down to a broadened chamber at the end of the tunnel, and begins to fashion the first of several brood balls. Each brood ball contains a single egg and is about 2 in (50 mm) in diameter. Males probably use their formidable array of head and pronotal horns against rival males.

### RELATED SPECIES
*Heliocopris* contains 49 sexually dimorphic and mostly African species; four species occur in the Oriental Realm. Aside from its large size, *Heliocopris* is distinguished from robust species of *Catharsius* by the distinct ridges above the sides of the elytra. Major males of *H. gigas* resemble those of *H. andersoni* and *H. midas*, but are distinguished by the shape of their horns.

Actual size

**Heliocopris gigas** is strongly convex, dark brown to black, and dull. Major males have a deep circular impression flanked by long, diverging curved horns on the head. The pronotum is steep and coarsely punctured in front with a sharp horn on each side, and a median, broad-based, forward-projecting, and flattened horn that extends over the head. The elytra are coarsely, irregularly punctate, creating a leathery appearance.

| FAMILY | Scarabaeidae |
|---|---|
| SUBFAMILY | Scarabaeinae |
| DISTRIBUTION | Afrotropical: Democratic Republic of Congo and Angola to Tanzania and northern South Africa |
| MACROHABITAT | Moist savanna with summer rainfall |
| MICROHABITAT | Deep sand habitats |
| FEEDING HABITS | Adults and larvae typically eat dung, especially of cattle and elephants |
| NOTE | Enlarged front legs are used to defend themselves and their dung supplies |

ADULT LENGTH
⅞–1¾ in
(23–45 mm)

206

# PACHYLOMERA FEMORALIS
(KIRBY, 1828)

Actual size

*Pachylomera femoralis* typically flies and moves dung during the day. It is often seen in large numbers on cattle and elephant dung, but is also attracted to omnivore feces, vertebrate and insect carrion, and crushed fruits of the Monkey Orange (*Strychnos spinosa*). Their distinct lumbering gait is the result of the characteristically enlarged front legs. Solitary females dig slanting burrows fairly close to the dung source and provision it with chunks of dung rolled with their hind legs or butted along with their heads. The dung is then fashioned into a pear-shaped brood mass that contains a single egg.

## RELATED SPECIES

The only other species of *Pachylomera*, *P. opaca*, is distributed in the arid southwest Kalahari and outlying sandy habitats in the Limpopo and Gauteng provinces of South Africa. It is distinguished from *P. femoralis* by the absence of both the spines on the enlarged front femora and the toothlike projection on the inner margins of the front tibiae.

**Pachylomera femoralis** is large, robust, somewhat flattened, dull black beetle. The broad head has four short teeth in front and is flanked with large cheek-like plates called genae. The front coxae and spined femora are disproportionately large, especially in the male. The inner margin of each front tibia has a small, broad toothlike projection.

| FAMILY | Scarabaeidae |
|---|---|
| SUBFAMILY | Scarabaeinae |
| DISTRIBUTION | Afrotropical: Botswana, Kenya, Mozambique, Namibia, South Africa, Tanzania, Zimbabwe |
| MACROHABITAT | Savanna |
| MICROHABITAT | Adults are found on various soils |
| FEEDING HABITS | Adults have been found on the dung of various animals; larvae feed on the liquid component of dung |
| NOTE | This dung beetle has amazing antler-like horns |

ADULT LENGTH
⅜–½ in
(10–13 mm)

*PROAGODERUS RANGIFER*

# PROAGODERUS RANGIFER

KLUG, 1855

207

The male of *Proagoderus rangifer* possesses one of the most amazing horn structures among all dung beetles and likely uses them to defend burrows with females from rival males. Both males and females fly during the day and are typically found in fresh elephant and rhinoceros feces. Little is known about the life histories of most *Proagoderus* species, but they likely construct one or more egg-shaped brood balls and bury them in tunnels directly beneath the dung. Their seasonal activity depends primarily upon warm temperatures and ample rainfall.

### RELATED SPECIES

One hundred and seven species of *Proagoderus* have been described, mostly from Africa. *Proagoderus ramosicornis* is very similar to *P. rangifer* in form, color, and distribution, but may be distinguished by its coarser punctation. Ten species of *Proagoderus* are listed on the IUCN Red List of Threatened Species in the category "Least Concern" as there is currently no data to suggest that their populations are under immediate threat.

Actual size

**Proagoderus rangifer** is a small dung beetle, the male of which bears amazing horns. The development of the cephalic horn may vary, but males with huge horns are quite common. The female lacks armature. The beetle is coppery red on the dorsal face and legs, and coppery red with greenish reflections on the ventral face. Some specimens are also metallic green and a lot of variation in coloration is possible.

| FAMILY | Scarabaeidae |
|---|---|
| SUBFAMILY | Scarabaeinae |
| DISTRIBUTION | Palearctic: southern and central Europe, North Africa, Middle East, portions of Asia |
| MACROHABITAT | Steppe, forest-steppe, and semidesert |
| MICROHABITAT | In the vicinity of accumulations of fresh dung |
| FEEDING HABITS | Adults strain nutrients from dung; larvae eat solid waste |
| NOTE | Regarded as a sacred symbol by the ancient Egyptians |

**ADULT LENGTH**
1¹⁄₃₂–1⁹⁄₁₆ in
(26–40 mm)

208

*SCARABAEUS SACER*
# SACRED SCARAB BEETLE
LINNAEUS, 1758

Actual size

*Scarabaeus sacer* uses its rakelike front legs to fashion balls from fresh dung, then buries it and remains with it before laying a single egg inside. The grub feeds and completes its development inside the ball. These beetles were revered in ancient Egypt as symbols of Khepri, a manifestation of the sun god Ra, because their dung-rolling activities were considered symbols of the forces that moved the sun, represented by the dung ball, across the sky. The species was also associated with rebirth, and the beetles, along with their likenesses carved in stone, were frequently buried with the dead.

### RELATED SPECIES
*Scarabaeus* contains 139 species in four subgenera that inhabit the Afrotropical, Palearctic, and Oriental realms. These small to relatively large dung beetles have four distinct teeth across the clypeus, front coxae and femora that are not enlarged, and lack front tarsi. *Scarabaeus sacer* is distinguished from other Palearctic species, in part,

**The Sacred Scarab Beetle** has a broad, smooth patch and narrow groove along the posterior margin of the pronotum. The middle tibiae each have two oblique rows of short setae. The tips of the hind tibiae are prolonged, forming a narrow plate beneath the tarsus. Males have a reddish fringe of setae along the inner margins of their hind tibiae.

| FAMILY | Scarabaeidae |
|---|---|
| SUBFAMILY | Scarabaeinae |
| DISTRIBUTION | Neotropical: northern Argentina, southern Bolivia, western Paraguay |
| MACROHABITAT | Dry forest, dry thorn forest, and pasture |
| MICROHABITAT | Often found in pastures in cattle-raising areas |
| FEEDING HABITS | Adults commonly found in cattle dung |
| NOTE | This is the most colorful and variable species of *Sulcophanaeus* |

ADULT LENGTH
$^{11}/_{16}$–1$^{1}/_{8}$ in
(18–28 mm)

*SULCOPHANEUS IMPERATOR*
# SULCOPHANEUS IMPERATOR
(CHEVROLAT, 1844)

209

*Sulcophanaeus imperator* adults reach their peak of activity from January to March. They fly during the day in search of fresh feces of humans and various domesticated animals, and can be common in cattle pastures. They typically work in pairs to dig their nests directly beside or underneath animal droppings. Males push plugs of dung down the tunnel to females, which fashion them into brood balls within the brood chamber. Dung burial reduces the loss of pasturage due to the growth of rank herbage, releases nutrients back to the soil, and disrupts the life cycles of pest organisms developing in the feces.

## RELATED SPECIES

The genus *Sulcophanaeus* consists of 14 species, all but four of which occur in South America. Three of the latter species inhabit Central America, including an endemic, while the fourth species is endemic to Jamaica. With its green, gold, and red color forms, *S. imperator* is by far the most colorful and variable species in the genus.

**Sulcophanaeus imperator** is a large and bulky beetle that is dull to weakly shining black mixed with brilliant metallic greens, golds, and blues, and coppery red reflections. Males have a distinct backward-pointing horn on the head, while the females lack this armature. Both males and females have front tarsi.

Actual size

| FAMILY | Scarabaeidae |
|---|---|
| SUBFAMILY | Melolonthinae |
| DISTRIBUTION | Neotropical: Peru |
| MACROHABITAT | Tropical forests |
| MICROHABITAT | On live or decaying vegetation |
| FEEDING HABITS | Adults feed on leaves and flowers; larvae feed on decaying plant matter |
| NOTE | A commonly occurring but little-known beetle |

ADULT LENGTH
1¹¹/₃₂–1³/₁₆ in
(26–30 mm)

210

*ANCISTROSOMA KLUGII*
# ANCISTROSOMA KLUGII
CURTIS, 1835

Although *Ancistrosoma klugii* is fairly common, little is known about its life history. The adults appear to be active during the day and at night, and have been found on the leaves and flowers of *Mimosa* species in Peru. The subterranean C-shaped larvae feed on roots and possibly plant detritus. The name *Ancistrosoma* is derived from the Greek word *ankistron* and refers to the hook-like projection on the abdomen of males. Species of *Ancistrosoma* occur in northern South America, including Colombia, Ecuador, Peru, Venezuala, and Trinidad and Tobago, as well as Argentina.

RELATED SPECIES

The genus *Ancistrosoma* contains 15 species. Males are distinguished from females by the presence of a blunt spine projecting from the underside of the first visible abdominal segment. The legs of *A. klugii* are reddish and the pronotum has a distinct groove down the middle and a short spine on the middle of the

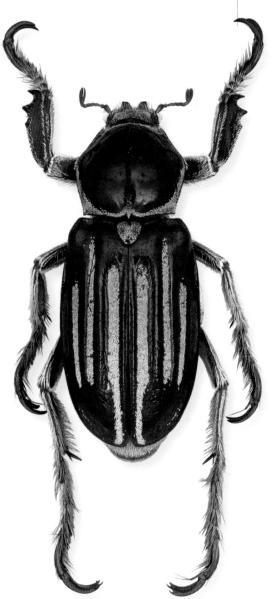

**Ancistrosoma klugii** is a medium-size, rather elongate beetle with a reddish-brown to black cuticle, covered in part with yellow to orange setae that are mostly pressed against the surface. The setae on the elytra form longitudinal stripes. The long legs are reddish or yellowish orange with large claws. Males have a distinct, slightly curved spine near the base of their abdomen.

Actual size

| FAMILY | Scarabaeidae |
|---|---|
| SUBFAMILY | Melolonthinae |
| DISTRIBUTION | Palearctic: Bhutan, China, Tibet, India, Nepal |
| MACROHABITAT | Forests |
| MICROHABITAT | On tree trunks; females have been found laying eggs in humus |
| FEEDING HABITS | Adults feeds on tree sap; larvae feed on decaying vegetation |
| NOTE | This uncommon species has unique sexual dimorphism |

*CHEIROTONUS MACLEAYI*
# MACLEAY'S LONG-ARMED CHAFER
HOPE, 1840

ADULT MALE LENGTH
1⅝–2⅜ in
(42–61 mm)

ADULT FEMALE LENGTH
1¾–2 in
(44–52 mm)

211

With its incredibly long front legs, the male Macleay's Long-armed Chafer is one of the largest and most remarkable insects in the world; females have much shorter legs. The larvae develop in decaying trunks of Bluejack Oak trees (*Quercus incana*) and pupate in cases with smooth interior walls and large, woody fibers externally. Adults are sometimes found among groups of stag beetles on tree trunks drinking sap. All species of *Cheirotonus* typically occur in high-elevation old-growth forests that furnish brood trees and sap to sustain both larvae and adults, habitats that are threatened by deforestation.

## RELATED SPECIES
*Cheirotonus* is distinguished from the two other genera of long-armed chafers in the tribe Euchirini (*Euchirus* and *Propomacrus*) by its coarsely punctured and brilliant shining green pronotum, and includes eight species (*C. arnaudi*, *C. battareli*, *C. formosanus*, *C. gestroi*, *C. jambar*, *C. jansoni*, *C. macleayi*, and *C. parryi*). *Cheirotonus macleayi* is distinguished by its elytral spots, characteristics of the male front tibiae, and distribution.

Actual size

**Macleay's Long-armed Chafer** is easy to recognize in that the male's front legs often exceed its entire body length. Major males have a very shiny pronotum. The male's head and the pronotum bear yellow and orange setae. The elytra are brown-black and bear orange and yellow spots.

| FAMILY | Scarabaeidae |
|---|---|
| SUBFAMILY | Melolonthinae |
| DISTRIBUTION | Palearctic: France, Spain, Switzerland |
| MACROHABITAT | Humid areas in fields |
| MICROHABITAT | Various shrubs |
| FEEDING HABITS | Feeds on foliage and flowers |
| NOTE | A common small scarab beetle |

ADULT LENGTH
⁵/₁₆–⁷/₁₆ in
(8–10.5 mm)

212

*HOPLIA COERULEA*
# CERULEAN CHAFER BEETLE
(DRURY, 1773)

The Cerulean Chafer Beetle is bright iridescent blue-violet, while the female is brownish. The male's spectacular color is the result of the photonic structure of the scales that cover its body, consisting of stacked plates of chitin supported by parallel rods. They often perch conspicuously on the highest branches of low-growing shrubs and remain motionless with one or both hind legs lifted upward. Both males and females are often found flying in swarms on warm, sunny summer days along stream banks or near swampy habitats, where they feed on foliage and flowers.

## RELATED SPECIES

Nearly 300 species of *Hoplia* have been described worldwide, except in Australia. The genus is especially diverse in the Palearctic and Neotropical realms. The genus is in need of revision, and it is likely that new species and genera will be discovered. Of the 170 species currently placed in *Hoplia* from the Palearctic Realm, the males of *H. coerulea* are easily separated by their brilliant iridescent hue.

Actual size

**The Cerulean Chafer Beetle** male is beautiful, with an iridescent blue dorsal surface, often with purplish hues. The female is larger and brown, brownish yellow, or dark gray. The body of this beetle is rather short. The head, thorax, and abdomen are covered with small scales. The ventral surface of both sexes has silver scales.

| FAMILY | Scarabaeidae |
| --- | --- |
| SUBFAMILY | Melolonthinae |
| DISTRIBUTION | Palearctic: Europe |
| MACROHABITAT | Forests, open areas |
| MICROHABITAT | On various trees, pastures, hedges, fodder crops, cereals, and vegetables |
| FEEDING HABITS | Adults feed on leaves of several trees; larvae feed on roots |
| NOTE | Children have used European Cockchafers as live toys since antiquity |

ADULT LENGTH
¾–1¹⁄₁₆ in
(20–30 mm)

*MELOLONTHA MELOLONTHA*
# EUROPEAN COCKCHAFER
(LINNAEUS, 1758)

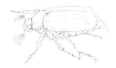

213

*Melolontha melolontha* is one of the best-known beetles in Europe. Since antiquity, children have tied thread to the legs of these beetles and flown them overhead as if they were living kites. At one time, the larvae, known as "white grubs," were served as food. The adults emerge in spring and are especially abundant in April and May. Females lay 50 to 80 eggs in the soil, where they hatch into C-shaped grubs and feed on roots. Their development may take three or four years, depending on the climate. Several species of *Melolontha* were once considered common, but since their larvae are often considered pests, the use of pesticides has reduced their populations.

RELATED SPECIES

*Melolontha* belongs to the tribe Melolonthini, which is the most diverse in the subfamily Melolonthinae. The tribe is distributed throughout the world and includes many species of economic importance. Other European species in the genus include *M. hippocastani* and *M. pectoralis*. North American members of Melolonthini such as *Phyllophaga* species are commonly referred to as May or June beetles.

**The European Cockchafer** is a large, robust beetle. The head and thorax are black with some gray. The elytra are brown and the legs are typically reddish. This species has a distinct fanlike antennal club. The males have a long, narrowly truncated pygidium at the tip of their abdomen; in the female, the pygidium is slightly longer and wider.

Actual size

| FAMILY | Scarabaeidae |
|---|---|
| SUBFAMILY | Melolonthinae |
| DISTRIBUTION | Nearctic: western North America |
| MACROHABITAT | Grasslands, oak woodlands, pine forests |
| MICROHABITAT | Adults found on pines and attracted to lights; larvae in sandy soils |
| FEEDING HABITS | Adults eat pine needles; larvae eat roots of grasses and other plants |
| NOTE | Most common and widespread *Polyphylla* in North America |

ADULT LENGTH
<sup>11</sup>⁄₁₆–1¼ in
(18–31 mm)

214

*POLYPHYLLA DECEMLINEATA*
# TEN-LINED JUNE BEETLE
(SAY, 1824)

The Ten-lined June Beetle is widely distributed in western North America and occurs from sea level to 9,000 ft (2,740 m) in elevation. Adults typically fly on warm summer evenings. They feed on the needles of Ponderosa Pine (*Pinus ponderosa*). With their incredibly sensitive antennal lamellae spread wide, airborne males track pheromones released by females. Copulation takes place on the ground or in trees. Both sexes are attracted to light, but especially males. The larvae eat the roots of plants growing in sandy soils, including grasses, coniferous seedlings, fruit trees, and various vegetable crops.

### RELATED SPECIES

The genus *Polyphylla* is widely distributed in the Northern Hemisphere, with 32 species known to occur in North America. Beetles in this genus are characterized by having robust and scaled bodies, and lamellate antennal clubs with five (females) or seven (males) antennomeres. The Ten-lined June Beetle is distinguished by the distinctly yellow scales in between the smooth-edged white stripes on the elytra, lack of erect setae on the pronotum, and male genitalic characters.

Actual size

**The Ten-lined June Beetle** is elongate and robust with distinct white stripes on the elytra. Its black head has large eyes and is rectangular and strongly concave in the front. The lamellate antennae consist of ten antennomeres with clubs long and curved in the male or short and straight in the female. Broad and convex, the pronotum lacks setae, except along the margins.

| FAMILY | Scarabaeidae |
|---|---|
| SUBFAMILY | Melolonthinae |
| DISTRIBUTION | Afrotropical: southern Africa |
| MACROHABITAT | Deserts, sandy grasslands |
| MICROHABITAT | Adults attracted to lights; larvae burrow in sandy soil beneath dung |
| FEEDING HABITS | Adults probably eat leaves; larvae eat antelope and sheep dung |
| NOTE | Larval feeding habits are unusual within the Melolonthinae |

ADULT LENGTH
¹¹⁄₁₆–⁷⁄₈ in
(17–23 mm)

*SPARRMANNIA FLAVA*

# SPARRMANNIA FLAVA

ARROW, 1917

215

Adult *Sparrmannia flava* emerge after the first summer rains in November to feed, mate, and lay eggs. They eat leaves, but specific information on their food plants is lacking. The vertical burrows of the larvae are indicated by "push-ups" on the surface and appear in and around springbok dung-middens in January. They leave their burrows at night to locate a suitable dung pellet and drag it back to the burrow and begin to feed. Mature larvae construct an earthen cell in April, enter diapause, and pupate within three weeks of the next summer's rains.

Actual size

## RELATED SPECIES

The sub-Saharan genus *Sparrmannia* contains 28 species, all of which are distinguished from other scarabs in the region by the long setae on the pronotum and their antennal characters. *Sparrmannia flava* is similar to *S. alopex*, *S. similis*, and *S. vicinus*, but can be distinguished by the shape of the male genitalia. All but two species in the genus are yellowish brown and crepuscular or nocturnal.

**Sparrmannia flava** is robust with a densely pilose head and thorax. The head has a notched and bare clypeus, and antennae with ten antennomeres, the last seven forming a lamellate club. The pronotum is wider than long and completely covered with long, dense whitish setae. The yellowish-brown elytra are long, exposing only the tip of the abdomen.

| FAMILY | Scarabaeidae |
|---|---|
| SUBFAMILY | Rutelinae |
| DISTRIBUTION | Australian: northern part of Australia (northern coastal Queensland and the western zones of Western Australia), Papua New Guinea |
| MACROHABITAT | Forests, woodlands |
| MICROHABITAT | Usually on leaves |
| FEEDING HABITS | Adults feed on leaves of various trees (e.g., *Eucalyptus*); larvae feed on roots |
| NOTE | The least common of the four species in the genus |

ADULT LENGTH
⅞–1 in
(22–25 mm)

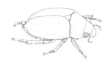

216

*CALLOODES ATKINSONI*
# ATKINSON'S CHRISTMAS BEETLE
WATERHOUSE, 1868

The name "Christmas beetle" is attributed to species of *Calloodes* and other closely related scarab genera because they typically appear in large numbers around the holidays during the austral summer. Atkinson's Christmas Beetle is nocturnal and feeds on the leaves of Red Bloodwood (*Eucalyptus gummifera*), *Acacia*, and other host trees. When feeding in large numbers, these beetles are capable of stripping an entire tree of its leaves. The distinctly C-shaped larvae feed on the roots of grasses and other plants. Although the Atkinson's Christmas Beetle is not rare, the populations of this and other species of *Calloodes* seem to be in decline.

## RELATED SPECIES

The other known species of *Calloodes* are *C. nitidissimus*, *C. grayianus*, and *C. rayneri*. Only the Atkinson's Christmas Beetle has been recorded outside Australia. The genus *Anoplognathus* is related to *Calloodes* and comprises around 40 species. Atkinson's Christmas Beetle is distinguished by having pointed elytral apices and deep metallic green legs, and by the lateral margins of the pronotum and elytra having a broad reddish-yellow band.

**The Atkinson's Christmas Beetle** is a fairly large ruteline beetle. The species is brilliant metallic and iridescent green with two large yellow bands on the edge of the elytra. The head and legs are also metallic green. The adults have small clubbed antennae. Like most species in the subfamily Rutelinae, the Atkinson's Christmas Beetle has large and unequal tarsal claws. No noticeable sexual dimorphism occurs in this species.

Actual size

| FAMILY | Scarabaeidae |
|---|---|
| SUBFAMILY | Rutelinae |
| DISTRIBUTION | Neotropical: Mexico (San Luis Potosí, Hidalgo, Puebla, Veracruz, Oaxaca, Guerrero) |
| MACROHABITAT | Moist montane forest, usually at 2,500–6,500 ft (750–2,000 m) |
| MICROHABITAT | Leaves of various trees |
| FEEDING HABITS | Adults feed on leaves; larvae feed in rotten logs |
| NOTE | A very common species, the males of which have unusually large hind legs |

ADULT LENGTH
1⅛–1⁹⁄₁₆ in
(28–40 mm)

*CHRYSINA MACROPUS*
# CHRYSINA MACROPUS
(FRANCILLON, 1795)

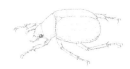

217

The species name of this beetle is derived from the Greek words *makros* ("long" or "large") and *pous* ("foot"), in reference to the abnormally large hind legs of males. Adults are active from May to October and are sometimes attracted to lights at night in large numbers; they are occasionally known to fly during the day in bright sunlight. The larvae feed and develop in the decaying logs of alder (*Alnus* spp.), sweetgum (*Liquidambar* spp.), and sycamore (*Platanus* spp.) and take about two years to reach adulthood. The charismatic male of this species was depicted on a stamp in Nicaragua in 1988.

### RELATED SPECIES

The genus *Chrysina* is well known for its colorful, metallic species that occur mostly in the Neotropical Realm. The species with large-legged males include *C. amoena*, *C. beckeri*, *C. erubescens*, *C. macropus*, *C. modesta*, and *C. triumphalis* from Mexico, and *C. karschi* from Honduras. *Chrysina erubescens* feeds on the leaves of oaks (*Quercus* spp.) at elevations of 5,250–9,500 ft (1,600–2,900 m).

Actual size

**Chrysina macropus** is a fairly large, colorful scarab beetle. The head, thorax, and abdomen are yellowish green, sometimes with a coppery tinge, and the legs are usually green with reddish reflections. The males of this species show a hypertrophication (abnormal enlargement) of the hind legs. The overall size of e beetle and the intensity of the body color vary between individuals.

| FAMILY | Scarabaeidae |
|---|---|
| SUBFAMILY | Rutelinae |
| DISTRIBUTION | Neotropical: Costa Rica (Puntarenas and Cartago provinces), Panama (Chiriquí province) |
| MACROHABITAT | Tropical rainforests, coffee plantations |
| MICROHABITAT | Adults live on foliage and are attracted to lights at night |
| FEEDING HABITS | Adults feed on foliage; larvae feed on rotting logs |
| NOTE | The spectacular color of this species has led to research into the optical properties of the exoskeleton. Recent studies have resulted in the synthetic re-creation of this beetle's cuticle |

ADULT LENGTH
¾–¹⁵⁄₁₆ in
(20–24 mm)

218

*CHRYSINA RESPLENDENS*
# GOLDEN SCARAB BEETLE
(BOUCARD, 1875)

The Golden Scarab Beetle is commonly found in tropical rainforests and coffee plantations at elevations of 1,300–9,200 ft (400–2,800 m). The nocturnal adults are active from January through June, and spend much of their lives in the forest canopy, where they likely eat leaves. Species of *Chrysina*, commonly referred to as jewel scarabs, are native mostly to the Neotropical Realm, although four species occur in the American Southwest. The brilliant metallic coloration of these beetles makes them very popular among collectors, and pristine specimens of rarer species can command high prices.

## RELATED SPECIES

The more than 100 species are distributed primarily in pine, juniper, and pine–oak forests at elevations of 160–12,500 ft (50–3,800 m). Most species are bright green, pink, purple, blue, red, silver, or gold. Other golden species of *Chrysina* include *C. aurigans*, *C. batesi*, *C. cupreomarginata*, *C. guaymi*, *C. pastori*, and *C. tuerckheimi*.

Actual size

**The Golden Scarab Beetle** is medium-size oval beetle with a brilliant metallic gold coloration on the dorsal surface. The front tibiae bear three triangular spines on their outer edge near the apex. The ventral face is gold with iridescent bronze. The apex of the hind tibia has several small spines.

| FAMILY | Scarabaeidae |
|---|---|
| SUBFAMILY | Rutelinae |
| DISTRIBUTION | Neotropical: Colombia, Ecuador, Peru |
| MACROHABITAT | Tropical forests |
| MICROHABITAT | Twigs of fresh leaves of shrubs |
| FEEDING HABITS | Feeds on leaves of various plants |
| NOTE | The elytra and other body parts of this beetle are used to make jewelry by native people |

ADULT MALE LENGTH
1⅛–1⁹⁄₁₆ in
(28–40 mm)

*CHRYSOPHORA CHRYSOCHLORA*
# SHINING LEAF CHAFER
(LATREILLE, 1811)

ADULT FEMALE LENGTH
1¹⁄₁₆–1⅛ in
(27–29 mm)

219

The Shining Leaf Chafer is a large, diurnal species that is active during the rainy season from September to November. Adults feed on the foliage of butterfly bush (*Buddleja* spp.), Martin Galviz (*Senna reticulata*), Wildcane (*Gynerium saggitatum*), and White Leadtree (*Leucaena leucocephala*). Indigenous people throughout the beetle's range use the elytra or dried bodies in handicrafts, earrings and necklaces, and other souvenirs. The larvae have been reared in captivity on rotten wood and sawdust, and reach adulthood in about a year.

## RELATED SPECIES

*Chrysophora* belongs to the tribe Rutelini, which is distributed worldwide but is most diverse in the Neotropical Realm. The 70-plus genera in the Americas (e.g., *Chrysina*, *Pelidnota*, *Rutela*) are generally recognized by their ten-segmented antennae and three teeth at the apex of their front tibiae. *Chrysophora chrysochlora* is the only species in the genus.

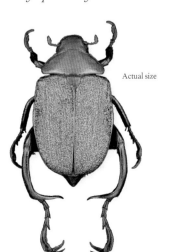

Actual size

**The Shining Leaf Chafer** is a large, dark metallic green beetle with gold reflections. The male has enlarged hind legs with sharply pointed spurs. The legs are the same color as the elytra but the tarsi are an attractive metallic blue, often with some green and red. The elytra have a coarse granulate texture.

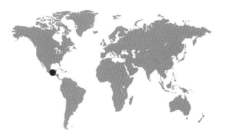

| FAMILY | Scarabaeidae |
|---|---|
| SUBFAMILY | Rutelinae |
| DISTRIBUTION | Neotropical: Mexico |
| MACROHABITAT | Humid forests |
| MICROHABITAT | Adults are attracted to lights; larvae develop in decaying logs |
| FEEDING HABITS | Adult habits are unknown; larvae eat decaying wood |
| NOTE | Males and females are strongly sexual dimorphic |

ADULT MALE LENGTH
1¾–2½ in
(44–63 mm)

ADULT FEMALE LENGTH
1⅝–1¾ in
(42–44 mm)

220

*HETEROSTERNUS BUPRESTOIDES*
# HETEROSTERNUS BUPRESTOIDES
DUPONT, 1832

Actual size

Males of *Heterosternus buprestoides* are among the largest and most striking of all ruteline scarabs because of their shape, rarity, and hyperdevelopment of the hind legs. They inhabit cloud forests, montane and tropical rainforests, and warm oak forests on the external slopes of the Sierra Madra Oriental, Sierra de los Tuxtlas, Sierra Madre del Sur, and Sierra Madre de Chiapas between 2,620 and 3,280 ft (800 and 1,000 m) in elevation. The larvae develop in rotten logs and may require two years to complete their life cycle. Adults fly from June through August and are occasionally attracted to light.

RELATED SPECIES

The genus *Heterosternus* includes three species that range from southern Mexico to western Panama, and is most easily distinguished from related genera by the extreme development of the hind legs and the nearly horizontal pygidium in the male. *Heterosternus buprestoides* is recognized by the extended tips of the elytra that are seen in the male and the toothed elytral tips of the female. The unarmed femora of the male's hind leg are also distinctive.

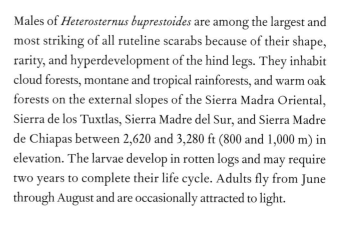

**Heterosternus buprestoides** males are large, oval-elliptical, and somewhat uniformly pale yellow, while the females are more oval with a reddish-brown pronotum and yellowish elytra. The tips of the elytra are narrowly extended in males, and spined or toothed in females. The hind legs of the male lack femoral spines, while the very long, curved tibiae lack setal brushes.

| | |
|---|---|
| FAMILY | Scarabaeidae |
| SUBFAMILY | Rutelinae |
| DISTRIBUTION | Oriental and Palearctic: Vietnam, China |
| MACROHABITAT | Forests |
| MICROHABITAT | Adults are found on trees; larvae are found in decaying wood |
| FEEDING HABITS | Adults and larvae feed on decayed wood flakes |
| NOTE | Males use their "calipers" to fight for food and females |

ADULT MALE LENGTH
$^{11}/_{16}-1^{5}/_{16}$ in
(17–33 mm)

ADULT FEMALE LENGTH
$^{9}/_{16}-^{3}/_{4}$ in
(15–19 mm)

*KIBAKOGANEA SEXMACULATA*

# KIBAKOGANEA SEXMACULATA

(KRAATZ, 1900)

221

Little is known about the biology or ecology of *Kibakoganea sexmaculata*, which is considered to be a rare species. As in other species of *Kibakoganea*, males have long, slender, curved mandibles that resemble calipers. The short-lived beetles emerge in April to mate and feed on flowers, and are sometimes attracted to lights at night. The larvae of other species of *Kibakoganea* have been raised in captivity on decaying wood chips and take 10–12 months to reach adulthood.

## RELATED SPECIES

More than 15 species of *Kibakoganea* have been described in Asia, including southern China and Taiwan. The male of *K. sexmaculata* is similar to *K. dohertyi* from Laos and *K. sinica* from China. Other genera that are similar to *Kibakoganea* are *Fruhstorferia*, *Masumotokoganea*, *Pukupuku*, *Ceroplophana*, *Dicaulocephalus*, and *Didrepanephorus*.

Actual size

**Kibakoganea sexmaculata** is a medium-size beetle that displays sexual dimorphism. The male has a small head with curved, sharply pointed, slender, curved, caliper-shaped, reddish-brown mandibles. The pronotum is green, sometimes black, with fine punctation. The males are olive-green to darker greenish overall, while the females are greenish yellow to reddish brown with brown spots on the elytra. The legs are green with red reflections. Some completely yellow specimens have also been recorded.

| FAMILY | Scarabaeidae |
|---|---|
| SUBFAMILY | Dynastinae |
| DISTRIBUTION | Oriental: from India to Indonesia (Sulawesi) |
| MACROHABITAT | Adults are found in tropical forests |
| MICROHABITAT | On tree trunks |
| FEEDING HABITS | Adult feed on tree sap and overripe fruit; larvae feed on humus and decaying wood |
| NOTE | One of the largest and strongest beetles in the world—one specimen was able to lift 850 times its own weight in a laboratory experiment |

**ADULT MALE LENGTH**
2³⁄₈–5¹⁄₈ in
(60–130 mm)

**ADULT FEMALE LENGTH**
1–2³⁄₈ in
(25–60 mm)

*CHALCOSOMA ATLAS*
# ATLAS BEETLE
(LINNAEUS, 1758)

Actual size

The Atlas Beetle is one of the largest beetles in the world. Males use their head and thoracic horns in intraspecific battles with rival males over food and nearby females. It has been suggested that the minor (i.e., smaller) males emerge earlier in nature, fly longer distances, and mate with receptive females before the emergence of the major (i.e., larger) males, thus avoiding confrontations that they are likely to lose. The larvae are very aggressive toward one another under crowded conditions. In some parts of Asia, gamblers bet substantial sums of money over the outcome of these beetles fighting.

## RELATED SPECIES

Although a number of subspecies of *Chalcosoma atlas* have been recognized (*C. a. atlas*, *C. a. butonensis*, *C. a. keyboh*, *C. a. mantetsu*, *C. a. simeuluensis*, and *C. a. sintae*), their status as valid taxa remains controversial. *Chalcosoma atlas* is readily distinguished from the otherwise similar *C. chiron* by the lack of a tooth on the frontal horn, while *C. moellenkampi* has a narrower pronotum. The other known species in the genus are *C. chiron* and *C. engganensis*.

**The Atlas Beetle** is black, sometimes with a metallic luster on the pronotum and elytra. The legs are black and the front tibiae bear strong spines on their outer edge near the apex. Males, which vary greatly in size, have a pair of horns on the pronotum and a single large upcurved horn on the head.

| FAMILY | Scarabaeidae |
|---|---|
| SUBFAMILY | Dynastinae |
| DISTRIBUTION | Neotropical: southern Mexico to Bolivia; Trinidad, Guadeloupe, Martinique, Dominica in the West Indies (extinct in Hispaniola) |
| MACROHABITAT | Tropical wet forests, premontane wet forests, premontane rainforests, montane rainforests |
| MICROHABITAT | Adults at sap flows on trees or at lights at night; larvae occur in rotting wood |
| FEEDING HABITS | Adults feed on fruit and tree sap; larvae feed in rotten wood |
| NOTE | One of the largest beetles in the world |

ADULT MALE LENGTH
1¹⁵⁄₁₆–6¾ in
(50–170 mm)

ADULT FEMALE LENGTH
1⁹⁄₁₆–3⅛ in
(40–80 mm)

*DYNASTES HERCULES*
# HERCULES BEETLE
(LINNAEUS, 1758)

223

Hercules Beetles are one of the most recognizable insect species in the world. Adults fly mostly at night, especially during the first two hours after sunset. They are commonly bred by hobbyists and live three to six months in captivity, but live almost two years in the wild. Males are capable of lifting nearly 4¼ lb (2 kg) with their head. Elytra of living and dead beetles change rapidly from yellowish olive to black and back in response to changes in humidity. Larvae feed and develop in rotting tree trunks. Hercules Beetles are protected by law in Guadeloupe and Martinique.

## RELATED SPECIES

*Dynastes* contains seven species of large to very large beetles; males have a long, forward-projecting horn mounted on the prothorax. Morphological characters to differentiate the species include differences in the tarsal segments and in coloration as well as in the thoracic and clypeal horns of the males. *Dynastes neptunus* and *D. satanas* are restricted to South America, while *D. moroni* occurs in Mexico. *Dynastes maya* and *D. hyllus* inhabit Mexico, Guatemala, and Honduras. *Dynastes tityus* and *D. granti* are distributed in the southeastern and southwestern United States, respectively.

**The Hercules Beetle** displays sexual dimorphism, the males reaching much greater lengths than the females. The head and smooth pronotum of the males are armed with distinct horns, while in the females they are unarmed, the head with small bump, and the pronotum and elytra rough. The elytra of males are mostly grayish olive to brownish olive, or yellowish green with dark spots, to nearly entirely black; the female elytra are entirely black, sometimes with the tips colored as in males. Numerous dubious subspecies have been described based solely on color and horn configuration.

Actual size

| FAMILY | Scarabaeidae |
|---|---|
| SUBFAMILY | Dynastinae |
| DISTRIBUTION | Nearctic: eastern North America |
| MACROHABITAT | Deciduous hardwood forest and mixed woodland |
| MICROHABITAT | Tree holes, rotten logs, and sapping ash branches |
| FEEDING HABITS | Adults imbibe sap laden with microorganisms, also fruit |
| NOTE | One of the largest horned beetles of North America |

**ADULT LENGTH**
1½ to 2½ in
(40 to 60 mm)

*DYNASTES TITYUS*
# EASTERN HERCULES BEETLE
(LINNAEUS, 1763)

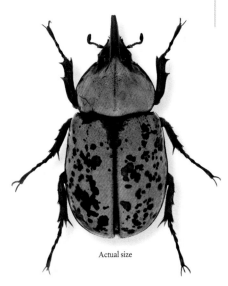

Actual size

**The Eastern Hercules Beetle** is large, olive, yellow-green, or gray, with irregular black or mahogany spots. Well-hydrated individuals may have one or both elytra completely dark. Males have a single curved horn on their head and one long and two short horns on the pronotum. Females have a single tubercle on the head, while their pronotum lacks any adornment.

Larvae develop in rotting hardwoods, including oaks (*Quercus* spp.), cherry (*Prunus* spp.), black locust (*Robinia* spp.), and willow (*Salix* spp.); they will also occasionally use pine (*Pinus* spp.). Two years are required to complete the life cycle. Pupation takes place in late summer inside a cell constructed from larval fecal pellets. Adults emerge in several weeks, but remain in the cell until the following summer. Both males and females are found at larval breeding sites and are attracted to lights at night. Males guard sapping wounds on ash trees that will attract females and use their forceps-like horns to grapple with rival males.

RELATED SPECIES
*Dynastes* is restricted to the Nearctic and Neotropical realms and includes seven species. *Dynastes granti*, the only other species in the United States, is restricted to the southwest. *Dynastes hyllus* and *D. maya* occur in Mexico and Central America, while *D. neptunus* and *D. satanas* are found only in South America. The Hercules Beetle, *D. hercules*, occurs from southern Mexico to South America.

| FAMILY | Scarabaeidae |
|---|---|
| SUBFAMILY | Dynastinae |
| DISTRIBUTION | Oriental and Palearctic: Thailand, Burma, China |
| MACROHABITAT | Tropical forests |
| MICROHABITAT | Associated with bamboo trees |
| FEEDING HABITS | Adults feed on young bamboo shoots and fruits; larvae feed on soft rotten wood |
| NOTE | The impressive fully grown larvae, which can be reared successfully in laboratory conditions, weigh up to 2⅛ oz (60 g) and can reach a length of 3⅞ in (100 mm) |

ADULT MALE LENGTH
1⅞–3⅞ in
(48–100 mm)

ADULT FEMALE LENGTH
1¾–1¹⁵⁄₁₆ in
(45–50 mm)

*EUPATORUS GRACILICORNIS*
# FIVE-HORNED RHINOCEROS BEETLE
ARROW, 1908

225

The Five-horned Rhinoceros Beetle is one of the largest beetles in the world. The male has four spectacular horns on the prothorax and one very long, curved, slender, sharply pointed cephalic horn, while the female is unarmed. Adults are primarily active during the months of September and October, and the males usually die soon after mating. The larvae develop in damp, decaying wood and reach adulthood in one to two years depending on environmental conditions. In northern Thailand, people keep these beetles as fighting pets. The larvae and gravid females are considered delicacies in some regions.

## RELATED SPECIES

The genus *Eupatorus* is placed in the tribe Dynastini and, based on DNA analysis and morphological characters, is closely related to *Beckius*, *Chalcosoma*, *Haploscapanes*, and *Pachyoryctes*. Three subspecies of the Five-horned Rhinoceros Beetle are recognized: *E. gracilicornis gracilicornis* from Thailand and China; *E. g. edai* from Thailand and Burma; and *E. g. kimioi* from Thailand.

Actual size

**The Five-horned Rhinoceros Beetle** is a large dynastine with a shiny black body except for the elytra, which vary in color from yellow to black, depending on the individual. The elytra also have a narrow, longitudinal black strip along the midline. In males, the pronotum has four large anteriorly projecting spines and the head has a long spine that curves upward. The flight wings are fully developed but these beetles do not fly very well.

| FAMILY | Scarabaeidae |
|---|---|
| SUBFAMILY | Dynastinae |
| DISTRIBUTION | Neotropical: Colombia and Venezuela |
| MACROHABITAT | Montane tropical forests |
| MICROHABITAT | Adults found on leafless stalks of bamboo |
| FEEDING HABITS | Adult males and females eat stalks of bamboo |
| NOTE | Males use their elaborate horns to defend feeding sites from other males |

**ADULT LENGTH**
1⁹⁄₁₆–2³⁄₈ in
(40–60 mm)

226

*GOLOFA PORTERI*
# GOLOFA PORTERI
HOPE, 1837

Adult *Golofa porteri* are active during the day and fly in the early morning in April and May. They are commonly found feeding and mating on the young stems of *Chusquea* bamboo that grows in tall, thick clumps at elevations between 6,600 and 8,500 ft (2,000 and 2,600 m). Males perch head down on a single stalk to feed and defend it from other males. An attacking male rakes its long front legs across the legs of its opponent in an attempt to raise it up, work its long head horn under the opponent's body, and flip it off the stalk. Females are occasionally attracted to lights.

RELATED SPECIES

There are 28 species of *Golofa* that range from Mexico to northern Argentina and Chile. Adult males are usually brownish yellow to dark reddish brown with a long slender horn on the head and a short to long, erect horn on the pronotum, while females lack horns and are typically black or yellowish brown. Male *G. porteri* are distinguished by their long horns that oppose one another like calipers.

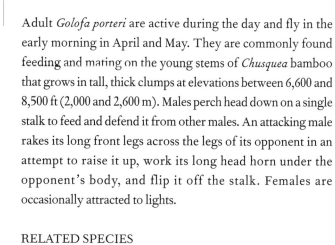

Actual size

***Golofa porteri*** males are smooth, shining, and reddish-brown beetles with long, slender, erect, and scythelike, toothed horns, one on their head and one on the pronotum that oppose one another. Their front legs are relatively long with thickened tarsal segments bearing tufts of golden setae on their undersides. All these features are lacking in the dark, shiny, and roughly sculptured females.

| | |
|---|---|
| FAMILY | Scarabaeidae |
| SUBFAMILY | Dynastinae |
| DISTRIBUTION | Afrotropical: Madagascar |
| MACROHABITAT | Several subspecies live near beaches; one subspecies occurs in forests |
| MICROHABITAT | On soil and sand |
| FEEDING HABITS | Adults feed on algae and mosses; larvae feed on dead and decaying matter |
| NOTE | All species of *Hexodon* are flightless and endemic to Madagascar |

*HEXODON UNICOLOR*

# HEXODON UNICOLOR

OLIVIER, 1789

ADULT MALE LENGTH
$^{11}/_{16}$–$^{15}/_{16}$ in
(18–24 mm)

ADULT FEMALE LENGTH
$^{3}/_{4}$–1 in
(20–25 mm)

227

While males in the subfamily Dynastinae sometimes have spectacular horns on their head and pronotum, those of the genus *Hexodon* are unarmed and resemble species in other families such as darkling beetles (Tenebrionidae) and some carrion beetles (Silphidae). Adults of *H. unicolor* are active during the day, when they can be encountered digging into the soil and sand. The C-shaped larvae are saprophagous, but will sometimes feed on the roots of rice. Sexual dimorphism in this species is not pronounced, although the females are generally larger and more oval than the males.

RELATED SPECIES

*Hexodon* is the only genus in the tribe Hexodontini. It includes ten species, all of which are endemic to Madagascar. They are distinguished from one another by the characteristics of their pronotum, elytra and male genitalia.

Actual size

**Hexodon unicolor** is an unusual, dark brown to black dynastine beetle with a nearly circular body. Some individuals have some gray on the elytra. The clypeus is short and rounded, and the mandibles are small and simple. The elytra are fused along the midline and individuals are flightless, which is an exceptional phenomenon within the subfamily Dynastinae.

| FAMILY | Scarabaeidae |
|---|---|
| SUBFAMILY | Dynastinae |
| DISTRIBUTION | Neotropical: southeastern Mexico to Colombia and Venezuela |
| MACROHABITAT | Tropical evergreen and deciduous forests below 3,280 ft (1,000 m) |
| MICROHABITAT | Adults found on trees and are attracted to light; larvae found in decaying wood |
| FEEDING HABITS | Adults eat twigs, drink sap and fruit juices; larvae eat wood |
| NOTE | Weigh up to 1¼ oz (35 g) |

ADULT LENGTH
2⅛–3½ in
(54–90 mm)

228

*MEGASOMA ELEPHAS*
# ELEPHANT BEETLE
(FABRICIUS, 1775)

Elephant Beetles fly late on warm, humid nights and are attracted to light. They have the ability to increase their body temperature metabolically as the air cools. During the day, adults feed on twigs, flowers, and sap flows from twigs cut the night before using their crossed front tibiae like scissors. Although adults may be locally abundant, the larvae are seldom found in rotten logs or stumps. Females may deposit their eggs in the detritus-filled hollows in the upper branches and trunks of standing living and dead trees, where the larvae would feed and develop in rotten wood.

RELATED SPECIES

There are 15 species of *Megasoma* that range from the southwestern United States to Argentina. They are distinguished from *Dynastes* and *Golofa* by having three long teeth on their mandibles and two horns on the male's pronotum. *Megasoma elephas* males are similar to those of *M. nogueirai* and *M. occidentalis*, but the pronotal horns are not curved and project forward, rather than to the side.

**The Elephant Beetle** is very large, and mostly velvety golden-brown. Males have a long, upcurved and bifurcate horn on the head and a pair of shorter, somewhat divergent horns on the pronotum. Females lack horns, and the head, pronotum, and bases of the elytra are coarsely sculpted.

Actual size

| FAMILY | Scarabaeidae |
|---|---|
| SUBFAMILY | Dynastinae |
| DISTRIBUTION | Palearctic: from Sweden to Algeria, and from Morocco to China |
| MACROHABITAT | Forest, agricultural pasture, human habitation |
| MICROHABITAT | Decaying wood and plants |
| FEEDING HABITS | Adults do not feed; larvae feed on decaying wood |
| NOTE | The related species *Oryctes rhinoceros* is an important pest of coconut and oil palms |

ADULT LENGTH
⁷⁄₈–1⁷⁄₈ in
(22–47 mm)

*ORYCTES NASICORNIS*
# EUROPEAN RHINOCEROS BEETLE
(LINNAEUS, 1758)

229

The male European Rhinoceros Beetle has a long, curved horn on its head, while the female possesses only a very small horn or tubercle. The adults emerge from the soil in spring, and although they do not feed, live for several months and reach their peak of activity in June and July. They begin flying at dusk and are attracted to lights at night. Females lay their eggs in decaying stumps and logs, where the larvae feed and develop in rotting wood. The entire life cycle, from egg to adult, takes two to four years.

## RELATED SPECIES
*Oryctes* is placed in the tribe Oryctini, and includes 42 large to very large species that occur primarily in Europe, Africa, Asia, and the Indo-Australia region that are similar in form and color. Most of the 20 subspecies of *O. nasicornis* that have been described thus far are taxonomically dubious.

Actual size

**The European Rhinoceros Beetle** is a very large beetle, one of the largest in Europe. The elytra are reddish brown, or occasionally blackish with some metallic reflections. The head and legs are darker. The male has a long, curved horn, while in the female this is absent or very reduced. The ventral surface is covered with reddish setae.

| FAMILY | Scarabaeidae |
|---|---|
| SUBFAMILY | Dynastinae |
| DISTRIBUTION | Neotropical: southern Mexico and Belize to Costa Rica |
| MACROHABITAT | Lowland, montane broadleaf, pine–oak, tropical dry forests |
| MICROHABITAT | Adults are attracted to lights |
| FEEDING HABITS | Unknown |
| NOTE | Big-horned males resemble small male *Dynastes hercules* |

ADULT LENGTH
1–1⅜ in
(24.8–34.5 mm)

230

*SPODISTES MNISZECHI*
# SPODISTES MNISZECHI
(THOMSON, 1860)

Actual size

Little is known of the biology of this and other species of *Spodistes*. Adults, mostly males, are attracted to light between 1,970 and 3,280 ft (600 and 1,000 m) in lowland and montane forests. They are sometimes attacked by bats while flying, as evidenced by individuals suddenly crashing to the ground with an array of small punctures in their elytra. Although found throughout most of the year, their peak flight activity occurs mainly during the early part of the rainy season in April and May. The larvae are unknown.

## RELATED SPECIES

The eight species of *Spodistes* are found from southern Mexico to Colombia and Ecuador. All are distinguished from other horned dynastine scarabs by their velvety covering. Males of *S. batesi*, *S. mniszechi*, and *S. monzoni* all have bifurcate cephalic (head) horns, but *S. mniszechi* has a completely velvety pronotum and lacks a ridge projecting from the ocular canthus to the base of the horn. Female *Spodistes* are difficult to distinguish from one another.

**Spodistes mniszechi** is velvety, grayish brown, with the clypeus, part of the male horn, and most of the female pronotum dark reddish brown. The head horn is bifurcate at the tip, projecting forward and curving upward in major and minor males; it is absent in females. The pronotal horn projects almost to (minor) or beyond (major) the base of the head horn in males, and curves down; it is absent in females.

| FAMILY | Scarabaeidae |
|---|---|
| SUBFAMILY | Dynastinae |
| DISTRIBUTION | Nearctic and Neotropical: southern United States to Brazil and Bolivia |
| MACROHABITAT | Deciduous woodlands, tropical forests, and rain forests |
| MICROHABITAT | At base of palms and at lights; larvae in rotten stumps and logs |
| FEEDING HABITS | Adults feed on tree roots; larvae develop in decaying wood |
| NOTE | Most widespread and morphologically variable species of *Strategus* |

ADULT LENGTH
1¼–2⅜ in
(31–61 mm)

*STRATEGUS ALOEUS*
# OX BEETLE
(LINNAEUS, 1758)

231

The Ox Beetle is the most abundant and widespread species of *Strategus*. Southern individuals are larger and darker than those found in the north. Eggs are deposited in dead or rotten wood. The larvae develop in decaying stumps, or under old hardwood logs, palm trunks, and boards. Mature larvae construct oval pupal chambers where they have been feeding. Adults are found in the refuse piles of leafcutter ants and feed on the roots of palms, agave leaves, and sugar cane. In spite of their preference for palms, Ox Beetles are seldom of any economic importance in palm plantations.

## RELATED SPECIES

The genus *Strategus* contains 31 species that are distinguished by having exposed mandibles with bidentate tips and prominent basal lobes, front tibiae each with four teeth, and the tips of the hind tibiae with three teeth. The pronotum usually has a deep pit with at least a tubercle in front. Major males of the Ox Beetle are best distinguished by their genitalia.

Actual size

**The Ox Beetle** is shiny reddish brown to black. The clypeus is broadly notched in males and somewhat straight or rounded in females. The pronotum of major males has a long, stout, and sharp front horn, while the rear horns are moderately long and flat with sharp, rounded or truncate tips. Elytra have a distinct and complete punctured groove along the elytral suture.

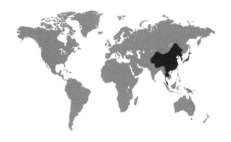

| FAMILY | Scarabaeidae |
|---|---|
| SUBFAMILY | Dynastinae |
| DISTRIBUTION | Palearctic and Oriental: Japan, China, Korea, Taiwan, Thailand |
| MACROHABITAT | Tropical forests |
| MICROHABITAT | Decaying wood, underground |
| FEEDING HABITS | Adults feed on tree sap and fruit; larvae feed on humus in the soil |
| NOTE | A very important beetle in Japanese culture, where it is known as *Kabutomushi*. It served as a model for the design of samurai battle headgear |

**ADULT MALE LENGTH**
1⁹⁄₁₆–3⅛ in
(40–80 mm)

**ADULT FEMALE LENGTH**
1⁹⁄₁₆–2⅜ in
(40–60 mm)

232

*TRYPOXYLUS DICHOTOMUS*
# JAPANESE RHINOCEROS BEETLE
(LINNAEUS, 1771)

The Japanese Rhinoceros Beetle is the largest and probably the best-known beetle in Japan, where children and amateur entomologists have been breeding the species for many years. *Trypoxylus dichotomus* is very popular and is sold as a pet in many stores and through vending machines. Males use their long, forked horn in battles with rival males over access to sapping wounds on trees that attract females. The most intense fighting occurs between males of equal size. Males are active all summer long, but the females soon die after mating and laying their eggs. The grubs feed on and develop in decaying wood. Gambling on the outcome of battles between males is a popular pastime.

## RELATED SPECIES

*Trypoxylus* is placed in the tribe Dynastini and is most closely related to *Xyloscaptes* from Vietnam and *Allomyrina* from Malaysia, Indonesia, and the Philippines. Several subspecies are recognized (e.g., *T. dichotomus dichotomus* from China and Korea, *T. d. septentrionalis* from Japan, and *T. d. tsunobosonis* from Taiwan), but the status of some of these taxa is doubtful.

**The Japanese Rhinoceros Beetle** males have a spectacular large frontal horn with four points apically as well as a prominent but relatively short, apically bifurcated pronotal horn. The legs are dark brown to black, and the elytra, which have no noticeable punctures, are typically reddish brown. Tiny sensory structures are found on the surface of the male's head horn; these are thought to enable the male to judge the strength of his opponent when they fight.

Actual size

| FAMILY | Scarabaeidae |
|---|---|
| SUBFAMILY | Dynastinae |
| DISTRIBUTION | Oriental: Indonesia (Java, Borneo, Lombok, Bali) |
| MACROHABITAT | Tropical forests |
| MICROHABITAT | Decaying wood, compost, manure |
| FEEDING HABITS | Adults feed on fruits, and sap; larvae feed on decaying wood |
| NOTE | A very common species, used for beetle fights in Asia |

ADULT LENGTH
1⅜–2¹⁵⁄₁₆ in
(35–75 mm)

*XYLOTRUPES GIDEON*
# SIAMESE
# RHINOCEROS BEETLE
(LINNAEUS, 1767)

ADULT MALE LENGTH
approximately 1⅝ in
(41 mm)

233

The nocturnal Siamese Rhinoceros Beetle is very common across its range and is attracted to light. The male has a pair of horns that it uses against rival males in battles for food or females. In captivity, the females lay 14 to 132 eggs and the adults live for up to four months. Species of the genus are used for beetle fights in Asia, mainly in Thailand, Burma, and Laos. Some species of *Xylotrupes* are pests of the Coconut Palm (*Cocos nucifera*) and other trees.

## RELATED SPECIES

To date, 22 subspecies of *Xylotrupes gideon* have been described, many of which are distinguished primarily by their geographic location. A thorough revision of the genus is needed, including molecular studies, to reveal valid species. Several subspecies of *X. gideon* have been described but the validity of many of these taxa is also in question.

Actual size

**The Siamese Rhinoceros Beetle** is a large black and reddish beetle with a shiny texture and a robust body. Males possess a large cephalic horn, bifurcated at the end, and another horn on the thorax. The size of the horns may be variable. Females have no horns or sometimes a small tubercle. The mandibles are well developed.

| FAMILY | Scarabaeidae |
|---|---|
| SUBFAMILY | Cetoniinae |
| DISTRIBUTION | Palearctic |
| MACROHABITAT | Open fields |
| MICROHABITAT | Adults are usually found on flowers of various plants, including roses |
| FEEDING HABITS | Adults feed on nectar and pollen; larvae feed on decaying matter |
| NOTE | Adults of this common species can sometimes damage the reproductive parts of the flowers of several ornamental plants and orchard trees |

ADULT LENGTH
⅝ –⅞ in
(16–23 mm)

*CETONIA AURATA*
# ROSE CHAFER
(LINNAEUS, 1761)

Adult Rose Chafers feed on nectar, pollen, and flower petals, especially those of rose during the warm, sunny days of spring and summer. They are clumsy fliers as they move about flowering plants in search of food. Wary, they are quick to take to the air when threatened. Once mated, the female lays eggs in decaying plant matter and dies soon after. The C-shaped larvae are detritivores and feed on decaying wood and accumulations of plant materials in manure and compost, and take about two years to reach adulthood.

## RELATED SPECIES

*Cetonia* contains many species in the Palearctic and Oriental realms, and is divided into several subgenera (e.g., *Cetonia, Eucetonia, Indocetonia*). *Cetonia aurata, C. aeratula, C. cypriaca, C. delagrangei,* and *C. carthami* are all included in the subgenus *Cetonia*. Of the six subspecies of *C. aurata* currently known, *C. a. aurata* is the most widely distributed.

Actual size

**The Rose Chafer** is a robust, large, metallic green flower beetle. The head, thorax, and abdomen are shiny metallic green. The elytra bear small white spots or a very tiny white line. A small number of individuals are completely metallic red. The ventral face of this species is often metallic green but sometimes violet, blue, or black and gray.

| FAMILY | Scarabaeidae |
|---|---|
| SUBFAMILY | Cetoniinae |
| DISTRIBUTION | Neotropical: Costa Rica, Guatemala, Honduras, Mexico, Nicaragua |
| MACROHABITAT | Tropical forests |
| MICROHABITAT | Adults are found on flowers and tree trunks; larvae probably live in dead wood |
| FEEDING HABITS | Adults feed on stems, leaves, and flowers; larvae presumably feed in dead wood |
| NOTE | An uncommon beetle with bright, iridescent markings, the larva of *Dialithus magnificus* is still unknown |

ADULT LENGTH
¼–⅞ in
(18.5–22 mm)

*DIALITHUS MAGNIFICUS*

# DIALITHUS MAGNIFICUS

PARRY, 1849

235

Although little is known about *Dialithus magnificus*, its habits are probably similar to those of other species in the tribe Trichiini. Adults feed on sugary secretions of stems, leaves, fruits, and flowers of different plants, while the larvae are likely to feed and develop in decaying hardwoods. As its name suggests, *D. magnificus* is a spectacularly marked insect with iridescent blue to green bands. In Mexico, these beetles have been encountered in wet forests during the month of May.

## RELATED SPECIES

The closest relative of *Dialithus* in the Neotropical Realm appears to be the *Giesbertiolus*, a genus that includes four species. *Dialithus*, which is distinguished by a deeper clypeal notch and large, symmetrical, iridescent markings, includes *D. magnificus* and *D. scintillans*, currently known from Panama. These two species are best distinguished by characters of the male genitalia.

Actual size

**Dialithus magnificus** is a reddish-brown to dark brown cetoniine with long tarsi (especially on the hind legs) and green or blue iridescent markings throughout. The bright markings appear on the head as two longitudinal lines, on the pronotum as two lines near the sides plus one line in the middle, on the elytra as symmetrical patterns, and on the pygidium as two broad spots. The ventral surface is also iridescent.

| FAMILY | Scarabaeidae |
|---|---|
| SUBFAMILY | Cetoniinae |
| DISTRIBUTION | Oriental and Palearctic: Himalayan foothills, Burma, Malaysia, Vietnam, mainland China, Hainan Island, Taiwan |
| MACROHABITAT | Forests |
| MICROHABITAT | Adults live on tree trunks; larvae live in burrows |
| FEEDING HABITS | Adults feed on sap flows and fruits; larvae feed on dead plant matter |
| NOTE | The species has a unique nesting behavior among flower chafers |

**ADULT MALE LENGTH**
1–1⁹⁄₁₆ in
24.8–39.5 mm

**ADULT FEMALE LENGTH**
⁷⁄₈–1 in
22.3–25.3 mm

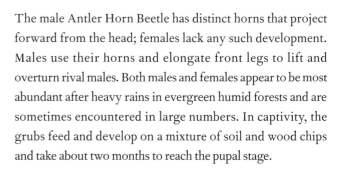

*DICRONOCEPHALUS WALLICHI*
# ANTLER HORN BEETLE
(HOPE, 1831)

The male Antler Horn Beetle has distinct horns that project forward from the head; females lack any such development. Males use their horns and elongate front legs to lift and overturn rival males. Both males and females appear to be most abundant after heavy rains in evergreen humid forests and are sometimes encountered in large numbers. In captivity, the grubs feed and develop on a mixture of soil and wood chips and take about two months to reach the pupal stage.

## RELATED SPECIES
*Dicronocephalus* is the only genus in the subtribe Dicronocephalina within the tribe Goliathini. It contains seven other species, including *D. bieti*, *D. dabryi*, and *D. adamsi* from China and surrounding areas, and *D. shimomurai*, *D. yui*, and *D. uenoi* from Taiwan. Three subspecies are generally recognized: *D. wallichi wallichi* from India, Vietnam, and Thailand; *D. w. bowringi* from China and *D. w. bourgoini* from Taiwan.

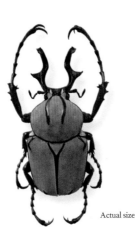

**The Antler Horn Beetle** is a medium to large cetoniine beetle with a flattened body. The males are larger and longer than the females and possess slender, upcurved, anteriorly projecting horns that originate at the anterior corners of their head. The color of the head, pronotum, and elytra varies from yellowish brown to dark brown. The pronotum bear two slightly curved, dark brown to black longitudinal lines. The legs have long tarsi and tarsal claws.

Actual size

| FAMILY | Scarabaeidae |
|---|---|
| SUBFAMILY | Cetoniinae |
| DISTRIBUTION | Afrotropical: endemic to Madagascar |
| MACROHABITAT | In forests, usually at 2,300–5,300-ft (700–1,600-m) altitude |
| MICROHABITAT | Feed on the inflorescence of palm trees |
| FEEDING HABITS | The adults feed on nectar and pollen |
| NOTE | One of the most beautiful flower beetles in the world and popular with collectors |

ADULT LENGTH
¾–1¼ in
(20–32 mm)

*EUCHROEA COELESTIS*
# EUCHROEA COELESTIS
BURMEISTER, 1842

237

The diurnal adults of *Euchroea coelestis* are active on warm and sunny days. Their C-shaped larvae feed and develop in various kinds of decaying plant matter. Adults of other species of *Euchroea* have been observed on the inflorescences of trees such as majesty palms (*Ravenea* spp.) and screw pines (*Pandanus* spp.), while others are recorded on *Dombeya* flowers. Species in this genus are uncommon and the widespread destruction of forests in Madagascar may negatively impact the populations of some species. Some of the more colorful species of *Euchorea* have been successfully reared in captivity.

RELATED SPECIES

The 20 species of *Euchroea* are all endemic to Madagascar. Most are easily distinguished by their distinctive and brilliant patterns. Several species have been featured over the years on postage stamps in Madagascar. The two recognized subspecies of *E. coelestis*, *E. c. coelestis* and *E. c. peyrierasi* are distinguished primarily in the amount of blue or green on their elytra.

Actual size

**Euchroea coelestis** is a distinctive, broadly oval flower beetle and arguably one of the most beautiful flower beetles in the world. The elytra are black with some irregular shiny green or blue spots that combine together to create somewhat regular transverse lines. The legs are black. The ventral face of the beetle is black, green, or blue.

| FAMILY | Scarabaeidae |
|---|---|
| SUBFAMILY | Cetoniinae |
| DISTRIBUTION | Nearctic and Neotropical: southern California to New Mexico and adjacent Mexico |
| MACROHABITAT | Deserts, thorn scrub |
| MICROHABITAT | Diurnal adults found on plants; larvae develop in woodrat nests |
| FEEDING HABITS | Adults visit flowers and eat mesquite beans |
| NOTE | *Euphoria fascifera* occurs in three different color forms |

ADULT LENGTH
7/16–9/16 in
(11–15 mm)

*EUPHORIA FASCIFERA*
# EUPHORIA FASCIFERA
(LECONTE, 1861)

This species consists of three different color forms: the shiny forms that occur in California to New Mexico and Chihuahua have four spots on the pronotum, while those on the Baja California peninsula usually have a single large mark; beetles from Sonora and Sinaloa also have a single large mark but are dull. Adults become active in late summer, especially right after thundershowers, and strongly resemble bees in flight. They visit flowers of various desert shrubs, presumably to drink nectar and sap and eat pollen, and are also attracted to fruit and molasses. The larvae are found in the nests of woodrats (*Neotoma* spp.).

## RELATED SPECIES

*Euphoria* comprises 59 species found in North, Central, and South America. They are characterized by having heads without horns, elytra each with two weakly raised ridges, straight sides on the scutellum, a long groove near the tip of the middle femur, and a pygidium with concentric or nearly concentric grooves. *Euphoria fascifera* is distinguished by its color patterns, concentric grooves on the pygidium, and the male genitalia.

Actual size

**Euphoria fascifera** is dull or shiny yellow to light orange. The elytra have three black bands that extend across the elytral suture. The underside and legs are shiny dark brown to black; the abdomen of the male is strongly concave when viewed from the side. Occasionally, individuals of two color forms are found at the same locality.

| FAMILY | Scarabaeidae |
|---|---|
| SUBFAMILY | Cetoniinae |
| DISTRIBUTION | Australian: eastern and southern coastal Australia (coasts of New South Wales, Queensland, South Australia, Victoria) |
| MACROHABITAT | Forest, bush |
| MICROHABITAT | Flowers |
| FEEDING HABITS | Adults feed on nectar and pollen; larvae feed in rotten wood |
| NOTE | This species is also known as the Horseshoe Beetle |

ADULT LENGTH
½–⅞ in
(12–22 mm)

*EUPOECILA AUSTRALASIAE*
# FIDDLER BEETLE
(DONOVAN, 1805)

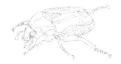

239

Adult Fiddler Beetles are so-named because of the distinctive lime-green to yellow violin pattern on their elytra, and are one of the most beautiful flower beetles found in Australia. The adults emerge from November through March, and frequent blossoms of flowering trees and shrubs, where they feed on nectar and pollen. Their preferred food plants include the Prickly Tea Tree (*Leptospermum juniperinum*), Austral Grass Tree (*Xanthorrhoea australis*), Snow in Summer (*Melaleuca linariifolia*) and various species of gum (*Eucalyptus*) and mallee (*Angophora*). The larvae develop in decaying wood.

## RELATED SPECIES

*Eupoecila australasiae* is a similar shape and color to *Chlorobapta frontalis*, another Australian species in the same tribe (Schizorhinini) that is thought to develop exclusively in decaying holes in the Yellow Gum (*Eucalyptus leucoxylon*). There are four additional species of *Eupoecila*: *E. evanescens*, *E. inscripta*, *E. miskini*, and *E. intricata*.

**The Fiddler Beetle** is a shiny beetle with contrasting colors and a rather flat dorsal surface. The elytra and pronotum have distinct yellow to green patches and lines. The resulting color pattern is reminiscent of the shape of a fiddle, hence the species' common name. The elytra are slightly concave behind the anterior corners in dorsal view. The legs are reddish brown.

Actual size

| FAMILY | Scarabaeidae |
|---|---|
| SUBFAMILY | Cetoniinae |
| DISTRIBUTION | Nearctic: eastern North America |
| MACROHABITAT | Deciduous hardwood forest and mixed woodland |
| MICROHABITAT | Adults found on flowering trees and shrubs |
| FEEDING HABITS | Adults feed on pollen |
| NOTE | Widespread, seldom encountered, with poorly known biology |

ADULT LENGTH
⁷⁄₁₆ in– ⅝ in
(11–16 mm)

240

*GNORIMELLA MACULOSA*
# GNORIMELLA MACULOSA
(KNOCH, 1801)

Actual size

Little is known about the biology of this conspicuous, yet seldom seen species. Adults are usually encountered in small numbers in wooded habitats on hot days in May and June. Strong fliers, they resemble bees as they buzz among the flowers. They prefer the blooms of dogwood (*Cornus* spp.) and viburnum (*Viburnum* spp.), but will also visit those of other deciduous hardwoods, including blackberry (*Rubus* spp.), hawthorn (*Crataegus* spp.), tuliptree (*Liriodendon* spp.), apple (*Malus* spp.), and maple (*Acer* spp.). The only published record of the larvae is that they develop in rotten trunks of Eastern Redbud (*Cercis canadensis*), although it is likely that they utilize other sources of decaying wood.

## RELATED SPECIES

The genus *Gnorimella* is restricted to the Nearctic Realm and includes only one species. Its nearest relative is the Palearctic *Gnorimus* that includes species in Europe and Asia. The two other closely related genera *Trichiotinus* and *Trigonopeltastes* also occurring in North America contain eight and two species in the region respectively. Species in those genera typically visit flowers in late spring and early summer.

**Gnorimella maculosa** is black with mottled brown and black elytra, with the rest of the body variably marked with cream or yellowish-orange spots. The elytra are bare, but the body and underside are clothed with long pale or yellowish setae. Males have strongly curved middle tibiae, while those of the female are straight. Northern populations are darker overall with fewer and smaller markings.

| | |
|---|---|
| FAMILY | Scarabaeidae |
| SUBFAMILY | Cetoniinae |
| DISTRIBUTION | Afrotropical: Sierra Leone, Guinea, Ghana, Ivory Coast, Nigeria, Burkina Faso |
| MACROHABITAT | Tropical forests |
| MICROHABITAT | Flowers and various trees |
| FEEDING HABITS | Feeds on tree sap and fruit |
| NOTE | Species in the genus are among the largest beetles in the world and appropriately known as Goliath beetles |

ADULT MALE LENGTH
1¹⁵⁄₁₆–4¼ in
(50–110 mm)

ADULT FEMALE LENGTH
1¹⁵⁄₁₆–3⅛ in
(50–80 mm)

*GOLIATHUS REGIUS*
# ROYAL GOLIATH BEETLE
KLUG, 1835

241

Males of *Goliathus regius* possess horns on their heads and use them to defend sap flows on host trees that are likely to attract females. They are relatively common throughout their range and have been reared successfully in captivity. Species of *Goliathus*, commonly known as Goliath beetles, are among the largest insects in the world, with some individuals reaching 6 in (150 mm) in length. Adults are often spotted early in the morning on *Vernonia* species or resting on the flower stems of other shrubs. Their larvae, which develop in decaying wood, are sometimes eaten and are considered a delicacy by people in Central Africa.

## RELATED SPECIES

Several subspecies in *Goliathus regius* have been described based on variations of their elytral color patterns, but these taxa are all considered invalid. Four equally spectacular species of *Goliathus* (*G. albosignatus*, *G. cacicus*, *G. goliatus*, and *G. orientalis*) also occur in Africa. They are distinguished by their overall size, the color patterns on their pronota and elytra, and their geographic distribution.

**The Royal Goliath Beetle** is a very large and strong insect. Adults have longitudinal black stripes on their pronotum. The elytra are black along the sides with a characteristic white pattern near the midline. The dark coloration of the body may vary from black to brownish black. The flight wings are fully developed and therefore adults can fly. Males have an anteriorly projecting Y-shaped extension on their head.

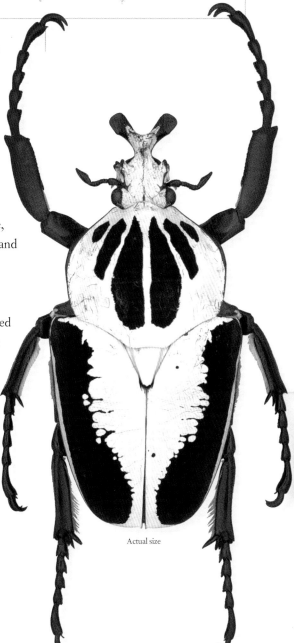

Actual size

| | |
|---|---|
| FAMILY | Scarabaeidae |
| SUBFAMILY | Cetoniinae |
| DISTRIBUTION | Neotropical: southern Mexico to central South America |
| MACROHABITAT | Tropical forests |
| MICROHABITAT | Adults on flowers; larvae live in rotting tree trunks |
| FEEDING HABITS | Adults feed on pollen, fruit, and tree sap; larvae feed on rotting wood |
| NOTE | This species is distinguished by the amazing patterns on its elytra |

ADULT LENGTH
¾–⅞ in
(19–23 mm)

242

*GYMNETIS STELLATA*

# GYMNETIS STELLATA

(LATREILLE, 1813)

*Gymnetis stellata* is a striking flower beetle with a distinctive pattern of yellow or orange markings. Adults are active mostly on hot, sunny days in deciduous or semi-deciduous forest habitats from sea level to 5,250 ft (1,600 m), and look and sound like bumblebees when in flight. Adults feed on the pollen and nectar of various flowers, fruits, and tree sap, and will accept various ripe fruits in captivity. This species appeared on a Guatemalan postage stamp in 1988.

## RELATED SPECIES

Some species of *Gymnetis* have showy patterns on the elytra that resemble those species in the closely related genus *Gymetosoma*. Species similar to *G. stellata* include *G. mediana* and *G. radiicollis* and each generally has distinctive color patterns. While the Gymnetini are mostly Neotropical flower beetles, some species are found in the southern United States. More than 29 species of *Gymnetis* have been described and the genus is currently being revised.

**Gymnetis stellata** is an attractive flower beetle with a showy pattern on the elytra. The head, pronotum, and elytra have irregular, dark black and yellow or orange stripes and/or lines radiating from the center. The legs are black. The lines may be lighter or darker on different specimens.

Actual size

| FAMILY | Scarabaeidae |
|---|---|
| SUBFAMILY | Cetoniinae |
| DISTRIBUTION | Neotropical: Honduras, Guatemala, Mexico, Belize, Nicaragua, Panama, Colombia, Ecuador |
| MACROHABITAT | Tropical areas |
| MICROHABITAT | Various trees |
| FEEDING HABITS | Adults feed on sap flows; larvae feed on decaying wood |
| NOTE | A common beetle with pronounced sexual dimorphism |

| ADULT MALE LENGTH |
|---|
| 1⁹⁄₁₆–2³⁄₁₆ in |
| (40–55 mm) |

| ADULT FEMALE LENGTH |
|---|
| 1⅜–1¾ in |
| (35–44 mm) |

*INCA CLATHRATA SOMMERI*

# INCA CLATHRATA SOMMERI
(WESTWOOD, 1845)

243

Male *Inca clathrata sommeri* tend to be larger than females and have two broad, obliquely projecting "horns" on their head. *Inca* species feed on sapping wounds of *Citrus*, Gliricidia (*Gliricidia sepium*), avocado (*Persea americana*), and holly (*Ilex arimensis*), usually early in the morning. They are also attracted to the rotting fruit of silk banana (*Musa sapentium*) and mangos. The larvae feed and develop in decaying wood.

### RELATED SPECIES

Most species of *Inca* are found in Brazil. Those species most closely related to *I. clathrata sommeri* are *I. beschkii*, *I. bonplandi*, *I. burmeisteri*, *I. irrorata*, and *I. pulverulenta*. The other subspecies of *I. clathrata* are *I. c. clathrata* in South America east of the Andes, and *I. c. quesneli* in Trinidad and the West Indies. The three subspecies are distinguished by the shape of the male's horns.

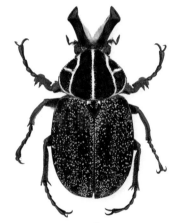

Actual size

**Inca clathrata sommeri** has a dark green to black head and pronotum, and brown or reddish elytra with small, pale spots. The pronotum has pale longitudinal and oblique lines. The clypeus of the male is divided into two rectangular-shaped horns, which are covered by dense yellowish setae on their inner side. The mandibles are not well developed. The front tibiae have broad, sharply pointed teeth on their outer edge.

| FAMILY | Scarabaeidae |
|---|---|
| SUBFAMILY | Cetoniinae |
| DISTRIBUTION | Afrotropical: from Ivory Coast to eastern Democratic Republic of the Congo |
| MACROHABITAT | Tropical forests |
| MICROHABITAT | Adults are found on various trees; larvae live in the soil |
| FEEDING HABITS | Adults have been seen feeding on tree sap and fruit; larvae feed on a range of substances |
| NOTE | Larvae of this species walk on their back |

**ADULT MALE LENGTH**
1⅜–2¹⁵⁄₁₆ in
(35–75 mm)

**ADULT FEMALE LENGTH**
1⁹⁄₁₆–1⅞ in
(40–47 mm)

*MECYNORHINA SAVAGEI*
# MECYNORHINA SAVAGEI
(HARRIS, 1844)

Actual size

The very attractive *Mecynorhina savagei* is an uncommon beetle ranging from Ivory Coast to the eastern Democratic Republic of the Congo. Little is known about its behavior or life history, but like most of the large flower beetles, the species feeds on tree sap and fruits. This species has been reared in captivity as a pet by beetle enthusiasts. The large C-shaped larvae of this species, like most other cetoniines, crawl on their backs and feed on various substances in natural and artificial conditions, including dead leaves, rotten wood, compost, dry dog food, cat food, and fish-food pellets, and are also cannibalistic. The life cycle lasts about one year.

RELATED SPECIES
According to a recent revision published in 2010, there are nine other species of *Mecynorhina* distributed in five subgenera. The species include *M. harrisi*, *M. kraatzi*, *M. mukengiana*, *M. oberthuri*, *M. passerinii*, *M. polyphemus*, *M. taverniersi*, *M. torquata* and *M. ugandaensis*. *Mecynorhina savagei* is distinguished by its color pattern and the shape of the horn in the males.

**Mecynorhina savagei** is a large, dark green-black flower beetle. On live specimens the black elytra sport bright yellow lines and spots; these turn duller orange in collection specimens. The border of the pronotum is also yellow. The male has a clypeal horn that is almost horizontal and that has divergent forks. The female is unarmed.

| FAMILY | Scarabaeidae |
|---|---|
| SUBFAMILY | Cetoniinae |
| DISTRIBUTION | Afrotropical: Cameroon, Central African Republic, Democratic Republic of the Congo, Gabon, Ghana, Ivory Coast |
| MACROHABITAT | Forests |
| MICROHABITAT | Flowers, various trees |
| FEEDING HABITS | Adults feed on tree sap, overripe fruit, and flowers; larvae feed on humus |
| NOTE | This large, common beetle has recently been used in experiments to develop radio-controlled "cyborg beetles" |

ADULT MALE LENGTH
1¹⁵⁄₁₆–3⁵⁄₁₆ in
(50–85 mm)

ADULT FEMALE LENGTH
1¾–2⅜ in
(45–60 mm)

*MECYNORHINA TORQUATA*
# MECYNORHINA TORQUATA
(DRURY, 1782)

245

*Mecynorhina torquata* is the second largest flower beetle in the world, second only to the Goliath beetle (*Goliathus*). Males have a prominent triangular horn on their head that is not present in females. The larvae, which have been successfully reared in captivity, can grow to 3⅛ in (80 mm) in length and weigh up to 1⅜ oz (40 g). Recent studies have successfully demonstrated that the flight of this beetle can be controlled remotely via an implantable radio-equipped miniature neural-stimulating system mounted on the pronotum; the system consists of neural stimulators (attached to the brain), muscular stimulators (attached to flight muscles), a radio transceiver-equipped microcontroller, and a microbattery.

## RELATED SPECIES

There are nine additional species of *Mecynorhina*, including *M. harrisi*, *M. kraatzi*, *M. mukengiana*, *M. oberthuri*, *M. passerinii*, *M. polyphemus*, *M. savagei*, *M. taverniersi*, and *M. ugandaensis*. Three subspecies of *M. torquata* are recognized: *M. t. torquata*, *M. t. immaculicollis*, and *M. t. poggei*, which are differentiated mostly by their color patterns.

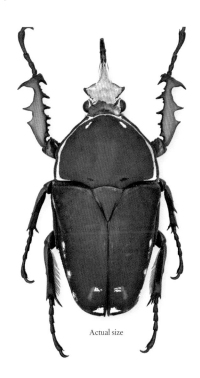

Actual size

**Mecynorhina torquata** is green with white lines, and sometimes white spots, on the elytra and pronotum. The head is mostly white with some black and green spots. The spectacular front legs are also green and have several sharply pointed spines, especially in males. The males have a strong, anteriorly projecting extension on the head, sometimes referred to as a clypeal sword.

| FAMILY | Scarabaeidae |
|---|---|
| SUBFAMILY | Cetoniinae |
| DISTRIBUTION | Afrotropical: from Senegal to the Democratic Republic of the Congo |
| MACROHABITAT | Forests, savanna |
| MICROHABITAT | Adults are found on flowers; larvae are found in the soil |
| FEEDING HABITS | Adults feed on nectar, pollen, and sap; larvae feed on decaying plant matter |
| NOTE | Because of its beautiful colors, this species is reared by beetle enthusiasts |

ADULT LENGTH
⅞–1¹⁄₁₆ in
(22–27 mm)

246

*STEPHANORRHINA GUTTATA*
# STEPHANORRHINA GUTTATA
(OLIVIER, 1789)

*Stephanorrhina guttata* is a common and very attractive African flower beetle, the males of which possess a cephalic armature. Adults feed at sap flows, as well as the nectar and pollen of *Acacia* and *Protea* flowers. There are three subspecies: *S. g. guttata* (the Democratic Republic of the Congo and the Central African Republic), *S. g. aschantica* (Togo), and *S. g. insularis* (Equatorial Guinea). This species is one of the easiest beetles to rear in captivity, and is commonly kept in terraria as a colorful pet.

## RELATED SPECIES

The genus *Aphelorhina* is closely related to *Stephanorrhina*, and is considered by some authors to be synonymous with the latter name having priority. The other known species of the genus *Stephanorrhina* are: *S. adelpha*, found in the Democratic Republic of the Congo, Uganda, Kenya, Sudan, and South Sudan; *S. julia* in Cameroon; *S. princeps* in Tanzania; and *S. simplex* in Zimbabwe and Mozambique.

**Stephanorrhina guttata** is a shiny green beetle with some spots on the ventral surface. The elytra are covered in round white dots, and the sutural band of the elytra is red. Some specimens are more reddish and some present a blue-red form as well. The male has two small clypeal horns.

Actual size

| FAMILY | Scarabaeidae |
|---|---|
| SUBFAMILY | Cetoniinae |
| DISTRIBUTION | Oriental: Borneo |
| MACROHABITAT | Tropical forest |
| MICROHABITAT | Flowers |
| FEEDING HABITS | Adults feed on sap and fruit, and probably also pollen; larvae feed on humus |
| NOTE | The impressive horns of males and other scarabs are rigid, hollow outgrowths of the body wall |

*THEODOSIA VIRIDIAURATA*
# THEODOSIA VIRIDIAURATA
(BATES, 1889)

ADULT MALE LENGTH
1–2³⁄₁₆ in
(25.4–55.5 mm)

ADULT FEMALE LENGTH
1–1¹⁄₃₂ in
(24.6–25.9 mm)

247

The male *Theodosia viridiaurata*, with its long and impressive horns, is one of the most attractive of all flower beetles. This species is restricted to eastern Borneo, where it is considered rare. These beetles are now being reared in laboratories for further study. Horned species in the superfamily Scarabaeoidea are mostly confined to the family Geotrupidae as well as the subfamilies Cetoniinae, Scarabaeinae, and Dynastinae within the Scarabaeidae.

## RELATED SPECIES
*Theodosia* is closely related to *Phaedimus* and both genera are placed in the tribe Phaedimini. Many of their species are native to Borneo and all are found in Southeast Asia. The other known species of *Theodosia* are *T. antoinei*, *T. chewi*, *T. howitti*, *T. katsurai*, *T. magnifica*, *T. maindroni*, *T. miyashitai*, *T. nobuyukii*, *T. perakensis*, *T. pilosipygidialis*, *T. rodorigezi*, and *T. telifer*.

**Theodosia viridiaurata** is a bright, metallic green flower beetle. The elytra are metallic green or metallic red with coppery reflections. The males have long, curved cephalic and thoracic horns that are metallic green and reddish pink in color. The ventral face of the male is also shiny metallic green. The horns vary in size, those in some individuals reaching a enormous lengths. The hornless females are brownish overall, although some specimens show a green thorax, and they have metallic green legs like the males.

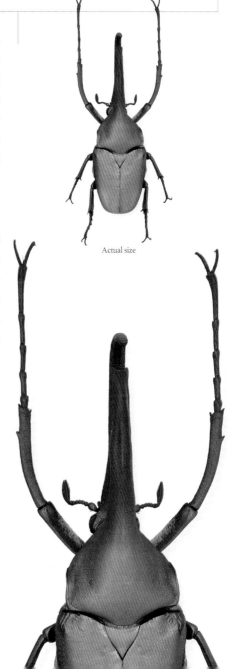

Actual size

| FAMILY | Scarabaeidae |
|---|---|
| SUBFAMILY | Cetoniinae |
| DISTRIBUTION | Palearctic |
| MACROHABITAT | Fields, open areas |
| MICROHABITAT | Adults are found on flowers; larvae are only found in tree stumps |
| FEEDING HABITS | Adults feed on flower petals; larvae feed on decaying tree stumps |
| NOTE | A common beetle whose coloration and pubescence give it the resemblance of a bee, hence its common name |

ADULT LENGTH
³⁄₈–¹⁄₂ in
(9–12 mm)

*TRICHIUS FASCIATUS*
# BEE BEETLE
(LINNAEUS, 1758)

The Bee Beetle is seen on warm, sunny summer days, mostly between the months of June and August. Adults are strong flyers and visit various flowers to feed on petals, especially in the genera *Thymus* and *Rosa*. Males and females mate on the flowers as they feed. The larvae feed and develop on decaying stumps, especially those of beech trees (*Fagus* spp.). The common name Bee Beetle was inspired by their bee-like behavior and appearance.

## RELATED SPECIES

*Trichius* is a genus placed in the tribe Trichiini and is absent from the New World. The species most closely related to *T. fasciatus* in Europe are *T. abdominalis*, *T. orientalis*, and *T. sexualis*. Characteristics to separate the species include differences in color patterns and structures on the legs.

**The Bee Beetle** is a small, stocky, very active beetle. The head and pronotum are black. The elytra are yellow to orange in color, and are crossed by six black bands of varying widths. This beetle has pronounced pubescence, especially on the head, pronotum and ventral surface. The large eyes are prominent.

Actual size

| FAMILY | Decliniidae |
| --- | --- |
| SUBFAMILY | |
| DISTRIBUTION | Palearctic: Russian Far East |
| MACROHABITAT | Mixed forest and forested wetlands |
| MICROHABITAT | Unknown |
| FEEDING HABITS | Adults feed on pollen; larval feeding habits unknown |
| NOTE | This phylogenetically important species is known only from females |

ADULT FEMALE LENGTH
$^3/_{16}$–$^1/_4$ in
(3.5–5.5 mm)

*DECLINIA RELICTA*
# DECLINIA RELICTA
NIKITSKY, LAWRENCE, KIREJTSHUK & GRACHEV, 1994

249

Actual size

This enigmatic species is known only from adult females mainly collected using flight-intercept traps in wet northern forests. Biological information is largely lacking, but dissection revealed the presence of pollen grains in the gut of one specimen, so pollenophagy is the presumed adult feeding habit. Larvae are unknown. The species is important phylogenetically because it appears to occupy a basal position relative to other members of the suborder Polyphaga. Analyses based on adult morphology place it in the superfamily Scirtoidea, which is considered by some experts to be the sister taxon of all other polyphagan beetles.

## RELATED SPECIES
Superficially, species of Decliniidae resemble members of the family Scirtidae, to which they apparently are related. Only two species are known in this family, *Declinia relicta* and *D. versicolor*, from Japan. *Declinia versicolor* can be diagnosed by its more rounded body shape as well as differences in its elytral striae and the shape of its antennal segments.

**Declinia relicta** is a rather generalized small brown beetle with a broad, somewhat flattened body, a large head, short antennae with weakly enlarged distal segments, and a short prothorax. The head is slightly declined, but differs from the heads of other possibly related species in that it rests on the prosternum instead of on the front coxae, which are widely separated.

| | |
|---|---|
| FAMILY | Eucinetidae |
| SUBFAMILY | |
| DISTRIBUTION | Australian: New Zealand |
| MACROHABITAT | Forests |
| MICROHABITAT | Moist organic litter |
| FEEDING HABITS | Mycophagous |
| NOTE | Members of this genus are among the most colorful of the entire family |

ADULT LENGTH
¹⁄₁₆ in
(1.5–1.9 mm)

250

# NOTEUCINETUS NUNNI
BULLIANS & LESCHEN, 2004

Actual size

These tiny beetles occur in southern beech (*Nothofagus* spp.) and broadleaf forests of New Zealand, where they have been collected using flight-intercept traps, insecticide fogging of foliage, and sifting moist organic forest litter. Direct collecting from fungus and slime mold on logs suggests feeding habits that are similar to other members of the family that have been associated with various fungus and slime-mold species. Eucinetids jump or flail about wildly through energetic thrusts of the hind legs when disturbed. This behavior, combined with the streamlined body shape, is an effective way of escaping into the substrate.

### RELATED SPECIES

Two species of this recently described genus occur in New Zealand. They differ in subtle details of coloration, and the anatomy of the legs and genitalia. A third species occurs in temperate forests of southern Chile. Temperate southern South America and New Zealand share many genera from taxa that show a Gondwanan distribution pattern—the ancient supercontinent Gondwana comprised what are now Africa, South America, Australia, Antarctica, and the Indian subcontinent.

**Noteucinetus nunni** adults are relatively spectacular among microcoleoptera occurring in forest-litter habitats. Most are uniformly brown, but this species is strikingly bicolored yellow and brown. The pattern is variable, particularly the extent of the dark markings of the elytra. The deflexed head and teardrop shape is typical for the family Eucinetidae, though this species is more broadly oval than most. The photograph above is of a recently emerged adult resulting in the color pattern being slightly paler.

| FAMILY | Clambidae |
|---|---|
| SUBFAMILY | Calyptomerinae |
| DISTRIBUTION | Palearctic: central and eastern Europe |
| MACROHABITAT | Forests |
| MICROHABITAT | Moist organic matter |
| FEEDING HABITS | Mycophagous |
| NOTE | Adults of these beetles conglobulate for protection |

ADULT LENGTH
¹⁄₁₆ in
(1.6–2 mm)

*CALYPTOMERUS ALPESTRIS*

# CALYPTOMERUS ALPESTRIS

REDTENBACHER, 1849

251

Actual size

This minute beetle has a patchy distribution in various forest types, particularly coniferous forests, across central Europe and the Caucasus border region of Europe and Asia. Larvae and adults are believed to feed on fungi, especially spores. Members of the family are capable of contracting themselves into an oblong ball for protection, a type of behavior described as conglobulation or enrollment. Profound reduction in size and orientation of the ventral parts of the thorax allow the lateral margins of the body to be pulled tightly against each other when the beetle contracts its muscles.

## RELATED SPECIES

Three species in this genus occur in Eurasia, with one additional species in northwestern North America. One species has been introduced to Australia and South Africa. Species differ externally in their body outlines, particularly details of the lateral margins of the heads, and in the morphology of the genitalia. The family as a whole is small, with about 150 species worldwide, most in the genus *Clambus*.

**Calyptomerus alpestris** is among the larger members of the family Clambidae, coming in at nearly ¹⁄₁₆ in (2 mm). The elytra are more elongate than in many other species. The reddish-brown color and short yellowish setae are typical of most members of the family. The eyes are not divided along the sides of the head as they are in *Clambus*.

| FAMILY | Clambidae |
|---|---|
| SUBFAMILY | Clambinae |
| DISTRIBUTION | Australian: New Zealand |
| MACROHABITAT | Forests |
| MICROHABITAT | Moist organic matter |
| FEEDING HABITS | Mycophagous |
| NOTE | The original description of this species was based on specimens collected at windows of the author's house |

ADULT LENGTH
¹⁄₃₂ in
(0.9–1 mm)

252

Actual size

### CLAMBUS DOMESTICUS
# CLAMBUS DOMESTICUS
(BROUN, 1886)

As is the case with other members of the family, adults of this species are capable of rolling into a nearly perfect ball (conglobulation) when disturbed. This species has a scattered distribution on both the North and South islands of New Zealand. It occurs in native southern beech (*Nothofagus* spp.) forests, but it has also been recorded from suburban Auckland from habitats such as compost heaps. Clambids are considered to be fungivorous and may specialize on fungal spores as their primary nutrient sources, but details of the biology of most species are undocumented.

### RELATED SPECIES

This genus includes five additional species from New Zealand. They differ in the shapes of external body parts, and degree of development of the eyes and the wings. The apparent closest relative of *Clambus domesticus*, *C. simsoni*, is an Australian and South African species that can be distinguished only by the shape of the male genitalia. The family includes about 150 species in five extant genera, of which *Clambus* is the most diverse.

**Clambus domesticus** is a minute beetle that appears to comprise three somewhat circular, convex parts corresponding to head, prothorax, and elytra. The latter are punctate near the apex on this species. When enrolled, these parts overlap, forming a ball. The predominant color of this and most other clambids is reddish brown, with varying coverings of short setae.

| FAMILY | Scirtidae |
|---|---|
| SUBFAMILY | Scirtinae |
| DISTRIBUTION | Australian: southern Australia, Tasmania |
| MACROHABITAT | Forests |
| MICROHABITAT | Moist forest litter, woody debris |
| FEEDING HABITS | Saprophagous |
| NOTE | The variable coloration of adults has led to a number of subspecies descriptions and synonymies |

ADULT LENGTH
⁵⁄₁₆–³⁄₈ in
(8–10 mm)

*MACROHELODES CRASSUS*
# MACROHELODES CRASSUS
BLACKBURN, 1892

253

*Macrohelodes crassus* occurs in upland and mountain habitats such as southern beech (*Nothofagus* spp.) forests in several southern Australian states and the island of Tasmania. Adults occur on foliage and have been collected on flowers and by fogging canopies. Larvae occur in wet microhabitats such as marshy areas, water-filled tree holes, and saturated coarse woody debris such as rotting logs. They are probably saprophagous or detritivorous on microbe- and fungus-infiltrated decomposing plant matter, but details of larval feeding habits are not well known.

## RELATED SPECIES

*Macrohelodes crassus* is one of 15 members of this Australian genus. Species are difficult to separate. The taxonomic history of *M. crassus* has been complicated through the proliferation of a number of named varieties. These were dealt with in a revision in 2010 and all are now synonymized under this single species name.

Actual size

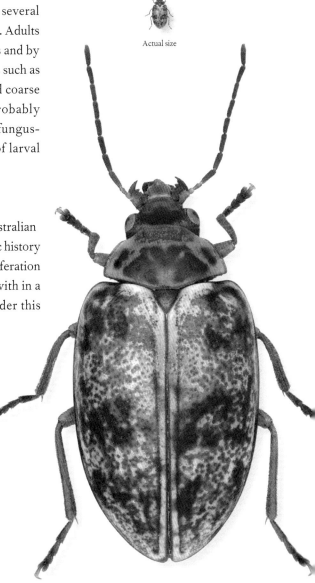

**Macrohelodes crassus** is a medium-size, variegated mahogany-brown and yellowish marsh beetle. The yellow and brown pattern is highly variable, with some specimens being nearly solid brown except for yellow transverse markings on the elytra, and others being strikingly bicolored or with the elytra largely yellow except for a brown humeral spot.

| FAMILY | Scirtidae |
|---|---|
| SUBFAMILY | Scirtinae |
| DISTRIBUTION | Nearctic: southeastern United States |
| MACROHABITAT | Wetlands |
| MICROHABITAT | Marshes, forested wetlands |
| FEEDING HABITS | Saprophagous |
| NOTE | The enlarged hind legs and overall appearance are similar to those of members of the unrelated family Chrysomelidae |

ADULT LENGTH
³⁄₁₆–¼ in
(4–6 mm)

254

*ORA TROBERTI*
# MARSH FLEA BEETLE
(GUÉRIN-MÉNEVILLE, 1861)

Actual size

These beetles are capable of jumping due to the massive musculature in the enlarged hind femora. They are relatively common in moist habitats from Florida to Texas in the United States, but may also occur some distance from aquatic larval habitats. Adults are frequently collected at lights, but can also be beaten from vegetation. The larvae feed on decomposing vegetable matter in shallow water of ponds, freshwater marshes, and margins of lakes and streams. Adults may graze on organic particles or fungi, but details of the life history are poorly known for this and other members of the family.

## RELATED SPECIES

Four species of *Ora* are known from the southeastern United States, and they can be difficult to distinguish due to variability of species and some unresolved taxonomic issues. Adults of this genus and the genus *Scirtes* possess enlarged hind femora. This character and the overall shape lead to an uncanny convergent resemblance to members of the chrysomelid beetle genus *Capraita*.

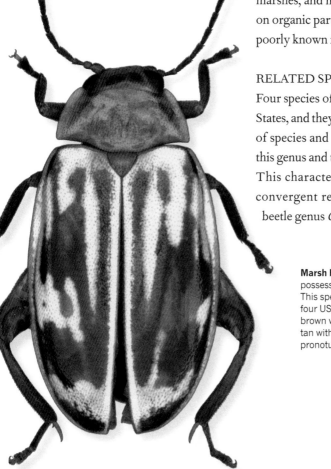

**Marsh Flea Beetle** adults are distinctive in possessing thick, heavily muscled hind femora. This species is the most variable among the four US species, with elytra ranging from dark brown with contrasting yellow markings to pale tan with slightly darker longitudinal stripes. The pronotum may be uniformly brown or bicolored.

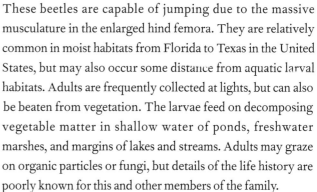

| FAMILY | Scirtidae |
|---|---|
| SUBFAMILY | Scirtinae |
| DISTRIBUTION | Australian: eastern Australia |
| MACROHABITAT | Forests |
| MICROHABITAT | Water-filled tree holes |
| FEEDING HABITS | Saprophagous |
| NOTE | This species is the dominant detritivore in tree holes in box forest in southeast Queensland |

ADULT LENGTH
⅛–³⁄₁₆ in
(3–3.5 mm)

*PRIONOCYPHON NIGER*

# PRIONOCYPHON NIGER

KITCHING & ALLSOPP, 1987

255

Actual size

This species was the subject of a detailed life-history study by the original describers. It is common in water-filled tree holes in southeast Queensland, Australia, and the authors were able to rear larvae to adulthood. Larvae possess complex brushes and spines on the internal surfaces of the mouthparts that function as combing and filtering devices for processing finely divided organic matter accumulated in the tree holes. Adults are terrestrial and occur on vegetation in the vicinity of larval habitats. Members of the genus *Prionocyphon* in other parts of the world also occur in flooded tree holes.

## RELATED SPECIES

At least 38 species of *Prionocyphon* are known from various parts of the world. *Prionocyphon niger* was the only described species in Australia until 2010, when an additional 16 species were described. Genitalia dissections are necessary to distinguish most species. Many more new species likely remain to be discovered and described worldwide.

**Prionocyphon niger** is a small, densely setose, oval marsh beetle. The dorsal surface is dark brown or black, with a slightly lighter brown head, and the setae are yellowish. The underside and antennae are yellowish brown. The legs are yellowish brown with dark margins. The head is strongly deflexed and the pronotum wider than long.

| FAMILY | Scirtidae |
|---|---|
| SUBFAMILY | Scirtinae |
| DISTRIBUTION | Australian: New Zealand |
| MACROHABITAT | Temperate forests |
| MICROHABITAT | Moist organic litter |
| FEEDING HABITS | Saprophagous |
| NOTE | One of many species collected by pioneering New Zealand coleopterist Captain Thomas Broun on the Coromandel Peninsula |

ADULT LENGTH
¼–⅜ in
(7–10 mm)

256

*VERONATUS LONGICORNIS*
# VERONATUS LONGICORNIS
SHARP, 1878

Actual size

The limited biological information about this and other members of the genus indicate occurrence in various moist south temperate forest habitats of New Zealand. The original description of this species is from Tairua, on the Coromandel Peninsula, which was a favorite collecting locality for Captain Thomas Broun, a prolific early collector and describer of the New Zealand beetle fauna. The only study of larvae or feeding habits of the genus is based on a related species, *Veronatus tricostellus*. Both larvae and adults of this species were found in smooth cells formed beneath rotting wood, and the larval gut contents consisted of dark organic matter.

## RELATED SPECIES

*Veronatus longicornis* is one of 19 species of the genus described from New Zealand, two by Sharp and 17 by Broun. Broun tended to describe more species than were actually represented in his collections, resulting in numerous synonymies when detailed studies are performed on his type material. Fortunately, most of his types are well preserved and located at the Natural History Museum, London.

**Veronatus longicornis** is a sparsely pubescent, medium-size beetle with a dark brown head and thorax, and lighter brown or tan elytra, antennae, and legs. The prominent, forward-projecting mandibles suggest a predatory lifestyle, but the adults are thought to feed on decaying organic matter. As with other members of the family, the larvae are unusual in possessing many-segmented antennae.

| FAMILY | Dascillidae |
|---|---|
| SUBFAMILY | Dascillinae |
| DISTRIBUTION | Nearctic: western United States (California) |
| MACROHABITAT | Chaparral and woodlands |
| MICROHABITAT | Adults occur on foliage; larvae live underground around trees and shrubs |
| FEEDING HABITS | Herbivorous on roots |
| NOTE | This is the largest species of Dascillidae in North America |

ADULT MALE LENGTH
⁵⁄₁₆–⁹⁄₁₆ in
(8–14 mm)

ADULT FEMALE LENGTH
³⁄₈–³⁄₄ in
(10–20 mm)

*DASCILLUS DAVIDSONI*
# DAVIDSON'S BEETLE
LECONTE, 1859

257

Actual size

Adults of these beetles occur on foliage of various trees and other vegetation during spring and can be collected by beating vegetation over a white sheet. Larval habits seem to be similar to those of some subterranean scarab beetles. The burrowing, grub-like larvae are root-feeders and have been recorded from sandy soil around fruit trees, *Acacia* species, and other native trees and shrubs. Detailed studies of mouthparts and head musculature of a related European species have been cited as evidence of a phylogenetic relationship with the cantharoid group of beetle families.

## RELATED SPECIES

Two species of *Dascillus* occur in California, with *D. plumbeus* differing mainly in being more evenly dark gray in color. At least 23 species of the genus occur in other parts of the world. A related European species is known as the Orchid Beetle (*D. cervinus*). Only one other genus, *Anorus*, in the family occurs in the western United States.

**Davidson's Beetle** is an oblong, parallel-sided beetle with prominent gray pubescence that is broken by transverse bands of dark integument on the elytra, giving the beetle a mottled appearance. The mandibles are distinctly projecting and strongly curved, and the antennae are slender and serrate.

| FAMILY | Dascillidae |
| --- | --- |
| SUBFAMILY | Karumiinae |
| DISTRIBUTION | Nearctic: California |
| MACROHABITAT | Open country and scrublands |
| MICROHABITAT | Males occur on foliage; females occur on the ground, and possibly live in burrows |
| FEEDING HABITS | Adults are probably non-feeding; larval feeding habits are unknown |
| NOTE | Larviform females wait on the ground while males fly in search of mating opportunities |

ADULT LENGTH
¼–⁷⁄₁₆ in
(7–11 mm)

258

*ANORUS PICEUS*
# ANORUS PICEUS
LECONTE, 1859

Actual size

The only biological information known about this species relates to the occurrence of winged males crawling on grasses, other vegetation, or flying to artificial lights at night during spring and early summer. Females are wingless, with a single published record of a specimen collected near a burrow along a wagon road in 1884. The only published description and illustration of the female is based on that single known specimen. Related members of the subfamily are believed to be associated with termite nests. Larvae probably feed on subterranean plant matter.

## RELATED SPECIES

The genus *Anorus* is the only North American representative of the subfamily Karumiinae, which typically occurs in arid and semiarid regions of the world, including South America, Africa, and Central Asia. Three species are described in the region. The males may be distinguished by differences in the shapes of the dorsal outlines of the pronota. Females are described only for *A. piceus*.

**Anorus piceus** is a fuzzy, elongate, parallel-sided brown beetle with elongate, slender antennae. The external integument is rather soft bodied. The eyes are large and bulging, and the mandibles are elongate, with prominent teeth. Females are similar, but have much shorter elytra and lack flight wings.

| FAMILY | Dascillidae |
|---|---|
| SUBFAMILY | Karumiinae |
| DISTRIBUTION | Palearctic: Iran |
| MACROHABITAT | Unknown |
| MICROHABITAT | Possibly associated with termites |
| FEEDING HABITS | Unknown |
| NOTE | Based on collecting data from a related species, this beetle may live in termite nests |

ADULT LENGTH
¼–⅜ in
(7–10 mm)

*KARUMIA STAPHYLINUS*

# KARUMIA STAPHYLINUS
(SEMENOV & MARTYNOV, 1925)

259

Actual size

Knowledge about this group of beetles has suffered from an extremely confusing taxonomic history, insufficient collecting, and lack of detailed notes associated with the few specimens available for study. Karumiines are part of an assemblage of taxa with soft bodies and a tendency for neotenic (persistent larva-like) development. Biological information about this species is inferred from collecting data on another, similar species, *Karumia estafilinoides*, published in a paper in 1964. That paper described a series of eight adult beetles included in a shipment of termites from Afghanistan. Presumably this species and others in the genus have some association with termites.

## RELATED SPECIES
The 11 species in this genus occur across the Middle East, especially Iran, and to Afghanistan, and differ from each other by the relative lengths of the elytra and characters of the head and genitalia. The species-level taxonomy in *Karumia* and the overall composition of the subfamily is unsettled due to the chaotic history of the descriptive literature, which includes the failure to interpret characters in any phylogenetically meaningful context.

*Karumia staphylinus* is an oddly proportioned beetle, with an oversize, elongate head, large, forward-projecting mandibles, and an anemic abdomen that is largely exposed dorsally by the unusually short elytra. The latter are reminiscent of typical members of the family Staphylinidae and this similarity is reflected in the species name.

| FAMILY | Rhipiceridae |
|---|---|
| SUBFAMILY | |
| DISTRIBUTION | Australian: southeastern Australia, Tasmania |
| MACROHABITAT | Forests |
| MICROHABITAT | Adults occur on foliage; larvae live underground |
| FEEDING HABITS | Adults are non-feeding; larvae are ectoparasites of cicada nymphs |
| NOTE | Adults of this species exhibit extreme sexual dimorphism in development of the antennae |

**ADULT MALE LENGTH**
½–¾ in
(13–19 mm)

**ADULT FEMALE LENGTH**
½–¹¹⁄₁₆ in
(12–17 mm)

*RHIPICERA FEMORATA*
# RHIPICERA FEMORATA
KIRBY, 1818

Larvae of rhipicerid beetles with known life histories are ectoparasites of immature cicadas. Presumably the larval feeding habits of this species are the same, and Australia has a high diversity of cicadas that could serve as hosts. *Rhipicera femorata* adults have been observed in grassy areas of *Eucalyptus* forests and in *Melaleuca* wetlands, and have been reported to emerge synchronously during August and September in New South Wales. They apparently do not feed and emerge only briefly to mate and lay eggs. Males outnumber females by as much as 8:1 in the few available observations of large numbers of individuals.

RELATED SPECIES

The genus *Rhipicera* is divided among three subgenera, with species occurring in Australia, New Caledonia, and South America. A modern taxonomic revision of this genus is needed to determine the actual number of species and their relationships. *Rhipicera femorata* is a distinctive species that is unlikely to be confused with any other Australian beetle.

**Rhipicera femorata** is a large black beetle boldly marked with white polka dots across the elytra and scattered white speckling on the pronotum. In the males, most segments of the antennae are profoundly expanded to a feather-like appearance, presumably in order to detect female pheromones. In the females, the antennae are only slightly expanded.

Actual size

| FAMILY | Rhipiceridae |
| --- | --- |
| SUBFAMILY | |
| DISTRIBUTION | Nearctic: Ontario to Florida, west to Colorado and Texas |
| MACROHABITAT | Eastern deciduous forest |
| MICROHABITAT | Adults live on tree trunks or undergrowth; larvae are subterranean |
| FEEDING HABITS | Adults do not feed; larvae are external parasitoids of cicadas |
| NOTE | The New World species of *Sandalus* are in need of revision |

ADULT LENGTH
$^{11}/_{16}$–1 in
(17–25 mm)

*SANDALUS NIGER*
# CEDAR BEETLE
KNOCH, 1801

261

Adults of *Sandalus niger* emerge from their burrows on
mornings in late summer and crawl up the trunks of hardwoods
to copulate, sometimes forming conspicuous mating
aggregations. The female lays large numbers of eggs
in the holes and cracks of bark. After hatching, the
highly active larva, or triungulin, enters the soil to
search of young cicada nymphs to parasitize. The rest of
the species' hypermetamorphic life cycle is known only from
a single pupa that was associated with a shed exoskeleton of a
sedentary grub-like larva found inside the hollowed-out
exoskeleton of a cicada nymph.

### RELATED SPECIES

The 41 species of *Sandalus* are distributed in the Afrotropical,
Nearctic, Neotropical, Palearctic, and Oriental realms. The
Nearctic fauna consists of five described species, three of
which (*S. niger*, *S. petrophya*, and *S. porosus*) occur in eastern
North America. *Sandalus niger* is distinguished from these
species in that the weakly keeled sides of the prothorax
uniformly diverge behind the head and the base of the elytra is
distinctly broader than the prothorax.

Actual size

**The Cedar Beetle** is coarsely punctate, and either uniformly
black or black with reddish-brown elytra. The head has
prominent hypognathous mandibles, bulging eyes, and bright
reddish-brown antennae that are flabellate (male) or serrate
(female). The cone-shaped prothorax becomes uniformly wider
behind the head, and the sides are weakly keeled, especially
at the basal third. At their base the elytra are wider than the
pronotum, and each has ridges that are only faintly indicated
or absent.

| FAMILY | Schizopodidae |
|---|---|
| SUBFAMILY | Schizopodinae |
| DISTRIBUTION | Nearctic: Arizona, California, Nevada, and northern Baja California |
| MACROHABITAT | Mojave, Colorado, and Sonoran Deserts |
| MICROHABITAT | Adults found on flowers or resting on other desert plants |
| FEEDING HABITS | Adults eat pollen |
| NOTE | The larvae are unknown |

ADULT LENGTH
⅜–¹¹⁄₁₆ in
(10–18 mm)

*SCHIZOPUS LAETUS*
# SCHIZOPUS LAETUS
LECONTE, 1858

*Schizopus laetus* is distributed in desert regions of North America and is often abundant in spring. Adults feed on the pollen and flowers of various desert plants during the day, especially the Hairy Desert Sunflower (*Geraea canescens*) in late March through early June. The oval eggs are pale yellowish white, but the larvae remain unknown. The only other species in the genus, *S. sallaei*, is active in May and June and is restricted to valley grassland habitats in the Great Central Valley of California. *Schizopus sallaei sallaei* inhabits the eastern slopes, while *S. s. nigricans* occurs along the western slopes.

## RELATED SPECIES

The Schizopodidae, or false jewel beetles, is a small family of stout and convex beetles that resemble jewel beetles (Buprestidae), but are distinguished by the deeply lobed fourth tarsomere on each leg. *Schizopus* contains two species that can be distinguished from other schizopodids by having 11 antennomeres. *Schizopus laetus* is partially or entirely iridescent green or blue in color, while *S. sallaei* is yellowish brown to black.

**Schizopus laetus** is stout, convex, with coarse surface sculpturing, becoming wrinkled on the elytra, and with slender, hairlike setae on the upper and lower surfaces of the body. Antennomeres 5–11 are strongly saw-toothed, or serrate. The females are entirely iridescent green or blue, while the males are similar in color, but have orange to orange-red elytra, tibiae, and tarsi.

Actual size

| FAMILY | Buprestidae |
|---|---|
| SUBFAMILY | Julodinae |
| DISTRIBUTION | Palearctic: Iran and Pakistan |
| MACROHABITAT | Baluchistan desert |
| MICROHABITAT | As for other species in this group, adults occur on leaves and flowers, and larvae are thought to feed underground |
| FEEDING HABITS | The feedings habits of the adults and the larvae are unknown |
| NOTE | This is one of the largest jewel beetles in the world |

ADULT LENGTH
2³⁄₁₆–2¾ in
(55–70 mm)

*AAATA FINCHI*
# AAATA FINCHI
(WATERHOUSE, 1884)

*Aaata finchi* has been qualified as the most "primitive" species within the subfamily Julodinae based on the venation pattern of its flight wings and the well-developed apical spine on the elytra. Waterhouse based his original description of the species on a single beetle found at Bir, a small village on the Makran Coast of Beluchistan, which was presented to the London Zoological Society by Mr. B. F. Finch of the Persian Gulf Telegraph Service in Karachi.

RELATED SPECIES

The subfamily Julodinae consists of five genera: *Aaata* (Palearctic), *Amblysterna* (Afrotropical), *Julodella* and *Julodis* (Afrotropical, Palearctic), *Neojulodis* (Afrotropical), and *Sternocera* (Afrotropical, Oriental). *Aaata* consists of a single species, *A. finchi*, which is distinguished from other julodines by its large size, and by its raised and wrinkled pronotal and elytral surfaces.

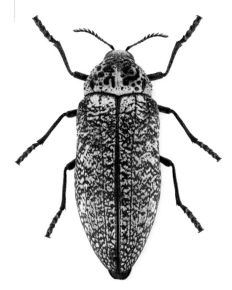

Actual size

**Aaata finchi** is very large, robust, and uniformly brown, except for the raised areas, and densely clothed in sandy-white or yellowish pubescence that forms no particular pattern. The surface of the convex pronotum is irregularly sculpted with raised spots and marks. The elytra have straight raised ridges separated by raised and irregular wrinkles.

| FAMILY | Buprestidae |
|---|---|
| SUBFAMILY | Julodinae |
| DISTRIBUTION | Afrotropical: Botswana, Mozambique, South Africa, Tanzania, Zambia |
| MACROHABITAT | Moist savanna |
| MICROHABITAT | Adults are found on trees; larvae live in soil |
| FEEDING HABITS | Adults feed on pollen; larvae probably feed on roots |
| NOTE | The species includes various color forms |

ADULT LENGTH
⁷⁄₁₆–⁹⁄₁₆ in
(11.2–14.5 mm)

264

*AMBLYSTERNA NATALENSIS*
# AMBLYSTERNA NATALENSIS
(FÅHRAEUS, 1851)

While most larvae in the family Buprestidae are wood-borers, species in some groups such as the subfamily Julodinae have larvae that are free-living, soil-dwelling, external root-feeders. Species in this subfamily often have depressions on their body that are filled with dense setae, as is the case for this species. *Amblysterna natalensis* is a very attractive jewel beetle that occurs in southeastern Africa. The adults of this species, which typically are present between January and April, visit Sicklebush (*Dichrostachys cinerea*) and *Acacia* trees.

RELATED SPECIES

*Amblysterna* belongs to the subfamily Julodinae, which also contains the genera *Sternocera*, *Julodis*, *Aaata*, *Neojulodis*, and *Julodella*. Two species are known in the genus *Amblysterna*: the smaller *A. natalensis* has elytra with continuous stripes from the base to the apex; and the larger *A. johnstoni* (⁷⁄₈–1⅛ in/ 21–28 mm) has spots that are rather evenly distributed over its elytra. *Amblysterna johnstoni* is found in Ethiopia, Kenya, the Seychelles, Somalia, and Tanzania.

**Amblysterna natalensis** is a torpedo-shaped, usually brilliant metallic green jewel beetle. The head is large and the pronotum has short pubescence in some areas, as well as a longitudinal groove along the midline. The elytra, which vary in color from green to blue, purple, and black, bear tomentose stripes that are continuous from the base to the apex.

Actual size

| | |
|---|---|
| FAMILY | Buprestidae |
| SUBFAMILY | Julodinae |
| DISTRIBUTION | Afrotropical: South Africa (Western Cape) |
| MACROHABITAT | Savanna, arid shrub biomes |
| MICROHABITAT | Flowers of various shrubs and trees; larvae live in the soil |
| FEEDING HABITS | Adults feed on pollen and foliage; larvae feed on roots |
| NOTE | A jewel beetle with amazing wax-coated setae |

ADULT LENGTH
⅞–1⁷⁄₁₆ in
(22.9–37.4 mm)

*JULODIS CIRROSA HIRTIVENTRIS*
# BRUSH JEWEL BEETLE
LAPORTE, 1835

265

The common Brush Jewel Beetle, found in South Africa's Western Cape province, is a diurnal species active mostly in hot, sunny conditions. The adults feed on pollen and foliage of various flowers of shrubs and trees, including *Lebeckia*, *Acacia*, and *Dichrostachys* species. The larvae are free-living root-feeders. Adults probably live up to several months, with the males dying before the females. During the reproduction season, females attract males with pheromones. In the laboratory, a female laid 46 white-greenish oval eggs measuring ³⁄₁₆ in (4.5–5 mm). When the beetles are disturbed, they fly off strongly or can also drop to the ground.

## RELATED SPECIES

The genus *Julodis* contains more than 77 species ranging from Africa to central Asia, with some species also found in Europe. Many species are extremely variable and polymorphism occurs. Like *J. cirrosa hirtiventris*, *J. fascicularis*, *J. hirsuta*, *J. sulcicollis*, and *J. viridipes* also have yellow-orange wax-coated setae on their body. The other known subspecies of *J. cirrosa* are *J. c. cirrosa* and *J. c. mellyi*, which are also found in South Africa.

**The Brush Jewel Beetle** is a fairly large buprestid beetle with a hard black body that has a metallic blue sheen. The dorsal surface of the head, thorax, and abdomen has many yellow wax-coated setae. Some specimens have darker yellow, yellow-orange, or white setae.

Actual size

| FAMILY | Buprestidae |
|---|---|
| SUBFAMILY | Julodinae |
| DISTRIBUTION | Oriental: China, India, Burma, Sri Lanka, Vietnam and Thailand |
| MACROHABITAT | Tropical forests |
| MICROHABITAT | Tree trunks and leaves |
| FEEDING HABITS | Adults feed on leaves and larvae presumably feed on roots in the soil |
| NOTE | This beetle has been described under fifteen other names over time |

ADULT LENGTH
1¼–2⅜ in
(31–60 mm)

266

*STERNOCERA CHRYSIS*
# STERNOCERA CHRYSIS
(FABRICIUS, 1775)

*Sternocera chrysis* is a very attractive jewel beetle, with both sexes similar in appearance. It feeds on the leaves of various trees and can be found on tree trunks, its preferred host plants being *Albizia* species and *Pithecellobium* species. Many species of *Sternocera* have a short lifespan of two to three weeks. The known subspecies of *S. chrysis* are *S. c. chrysis* which is more broadly distributed, and *S. c. nitidicollis* in India. In Asia—especially Thailand—the elytra of *Sternocera* are used to create brooches and necklaces, as well as to decorate clothing.

RELATED SPECIES
The subfamily Julodinae contains more than 150 species. The genus *Sternocera* includes approximately 25 species. Most of the species in this genus (e.g., *S. castanea* and *S. discedens*) are found in Africa. Differences in color patterns on the pronotum, elytra, and legs of these species are useful to distinguish many of them.

**Sternocera chrysis** is a large oval jewel beetle with a metallic green head and shiny brown elytra. Some rare specimens are darker brown or nearly black. The pronotum is strongly punctured and usually green, but may be blue, brown, or black in some specimens. The legs, tibiae, and tarsi are brown, sometimes with a green sheen. The antennae are brown or black. The venter is brown, sometimes with a metallic sheen.

Actual size

| FAMILY | Buprestidae |
|---|---|
| SUBFAMILY | Polycestinae |
| DISTRIBUTION | Nearctic and Neotropical: United States (southern California, Texas, Nevada, Arizona, New Mexico, Utah), Mexico (Baja California) |
| MACROHABITAT | Desert areas |
| MICROHABITAT | Adults occur on various flowers; larvae develop in several desert thorn trees |
| FEEDING HABITS | Adults feed on pollen and foliage; larvae are wood-borers |
| NOTE | The beetle has characteristic spots on its elytra |

ADULT LENGTH
⅛–½ in
(10–12 mm)

*ACMAEODERA GIBBULA*

# ACMAEODERA GIBBULA

LECONTE, 1858

267

*Acmaeodera gibbula* is an attractive small wood-boring beetle that can be found in desert regions of the southwestern United States and parts of Mexico. The adults feed on the pollen and foliage of a variety of plants, including the leaves of Desert Twinbugs (*Dicoria canescens*), while larvae bore into dead or injured branches, stems, and roots of trees and shrubs. The larvae are known to develop in a variety of thorn trees, including mesquite (*Prosopis* spp.), Catclaw (*Acacia greggii*), and willow (*Salix* spp.).

### RELATED SPECIES

*Acmaeodera* is a large genus (more than 500 species) that occurs in Africa and the Palearctic and Oriental realms as well as North and Central America. This genus is typically subdivided in nine subgenera. During flight, the adults of *Acmaeodera* fly with their elytra fused over the body rather than held out as in other buprestids. Because of their coloration patterns, several species of *Acmaeodera* are considered mimics of hymenopterans (bees and wasps).

Actual size

**Acmaeodera gibbula** is a small jewel beetle with a convex head that is flattened above the clypeus and has large oblong eyes. This species is black with bright yellowish-white and red spots on the elongate elytra. The legs, head, prothorax, and ventral surface of the body are covered with fine white setae.

| FAMILY | Buprestidae |
|---|---|
| SUBFAMILY | Polycestinae |
| DISTRIBUTION | Australian: Western Australia |
| MACROHABITAT | Temperate forest |
| MICROHABITAT | Flowers of various plants, mainly *Daviesia* and *Hakea* spp. |
| FEEDING HABITS | Adults feed on pollen and petals; larvae feed on wood |
| NOTE | An unusual "clicking" jewel beetle |

**ADULT LENGTH**
⁵⁄₁₆–³⁄₈ in
(8–9 mm)

*ASTRAEUS FRATERCULUS*
# ASTRAEUS FRATERCULUS
VAN DE POLL, 1889

Actual size

*Astraeus fraterculus* is found along the southern coast of Western Australia, from Perth to Albany. This species has been recorded feeding during the daytime on the leaves of *Daviesia divaricata* and the Kerosene Bush (*Hakea trifurcata*). The larvae are wood-borers. It seems that this species is not easy to find and therefore uncommon in collections. Like all other *Astraeus* species, it flies well. One of the remarkable features about the beetle is that it is able to "drop" to avoid predators and as a second measure of escape will "click" like a click beetle (Elateridae) and jump more than 20 in (50 cm).

RELATED SPECIES

The genus *Astraeus*, which is restricted to Australia and New Caledonia, is the sole representative of the tribe Astraeini. More than 50 species of *Astraeus* have been described to date, including *A. aberrans*, *A. carnabyi*, and *A. dedariensis*, also from Western Australia; *A. adamsi* from Queensland; and *A. caledonicus* from New Caledonia. Illustrations of some larvae of the genus have been published.

**Astraeus fraterculus** is a small but very attractive beetle. The head, antennae, and pronotum are coppery blue or black. The dorsal surface is usually bright metallic blue or black. Each elytron is marked with a pair of yellow-orange patches, and the apex of each ends in a pair of sharply pointed spines. Metallic reflections are also present on the ventral surface.

| FAMILY | Buprestidae |
| --- | --- |
| SUBFAMILY | Polycestinae |
| DISTRIBUTION | Neotropical: central Chile |
| MACROHABITAT | Sclerophyll forests along coastal and Andean foothills |
| MICROHABITAT | Adults are found on branches of conifers and hardwoods; larvae develop within dead branches of various conifers and hardwoods |
| FEEDING HABITS | Adults eat leaves and pollen; larvae feed on dead wood |
| NOTE | This handsome species occurs only in central Chile |

ADULT LENGTH
⁹/₁₆–1 in
(15–25 mm)

*POLYCESTA COSTATA COSTATA*

# POLYCESTA COSTATA COSTATA

(SOLIER, 1849)

269

*Polycesta costata costata* is restricted to central Chile in the Valparaíso, Metropolitan, and O'Higgins regions at altitudes of 2,600–5,900 feet (800–1,800 m). The larvae of this attractive jewel beetle have a flattened white body; they feed and develop in the dead branches of various coniferous and hardwood trees and shrubs, including Peumo (*Cryptocarya alba*), Litre (*Lithraea caustic*), and Chilean Romerillo (*Baccharis linearis*). The adults are often found resting on the branches of Soapbark (*Quillaja saponaria*).

Actual size

## RELATED SPECIES

*Polycesta* includes 55 species in the Afrotropical, Australian, Nearctic, and Neotropical realms. Of the 39 Neotropical species, only *P. costata* and *P. tamarugalis* occur in Chile. *Polycesta tamarugalis* is black, while *P. costata* is blue or green with small spots. *Polycesta costata paulseni* is larger and dark blue or green with orange or yellowish spots, while *P. c. costata* is a lighter blue-green, often with red spots.

**Polycesta costata costata** is a shiny metallic blue-green color and coarsely punctured. The distinctly ridged elytra are occasionally unmarked, but typically have small red spots that are not quite symmetrical in either size or location. The last abdominal segment of the male is narrowed at the tip, while that of the female is broadly rounded with a small notch in the middle.

| FAMILY | Buprestidae |
|---|---|
| SUBFAMILY | Polycestinae |
| DISTRIBUTION | Nearctic and Neotropical: southwestern United States and northern Mexico |
| MACROHABITAT | Deserts, semiarid highlands |
| MICROHABITAT | Adults and larvae on select agaves |
| FEEDING HABITS | Adults eat leaf edges; larvae feed in stalks and leaf bases |
| NOTE | Possibly hybridizes with *Thrincopyge ambiens* |

ADULT LENGTH
⅝ –⅞ in
(16–23 mm)

270

# THRINCOPYGE ALACRIS
LECONTE, 1858

Adult *Thrincopyge alacris* are active primarily during the summer months and chew notches along the margins of young sotol (*Dasylirion* spp.) and beargrass (*Nolina* spp.) leaves as they feed. The larvae mine and develop in dead flower stalks and the leaf bases of Green (*Dasylirion leiophyllum*) and Common (*D. wheeleri*) Sotol. In some individuals, the surface sculpturing and markings of the pronotum and elytra, and male genitalic characters suggest that *T. alacris* and *T. ambiens* may hybridize in the northern portions of their broadly overlapping ranges.

### RELATED SPECIES

*Thrincopyge* includes three species from the southwestern United States and northern Mexico. Distinctive features include an elongate, parallel-sided body that is flat on top and convex underneath, with plates at the hind-leg bases, which are distinctly expanded at the midline, and a deep groove around the apical half of the last visible abdominal segment. *Thrincopyge alacris* is the only species with yellow markings that are not confined to the pronotal and elytral margins.

**Thrincopyge alacris** ranges from blue with yellow pronotal margins and no elytral spots to having mostly yellow elytra. It is typically blue or green with the pronotum yellow on the sides and front, with a single median spot at the base. The elytra have two pairs of yellow bars before the middle and elongated spots on the tips.

Actual size

| FAMILY | Buprestidae |
|---|---|
| SUBFAMILY | Galbellinae |
| DISTRIBUTION | Palearctic: Cyprus, Israel, Jordan, Lebanon, Syria, Turkey |
| MACROHABITAT | Savanna |
| MICROHABITAT | Adults are found on shrubs or trees; larvae are found in twigs |
| FEEDING HABITS | Adults probably feed on pollen; larvae feed on host tissue |
| NOTE | The two known larvae described in *Galbella* to date, including that of *G. felix*, share unique structures in their mouthparts that are not found in any other buprestid larvae |

ADULT LENGTH
³⁄₁₆ in
(3.9–5.4 mm)

*GALBELLA FELIX*
# GALBELLA FELIX
(MARSEUL, 1866)

271

Actual size

Adults in the subfamily Galbellinae have deep grooves on the ventral surface of the prothorax for the reception of the antennae in repose. The femora of these beetles are also flattened and expanded to hide the tibiae and tarsi when the legs are folded under the body. Adults of *Galbella felix* are typically active from April through July. The larval stage of this species was described in 2001 from three individuals found in twigs of Barberry (*Phillyrea latifolia*). The larval stage of only one other species in this diverse genus, *G. acacia*, was found in twigs of *Acacia raddiana*.

### RELATED SPECIES

The genus *Galbella* contains more than 80 species and is present in the Afrotropical, Oriental, and Palearctic zones. Many species are known only by the single type specimens, so are usually rare in collections. Species within the three recognized subgenera (*Galbella*, *Progalbella*, and *Xenogalbella*) are distinguished by their color, ranging from all black to having blue, green, purple, or bronze reflections, and male genitalia.

**Galbella felix** is a small, bright blue buprestid beetle with an oval body. The head has large, coarse and sparse punctures. The pronotum is wider than it is long and has coarse punctures also. The eyes are large and convex. The abdominal ventrite 2 has a curved patch of setae near the middle.

| FAMILY | Buprestidae |
|---|---|
| SUBFAMILY | Chrysochroinae |
| DISTRIBUTION | Afrotropical: South Africa, Namibia, Botswana, Mozambique, Zimbabwe, Tanzania, Kenya, Ethiopia |
| MACROHABITAT | Savanna |
| MICROHABITAT | Adults are found on flowers |
| FEEDING HABITS | Adult feed on pollen of flowers of Sicklebush (*Dichrostachys cinerea*), Mopane (*Colophospermum mopane*), *Aloe littoralis*, and various species of *Grewia*; larvae are probably wood-borers |
| NOTE | This species mimics blister beetles from the family Meloidae |

ADULT LENGTH
$^{11}/_{16}$–1⅛ in
(17.5–28 mm)

*AGELIA PETELII*
# MELOID-MIMICKING JEWEL BEETLE
(GORY, 1840)

The Meloid-mimicking Jewel Beetle is often found in association with blister beetles in the genus *Mylabris*. The blister beetles are well known for their toxicity and therefore *Agelia petelii* is thought to obtain protection from predators from this association. Adults are active during the day and have been found on a variety of arid vegetation; they are known to feed on the Sicklebush (*Dichrostachys cinerea*), Mopane (*Colophospermum mopane*), *Aloe littoralis*, and various species of *Grewia*.

## RELATED SPECIES

The genus *Agelia* contains nine species: *A. burmensis*, *A. chalybea*, *A. fasciata*, *A. limbata*, *A. pectinicornis*, and *A. theryi*, which occur in the Oriental Realm; and *A. lordi* and *A. obtusicollis*, in Africa. The African species of *Agelia* seem to be more active during the rainy season and have aposematic (warning) coloration on their elytra that resembles color patterns of blister beetles in the genus *Mylabris*.

**The Meloid-mimicking Jewel Beetle** has an elongate body that is flattened above. The head is black and the pronotum sometimes has lateral metallic spots ranging from greenish gold to red. The elytra are black with four large yellow patches, the basal patches reaching or partially extending to the elytral base. The pronotum is broader than long, devoid of setae, and heavily punctured. Individuals of this species show a large range of variation in the coloration pattern of their elytra.

Actual size

| FAMILY | Buprestidae |
|---|---|
| SUBFAMILY | Chrysochroinae |
| DISTRIBUTION | Palearctic: Europe and Asia |
| MACROHABITAT | Forest and agricultural areas, especially fruit orchards |
| MICROHABITAT | Adults are found on foliage |
| FEEDING HABITS | Adults feed on foliage; larvae feed on the roots of their hosts |
| NOTE | Adults of this species have very heavily sclerotized (i.e., hard) elytra |

ADULT LENGTH
1¹/₃₂–1⅝ in
(26–41 mm)

*CAPNODIS MILIARIS MILIARIS*

# CAPNODIS MILIARIS MILIARIS

(KLUG, 1829)

273

*Capnodis miliaris miliaris* adults are mostly active from 10am to 6pm in tree tops, where they feed on foliage, including leaves of *Populus* species. Before and after feeding they are often seen on tree trunks. The white larvae are long, reaching 2⅝ in (65 mm) when fully grown, and develop in the roots of various trees. Many species of *Capnodis* are pests of fruit trees. Examples include *C. tenebrionis* and *C. carbonaria*, which attack stonefruit trees in the Mediterranean region, and *C. cariosa*, which impacts pistachio plantations in eastern Asia.

## RELATED SPECIES

*Capnodis miliaris metallica* is the other known subspecies and can be found in Afghanistan, Tajikistan, and Uzbekistan. The genus forms a homogenous group across the Palearctic and the Oriental realms, and to date 18 species (including one fossil) have been described. A 2010 study showed that *Capnodis* females are more abundant than males in nature, outnumbering them nine to one.

**Capnodis miliaris miliaris** has a large, solid, robust black or bronze body and large head. The pronotum is always inflated. Members of the genus *Capnodis* have the hardest integuments among buprestids. The solid, robust elytra have white patches and, along with the pronotum, are covered with white spots. The males are generally smaller than the females.

Actual size

| FAMILY | Buprestidae |
|---|---|
| SUBFAMILY | Chrysochroinae |
| DISTRIBUTION | Oriental: Malaysia, Thailand, India, Indonesia, Philippines |
| MACROHABITAT | Tropical forests |
| MICROHABITAT | Found on tree trunks |
| FEEDING HABITS | Adults feed on leaves; larvae feed in wood |
| NOTE | A common large beetle |

**ADULT LENGTH**
1⁷⁄₁₆–2³⁄₈ in
(37 mm–60 mm)

274

# CATOXANTHA OPULENTA

(GORY, 1832)

The adults of *Catoxantha opulenta* are commonly found on the leaves of the Giant Crape-myrtle (*Lagerstroemia speciosa*) and the Bastard Cedar (*Chukrasia tabularis*). The eggs are laid on the surface of bark, either on standing or fallen trees. The emerging larvae feed on bark for a short time and then burrow into the wood for further development. Larval galleries in infested wood are usually ³⁄₁₆–³⁄₈ in (5–10 mm) wide. The adults fly with their body held in a vertical position, as is typical of some adult Lucanidae. The well-known British naturalist and explorer Alfred Russel Wallace collected these impressive beetles in Borneo during his travels in the Malay Archipelago in the mid-1850s.

Actual size

## RELATED SPECIES

The other known species of *Catoxantha* are *C. bonvouloirii* from Sikkim and Assam in India, Bhutan, Burma, Thailand, Laos, and Vietnam; *C. eburnea* from the Andaman Islands; *C. pierrei* from Thailand; *C. purpurea* from the Philippines; and *C. nagaii* from Malaysia. The subspecies *C. opulenta opulenta* occurs in Thailand and Indonesia (Sumatra), while *C. o. borneensis* is found in northern Borneo and Palawan (the Philippines).

**Catoxantha opulenta** is a large, bright metallic green jewel beetle with large, prominent eyes. The pronotum is noticeably narrower than the elytra and usually has some coppery green color. The flattened antennae reach the base of the pronotum. The elytra sometimes have bluish reflections and there is a conspicuous transverse yellowish band on each elytron. The ventral surface of the body is yellow.

| FAMILY | Buprestidae |
|---|---|
| SUBFAMILY | Chrysochroinae |
| DISTRIBUTION | Oriental and Palearctic: India (Chota Nagpur Plateau, Sikkim), Indonesia (Java), Laos, Thailand, Vietnam, China (Fujian, Guangdong, Guangxi, Yunnan), Nepal |
| MACROHABITAT | Forests |
| MICROHABITAT | Adults occur on leaves and tree trunks of *Sterculia pexa* |
| FEEDING HABITS | Feeds on the leaves of trees |
| NOTE | A very common beetle |

ADULT LENGTH
1½–2 in
(38–52 mm)

*CHRYSOCHROA BUQUETI*

# RED SPECKLED JEWEL BEETLE

(GORY, 1833)

275

*Chrysochroa* is a diverse genus of jewel beetles that includes more than 50 described species. The Red Speckled Jewel Beetle is a very attractive and common jewel beetle. There is no pronounced sexual dimorphism, although considerable variation occurs in color and color patterns between individuals. This species can be found on tree trunks of *Sterculia pexa* and appears to be more abundant in June. This jewel beetle feeds on the leaves of its host. The larvae probably bore into the same species of tree but this requires confirmation.

## RELATED SPECIES

Most of the species in *Chrysochroa* are from the Oriental, Palearctic, and Australian realms, but one is from Africa. *Chrysochroa castelnaudi* closely resembles *C. buqueti* but is entirely blue with a broad yellow band in the middle of the elytra. The following subspecies are currently recognized: *C. b. rugicollis*, *C. b. suturalis*, *C. b. trimaculata*, and *C. b. kerremansi*.

**The Red Speckled Jewel Beetle** is a fairly large, flattened beetle with bright metallic patches. The head is blue and the pronotum is typically blue with red sides. Some subspecies have a bright metallic red head and pronotum. The elytra are yellowish with two blue spots near the middle that vary considerably in size and the apex is also blue. The ventral surface is spectacular with its various metallic colors.

Actual size

| FAMILY | Buprestidae |
|---|---|
| SUBFAMILY | Chrysochroinae |
| DISTRIBUTION | Neotropical: Mexico to Argentina, also Antilles |
| MACROHABITAT | Forests |
| MICROHABITAT | Adults on tree trunks of ceiba trees and relatives |
| FEEDING HABITS | Larvae tunnel in trunks and roots |
| NOTE | Adults and larvae sometimes eaten; durable elytra used as jewelry |

ADULT LENGTH
1¹⁵⁄₁₆–2³⁄₈ in
(50–60 mm)

*EUCHROMA GIGANTEA*
# GIANT METALLIC CEIBA BORER
(LINNAEUS, 1758)

The Giant Metallic Ceiba Borer is one of the largest jewel beetles in the world. On sunny days they are found flying around or walking on tree trunks of living Giant Ceiba or Kapok trees (*Ceiba pentandra*), and its relatives, as well as *Araucaria* and *Ficus*. Males apparently attract females by clicking their elytra. Females lay small batches of eggs in the crevices of bark. As the larvae grow, they mine down into the roots to complete their development and are sometimes a pest of managed trees. Mature larvae are quite large and may reach 4¾–6 in (120–150 mm) in length.

RELATED SPECIES
*Euchroma gigantea* is the only species in the genus and is readily distinguished from all other genera and species of Buprestidae in the region and the world by its large size, color, and surface sculpturing.

Actual size

**The Giant Metallic Ceiba Borer** is a large, elongate, and metallic beetle. The metallic green pronotum bears a black spot on each side, while the bright golden-green elytra are wrinkled and have reddish or purplish reflections. Freshly emerged adults are covered with or will soon develop a one-time layer of waxy yellow powder that is easily worn off.

| FAMILY | Buprestidae |
|---|---|
| SUBFAMILY | Chrysochroinae |
| DISTRIBUTION | Afrotropical: Democratic Republic of Congo, Mozambique, Senegal, South Africa, Togo |
| MACROHABITAT | Savanna |
| MICROHABITAT | Adults are found on Anacardiaceae trees; larvae are unknown |
| FEEDING HABITS | Adults feed on pollen; larvae probably feed on the same host tree as the adults |
| NOTE | A stunning, iridescent green jewel beetle |

ADULT LENGTH
¾–1 in
(20–25 mm)

*EVIDES PUBIVENTRIS*

# EMERALD JEWEL BEETLE

(LAPORTE & GORY, 1835)

277

The Emerald Jewel Beetle is one of the most attractive jewel beetles of Africa. This species lives in South Africa and can be found in savanna supporting Anacardiaceae trees. Adults have been found during the daytime on the upper branches of their host trees, Marula (*Sclerocarya birrea*) and Live-long (*Lannaea discolor*). When disturbed, some drop from the foliage while others quickly take flight. Adults are typically encountered from November through March.

RELATED SPECIES

The genus *Evides* contains around 11 species (including two from the Oriental Realm), all of which have been found on Marula and Live-long trees. Three species occur in South Africa, all of them similar in size, color, and distribution. However, a 2007 study showed that *E. pubiventris* is the largest of the three species, *E. interstitialis* is intermediate in size, and *E. gambiensis* is the smallest.

Actual size

**The Emerald Jewel Beetle** has a large torpedo-shaped body, handsomely colored iridescent metallic green. The head is metallic copper and green in color, the abdomen shows a rainbow coloration, and the legs are metallic green. The ventral face has short white setae.

| FAMILY | Buprestidae |
|---|---|
| SUBFAMILY | Chrysochroinae |
| DISTRIBUTION | Nearctic and Neotropical: southwestern United States and northern Mexico |
| MACROHABITAT | Sonoran and Chihuahuan deserts |
| MICROHABITAT | Adults typically found on twigs of acacias |
| FEEDING HABITS | Adults found on various species of *Acacia* |
| NOTE | Freshly emerged adults are covered in a yellow waxy bloom |

ADULT LENGTH
$^{11}/_{16}$–1$^{3}/_{16}$ in
(18–30 mm)

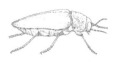

278

*GYASCUTUS CAELATUS*
# GYASCUTUS CAELATUS
(LECONTE, 1858)

Actual size

**Gyascutus caelatus** is a robust and convex beetle with a steel-blue body irregularly sculpted with raised bumps and patches of brassy punctures, and coated with a bright yellow, waxy bloom. The inner margins of the eyes converge on top of the head, and the antennae are notched at their tips. The male's antennae are distinctly bicolored.

The adults are found on hot summer days resting on the branches of several species of *Acacia*, especially Whitethorn (*A. constricta*) and Viscid (*A. neovernicosa*) acacias. When disturbed, they take to the air with a loud buzz. Other plants often visited by the adults include Catclaw Acacia (*A. greggii*) and Mesquite (*Prosopis juliflora*). The larvae and larval host plant are unknown. The beetle occurs in the states of Arizona, New Mexico, and Texas in the United States, and in Chihuahua, Coahuila, Durango, and Sonora in Mexico.

RELATED SPECIES

The genus *Gyascutus* consists of 12 species distributed mostly in the southwest United States. *Gyascutus caelatus* is the only species in the subgenus *Stictocera*, and in light the interrupted raised line along the posterior margin of the pronotum and the bicolorous male antennae are unlikely to be confused with those of any other species in the genus.

| FAMILY | Buprestidae |
|---|---|
| SUBFAMILY | Chrysochroinae |
| DISTRIBUTION | Afrotropical: Madagascar |
| MACROHABITAT | Presumably forest |
| MICROHABITAT | Unknown |
| FEEDING HABITS | Unknown |
| NOTE | A buprestid beetle with a false pair of eyes on its pronotum |

ADULT LENGTH
1¼–1¹³⁄₁₆ in
(32–46 mm)

*MADECASSIA ROTHSCHILDI*
# ROTHSCHILD'S
# JEWEL BEETLE
(GAHAN, 1893)

279

Rothschild's Jewel Beetle is a large beetle that seems to be rather common even with the disappearance of much of the native forest in Madagascar. Many individuals of this prized jewel beetle are available from commercial insect dealers for sale to collectors. The biology and ecology of this characteristic species remain unknown. No host plants have been recorded for the adults or the larval stages. Adults of *Madecassia* have eyespots on their pronotum, giving an overall appearance similar to the thorax of click beetles in the genus *Alaus*. Although this remains to be tested, the two large eyespots are presumed to have evolved as antipredator adaptations.

Actual size

## RELATED SPECIES
The genus *Madecassia* belongs to the subtribe Chalcophorina within the tribe Chrysochroini. Only three species are included in the genus, all of which are endemic to Madagascar. The other known species are *M. ophthalmica*, found in the southern part of Madagascar; and *M. fairmairei*, for which we know little about the distribution. Individuals of *M. ophthalmica* are generally shorter (1¹⁄₁₆–1½ in, or 27–38 mm) than *M. rothschildi* and have a distinctive coloration and punctation pattern on the elytra.

**Rothschild's Jewel Beetle** is a large buprestid beetle, although its size does not match that of the largest buprestids such as *Megaloxantha* and *Euchroma*. The dorsal surface of the head and pronotum is primarily metallic green, although the elytra are reddish bronze. The head is fairly large with two large reddish-brown eyes. The legs are metallic green with turquoise reflections. The broad pronotum has two isolated black spots surrounded by a distinctive yellow-lime area, giving the appearance of a pair of eyes.

| FAMILY | Buprestidae |
|---|---|
| SUBFAMILY | Chrysochroinae |
| DISTRIBUTION | Oriental: Indonesia (Java, Bali) |
| MACROHABITAT | Tropical forests |
| MICROHABITAT | Tree trunks |
| FEEDING HABITS | Feeds on the leaves of trees |
| NOTE | This species is among the largest in the family Buprestidae |

ADULT LENGTH
2⅜–2⅞ in
(60–71.5 mm)

*MEGALOXANTHA BICOLOR*
# MEGALOXANTHA BICOLOR
(FABRICIUS, 1775)

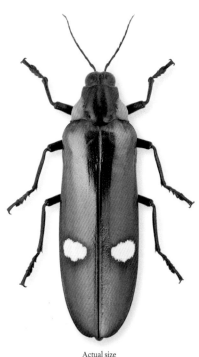

Actual size

*Megaloxantha* includes some of the largest jewel beetles in the world, the size of which can reach 2¹⁵⁄₁₆ in (75 mm) in *M. gigantea* from India, Burma, Bhutan, and Nepal. The taxonomy of *M. bicolor* and related species has changed considerably over time and is still unsettled. A number of coleopterists have included six subspecies, some of which (such as *M. gigantea*) are currently recognized as distinct, valid species. Following this taxonomic framework, three subspecies remain: *M. b. bicolor* and *M. b. ohtanii* from Java; and *M. b. ryoi* from Bali.

RELATED SPECIES

The genus *Megaloxantha* contains nearly 20 species that occur in the Oriental Realm, with the greatest diversity in Malaysia, Indonesia, and the Philippines. It belongs to the tribe Chrysochroini along with *Chrysochroa*, *Demochroa*, *Catoxantha*, and related genera. Color patterns as well as characteristics of the pronotum are typically used to separate the species in this genus, which include *M. concolor* from Malaysia and *M. netscheri* from Indonesia.

**Megaloxantha bicolor** is a very large, elongate, more or less parallel-sided jewel beetle with a primarily metallic green surface except for a pair of white to yellow oval patches on the elytra and the yellowish-orange posterior corners of the pronotum. The large eyes are reddish brown. The pronotum is distinctly narrower anteriorly than at the base. The ventral surface is mostly yellowish or brownish ivory.

| FAMILY | Buprestidae |
|---|---|
| SUBFAMILY | Chrysochroinae |
| DISTRIBUTION | Afrotropical: Madagascar |
| MACROHABITAT | Forests |
| MICROHABITAT | Adults are often found on the bark of trees |
| FEEDING HABITS | Little is known about the feeding habits of this species |
| NOTE | An unusual jewel beetle with a broadly oval body |

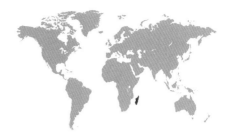

ADULT LENGTH
⅞–1⅛ in
(22–28 mm)

*POLYBOTHRIS AURIVENTRIS*
# POLYBOTHRIS AURIVENTRIS
(LAPORTE & GORY, 1837)

281

*Polybothris auriventris* is endemic to Madagascar. It is distributed in the eastern part of the country and occurs in forests of the Sandrangato area of Antsianaka. The biology of this and related species is not well known. The larva of the related *P. angulosa*, which has a strongly dilated prothorax and a ten-segmented abdomen, was described in 2001 from individuals found in its host in the genus *Ziziphus*. Like many jewel beetles, *Polybothris* species have cryptic coloration and adults are very difficult to notice on the bark of trees.

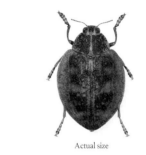

Actual size

## RELATED SPECIES
The genus *Polybothris* contains over 200 species in several subgenera that are endemic to Madagascar and the Comoros. *Polybothris* species share highly metallic iridescent exoskeletons and many are similar in shape and color. While most species in Buprestidae are more colorful dorsally, this is not the case in *Polybothris*. Remarkably, species in this genus typically have cryptic coloration dorsally but have brilliant metallic patterns ventrally, which is useful to separate the species.

**Polybothris auriventris** is a rather large, flattened, broadly rounded jewel beetle. The head, pronotum, and elytra are usually brown with a metallic brownish to green tinge, and the elytra have a small number of circular depressions, these sometimes appearing creamy white or yellow. The pronotum is distinctly broader posteriorly and the elytra are widest near the middle. The ventral surface is bright metallic, usually with green or copper reflections.

| FAMILY | Buprestidae |
|---|---|
| SUBFAMILY | Chrysochroinae |
| DISTRIBUTION | Neotropical: Argentina (Misiones), Paraguay, Brazil (Minas Gerais) |
| MACROHABITAT | Some adults have been found in plantations |
| MICROHABITAT | Adult are found on leaves |
| FEEDING HABITS | Adults have been found feeding on foliage of *Eucalyptus* trees; larvae are probably wood-borers |
| NOTE | This species has sometimes been considered a pest of forest plantations |

ADULT LENGTH
1–1⁷⁄₁₆ in
(25–37 mm)

*PSILOPTERA ATTENUATA*

# PSILOPTERA ATTENUATA
(FABRICIUS, 1793)

Actual size

**Psiloptera attenuata** is an elongate jewel beetle with a rather slender body that is tapered toward the apex of the elytra. The head, pronotum, and elytra are mostly metallic green. The antennae are short. The legs are also metallic green with golden to reddish reflection. Some individuals have a yellowish line along the border of the elytra, while coppery red reflections are typically noticeable along the midline of the elytra.

*Psiloptera attenuata* can be encountered in Argentina, Paraguay, and Brazil. Adults have been found feeding on the foliage of imported *Eucalyptus* trees in plantations; otherwise little is known about the biology or ecology of this species. The larvae are probably wood borers. Adults seem to be more active during sunny days. Some species currently placed in this genus, e.g., *P. acroptera* and *P. transversovittata*, have interestingly been described as Eocene fossils originating from Germany.

## RELATED SPECIES

The genus *Psiloptera* contains more than 30 extant species, all of which occur in the Neotropical Realm and have a moderately slender body. The majority of species occur in Brazil. Species in this genus normally have metallic green coloration with brownish, reddish, and golden reflections. Features of the pronotum and elytra are generally used to separate the species.

| FAMILY | Buprestidae |
|---|---|
| SUBFAMILY | Buprestinae |
| DISTRIBUTION | Palearctic: North Africa, central and southern Europe |
| MACROHABITAT | Forests, especially montane Oak (*Quercus* spp.) forests |
| MICROHABITAT | Adults found on branches and trunks of Oak trees |
| FEEDING HABITS | Adults feed on pollen |
| NOTE | This beetle has many color forms |

ADULT LENGTH
⁵⁄₁₆–⁹⁄₁₆ in
(7.5–15 mm)

*ANTHAXIA HUNGARICA*

# ANTHAXIA HUNGARICA

(SCOPOLI, 1772)

283

*Anthaxia hungarica* is a very well-known, common buprestid beetle of central and southern Europe and North Africa, and is the largest species in the genus. The adults are mostly active on sunny days in spring and summer. They feed on the pollen of various flowers (Asteraceae, Poaceae), while the larvae perforate branches and trunks of oaks (*Quercus ilex*, *Q. pubescens*, and *Q. coccifera*). This species is most often seen in oak forests in mountainous and hilly regions. The life cycle takes two to three years to complete.

### RELATED SPECIES

The subspecies *Anthaxia hungarica sitta* has a smaller geographic distribution than the nominate subspecies, being limited to the Caucasus, and has green elytra. *A. h. hungarica* has blue-green to violet elytra and is found in central and southern Europe. The genus *Anthaxia* contains more than 717 described species from the Afrotropical, Nearctic, Neotropical, Oriental, and Palearctic realms. Tarsal claw structure and coloration are useful characters for the identification of many species. The hosts of *Anthaxia* are trees, herbaceous plants, and shrubs.

Actual size

**Anthaxia hungarica** is brilliant metallic green, or sometimes golden, blue, or violet. The body is oblong and the elytra are elongate. The vertical head has two very big eyes. The males have longer antennae and expanded femora, and the ventral face is metallic green. In the female, the forehead, flanks of the pronotum, and ventral face are all purple. Some adults have a white pubescence.

| FAMILY | Buprestidae |
|---|---|
| SUBFAMILY | Buprestinae |
| DISTRIBUTION | Nearctic: western North America |
| MACROHABITAT | Montane coniferous forests |
| MICROHABITAT | On conifer trunks and needles; also in lumber |
| FEEDING HABITS | Adults eat needles; the larvae consume wood |
| NOTE | A larva emerged from a staircase as an adult after 51 years |

ADULT LENGTH
½–⅞ in
(12–22 mm)

*BUPRESTIS AURULENTA*
# GOLDEN BUPRESTID BEETLE
LINNAEUS, 1767

The Golden Buprestid Beetle is one of the most spectacular beetles in North America. Soon after mating and feeding on conifer needles, females select exposed wood on dead and dying conifer trees, especially in and around fire or lightning scars and wounds on Ponderosa Pine (*Pinus ponderosa*) and Douglas-fir (*Pseudotsuga menziesii*), or unseasoned lumber, and lay their eggs singly or in flat masses. Under natural conditions, the larvae take two to four years to develop, but they may take more than 50 years to reach adulthood under exceptional conditions. Emerging adults sometimes damage building timbers and wooden storage tanks constructed from infested lumber.

## RELATED SPECIES

This species is morphologically similar to *Buprestis sulcicollis* from North American, *B. striata* and *B. splendens* from Europe, and *B. niponica* from Japan. It is distinguished from these species by the smooth, not punctate, elytral ridges, and brilliant metallic green or blue-green color with coppery elytral margins.

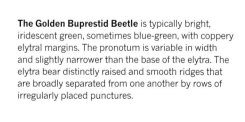

**The Golden Buprestid Beetle** is typically bright, iridescent green, sometimes blue-green, with coppery elytral margins. The pronotum is variable in width and slightly narrower than the base of the elytra. The elytra bear distinctly raised and smooth ridges that are broadly separated from one another by rows of irregularly placed punctures.

Actual size

| | |
|---|---|
| FAMILY | Buprestidae |
| SUBFAMILY | Buprestinae |
| DISTRIBUTION | Australian: Australia (Queensland, New South Wales) |
| MACROHABITAT | Rainforests |
| MICROHABITAT | Various flowers |
| FEEDING HABITS | Adults feed on nectar and pollen of flowers |
| NOTE | Arguably the most beautiful of all Australian jewel beetles, and highly prized among beetle collectors |

ADULT LENGTH
1½–1¹³⁄₁₆ in
(38–46 mm)

*CALODEMA REGALIS*

# REGAL JEWEL BEETLE

(GORY & LAPORTE, 1838)

285

*Calodema regalis* is an extremely large jewel beetle. Adults of this species fly high in the forest canopy, occurring at heights of 65 ft (20 m) or more. They feed on flowers of *Eucalyptus gummifera*, *E. hemiphloia*, *Bauhinia monandra*, *Melicope micrococca*, and *Cuttsia viburnea*, and live in rainforests from northern Queensland to northern New South Wales. The species appears to be less common than in the past due to pressures on its habitat from logging. The egg, larva, and pupa have not yet been described, but the larva is probably a borer of trees.

## RELATED SPECIES

The genus *Calodema* and the related *Metaxymorpha* share many characteristics, including the elongated mouthparts adapted to feeding on nectar. *Calodema* contains 15 species: *C. bifasciata*, *C. blairi*, *C. hanloni*, *C. hudsoni*, *C. longitarsis*, *C. mariettae*, *C. plebeia*, *C. regalis*, *C. ribbei*, *C. rubrimarginata*, *C. ryoi*, *C. sainvali*, *C. suhandae*, *C. vicksoni*, and *C. wallacei*.

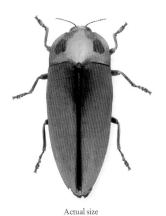

Actual size

**The Regal Jewel Beetle** is a large, elongate jewel beetle. The pronotum is elongate and metallic green, with one red spot on each side. The elytra are yellow-brown with a narrow, longitudinal black band along the midline. The antennae are metallic green. The ventral surface is metallic green with yellow spots. The mouthparts are elongate to allow the beetle to feed on nectar.

| FAMILY | Buprestidae |
|---|---|
| SUBFAMILY | Buprestinae |
| DISTRIBUTION | Nearctic: USA (southern Virginia to Florida and west to Texas) |
| MACROHABITAT | Found near conifers and deciduous trees |
| MICROHABITAT | Dead or dying tree trunks |
| FEEDING HABITS | Adults are found on their hosts; larvae develop in both hardwood and conifers |
| NOTE | A unique *Chrysobothris* with five golden-green spots on each elytron |

ADULT LENGTH
¼–⅜ in
(7–9.5 mm)

286

CHRYSOBOTHRIS CHRYSOELA
# CHRYSOBOTHRIS CHRYSOELA
(ILLIGER, 1800)

Actual size

*Chrysobothris chrysoela* is a beautiful jewel beetle of the southern United States with noticeable iridescent spots. Larvae of the species develop in both hardwoods and conifers—the wide variety of hosts include Buttonwood (*Conocarpus erectus*), Bald Cypress (*Taxodium distichum*), Persimmon (*Diospyros virginiana*), oaks (*Quercus* spp.), ash trees (*Fraxinus* spp.), plane trees (*Platanus* spp.), fig trees (*Ficus* spp.), pine trees (*Pinus* spp.), and the Yellow Plum (*Ximenia americana*). Adults are mostly active during sunny days. The North American relative *C. azurea* is also striking with its dorsal surface ranging from bright violet-blue to purple.

## RELATED SPECIES

The genus *Chrysobothris* is cosmopolitan and includes more than 650 described species, with more than 130 of them known to occur in North America. Many of the species are similar in appearance but *C. chrysoela* can be distinguished by the color pattern of the elytra. Larvae of *Chrysobothris* have been found in both coniferous and deciduous trees, and some attack shrubs and herbaceous plants.

**Chrysobothris chrysoela** is a broadly elongate, moderately convex jewel beetle with a flat bronzy head and large, elongate eyes. The dorsal surface is coarsely punctured. The pronotum is wider than long and the elytra are purplish black to reddish purple. Each elytron has five spots that may vary from golden green to green and copper red. The legs are robust.

| | |
|---|---|
| FAMILY | Buprestidae |
| SUBFAMILY | Buprestinae |
| DISTRIBUTION | Australian: southwestern Australia |
| MACROHABITAT | Mallee scrub |
| MICROHABITAT | On various shrubs growing in sandy substrates |
| FEEDING HABITS | Adults probably do not feed; larval host plant records have not been verified |
| NOTE | This species is frequently misidentified as *Julodimorpha bakewellii* |

ADULT LENGTH
1⅜–2⅝ in
(35–65 mm)

*JULODIMORPHA SAUNDERSII*
# JULODIMORPHA SAUNDERSII
THOMSON, 1878

287

*Julodimorpha saundersii* is one of the largest and most taxonomically enigmatic species of Australian jewel beetles. Adults become active in August and September. Flying males sometimes congregate on, and attempt to mate with, discarded "stubbie" beer bottles and orange peels. The color and shape of these items, combined with the small and regularly spaced dimples, strongly resembles the elytral sculpturing of the larger and flightless female and triggers the male's sexual response. Females lay their eggs in damp sand where the larvae burrow, develop, and feed externally on the roots of various trees and woody shrubs.

## RELATED SPECIES
This species is often confused with the only other described species in the genus, *Julodimorpha bakewellii*, which is more slender, and has sparse setae on the front of the head and underside, short curved mandibles, a coarsely punctate pronotum with distinct lateral margins, elytra sculpted with rows of regular punctures, and has entirely iridescent abdominal ventrites.

**Julodimorpha saundersii** is large, robust, cylindrical, and uniformly orangish brown, with long robust mandibles, and longer and denser setae on the front of the head and underside. The pronotum is shallowly punctate with weakly defined lateral margins, the elytra are sculpted with lines of irregular punctures, and the iridescent coloration on the abdominal ventrites is restricted to the ventral margins.

Actual size

| FAMILY | Buprestidae |
|---|---|
| SUBFAMILY | Buprestinae |
| DISTRIBUTION | Nearctic: Transverse and Peninsular ranges of southern California |
| MACROHABITAT | Juniper woodlands |
| MICROHABITAT | Adults rest on juniper foliage; larvae feed in juniper trunks |
| FEEDING HABITS | Unknown for adults; larvae feed and develop in wood |
| NOTE | Very little is known about this very rare species |

ADULT LENGTH
¼–⅞ in
(19–21 mm)

288

*JUNIPERELLA MIRABILIS*
# JUNIPERELLA MIRABILIS
KNULL, 1947

*Juniperella mirabilis* is a spectacular, yet rarely encountered beetle that lives among belts of juniper woodland flanking the inland slopes of the Transverse and Peninsular ranges of southern California. Eggs are probably laid at the base of thick trunks of California Juniper (*Juniperus californica*). The larvae mine the roots and trunks, boring under the bark and outer sapwood, where pupation takes place. Adults emerge in summer from large, elliptical emergence holes that are low to the ground, and hence are mostly hidden by the gray, fibrous, exfoliating bark. They rest among the dense foliage and take to the air with a loud buzzing sound when disturbed.

### RELATED SPECIES

The genus *Juniperella* contains only one species, *J. mirabilis*. This species is immediately distinguished from all other North American jewel beetles by its large size, robust and convex shape, and relatively smooth and boldly marked elytra. It was originally placed in the tribe Buprestini, but a recent study has moved it to the Melanophilini.

**Juniperella mirabilis** is very stout, convex, and with short setae only on the head and underside. The head and metallic green pronotum are broad and coarsely punctate, with the pronotum widest at its base. The dark greenish-black elytra are wider than the pronotum, widest behind the middle, and have four broad yellow bands that do not cross the elytral suture.

Actual size

| FAMILY | Buprestidae |
|---|---|
| SUBFAMILY | Buprestinae |
| DISTRIBUTION | Holarctic, Neotropical, Oriental |
| MACROHABITAT | Coniferous forest |
| MICROHABITAT | Adults are found on the trunks of conifers; larvae develop in recently burnt wood |
| FEEDING HABITS | Adults feed primarily on foliage of host plants; larvae feed on recently burnt coniferous trees |
| NOTE | Females lay their eggs on scorched and still smoldering wood |

ADULT LENGTH
⁵⁄₁₆–½ in
(8–12 mm)

*MELANOPHILA ACUMINATA*

# BLACK FIRE BEETLE

(DEGEER, 1774)

289

The Black Fire Beetle is a Holarctic species that is widely distributed throughout coniferous forests in North and Central America, as well as Cuba, and also occurs in Europe and Asia. Adults are found on the trunks of cedar (*Cupressus* spp.), spruce (*Picea* spp.), and pine (*Pinus* spp.) trees. The larvae utilize many species of conifers as food and are adapted to develop only in recently burnt wood. Heat-killed trees are incapable of defending themselves by producing sap and recently burnt habitats harbor few beetle predators. Adults locate egg-laying sites with thoracic infrared sensors that detect smoke and fires up to 80 miles (130 km) away.

### RELATED SPECIES

The genus *Melanophila* includes 14 species, most of which attack conifers. Several North American species are sometimes called "firebugs" because they are attracted to smoke and flames and will flock to forest fires. *Melanophila acuminata* is distinguished from other species in the genus by the form of its elytral tips and long antennae.

Actual size

**The Black Fire Beetle** is elongate-oval and uniformly dull black dorsally and ventrally. Its relatively long antennae extend beyond the hind angles of the prothorax. The pronotum is narrower than the elytra. Both the pronotal and elytral surfaces appear somewhat rough, or finely granulate. The tips of the elytra are sharply pointed, or acute.

| FAMILY | Buprestidae |
|---|---|
| SUBFAMILY | Buprestinae |
| DISTRIBUTION | Australian: Western Australia |
| MACROHABITAT | Southwest Australia botanical region |
| MICROHABITAT | Coastal scrub and heath |
| FEEDING HABITS | Adults feed on leaves, and larvae likely on wood tissue, of *Mirbelia* |
| NOTE | Many new species were described in a 2012 revision of the genus |

ADULT LENGTH
⅜–⁹⁄₁₆ in
(9–14 mm)

290

# MELOBASIS REGALIS REGALIS

CARTER, 1923

*Melobasis regalis regalis* is a common jewel beetle found in southwestern Australian coastal scrub heathlands from September through December, where it is typically encountered feeding on the leaves of Yilgara Poison (*Mirbelia seorsifolia*). The larvae are unknown, but are likely to feed on, and develop in, woody plant tissues, as do the known larva of other species of *Melobasis*. The genus contains 156 species in the Oriental Realm, Australia, and Papua New Guinea, and reaches its greatest diversity in the Southwest Australia botanical region of Australia with 82 species, 60 of which are endemic.

## RELATED SPECIES

Some forms of *Melobasis gloriosa gloriosa* are similar to both subspecies of *M. regalis*, but have translucent silvery, rather than opaque white, pubescence on their head and underside. *Melobasis r. carnabyorum* has reddish-purple elytra, each with a broad and sinuate green stripe almost along its entire length.

Actual size

**Melobasis regalis regalis** is brownish bronze or greenish bronze with coppery reflections on the head, underside, and most of the legs, while the tarsi are blue or green. The middle of the pronotum is broadly blue-green, golden green, or coppery, flanked on each side by stripes of variable color. The bluish, greenish, or violet elytra have greenish, golden, or coppery markings. Both males and females have tibiae that are not modified sawtoothlike structures or setae-filled pits.

| FAMILY | Buprestidae |
|---|---|
| SUBFAMILY | Buprestinae |
| DISTRIBUTION | Australian: Western Australia |
| MACROHABITAT | Forests |
| MICROHABITAT | Adults occur on flowers; larvae live in wood |
| FEEDING HABITS | Adults feed on nectar and pollen; larvae feed in wood |
| NOTE | Beetles in the tribe Stigmoderini are among the most important pollinators of myrtaceous and myoporaceous trees and shrubs in Australia |

ADULT LENGTH
⅞–1¹/₃₂ in
(23–26 mm)

*STIGMODERA ROEI*

# STIGMODERA ROEI

SAUNDERS, 1868

291

The genus *Stigmodera* is a member of the tribe Stigmoderini, which contains four additional genera in Australia: *Calodema*, *Castiarina*, *Metaxymorpha*, and *Temognatha*. This tribe is characterized by unique structures associated with the female ovipositor. *Stigmodera roei* is a common jewel beetle found only in Western Australia. Adults of this species have been found feeding in large numbers on Geraldton Wax (*Chamelaucium uncinatum*) flowers and on *Leptospermum* species, *Melaleuca* species, and *Hakea costata*. Larvae have been reported feeding on the Western Australian Peppermint (*Agonis flexuosa*) along coastal areas in the southwest of the state. Adults of this diurnal species are active mostly in September and October.

### RELATED SPECIES

When combined, the genera within the tribe Stigmoderini include several hundred species in Australia, nearly 500 in the genus *Castiarina* alone. Five other genera (e.g., *Conognatha* and *Lasionota*) also occur in the Neotropical Realm. *Stigmodera* contains seven species, all of which occur in Australia, from Western Australia east to Queensland. Differences in color patterns are useful to separate most of the species.

**Stigmodera roei** is a stocky, elongate-oval, hard-shelled, heavily punctate jewel beetle. The head and thorax are bright metallic green and the elytra are blue or green, each with three red or orange patches. The sides and the apex of the elytra are also red or orange. The antennae are rather small. The legs are metallic green or reddish depending on the individuals.

Actual size

| FAMILY | Buprestidae |
|---|---|
| SUBFAMILY | Buprestinae |
| DISTRIBUTION | Australian: Western Australia |
| MACROHABITAT | Forests |
| MICROHABITAT | Adults occur on flowering trees; larvae in wood |
| FEEDING HABITS | Adults feed on flowers and pollen; larvae bore into wood |
| NOTE | Larval development may take up to 17 years to complete |

**ADULT LENGTH**
1⁷⁄₁₆–1¾ in
(37–45 mm)

292

*TEMOGNATHA CHEVROLATII*
# TEMOGNATHA CHEVROLATII
GÉHIN, 1855

Most of the adults of *Temognatha*, which are active during the day, feed on flowers and pollen; reported host plants include the White Mallee (*Eucalyptus cylindriflora*), *E. foecunda*, and Hook-leaf Mallee (*E. uncinata*), as well as a species of *Melaleuca*. Larvae in this genus are wood-borers and have been reported feeding in species of *Melaleuca*, *Casuarina*, and *Eucalyptus*. It has been reported that it can take seven to 17 years for *Temognatha* larvae to complete their development. The adults are short-lived and typically die soon after mating. *T. chevrolatii* is one of the most attractive Australian jewel beetles and as such is sought after by collectors.

## RELATED SPECIES

*Temognatha* is a diverse genus in the tribe Stigmoderini that contains more than 85 species and subspecies, which occur in continental Australia, although one species (*T. mitchelii*) can also be found in Tasmania. The species in this genus differ primarily in their overall color patterns, including the presence and shape of the transverse lines and patches on their elytra.

**Temognatha chevrolatii** is a relatively large and very attractive jewel beetle, with a bright metallic green head, legs, and prothorax. The prothorax bears small orange spots that sometimes combine to form irregular lines. The elytra are orange or dark yellowish and have two or four transverse, zigzagging black lines. The elytra each end with a pair of sharp spines at the apex.

Actual size

| FAMILY | Buprestidae |
|---|---|
| SUBFAMILY | Buprestinae |
| DISTRIBUTION | Nearctic: British Columbia to California, Arizona, and New Mexico |
| MACROHABITAT | Cedar, cypress, and juniper woodlands up to 7,500 ft (2,300 m) |
| MICROHABITAT | Adults probably live high in the canopy; larvae mine sapwood of tree boles |
| FEEDING HABITS | Adults feed on foliage; larvae eat wood |
| NOTE | Adult *Trachykele* are seldom seen but can be abundant locally |

ADULT LENGTH
7/16–3/4 in
(11–20 mm)

*TRACHYKELE BLONDELI BLONDELI*
# WESTERN CEDAR BORER
MARSEUL, 1865

293

*Trachykele blondeli* feeds on, and lays its eggs under, the bark scales on branches of living, injured, dying, or dead Western Redcedar (*Thuja plicata*), Arborvitae (*Thuja occidentalis*), Port Orford Cedar (*Chamaecyparis lawsoniana*), Western Juniper (*Juniperus occidentalis*), and western cypresses (*Hesperocyparis* spp.). The larvae bore down to the bole to mine and develop in the outer sapwood for two or more years. The one-month pupal stage occurs in the fall and is followed by the emergence of adults, which remain in the pupal cell until the following spring. Adults remain active through summer. They apparently spend much of their time high in the tree canopy.

Actual size

### RELATED SPECIES
The six species of *Trachykele* all inhabit North America, two (*T. fattigi* and *T. lecontei*) occurring in the southeastern United States and four (*T. blondeli*, *T. hartmani*, *T. nimbosa*, and *T. opulenta*) in the West. *Trachykele blondeli* is distinguished from other members of the genus by its bright green color, and sculpturing on the pronotal and elytral surfaces. The subspecies *T. b. cuperomarginata* occurs mainly along the central coast of California, while *T. b. juniperi* inhabits eastern California.

**The Western Cedar Borer** is bright, shiny, emerald green with golden reflections and is coarsely punctured. The pronotum is deeply excavated and its sides are moderately angulate. Each elytron has six small, dark spots and an oblique smooth area behind the middle. *Trachykele b. cuperomarginata* has coppery elytral margins, while *T. b. juniperi* is smaller and a more brilliant green.

| FAMILY | Buprestidae |
|---|---|
| SUBFAMILY | Agrilinae |
| DISTRIBUTION | Palearctic, Oriental, and Nearctic: native to the Russian Far East, China, Japan, Korea, Laos, Mongolia; accidentally introduced to North America and Moscow (Russia) |
| MACROHABITAT | Open settings and closed forests with ash (*Fraxinus*) trees |
| MICROHABITAT | Adults are found on trunks and foliage of ash (*Fraxinus*) trees; larvae are wood-borers |
| FEEDING HABITS | Adults feed on foliage of host trees; larva excavate galleries under the bark of the host tree |
| NOTE | This invasive species in North America and the European part of Russia probably entered the regions in wooden packing material shipped from Asia |

ADULT LENGTH
⁵⁄₁₆–⁹⁄₁₆ in
(8–14 mm)

*AGRILUS PLANIPENNIS*
# EMERALD ASH BORER
FAIRMAIRE, 1888

294

In its native range, the Emerald Ash Borer is relatively uncommon and can cause minor damage to unhealthy or stressed native tree species (mostly in the genus *Fraxinus*), but in North America, where it has been introduced accidentally, it infests and kills both stressed and healthy ash tree species (e.g., *F. pennsylvanica*, *F. nigra*, and *F. americana*). As a result, this beetle has become one of eastern North America's most serious invasive insect pests, killing tens of millions of healthy ash trees there since its discovery in 2002. While large-scale treatment options against the strong flyer *Agrilus planipennis* are limited in North America, species of tiny parasitic wasps that attack either the larval or eggs stages of the pest are being explored (and released in some cases) as potential biological control agents.

### RELATED SPECIES

*Agrilus* is thought to be the most diverse animal genera and includes approximately 3,000 described species. The related species of *A. planipennis* are distributed in east and Southeast Asia and include *A. tomentipennis*, *A. crepuscularis*, and species in the *A. cyaneoniger* group. *Agrilus planipennis* can be separated from these species by the presence of a pygidial spine and the absence of pubescence on the elytra.

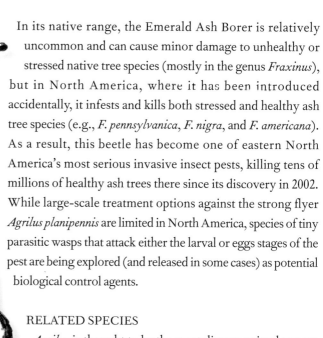

**The Emerald Ash Borer** is an elongate, bright metallic blue-green jewel beetle with a head that is flattened anteriorly. The body lacks setae. The kidney-shaped eyes are bronze to black. The dorsal surface is usually bright metallic green, but sometimes has a bluish or violet tinge. The flight wings are well developed and the beetle is a strong flyer.

Actual size

| FAMILY | Buprestidae |
|---|---|
| SUBFAMILY | Agrilinae |
| DISTRIBUTION | Oriental: Malaysia, Tioman Island |
| MACROHABITAT | Tropical forest |
| MICROHABITAT | Adults presumably live on foliage of monocots; larvae are unknown |
| FEEDING HABITS | Unknown; larvae are possibly leaf-miners |
| NOTE | Beetles in this genus are active during sunny days and some are attracted to bright colors such as orange or yellow |

ADULT LENGTH
⅛–³⁄₁₆ in
(2.9–4.1 mm)

*APHANISTICUS LUBOPETRI*

# APHANISTICUS LUBOPETRI

KALASHIAN, 2004

295

The numerous species of *Aphanisticus* all originate from the Old World, although *A. cochinchinae seminulum*, associated with sugarcane (*Saccharum* spp.), was introduced accidentally to the New World via the southern United States and has since spread into various areas of Latin America. *A. lubopetri* was described in 2004 from a small number of individuals and is known from Tioman Island in Malaysia. Little is known regarding the biology and ecology of this species. Adults in this group often feed on leaves. In Europe, larvae of some species of *Aphanisticus* mine the leaves of Cyperaceae and Juncaceae.

RELATED SPECIES

*A. lubopetri* belongs to a relatively large genus of buprestid beetles that contains more than 350 species. Most of the species in the genus have an elongate and slender body in the adult stage, with a metallic gray or black dorsal surface. Species of *Aphanisticus* in the Oriental and eastern Palearctic realms are typically separated based on features of the antennae, elytra, eyes, and pronotum.

Actual size

**Aphanisticus lubopetri** is a small, rather elongate jewel beetle with the flattened dorsal surface that is black with metallic gray or blackish reflections. The head has a noticeable notch in the middle anteriorly and the elytra are distinctly narrowed just before the middle. The area between the longitudinal ridges on the surface of the elytra does not have punctation and is covered instead with fine microsculpture.

| FAMILY | Buprestidae |
|---|---|
| SUBFAMILY | Agrilinae |
| DISTRIBUTION | Palearctic: Europe and Asia |
| MACROHABITAT | Cork Oak (*Quercus suber*) forests |
| MICROHABITAT | On foliage and trunks of Cork Oak |
| FEEDING HABITS | Adults feed on leaves of host: larvae excavate galleries in Cork Oaks |
| NOTE | The main insect pest of Cork Oaks worldwide |

ADULT LENGTH
⅜–⅝ in
(10–16 mm)

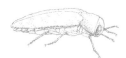

*CORAEBUS UNDATUS*
# CORK OAK JEWEL BEETLE
(FABRICIUS, 1787)

This beetle can be found in large quantities in the Andalucía region of Spain, and is a serious pest of the Cork Oak (*Quercus suber*) industry, mainly in Spain. The larvae excavate galleries in the cork tissue of Cork Oaks, thereby diminishing its quality but leaving the tree otherwise unaffected. It has been stated that the annual economic cost in Spain's Extremadura region alone is €5 million. The larva has been described and has also been found in *Castanea*, *Diospyros*, and *Fagus* species.

## RELATED SPECIES

The genus *Coraebus* contains around 230 species. Like most other members of *Coraebus*, the adults of *C. undatus* fly mainly in May, June, and July. The females lay their eggs in holes of the Cork Tree, and the size of the galleries excavated by the larvae can reach 6 ft (1.80 m) in length. The life cycle is presumed to take one to three years depending on the conditions. Economically significant damages have been reported in Spain, Portugal, and France.

Actual size

**The Cork Oak Jewel Beetle** is a small jewel beetle well known in Europe. The species has an elongate subcylindrical body. The clypeus is shaped like an upside-down letter "Y." The elytra are black with green reflections and pubescence forming wavy white stripes and spots. Sexual dimorphism is recognizable in the length of antennae, and the females are more robust than the males.

| FAMILY | Buprestidae |
| --- | --- |
| SUBFAMILY | Agrilinae |
| DISTRIBUTION | Neotropical: Brazil, French Guiana, Guyana, Guatemala, Panama, Mexico |
| MACROHABITAT | Tropical forests |
| MICROHABITAT | Leaves of various plants |
| FEEDING HABITS | Larvae are leaf-miners and feed on herbaceous vegetation |
| NOTE | The known larvae in this genus are legless and very flattened |

ADULT LENGTH
$\frac{1}{16}-\frac{3}{16}$ in
(2–4 mm)

*PACHYSCHELUS TERMINANS*

# PACHYSCHELUS TERMINANS

(FABRICIUS, 1801)

297

*Pachyschelus terminans* can be found in Brazil, French Guiana, Guyana, Guatemala, Panama, and Mexico. The biology of this very small species is unknown. The adults generally occur on the leaves of their larval hosts. The larvae are known to feed on various species in the families Sapindaceae, Euphorbiaceae, Brassicaceae, Combretaceae, and Fabaceae. The eggs are generally elliptic in shape. A 2013 study on the related species *P. laevigatus* reported that the leaf-mining larva molts by splitting its old cuticle laterally, instead of dorsally as in other insects. The only other known case of lateral cuticle split in insect larvae occurs in a species of the leaf-mining lepidopteran genus *Cameraria*.

Actual size

## RELATED SPECIES

*Pachyschelus* is a large genus found primarily in the Neotropical and Oriental realms. All the species are small to very small jewel beetles, and to identify them, details of coloration, host plant, and genitalia are all important. Around 269 species are known to date; they are leaf-miners of herbaceous vegetation. The genus *Hylaeogena* is related to *Pachyschelus*; members of both share many characteristics.

**Pachyschelus terminans** is a very small jewel beetle with attractive metallic coloration. The punctate body is teardrop-shaped. The tibiae are distinctly flattened. The head and pronotum are metallic blue with green reflections. The first two-thirds of the elytra are metallic blue, and the last one-third is yellow with greenish reflections at the apex. There are many color variations of this species.

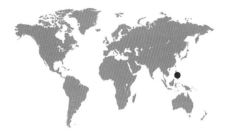

| FAMILY | Buprestidae |
|---|---|
| SUBFAMILY | Agrilinae |
| DISTRIBUTION | Oriental: Philippines (Romblon and Sibuyan islands) |
| MACROHABITAT | Tropical forests |
| MICROHABITAT | Adults are found on flowers |
| FEEDING HABITS | Adults probably feed on pollen and foliage; larvae probably feed on and tunnel into their hosts |
| NOTE | One of the most beautiful buprestid species in the world |

ADULT LENGTH
7/16–9/16 in
(11–14 mm)

*SIBUYANELLA BAKERI*
# SIBUYANELLA BAKERI
(FISHER, 1924)

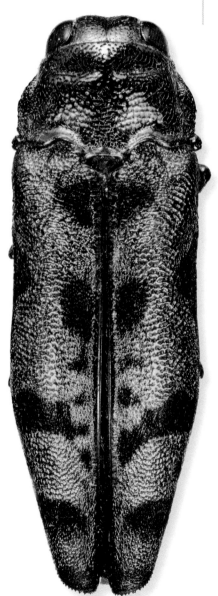

*Sibuyanella bakeri* is an attractive jewel beetle found on Romblon and Sibuyan islands in the Philippines. Little is known about the biology of the species, but experts suggest that the adults visit flowers and stay on the host plant to feed on the foliage. The members of this tribe (Coraebini) are associated with woody shrubs, thorn trees, and some monocot groups. The larvae tunnel into their hosts. The coloring of some of these and related species might be mimetic of scutellerids of the genus *Chrysocoris* or *Peocilocoris*.

RELATED SPECIES

*Sibuyanella bakeri* belongs to a small genus that contains two other species described in 2005 from the Philippines. The other known species are *S. boudanti* from Bohol and *S. mimica* from Marinduque and Mindoro. *Sibuyanella bakeri* can be separated by its shining dorsal surface and the elytral apex without black setae.

Actual size

**Sibuyanella bakeri** is iridescent green on its upper surface, sometimes with yellow or red reflections. The body is slender and robust. The elytra show a pattern of five pairs of blue spots but the maculations vary in placement and shape. The pronotum is wider than it is long. The legs are metallic green and in males the inner claw is bifid.

| | |
|---|---|
| FAMILY | Buprestidae |
| SUBFAMILY | Agrilinae |
| DISTRIBUTION | Palearctic: Armenia, Azerbaijan, Bulgaria, Greece, Iran, Romania, European Russia, Turkey, Turkmenistan, Ukraine |
| MACROHABITAT | Primarily in dry meadows, steppes, and near forests at low altitude |
| MICROHABITAT | Adults occur on foliage; larvae mine leaves |
| FEEDING HABITS | Adults presumably feed on leaves of their host; the only known larval host plant is *Phlomis pungens* |
| NOTE | Some species in the diverse Old World genus *Trachys* have been accidentally introduced to North America |

ADULT LENGTH
⅛ in
(2.8–3.2 mm)

*TRACHYS PHLYCTAENOIDES*
# TRACHYS PHLYCTAENOIDES
KOLENATI, 1846

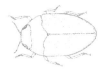

299

The leaf-mining larva of *Trachys phlyctaenoides* was described in 1996 from individuals extracted from leaves of their host, *Phlomis pungens*. These greatly flattened larvae do not have functional legs but instead use tubercles on the dorsal and ventral surfaces of their metathorax and abdomen for locomotion within leaf mines. The closely related Palearctic species *T. troglodytiformis* has been established on Hollyhock (*Alcea rosea*) in New Jersey, and the discovery of the exotic *T. minutus* in Massachusetts was reported in 2012.

Actual size

## RELATED SPECIES

The genus *Trachys* occurs in the Afrotropical, Australian, Oriental, and Palearctic realms, and is a member of the diverse tribe Tracheini, along with *Habroloma*, *Pachyschelus*, *Brachys*, and other genera. *Trachys phlyctaenoides* is one of more than 600 species that belongs in this genus. This large and important group of beetles needs a thorough revision of species concepts.

**Trachys phlyctaenoides** is a small, oval, brilliant black jewel beetle with bronze reflections on the dorsal surface. White setae pressed against the cuticle are visible on the dorsal face. The short antennae and the legs are black, usually with some metallic reflections. The broad pronotum is distinctly sinuate along the posterior edge.

| FAMILY | Byrrhidae |
|---|---|
| SUBFAMILY | Byrrhinae |
| DISTRIBUTION | Nearctic: transcontinental in Canada and northern USA |
| MACROHABITAT | Damp environments |
| MICROHABITAT | Associated with mosses |
| FEEDING HABITS | Mainly bryophagous |
| NOTE | Adults and larvae are surface grazers on mosses |

ADULT LENGTH
³⁄₁₆–¼ in
(4.5–5.5 mm)

*CYTILUS ALTERNATUS*
# CYTILUS ALTERNATUS
(SAY, 1825)

300

Actual size

Adults and larvae of this species prefer wet, moss-covered habitats, and live on or in the soil under the moss. Adults, which bring their appendages close to the body and remain immobile when disturbed, probably feed on bryophytes (mosses, hornworts, and liverworts). Analysis of gut contents revealed that the larvae are detritivorous and feed on dead leaves, dead wood, moss, liverworts, and other vegetable matter. Infestations of larvae of *Cytilus alternatus* have been reported in conifer-seedling farms in Ontario, Canada, resulting in economic losses.

### RELATED SPECIES

This species is closely related to *Cytilus mimicus*, which is found in montane western Canada and western United States. The two species can be separated externally mainly by the overall shape of the body, which is more elongate and subparallel in *C. mimicus*. The genus *Cytilus* includes five species, three in the Palearctic and two in the Nearctic.

**Cytilus alternatus** is a compact, strongly convex, ovoid blackish beetle. The elytra are covered with short, appressed, pale and dark setae, suggesting a checkered pattern on alternate intervals. The head is concealed under the pronotum in dorsal view. The antennae are relatively short and the last five antennomeres form a loose club. Abdominal ventrite 1 lacks femoral depressions.

| FAMILY | Byrrhidae |
|---|---|
| SUBFAMILY | Byrrhinae |
| DISTRIBUTION | Australian: southern Australia |
| MACROHABITAT | Forests |
| MICROHABITAT | Mosses and moist forest litter |
| FEEDING HABITS | Herbivorous on mosses and liverworts |
| NOTE | One of the most spectacularly colored members of the diverse fauna of south temperate byrrhid beetles |

ADULT LENGTH
³⁄₁₆–¼ in
(4.5–5.5 mm)

*NOTOLIOON GEMMATUS*

# NOTOLIOON GEMMATUS

(LEA, 1920)

301

Members of the family Byrrhidae are most diverse in cool, moist, high-latitude forests and montane habitats. Members of *Notolioon* occur in wet, mossy habitats in south temperate Australian forests, including Tasmania. Insofar as is known, both larvae and adults of this byrrhid subfamily feed on mosses and liverworts growing on the rich matrix of organic matter that forms the substrate of these forests. Data associated with specimens in museums corroborate these habitat and feeding associations for this species. Adults of *Notolioon* are wingless.

Actual size

### RELATED SPECIES

Thirteen species of *Notolioon* occur across the genus's range in the temperate forests of the southern Australian mainland and Tasmania, and some additional species are as yet undescribed. They differ from each other in the color and setal arrangements on the dorsal surface and in their distribution. *Notolioon gemmatus* and other members of this recently described genus were previously included in the genus *Pedilophorus*.

**Notolioon gemmatus** is a spectacularly colorful little beetle with a bright metallic green dorsal surface and a regularly arranged series of copper-colored metallic tumosities on the elytra. The appendages and ventral surfaces are darker in color. The head is visible from above, unlike the completely concealed heads of many other members of the family.

| FAMILY | Elmidae |
|---|---|
| SUBFAMILY | Larainae |
| DISTRIBUTION | Afrotropical: Zambia |
| MACROHABITAT | Aquatic |
| MICROHABITAT | Unknown, presumed to be shallow stream habitats |
| FEEDING HABITS | Presumed detritivorous |
| NOTE | Carries a layer of air trapped by hydrofuge setae for respiration while submerged |

ADULT LENGTH
⁵⁄₁₆–³⁄₈ in
(8–8.5 mm)

302

*POTAMODYTES SCHOUTEDENI*
# POTAMODYTES SCHOUTEDENI
DELÈVE, 1937

*Potamodytes schoutedeni* was described from individuals collected during an African expedition, we know very little about their natural history. Members of the subfamily Larainae typically occur in shallow, flowing water, particularly on water-splashed rocks (hygropetric habitats) and organic matter adjacent to streams. A trapped layer of air beneath specialized hydrofuge setae enables the adults to breathe while submerged. Secretions from specialized glands are continually applied to the setae to maintain their hydrophobic air-trapping function. Both adults and larvae are considered completely aquatic, though adults are active flyers and readily disperse among suitable habitats.

## RELATED SPECIES

At least 35 species of *Potamodytes* are described, all from Africa, with a concentration of species in equatorial and southern parts of the continent. They are similar in external appearance and differ mainly in the shape, presence or absence, and arrangement of spines on the apex of the elytra, and in details of the male genitalia.

Actual size

**Potamodytes schoutedeni** is a medium-size member of one of the long-toed water beetle family. The common name derives from the unusually long last tarsomere. This species is typical of the subfamily Larainae, with an elongate, tapering body densely clothed in specialized hydrofuge pubescence. The configuration of the apical elytral spines is species diagnostic and sexually dimorphic in many species.

| FAMILY | Elmidae |
|---|---|
| SUBFAMILY | Elminae |
| DISTRIBUTION | Nearctic: southern Canada (Alberta, Manitoba, Ontario, Quebec), USA (Wisconsin, Indiana, Illinois) |
| MACROHABITAT | Freshwater ecosystems |
| MICROHABITAT | On surfaces of rocks and vegetation |
| FEEDING HABITS | Detritivorous or algivorous |
| NOTE | Aquatic adult beetles in the subfamily Elminae do not need to come to the water surface to breathe; instead, they breathe using a very thin layer of air kept in place by hydrofuge structures around the body |

ADULT LENGTH
⅛ in
(3–3.4 mm)

*DUBIRAPHIA BIVITTATA*

# DUBIRAPHIA BIVITTATA

(LECONTE, 1852)

303

Actual size

The subfamily Elminae includes approximately 1,200 species worldwide. The adults and larvae are aquatic and typically live in running water, particularly shallow riffles and the rapids of streams and rivers. The adults are usually found on rocks, boulders, decaying wood, or vegetation, and use their long legs and strong tarsal claws to grip the substrate firmly. The five species of *Dubiraphia* found in northeastern North America, including *D. bivittata*, are known to tolerate a rather broad range of microhabitats, from cold springs to the margins of lakes.

### RELATED SPECIES

The genus *Dubiraphia* contains 11 species restricted to America, north of Mexico. Adults are difficult to distinguish and examination of the male genitalia is often required for reliable identification of the species. *Dubiraphia bivittata* is the largest species of the genus found east of the Rocky Mountains. The relationships among the species have not been studied.

**Dubiraphia bivittata** is an elongate beetle with a black head dorsally, and a yellowish pronotum and elytra, the latter with black suture and lateral margins. The antenna is 11-segmented and the maxillary palp four-segmented. The pronotum is smooth, without sublateral carinae or bumps. The front tibia has a fringe of setae. The tarsomeres are long.

| FAMILY | Dryopidae |
|---|---|
| SUBFAMILY | |
| DISTRIBUTION | Neotropical: Chile |
| MACROHABITAT | Aquatic habitats |
| MICROHABITAT | Unknown |
| FEEDING HABITS | Unknown |
| NOTE | A synonym of this species was used as the basis for the name of a different beetle family, the Chiloeidae |

**ADULT LENGTH**
³⁄₁₆ in
(3.5–4 mm)

304

*SOSTEAMORPHUS VERRUCATUS*

# SOSTEAMORPHUS VERRUCATUS

HINTON, 1936

Actual size

The original description of *Sosteamorphus verrucatus* simply states "Chile" as the origin of the specimens on which the description was based. In 1973 this species was again described, by Roger Dajoz, who gave it the name *Chiloea chilensis* and the type locality as Chiloé Island in southern Chile. That name was used as the basis of a separate family, Chiloeidae, which contained only this single species. The species was later synonymized under Hinton's older name, along with the short-lived family Chiloeidae. Nothing is known of the life history of *S. verrucatus*, but most other members of the family are aquatic and graze on biofilms.

RELATED SPECIES

This species is the single member of the genus. It may represent a south temperate, Gondwanan lineage of dryopids because it shares some morphological features with the New Zealand genus *Protoparnus*. Dryopids and members of the family Limnichidae share many morphological features and may be difficult to separate.

**Sosteamorphus verrucatus** adults are short, robust, heavily sculptured beetles with numerous tubercles and callosities that are covered by coarse golden pubescence. The pubescence traps a layer of air in many aquatic dryopids and is referred to as hydrofuge pubescence. The head is deflexed under the prothorax and not visible from above.

| FAMILY | Lutrochidae |
|---|---|
| SUBFAMILY | |
| DISTRIBUTION | Neotropical: Brazil (São Paulo, Paraná) |
| MACROHABITAT | Freshwater ecosystems |
| MICROHABITAT | In submerged wood |
| FEEDING HABITS | Algivorous and detritivorous |
| NOTE | A rare case among aquatic beetles of gallery-forming behavior in submerged woody debris |

ADULT LENGTH
$\frac{3}{16}$–$\frac{1}{4}$ in
(4.5–6 mm)

*LUTROCHUS GERMARI*

# LUTROCHUS GERMARI

GROUVELLE, 1889

305

Adults and larvae of this species are found in decaying submerged wood of various sizes in shallow streams with weakly alkaline or slightly acid water. The adults remain submerged with an air bubble held by the numerous hydrofuge setae that cover most of the body. The larvae excavate galleries deep into the woody debris. The few known pupae were found in cells in rotten logs above the water line. Adults and larvae apparently feed on algae and waterlogged wood.

## RELATED SPECIES

*Lutrochus* is the only genus in the family and includes 17 described species inhabiting the Western Hemisphere, from southeastern Canada to Brazil and Bolivia. There are few taxonomic studies available for this group and several new species await description. Morphological characters used to separate the species include, among others, the overall body size, characteristics of the legs, and the shape of the scutellum.

Actual size

**Lutrochus germari** is an oval, strongly convex, dark brown beetle with dense, decumbent golden pubescence. The 11-segmented antennae are very short, with antennomeres 1 and 2 broad and with conspicuous setae; antennomeres 3–11 are closely appressed, somewhat clavate and about as long as the first two antennomeres combined. The pronotum is wider than the head. The tarsal formula is 5-5-5.

| | |
|---|---|
| FAMILY | Limnichidae |
| SUBFAMILY | Hyphalinae |
| DISTRIBUTION | Australian: Australia (Heron Island, Queensland) |
| MACROHABITAT | Tropical beaches |
| MICROHABITAT | Temporarily submerged rocks |
| FEEDING HABITS | Adults and larvae feed on algae |
| NOTE | *Hyphalus* is the only wingless genus in the family |

ADULT LENGTH
¹⁄₃₂ in
(1.1–1.4 mm)

306

*HYPHALUS INSULARIS*
# HYPHALUS INSULARIS
BRITTON, 1971

Actual size

Beetles in this genus are unusual in that they live in the interstices of consolidated coral rocks in the intertidal area of tropical beaches. *Hyphalus insularis* is found on the rough undersides of flat, detached pieces of beach rock submerged at each high tide under 12–35 in (30–90 cm) of water for a period of three to six hours. The beach rock is usually coated with a thin film of algae (Cyanophyta), on which the adults and their larvae apparently feed. Three tufts of gill filaments protrude from the tip of the abdomen of submerged larvae, enabling them to survive underwater during high tides.

### RELATED SPECIES

*Hyphalus*, which contains eight species in Australia, New Zealand, Taiwan, Japan, and some islands (Seychelles) in the Indian Ocean, is the only genus in the subfamily Hyphalinae. The position of *Hyphalus* is still problematic as a phylogenetic study in 1995 based on adult and larval characters did not provide clear evidence that it belongs in the Limnichidae. Species in the genus can generally be separated by differences in structures of the elytra, abdominal ventrites, and male genitalia.

**Hyphalus insularis** is a minute, stout, blackish beetle. The last three antennomeres form a club. The maxillary palpus is four-segmented with the last segment enlarged and ovoid; the labial palpus is two-segmented. Flight wings are absent. The elytra bear minute round tubercles. The tarsal formula is 4-4-4; none of the tarsal segments is bilobed or emarginated, and the last tarsomere is longer than the other tarsomeres combined. The tibia does not have apical spurs.

| | |
|---|---|
| FAMILY | Limnichidae |
| SUBFAMILY | Thaumastodinae |
| DISTRIBUTION | Neotropical: Bahamas |
| MACROHABITAT | Islets with few or no vascular plants |
| MICROHABITAT | Intertidal rocks |
| FEEDING HABITS | Possibly algivorous |
| NOTE | The species in this genus are referred to as jumping shore beetles |

ADULT LENGTH
¹⁄₁₆ in
(1.6–2 mm)

*MEXICO MORRISONI*
# MEXICO MORRISONI
SKELLEY, 2005

307

Equipped with highly modified hind coxae, most thaumastodines—including *Mexico morrisoni*—are known to jump and are difficult to catch. Very little is known about the bionomics of this species. Adults of this species were collected by pan traps on marine limestone islets with little or no sand in the Bahamas. Most of the islets had no naturally occurring vascular plants and therefore algae are possibly the food source for this species. At least one other limnichid species is known to feed on algae.

Actual size

## RELATED SPECIES
Only two species are known in the genus *Mexico*, the other, *M. litoralis*, described from the Mexican state of Jalisco. Amongst other characters, *M. litoralis* differs in being slightly broader and having dark brown legs instead of black. This genus is morphologically very similar to *Babalimnichus*, which includes three species in the Palearctic, Oriental, and Australian realms.

**Mexico morrisoni** is a small oval beetle covered with dense, mixed coarse and fine seta-bearing punctures. The setae on the elytra form a noticeable pattern of color bands. The antenna is 11-segmented, with the last four antennomeres forming a club. The apical edge of the elytra is serrulate. The tarsal formula is 4-4-4. The hind tibiae have sharp spines.

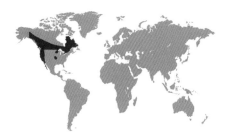

| FAMILY | Heteroceridae |
|---|---|
| SUBFAMILY | Heterocerinae |
| DISTRIBUTION | Nearctic and Neotropical: Canada (Yukon east to Quebec), USA, Mexico (Baja California) |
| MACROHABITAT | Riparian habitats |
| MICROHABITAT | In tunnels in sand or mudflats near water bodies |
| FEEDING HABITS | Adults and larvae feed on algae, plankton, and organic material |
| NOTE | Both adults and larvae have strong front legs, used for digging in the substrate |

ADULT LENGTH
³⁄₁₆–¼ in
(3.5–7 mm)

*HETEROCERUS GNATHO*
# HETEROCERUS GNATHO
LECONTE, 1863

Actual size

The family Heteroceridae, which includes approximately 300 rather morphologically uniform species worldwide, are commonly referred to as variegated mud-loving beetles. Adults are characterized by their relatively large mandibles and tibiae armed with a row of large spines. The legs of adults are used to dig tunnels in substrate near water bodies, where they feed on organic debris and other food items. Larvae use the tunnels created by adults but eventually dig their own. Adults of *Heterocerus gnatho* and related species have well-developed flight wings and can occur in large number at artificial lights in the summer.

### RELATED SPECIES

*Heterocerus gnatho* belongs to a group that contains 13 species in North America (including Mexico) previously known under the generic name *Neoheterocerus*. The best character to separate them morphologically is the male genitalia. A study on molecular data published in 2011 suggested that *H. gnatho* is closely related to *H. angustatus*, a species occurring in the southeastern United States and the West Indies.

**Heterocerus gnatho** is a relatively small beetle with brownish elytra bearing a darker zigzag banding pattern. Hypermandibulate males have greatly elongated mandibles and the labrum prolonged anteriorly into a process. The antennae have 11 antennomeres. In the male the pronotum is as wide as, or slightly wider than, the elytra, while in the female it is narrower. The beetle lacks middle coxal lines on the metaventrite and hind coxal lines on the first abdominal ventrite. The tarsal formula is 4-4-4.

| FAMILY | Psephenidae |
|---|---|
| SUBFAMILY | Eubrianacinae |
| DISTRIBUTION | Nearctic: USA (California, Oregon, Nevada) |
| MACROHABITAT | Freshwater habitats |
| MICROHABITAT | In or near water |
| FEEDING HABITS | Probably algivorous and/or detritivorous |
| NOTE | The aquatic larvae in this family have an unusual shape and are referred to as water pennies |

ADULT LENGTH
³⁄₁₆ in
(3.5–5 mm)

*EUBRIANAX EDWARDSI*

# EUBRIANAX EDWARDSI

(LECONTE, 1874)

309

Actual size

Adults of this species are found in riparian habitats, mainly along streams but also near lakes. The females lay eggs on rocks below the water. Larvae develop on or under submerged rocks. They probably graze during the night and on cloudy days upon the crop of diatoms and other algae covering stones in riffles, and retire to the undersides of stones during sunny periods. Mature larvae leave the water and pupate on a solid substrate in a moist area beneath or on the side of a rock or log. Pupation takes place above the water line, up to a few feet or several meters from the water's edge.

## RELATED SPECIES

The genus *Eubrianax* contains 18 species, all occurring in Asia (Japan, China, Taiwan, Philippines), except for *E. edwardsi*, which is found in the western United States. Relationships between the North American and Asiatic species have not yet been studied. A phylogenetic analysis using adult, larval, and pupal characters suggests that *Afrobrianax*, with representatives in Africa, is most closely related to *Eubrianax*.

**Eubrianax edwardsi** is a soft-bodied, oval-shaped beetle with a pale body except for the darker antennae, pronotum, and femora. The head is concealed beneath the pronotum in dorsal view. Male antennae are pectinate, while those of females are serrate. The posterior edge of the pronotum is smooth. The larvae, like those of all Psephenidae, are broadly oval, conspicuously flattened, and colored like the rocks to which they cling.

| FAMILY | Cneoglossidae |
|---|---|
| SUBFAMILY | |
| DISTRIBUTION | Neotropical: Mexico, Nicaragua |
| MACROHABITAT | Tropical streams |
| MICROHABITAT | Adults live near shallow streams with moderate to fast running water; larvae are unknown but presumably occur in submerged rotten wood |
| FEEDING HABITS | Feeding habits of adults are uncertain; the larvae presumably feed on submerged rotten wood |
| NOTE | The pronotum of *Cneoglossa* pupae has a pair of long, narrow, soft, anteriorly directed projections of unknown function in appearance on an unpalatable model |

ADULT LENGTH
³/₁₆ in
(3.5–4 mm)

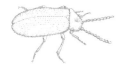

*CNEOGLOSSA LAMPYROIDES*
# CNEOGLOSSA LAMPYROIDES

CHAMPION, 1897

310

Actual size

Very little is known about the biology of this small and enigmatic family of beetles. Most of our knowledge of the group is based on *Cneoglossa edsoni*, described in 1999, but likely applies to all other species in the genus. The larvae occur in submerged rotten wood in small, shallow streams with clear, slightly acid water. The streams typically have a muddy or sandy bottom. The larvae of *C. edsoni* were found together with larvae of other aquatic beetles in the families Lutrochidae and Elmidae.

## RELATED SPECIES

The family Cneoglossidae includes only eight species in a single genus (*Cneoglossus*) and is distributed from Mexico south to Brazil. From the results of a phylogenetic analysis published in 1999, it appears that this family is closely related to the water penny beetles (Psephenidae) based on the shared presence of unique paired dorsal openings on the abdominal tergites of adult. Overall body shape and characters of the antennae, elytra, and prothorax are typically used to separate the species.

**Cneoglossa lampyroides** is a small, elongate-oval, weakly sclerotized beetle with a superficial resemblance to members of the family Lampyridae. The antennae of males are longer than those of females and are serrated from the third antennomere. The head is deeply retracted into the prothorax and difficult to see from above. The elytra are dark brown and the semicircular pronotum is distinctly paler except for a narrow, dark band along the midline. The sides of the pronotum are semitransparent.

| FAMILY | Ptilodactylidae |
| --- | --- |
| SUBFAMILY | Ptilodactylinae |
| DISTRIBUTION | Neotropical: Central America, South America, Caribbean |
| MACROHABITAT | Tropical forests |
| MICROHABITAT | Adults are found on foliage; larvae are found in moist forest litter |
| FEEDING HABITS | Mycophagous |
| NOTE | Part of a Batesian mimicry complex in which unrelated insects all converge in appearance on an unpalatable model |

ADULT LENGTH
¼ in
(6–6.5 mm)

*STIROPHORA LYCIFORMIS*

# STIROPHORA LYCIFORMIS

(CHAMPION, 1897)

311

Several types of mimicry complexes are known among insect species. This species is part of a complex of Batesian mimics in which the adults have converged in appearance to approximate that of lycid (net-winged) beetles. The latter are unpalatable to predators and the mimics benefit from the resemblance. Other insects within the lycid mimicry complex include unrelated members of other families of beetles and even other orders, including Lepidoptera. Details of the life history of *Stirophora lyciformis* are unknown, but the larvae are presumed to be mycophagous in moist organic matter and the adults grazers on exposed leaf surfaces.

## RELATED SPECIES

Two species of *Stirophora* are described, with *S. lyciformis* being the more widespread. Due to the diversity of insect taxa that share the general appearance of lycid beetles in the mimicry complex, members are often misplaced in collections. Knowledge of the constituent taxa in the complex is important to ensure correct identification in the field and to recovering specimens in collections.

**Stirophora lyciformis** is unusual among members of the family Ptilodactylidae in possessing boldly bicolored orange and brown elytra and pronotum. This color pattern is typical of other members of the Batesian lycid mimicry complex. The strongly pectinate antennae are typical of other members of the family, which are usually drab brown in dorsal coloration.

Actual size

| FAMILY | Podabrocephalidae |
|---|---|
| SUBFAMILY | |
| DISTRIBUTION | Oriental: southern India |
| MACROHABITAT | Forests |
| MICROHABITAT | On branches lying on the ground |
| FEEDING HABITS | Unknown |
| NOTE | This species is known from only a small number of adult males |

ADULT LENGTH
³⁄₁₆ in
(3.8–5.2 mm)

312

*PODABROCEPHALUS SINUATICOLLIS*
# PODABROCEPHALUS
# SINUATICOLLIS
PIC, 1913

Actual size

Beetles such as *Podabrocephalus sinuaticollis* have provided and continue to provide a source of curiosity and wonder for experts and non-experts alike. This species is known only from male specimens from southern India, and nothing is known about its ecology or feeding habits. The unique mandibles of the species are modified into long, narrow, unidentate, strongly curved structures, and their function remains unknown. We hope that this book will stimulate the discovery of more knowledge concerning this and other poorly understood species.

### RELATED SPECIES

The classification of the family Podabrocephalidae, which contains only *Podabrocephalus sinuaticollis*, has been a source of debate that continues to this day. Affinities with the family Ptilodactylidae seem likely since both groups share similar features (e.g., cells in the flight wings and the first three abdominal ventrites fused), but this has not been confirmed. The lack of knowledge is hampering efforts toward understanding the relationships of this species with other beetles.

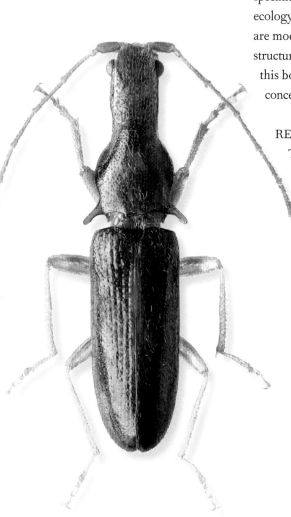

**Podabrocephalus sinuaticollis** is an unusual-looking elongated, parallel-sided, flattened beetle. The head, thorax, and elytra are reddish brown to dark brown, while the legs and antennae are yellowish. The long head bears circular and protruding eyes. The long, narrow antennae give the beetle a superficially similar appearance to that of some longhorn beetles. The pronotum ends posteriorly with a narrow, oblique projection at each corner.

| FAMILY | Chelonariidae |
| --- | --- |
| SUBFAMILY | |
| DISTRIBUTION | Neotropical: Colombia (Bogotá), Brazil (Minas Gerais, São Paulo), Argentina |
| MACROHABITAT | Poorly known, but probably forested areas |
| MICROHABITAT | Soil surface |
| FEEDING HABITS | Larvae are presumed to be detritivorous; feeding habits of adults are uncertain |
| NOTE | The head of these beetles rests in the prosternum, exposing only the eyes and the antennae in ventral view |

ADULT LENGTH
³⁄₁₆–¼ in
(5–6.5 mm)

*CHELONARIUM ORNATUM*

# CHELONARIUM ORNATUM

KLUG, 1825

313

The genus *Chelonarium* is mainly represented in the Neotropical Realm (215 species and subspecies), but also occurs in Asia and the Nearctic (one species), and in Australia (one species). Adults of *Chelonarium* are attracted to lights and have been collected from vegetation with sweep nets or in refuse heaps of ants. The larvae, once presumed to be aquatic, are in fact terrestrial since they lack retractile anal gills. Larvae of some tropical species were found in litter on the forest floor and under bark or in packing around roots of plants (mainly Orchidaceae). Data suggest that some species may be associated with ants or termites as inquilines or refuse-feeders.

Actual size

## RELATED SPECIES

*Chelonarium* is apparently closely related to the genus *Pseudochelonarium*, species of which are found in India, Southeast Asia, and New Guinea. Although the relationships between the species have not been studied, *C. ornatum* belongs to a species group that contains only one other species, *C. signatum*. The two species can be separated by their overall body shape and color patterns.

**Chelonarium ornatum** is a small, compact, oblong, brownish beetle with a glabrous dorsal surface. The elytra have a sinuous, longitudinal, lightly colored band on each side. The head is strongly declined and not visible in dorsal view. Antennal segments 3 and 4 are enlarged, fitting into a cavity on the mesoventrite. The pronotum is bordered by a strong ridge anteriorly and laterally.

| FAMILY | Eulichadidae |
|---|---|
| SUBFAMILY | |
| DISTRIBUTION | Oriental: Peninsular Malaysia (Kelantan, Pahang, Perak) |
| MACROHABITAT | Forest |
| MICROHABITAT | In or near streams |
| FEEDING HABITS | Adults possibly do not feed; larvae are presumably detritivorous |
| NOTE | The adults superficially resemble species of click beetles (Elateridae) |

ADULT MALE LENGTH
¾–¹⁵⁄₁₆ in
(20–24 mm)

ADULT FEMALE LENGTH
1¹⁄₃₂–1³⁄₁₆ in
(26–30 mm)

314

*EULICHAS SERRICORNIS*
# EULICHAS SERRICORNIS
HÁJEK, 2009

Known larvae in *Eulichas* are aquatic and found mainly in the sandy substrate of clean forest streams. A study of the gut content of larvae of one species showed that they feed on wood particles. Adults are considered to be short-lived and are particularly attracted to artificial lights, where males are much more common than females. Adults of *E. serricornis* are typically found sitting on vegetation near riverbanks or streams in mountain rainforests.

### RELATED SPECIES

Two genera are included in this small family: *Eulichas*, with about 30 species, mostly in the Oriental Realm although a few species reach the border of the Palearctic Realm in Nepal, Bhutan, northern India, and China; and *Stenocolus*, with a single species in California. *Eulichas sausai* from Sumatra is morphologically most similar to *E. serricornis* but differs mainly in having less serrate antennomeres, the last one being rectangular instead of filiform.

**Eulichas serricornis** is an elongate, fusiform reddish-brown to brown beetle covered with recumbent setae that form a distinctly colored pattern on the elytra. The eyes are large. Antennomeres 3–10 are markedly serrate and the last antennomere is filiform, four to five times as long as it is broad. The pronotum is trapezoidal, with almost regularly rounded sides. The elytra have punctures arranged in distinct longitudinal rows. The flight wings are well developed.

Actual size

| FAMILY | Callirhipidae |
| --- | --- |
| SUBFAMILY | |
| DISTRIBUTION | Neotropical: Colombia, Costa Rica, Guatemala, Mexico, Nicaragua, Panama |
| MACROHABITAT | In forests, sometimes at higher elevation |
| MICROHABITAT | Adults on bushes, under loose bark; larvae in dead wood |
| FEEDING HABITS | Adult feeding habits are uncertain—they probably do not feed; larvae feed in rotting wood |
| NOTE | Larvae in this family are known to take two years or more to develop, while the adults are very short-lived |

*CELADONIA LAPORTEI*

# CELADONIA LAPORTEI

(HOPE, 1846)

ADULT LENGTH
³⁄₈–⁹⁄₁₆ in
(9–15 mm)

315

The correct position of this family within the classification of beetles has been difficult to determine, due in part to the great variability in external and internal structures, as well as pronounced differences between the sexes, in most species. Although adults of most species in this family are nocturnal and are sometimes attracted to artificial lights, the bicolored species in *Celadonia* and the Asian *Horatocera* are thought to have diurnal habits. The elongate, cylindrical, dark reddish-brown larvae of *C. laportei* have been encountered in standing rotten trunks and can reach more than ⅞ in (22 mm) in length.

Actual size

## RELATED SPECIES

Callirhipidae currently includes ten genera and approximately 200 species, which are distributed worldwide throughout warmer regions. A single species, *Zenoa picea*, occurs in the United States. The Neotropical genus *Celadonia* includes eight species and the two subspecies, *C. laportei laportei* (widespread) and *C. l. nigroimpressa* (restricted to Panama).

**Celadonia laportei** adults are extremely variable in color and size. The pronotum can vary from completely yellowish orange to having a conspicuous longitudinal black band in the center. The elytra, which have four longitudinal costae, can vary from entirely yellowish orange to completely black, with intermediates showing various combinations of both colors. The 11-segmented antennae have extensions on antennomeres 3–11, these being much longer in the males.

| FAMILY | Rhinorhipidae |
|---|---|
| SUBFAMILY | |
| DISTRIBUTION | Australian: Australia (southeast Queensland) |
| MACROHABITAT | At the edge of high-elevation rainforest |
| MICROHABITAT | Near creeks on low vegetation |
| FEEDING HABITS | Unknown |
| NOTE | When disturbed, adults feign death and drop to the ground |

**ADULT MALE LENGTH**
³⁄₁₆–⁵⁄₁₆ in
(5.1–7.5 mm)

**ADULT FEMALE LENGTH**
¼–³⁄₈ in
(6.4–8.5 mm)

316

*RHINORHIPUS TAMBORINENSIS*
# RHINORHIPUS TAMBORINENSIS
LAWRENCE, 1988

Actual size

*Rhinorhipus tamborinensis* is one the rarest beetles in Australia. It has been assigned to its own family (Rhinorhipidae) and its relationships to other beetles are not clear, although it is currently considered a likely relative of the click beetles (family Elateridae). Several morphological characters are unique to the species. Females differ from males by the shorter antennae and shorter, straight legs. The larvae are unknown. Most of the specimens known to science are males that were collected during four days in October 1978 on low vegetation by John Lawrence and Tom Weir of the Australian National Insect Collection. Several subsequent attempts to recapture this species, including by authors of this book, have failed to discover more individuals.

## RELATED SPECIES
The family Rhinorhipidae contains a single species worldwide, the enigmatic Australian *Rhinorhipus tamborinensis*. It has been classified as a member of the superfamily Elateroidea in recent literature, although some analyses indicate that it could also be related to beetles in the superfamily Dascilloidea (families Rhipiceridae and Dascillidae). When found, the larvae will undoubtedly shed light on the affinities of this species.

**Rhinorhipus tamborinensis** is a small grayish-black beetle whose dorsal surface is covered with pale setae. The eyes are large and protuberant. The antennae are long and filiform, much longer in males. The body is elongate, slightly flattened above, with elytra that are nearly parallel in dorsal view. At its base, the pronotum is narrower than the width of the elytra. The legs are long and adapted for climbing on vegetation.

| FAMILY | Artematopodidae |
|---|---|
| SUBFAMILY | Artematopodinae |
| DISTRIBUTION | Nearctic: Ontario in Canada, south to Kansas and Virginia in the USA |
| MACROHABITAT | Granitic rocks |
| MICROHABITAT | Under lichen (*Umbilicaria* spp.) |
| FEEDING HABITS | Probably bryophagous (feeds on lichens) |
| NOTE | Species in this family have an unusual tongue-like structure on the ventral surface of the elytra near the apex |

ADULT LENGTH
³⁄₁₆ in
(3.5–4.5 mm)

*EURYPOGON NIGER*

# EURYPOGON NIGER

(MELSHEIMER, 1846)

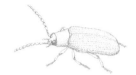

317

Actual size

The small family Artematopodidae includes eight extant genera worldwide (e.g., *Carcinognathus* from Peru, and *Macropogon*, which occurs throughout the north of North America and in eastern Asia), in addition to *Proartematopus* and *Electrapate*, which are known only from Baltic amber fossils. A study based on molecular data published in 2013 suggests that this family might be closely related to Omethidae and Telegeusidae, which are also included in the superfamily Elateroidea. The only biological information associated with *Eurypogon niger* is that a teneral adult (recently emerged from the pupal case) and a full-grown larva of this species were found under growths of a lichen (*Umbilicara* spp.) on granitic rocks in the Great Smoky Mountains of Tennessee.

RELATED SPECIES

In addition to *Eurypogon niger*, there are another ten species in the genus *Eurypogon*, two in North America (*E. californicus* and *E. harrisii*) and the others in Europe, Japan, Taiwan, and China (e.g., *E. brevipennis* and *E. japonicus*). *Eurypogon niger* can be distinguished from the other species in that the coarse and dense punctures of the elytra form longitudinal striae.

**Eurypogon niger** is a small, dark brown beetle with fine punctures on the pronotum and elytra. The dorsal surface of the body is covered with dense, fine yellowish setae and the antennae are quite long. The head is not usually visible in dorsal view and the prothorax is narrower than the elytra. The elytra have well-defined longitudinal punctate striae.

| FAMILY | Brachypsectridae |
| --- | --- |
| SUBFAMILY | |
| DISTRIBUTION | Nearactic and Neotropical: California to Colorado, Texas, and northern Mexico |
| MACROHABITAT | Wide variety of dry desert and wooded habitats |
| MICROHABITAT | Adults and larvae under bark, bits of wood, and other debris |
| FEEDING HABITS | Larvae prey on small insects and arachnids |
| NOTE | It took 25 years to associate the adult with its enigmatic larva |

ADULT LENGTH
³⁄₁₆–¼ in
(4–7 mm)

318

*BRACHYPSECTRA FULVA*
# TEXAS BEETLE
LECONTE, 1874

Actual size

Rarely encountered, Texas Beetles are short-lived and active in late spring and summer. Only the males are attracted to lights at night. Their slow-moving larvae are broad, flat, and covered with tough, highly modified scales. They are armed with finely branched thoracic and abdominal processes and a flexible spine on the abdomen. They live under flaking pine bark or pieces of wood, or in rock crevices, and prey on small arthropods. The larva ambushes its victims by arching its back and trapping prey between its perforated sucking mandibles and abdominal spine. Mature larvae pupate within delicate, loosely constructed silken cocoons.

## RELATED SPECIES
The family Brachypsectridae consists of three additional extant and rarely encountered species, all in the genus *Brachypsectra*: *B. vivafosile*, from the Dominican Republic; *B. lampyroides*, from southern India; and *B. fuscula*, from Singapore. Another undescribed species from northern Australia is known only from larvae. Adults and larvae of *B. moronei* were described from Miocene amber found in the Dominican Republic.

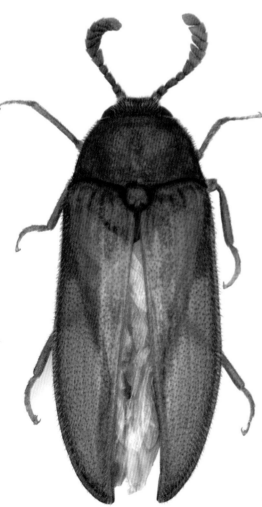

**The Texas Beetle** is oblong, broad, somewhat soft bodied and flattened, yellowish brown, and clothed with sparse, fine pubescence. The antennae are 11-segmented with antennomeres 4, 5, or 6–11 weakly comb-like, or pectinate. The pronotum is wider than long. The elytra are weakly grooved and cover the abdomen completely. The claws lack teeth, or are simple. The heavier-bodied female has less developed antennae.

| FAMILY | Cerophytidae |
|---|---|
| SUBFAMILY | |
| DISTRIBUTION | Palearctic: Japan |
| MACROHABITAT | Forested areas |
| MICROHABITAT | Low vegetation and bark |
| FEEDING HABITS | Unknown |
| NOTE | The only species of the family Cerophytidae that occurs in Asia |

ADULT LENGTH
¼–⁵⁄₁₆ in
(7–7.5 mm)

*CEROPHYTUM JAPONICUM*

# CEROPHYTUM JAPONICUM

SASAJI, 1999

319

Actual size

The small family Cerophytidae, which contains three genera and 21 species, occurs primarily in Europe and the Americas, although fossil records indicated that the group was once more diverse and more widely distributed. *Cerophytum japonicum* is the only representative of the family in Asia. Adults and larvae of the family have been associated with rotten wood, bark, leaf litter, and underground debris. Adults of *C. japonicum* have tarsal claws with a small comb-like structure at the base, and seem to be very uncommon.

**Cerophytum japonicum** is a brown beetle with fine setae covering the dorsal surface, well-marked striae on the elytra, and a densely punctured pronotum that is narrower than the elytra. The antennae are long and moderately to strongly pectinated. The eyes are large and slightly protuberant. The legs are brown and are adapted for walking.

## RELATED SPECIES

The shape of the antenna in *Cerophytum japonicum* resembles that of the North American *C. convexicolle*, specifically the third antennomere of the males, where the ramus is inserted medially instead of basally as in other species. A detailed study of the male genitalia is necessary to establish the boundaries and relationships of this species.

| | |
|---|---|
| FAMILY | Eucnemidae |
| SUBFAMILY | Palaeoxeninae |
| DISTRIBUTION | Nearctic: Transverse and Peninsular ranges of southern California |
| MACROHABITAT | Montane coniferous forests |
| MICROHABITAT | Adults found under bark of decaying Incense Cedar logs and stumps |
| FEEDING HABITS | Adult feeding habits are unknown; larvae bore into bark and wood |
| NOTE | One of the most striking eucnemids in the world |

ADULT LENGTH
½–¾ in
(13–19 mm)

320

*PALAEOXENUS DORHNI*
# DORHN'S ELEGANT EUCNEMID BEETLE
(HORN, 1878)

In a family of beetles with species typically brown or black, the bicolored Dorhn's Elegant Eucnemid Beetle stands out. Both adults and larvae are found in the lower portions of Incense Cedar (*Calocedrus decurrens*) stumps and under the bark of old trunks of Bigcone Douglas-fir (*Pseudotsuga macrocarpa*). Adults are reported from logs of dead Sugar Pine (*Pinus lambertiana*), perhaps erroneously, and flying at dusk. The rarity of this species, combined with its limited range and lack of close relatives, has resulted in its placement on California's Special Animal List by the Department of Fish and Game for further monitoring.

RELATED SPECIES
The popular name of this family, "false click beetles," is misleading because many species do have the ability to "click" like click beetles. Eucnemids are distinguished from click beetles by lacking a labrum and by having all five abdominal ventrites fused together. Dorhn's Elegant Eucnemid Beetle is the only species in the genus and is easily distinguished from all other North American eucnemids by its red and black color.

**Dorhn's Elegant Eucnemid Beetle** is boldly bicolored. The head, first antennal segment, pronotum, "shoulders" and tips of elytra, and the ventral surface are blood red, while the remainder of the body is black. The last three antennomeres are enlarged and the very tip is not hollowed out. The front tibiae have two spurs at the very tip. All claws are simple underneath, that is, they lack teeth or a comb.

Actual size

| FAMILY | Eucnemidae |
|---|---|
| SUBFAMILY | Eucneminae |
| DISTRIBUTION | Oriental and Australian: India, Indonesia, Philippines, Papua New Guinea, Solomon Islands |
| MACROHABITAT | Tropical forest |
| MICROHABITAT | Adults and larvae live on logs |
| FEEDING HABITS | Larvae feed on dead wood |
| NOTE | Females in this species are typically slightly larger than males |

ADULT LENGTH
¼–⁹⁄₁₆ in
(6.5–14 mm)

*GALBITES AURICOLOR*
# GALBITES AURICOLOR
(BONVOULOIR, 1875)

321

As in related beetles in the click beetle family Elateridae, adult eucnemids (including *Galbites auricolor*) are elongate and cylindrical, and are capable of clicking by using a prosternal spine and its associated mesoventral cavity. *Galbites*, the type genus for the tribe Galbitini, comprises 31 described species spread in the Indo-Malaysian region. Most of its species have partially pectinate antennae and their pronota have gibbosities (convex projections). The biology of this species is poorly known, but larvae of related species develop in dead wood, while adults are attracted to artificial lights and can be collected with flight-intercept traps.

Actual size

### RELATED SPECIES
*Galbites auricolor* belongs to a species group characterized by having a median ridge on the head and dense scales on the body. The *auricolor* species group includes: *G. albiventris*, *G. australiae*, *G. bicolor*, *G. chrysocoma*, *G. modiglianii*, *G. sericata*, and *G. tigrina*. The species in this group can be primarily separated by differences in the patterns of scales on their pronotum, scutellum, and elytra, as well as examination of the male genitalia.

**Galbites auricolor** adults have a black to dark brown integument and brown tarsi. The dorsal surface is covered with dense golden-yellow setae. The head is partially visible in dorsal view. The antenna is short, compact, and pectinated. The prothorax is large and as broad as the base of the elytra. The elytral striae are vaguely impressed.

| FAMILY | Elateridae |
| --- | --- |
| SUBFAMILY | Cebrioninae |
| DISTRIBUTION | Nearctic: Louisiana and Texas |
| MACROHABITAT | Semiarid prairies and southeastern plains |
| MICROHABITAT | Males are found on vegetation or are attracted to lights |
| FEEDING HABITS | Unknown |
| NOTE | The flight of males is usually triggered by heavy rain. The female of this species, presumed to be flightless, is unknown |

ADULT LENGTH
⅝ –¾ in
(16–20 mm)

*SCAPTOLENUS LECONTEI*
# LECONTE'S RAIN CLICK BEETLE
CHEVROLAT, 1874

John LeConte erected the genus *Scaptolenus* for his species *femoralis* in 1853. However, French coleopterist Louis Chevrolat had previously described *Cebrio femoralis* from Mexico and later decided that it, too, belonged in *Scaptolenus*. Due to the rules of priority, Chevrolat renamed LeConte's *femoralis* and chose the epithet *lecontei* in honor of his American colleague. Males of several species of *Scaptolenus* are reported to take flight during or just after heavy afternoon or evening rain showers to search for the flightless females. *Scaptolenus lecontei* males are typically found on vegetation or at lights in fall and winter, and emit a strong odor.

## RELATED SPECIES

*Scaptolenus*, with 32 species distributed from Arizona, Texas, and Louisiana south to Panama, reaches its greatest diversity in Mexico and Guatemala, and is in need of revision. Only three described species are known to occur in the United States. *Scaptolenus lecontei* is distinguished from *S. estriatus* and *S. ocreatus* by its larger size and distinctly grooved elytra.

**LeConte's Rain Click Beetle** is dark brown to blackish and moderately shiny, with pale chestnut elytra. The head is coarsely punctate. The pronotum is narrowed in front and sinuate at the base, with a densely punctate surface covered with long brown setae. The ventral surface is clothed in moderately long and dense yellowish setae. In mature adults, the legs are bicolored, with the femora pale yellowish and the tibiae and tarsi blackish.

Actual size

| FAMILY | Elateridae |
|---|---|
| SUBFAMILY | Agrypninae |
| DISTRIBUTION | Nearctic: mountains of southeastern Arizona |
| MACROHABITAT | Canyon bottoms along streams |
| MICROHABITAT | Tree limbs riddled with wood-boring beetle larvae |
| FEEDING HABITS | Adults and larvae probably prey on wood-boring beetles and larvae |
| NOTE | Known only from Arizona |

ADULT LENGTH
1⁹⁄₁₆–1¹⁵⁄₁₆ in
(39–49 mm)

*ALAUS ZUNIANUS*

# ALAUS ZUNIANUS

CASEY, 1893

323

*Alaus zunianus* is known only from the canyons of the Sky Islands of southeastern Arizona. Adults are active from spring through late summer, but peak during the summer monsoons in July and August. Although occasionally attracted to lights at night, they are usually found on the larger limbs and trunks of hardwoods, especially Arizona Sycamore (*Platanus wrightii*), that are infested with wood-boring beetles. The adults, larvae, and pupae are found in the galleries of longhorn wood-boring beetles (Cerambycidae) chewed in American Sycamore trees. The larva has never been formally described.

## RELATED SPECIES

*Alaus* includes 11 species distributed mostly in North and Central America, and the West Indies. All but one Mexican species are distinguished from other New World click beetle genera by the eyelike spots on the pronotum. *Alaus lusciosus*, from the south-central United States, has eye-spots closer to the sides of the pronotum than *A. zunianus*.

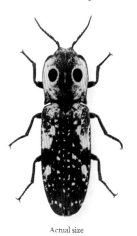

**Alaus zunianus** is black and covered with yellowish-white or white and black scales. The two velvety, round eyelike spots are either equidistant or closer to the middle than the sides, and are ringed by whitish pubescence that blends with the bands along the sides. The elytra each have three larger and some smaller uneven patches of pubescence.

Actual size

| FAMILY | Elateridae |
|---|---|
| SUBFAMILY | Agrypninae |
| DISTRIBUTION | Oriental and Australian: southern India; Sri Lanka; Samoa; Viti Levu, Fiji |
| MACROHABITAT | Coconut groves and rubber plantations |
| MICROHABITAT | Adults on trunks and stems; larvae bore into insect-infested wood |
| FEEDING HABITS | Adults and larvae are predators of wood-boring insect larvae |
| NOTE | Used as a biological control for the Coconut Rhinoceros Beetle (*Oryctes rhinoceros*) |

ADULT LENGTH
1–1½ in
(25–38 mm)

324

*CALAIS SPECIOSUS*
# CALAIS SPECIOSUS
(LINNAEUS, 1767)

Adults of *Calais speciosus* occur on felled and sawn timber, and the trunks and logs of palms and rubber trees (*Hevea brasiliensis*). Their black and white pattern camouflages them on fungus-ridden wood. The predatory larvae hunt for *Oryctes* grubs burrowing inside palm trunks, and they have been used as a biological control in Samoa since 1955 to control the Coconut Rhinoceros Beetle, a major pest of the Coconut Palm (*Cocos nucifera*) and other palm species. They also inhabit other infested logs, especially of Kapok (*Ceiba pentandra*), where they attack the larvae of longhorn beetles such as *Olethrius*.

RELATED SPECIES

The genus *Calais* is included in the Hemirhipini, a tribe that contains 30 genera from around the world, several of which are large and distinctly patterned. *Calais* contains 183 species inhabiting the Afrotropical, Australian, Oriental, and Palearctic realms. *Calais speciosus* is distinguished by its relatively round and convex prothorax, dense pubescence, bold black and white pattern, and truncate elytral tips.

**Calais speciosus** is boldly marked with patches of dense black and white pubescence over a shining black integument. The antennae are black. The convex prothorax is sinuate along its sides, with medial black markings not extended to the front, two round black spots, and black posterior angles. The elytra are widest at the middle and truncate at the tips. The legs are white with black tips to the femora and tarsi.

Actual size

| FAMILY | Elateridae |
| --- | --- |
| SUBFAMILY | Agrypninae |
| DISTRIBUTION | Neotropical: Virgin Islands, northern and central South America |
| MACROHABITAT | Tropical forests |
| MICROHABITAT | Adults are likely found on trees; the larvae probably develop in infested wood |
| FEEDING HABITS | Adults and larvae likely prey on wood-boring beetles and larvae |
| NOTE | The genus *Chalcolepidius* contains many colorful and boldly marked species |

ADULT LENGTH
⅞–1⅝ in
(22–42 mm)

*CHALCOLEPIDIUS LIMBATUS*
# CHALCOLEPIDIUS LIMBATUS
ESCHSCHOLTZ, 1829

325

The physician and naturalist Johann Friedrich Eschscholtz (1793–1831) erected *Chalcolepidius* in 1829, and *C. limbatus* was one of the first seven species he included in the genus. Little is known of the species' biology other than that individuals have been kept in captivity for six months on a diet of honey and water. *Chalcolepidius* adults are typically collected on sapping branches and tree trunks, under bark, or on flowers. The predatory larvae usually develop in deciduous trees, where they prey on wood-boring beetle larvae and termites.

RELATED SPECIES

The genus *Chalcolepidius* contains 63 species that are widely distributed in the New World, in the southern United States and throughout most of South America. *Chalcolepidius limbatus* is distinguished from the other 21 South American species in the genus by its overall color, whitish or yellow stripes on the sides of the pronotum and elytra, elytral grooves, and elytral margins that are turned under (epipleura).

Actual size

**Chalcolepidius limbatus** is broad, black, and densely clothed with metallic olive-green, olive-gray, olive-brown, bluish, or violet pubescence, and yellowish-white or yellowish-brown stripes. The dark area between the broad stripes along the sides of the pronotum is elliptical. The elytra have broad, complete side stripes and embrace three rows of punctures. Males have fringes of setae on their tibiae.

| | |
|---|---|
| FAMILY | Elateridae |
| SUBFAMILY | Agrypninae |
| DISTRIBUTION | Afrotropical: Madagascar |
| MACROHABITAT | Forested areas |
| MICROHABITAT | On tree branches and trunks |
| FEEDING HABITS | Herbivore |
| NOTE | This charismatic species is well known for its large size and the eye-shaped color pattern on its pronotum |

ADULT LENGTH
⅞–1⅜ in
(23–35 mm)

326

*LYCOREUS CORPULENTUS*
# ONE-EYED MADAGASCAR CLICK BEETLE
CANDÈZE, 1889

*Lycoreus* is an endemic genus of click beetles that occurs on the island of Madagascar. *Lycoreus corpulentus* is arguably the most popular species in the genus among beetle collectors, specifically because of its large size and the characteristic, unusual color pattern on its dorsal surface. The biology of this species is poorly known. A study published in the late 1970s revealed that the short, slightly overlapping white scales on the dorsal surface of *L. corpulentus* contribute to ultraviolet reflectance, a widely distributed phenomenon among species in certain families of beetles such as Carabidae, Scarabaeidae, Elateridae, and Tenebrionidae.

## RELATED SPECIES

Twelve species of *Lycoreus* occur in Madagascar, and most of the information available for each species is based on their very brief original descriptions. There are very few illustrations or comparative keys available for the species. The relationships between the species are not well understood and are in need of modern comparative attention. *Lycoreus corpulentus* is separated by its distinctive color pattern.

**The One-eyed Madagascar Click Beetle** is a large and robust beetle with black integument and pale scales. The pronotum has a large median circular glabrous area surrounded by bands of scales and additional glabrous areas, which produces the shape of an eye. The elytra are covered with patchy patterns of pale scales on the basal half and lines of scales toward the apex.

Actual size

| FAMILY | Elateridae |
|---|---|
| SUBFAMILY | Agrypninae |
| DISTRIBUTION | Neotropical: Mexico to South America and the Caribbean |
| MACROHABITAT | Tropical forests |
| MICROHABITAT | Adults are active on vegetation at night; larvae live in the soil |
| FEEDING HABITS | Adults and larvae eat plant materials and small insects |
| NOTE | *Pyrophorus* and fireflies use the same light-producing system |

ADULT LENGTH
¾–1⁹⁄₁₆ in
(20–40 mm)

*PYROPHORUS NOCTILUCUS*
# PYROPHORUS NOCTILUCUS
(LINNAEUS, 1758)

327

Species of *Pyrophorus* are sometimes called "headlight beetles" because they produce an intense and steady greenish glow from a pair of bioluminescent spots on the pronotum. They also have a broad orangish light-producing area underneath the first visible abdominal segment. The larvae and pupae are also bioluminescent. The first recognition that light emission from bioluminescent organisms is due to a luciferin–luciferase reaction came from studying extracts from *P. noctilucus* in the late 19th century. This important observation was the starting-point for studies with many other bioluminescent organisms including bacteria, fungi, dinoflagellates, mollusks, crustaceans, other insects, and many other groups.

RELATED SPECIES

The genus *Pyrophorus* includes 32 species living in tropical forests from Mexico to South America. Species are distinguished from other bioluminescent genera of click beetles by their large size, short antennae that do not extend to the posterior pronotal angles, convex light-producing organs closer to the sides than the posterior margin of the pronotum, and lack of apparent sexual dimorphism.

**Pyrophorus noctilucus** is robust, plain dark brown, and clothed in short, dense yellowish pubescence. The antennae are short and serrate after the third antennomere. The pronotum is convex, with prominent, sharp, more or less divergent spines, and convex light-producing organs. The abdomen has a transverse elliptical light-producing organ in the gap between the first visible abdominal ventrite and the metathorax. This light organ is usually concealed when the beetle is at rest.

Actual size

| FAMILY | Elateridae |
|---|---|
| SUBFAMILY | Thylacosterninae |
| DISTRIBUTION | Neotropical: Peru, Bolivia, French Guiana; also reported from Brazil, but without more precise data |
| MACROHABITAT | Forested areas |
| MICROHABITAT | On tree branches and trunks |
| FEEDING HABITS | Probably feeds on plants |
| NOTE | Adults of this rare species possess a pair of rounded, bioluminescent green tubercles on the pronotum |

ADULT LENGTH
¾–1³⁄₁₆ in
(20–30 mm)

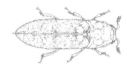

*BALGUS SCHNUSEI*
# BALGUS SCHNUSEI
(HELLER, 1914)

Species in the unusual-looking Neotropical genus *Balgus* have been occurring in the family Throscidae (e.g., because of their very small labrum) or in the family Eucnemidae (e.g., because of their deeply flabellate antennae), and for some time *B. schnusei* was regarded as the only bioluminescent species within the Throscidae. However, phylogenetic analyses based on morphological and molecular data have confirmed that *Balgus* belongs to the click beetle family Elateridae. In this family, approximately 200 species in the tribe Pyrophorini, one species in the subfamily Campyloxeninae (*Campyloxenus pyrothorax*), and *B. schnusei* are the only species with bioluminescent organs placed on the prothorax.

RELATED SPECIES
The click beetle subfamily Thylacosterninae contains five genera (*Lumumbaia* in tropical Africa, *Cussolenis* in Asia and Australia, plus *Balgus*, *Thylacosternus*, and *Pterotarsus* in the Neotropical Realm) and approximately 45 described species. The genus *Balgus* includes the following species: *B. albofasciatus*, *B. eganensis*, *B. eschscholtzi*, *B. humilis*, *B. obconicus*, *B. rugosus*, *B. subfasciatus*, and *B. tuberculosus*; *B. schnusei* is the only one with a pair of bioluminescent organs on its pronotum.

**Balgus schnusei** is a small brown click beetle. Its head is poorly visible from above. The prothorax is as broad as the base of the elytra and detailed examination shows prominent tubercles on the pronotum, two of which (laterally) are bioluminescent organs. The antennae are flabellate, short, and compact, with a large first antennomere. The elytra have small elongate tubercles covered with scales.

Actual size

| | |
|---|---|
| FAMILY | Elateridae |
| SUBFAMILY | Lissominae |
| DISTRIBUTION | Palearctic: Europe and Asia |
| MACROHABITAT | Temperate forest |
| MICROHABITAT | Logs and tree trunks |
| FEEDING HABITS | Dead wood |
| NOTE | This small species is more broadly distributed in the Palearctic Realm than other species in *Drapetes* |

ADULT LENGTH
⅛ –¼ in
(3–5.5 mm)

*DRAPETES MORDELLOIDES*
# DRAPETES MORDELLOIDES
(HOST, 1789)

329

*Drapetes mordelloides*, which has a life cycle that lasts approximately two years, feeds on dead wood and is hence a saproxylophagous beetle. This species is distributed in the southern and central parts of Europe, reaching north to Denmark, Fennoscandia, the southern province of Leningrad, and east through Siberia. *Drapetes mordelloides* apparently prefers trees with fungi that are exposed to the sun. The genus *Drapetes* was classified in the family Throscidae for a long time, although its systematic position as a member of the click beetle subfamily Lissominae is now well established and supported by larval characters.

RELATED SPECIES

The genus *Drapetes* comprises several species and is worldwide in distribution. A comprehensive study of all the species is essential to identify the related species of *D. mordelloides*. In the Palearctic Realm, there are eight species and subspecies known within *Drapetes* (e.g., *D. abei* in Japan and *D. flavipes flavipes* in Cyprus).

Actual size

**Drapetes mordelloides** is a small click beetle whose body is mainly black except for the bicolored elytra. The entire dorsal surface is sparsely setose and the integument is shiny. The head is partially withdrawn within the prothorax. The antennae are serrated and moderately long. The prothorax is as broad as the base of the elytra.

| FAMILY | Elateridae |
|---|---|
| SUBFAMILY | Semiotinae |
| DISTRIBUTION | Neotropical: southern Argentina and Chile |
| MACROHABITAT | Southern temperate oceanic forest |
| MICROHABITAT | Coniferous forests |
| FEEDING HABITS | Adults and larvae are probably predators on insects that infest *Araucaria* |
| NOTE | This species occurs the farthest south of any *Semiotus* |

ADULT LENGTH
⅞–1⅜ in
(21–35 mm)

330

*SEMIOTUS LUTEIPENNIS*
# SEMIOTUS LUTEIPENNIS
(GUÉRIN-MÉNEVILLE, 1839)

Adults and larvae of *Semiotus luteipennis* have been collected on the Monkey Puzzle Tree (*Araucaria araucana*). The larvae develop in decaying logs of this and other species, where they presumably feed on the larvae of flies and wood-boring beetles infesting the wood. The dirty yellowish-white pupae have antennae detached along their length from the rest of the body, two spines on the anterior margin of the pronotum, wings and elytra folded beneath the body, and various spines on the dorsal and ventral surfaces of the abdomen. Adults begin emerging in November and remain active through March.

## RELATED SPECIES

The Neotropical genus *Semiotus* consists of 82 mostly brightly colored and distinctively patterned species, and reaches its greatest diversity in Colombia, Ecuador, and Brazil. *Semiotus luteipennis* has the most southerly distribution of all members of the genus and is distinguished by its nearly black underside, orangish pronotal and elytral side margins, and the configuration of the elytral tips.

**Semiotus luteipennis** has a black head that is lobed, not spiny, in front. The black antennae are serrate. The pronotum is black and flanked by orange or orange-brown stripes, is not evenly convex, and has narrow grooves along each side. The elytra are orangish brown with the tips each bearing two small spines or teeth. The underside is almost entirely black. The tarsal pads are membranous.

Actual size

| FAMILY | Elateridae |
|---|---|
| SUBFAMILY | Campyloxeninae |
| DISTRIBUTION | Neotropical: Chile (Arauco, Cautín, Valdivia, Llanquihue, Chiloé, Aysén), Argentina (Río Negro) |
| MACROHABITAT | Southern temperate forest |
| MICROHABITAT | On tree branches and trunks |
| FEEDING HABITS | Probably feeds on plants |
| NOTE | This species of click beetle is remarkable for its taxonomic isolation within the family Elateridae |

ADULT LENGTH
½–⁹⁄₁₆ in
(13–14 mm)

*CAMPYLOXENUS PYROTHORAX*

# CAMPYLOXENUS PYROTHORAX

FAIRMAIRE & GERMAIN, 1860

331

The unique click beetle *Campyloxenus pyrothorax* used to be classified in the subfamily Agrypninae because of the presence of bioluminescent organs on its pronotum (which are vaguely reminiscent of those present in members of the tribe Pyrophorini). However, the new subfamily Campyloxeninae was proposed by click beetle expert Cleide Costa in 1975, since the adults of *C. pyrothorax* lack some important morphological structures found in Agrypninae species. The larvae of *C. pyrothorax* remain unknown and the biology of the species is poorly understood. Abdominal luminous organs are absent in adults.

RELATED SPECIES

*Campyloxenus pyrothorax* is the only species in this Neotropical genus and the only member of the subfamily Campyloxeninae. It differs from members of other Elateridae subfamilies in having tarsal claws without setae near the base, as well as unique characteristics on its hind wings and the female genitalia.

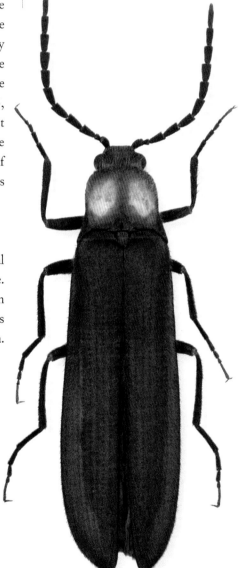

**Campyloxenus pyrothorax** resembles a typical elongate click beetle, its dark brown body covered with fine, dense brown setae. The slightly convex pronotum is reddish and has prominent bioluminescent organs on either side of the midline. The elytral striae are well defined. The eyes are small and the elongate antennae are slightly serrated starting from the fourth segments.

Actual size

| FAMILY | Elateridae |
|---|---|
| SUBFAMILY | Oxynopterinae |
| DISTRIBUTION | Oriental: Malaysia, Singapore |
| MACROHABITAT | Tropical forests |
| MICROHABITAT | On tree branches and trunks |
| FEEDING HABITS | Adults probably feed on plants; larvae are probably predaceous |
| NOTE | This beetle is very popular among collectors because of its colorful and iridescent body |

ADULT LENGTH
1 ¹⁵⁄₁₆–2 in
(49–52 mm)

*CAMPSOSTERNUS HEBES*
# JEWEL CLICK BEETLE
CANDÈZE, 1897

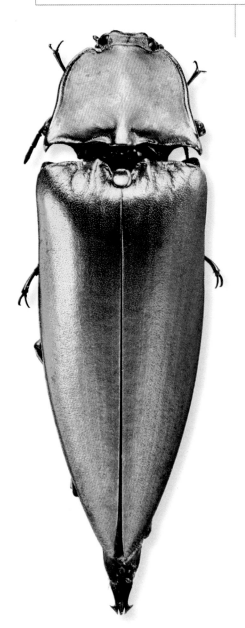

The genus *Campsosternus*, a member of the pantropical subfamily Oxynopterinae, is widely distributed in the Oriental Realm but especially diverse in Southeast Asia. Known oxynopterine larvae are predaceous and at least one species of *Oxynopterus* is a predator in termite nests. The magnificent species in *Campsosternus* are known for their large size and bright metallic colors. The adults are quite characteristic morphologically in that their mesoventrite and metaventrite are fused together (in ventral view). *Campsosternus hebes* is distributed in maritime Southeast Asia.

## RELATED SPECIES

There are approximately 60 species and subspecies described in the genus *Campsosternus*, with newly discovered taxa being described on a regular basis. The current taxonomy of the genus is unfortunately in a state of chaos, which impedes the discussion of relationships between the species. *Campsosternus watanabei* is a legally protected species in Taiwan.

**The Jewel Click Beetle** is a striking species with an iridescent green dorsal surface. The margins of the prothorax and middle of the elytra usually have a yellowish tinge. The pronotum is distinctly broader posteriorly and extends into sharply triangular spines at the posterior corners. The antennae are filiform and the legs are adapted for walking. The elytra are sharply pointed at their apex.

Actual size

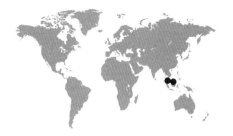

| FAMILY | Elateridae |
|---|---|
| SUBFAMILY | Oxynopterinae |
| DISTRIBUTION | Oriental: Malaysia |
| MACROHABITAT | Tropical forest |
| MICROHABITAT | On tree branches and trunks |
| FEEDING HABITS | Adults probably feed on plants; larvae presumably feed on termites |
| NOTE | The known larvae of *Oxynopterus* feed on termites, a rare occurrence among beetles in the family Elateridae |

ADULT LENGTH
1⁹⁄₁₆–2¹¹⁄₁₆ in
(40–69 mm)

*OXYNOPTERUS AUDOUINI*
# OXYNOPTERUS AUDOUINI
HOPE, 1842

333

*Oxynopterus audouini* belongs to a genus that contains probably the largest click beetles and lives in the forests of maritime Southeast Asia. The Oxynopterinae have morphological characters that include the fusion of parts of the middle and posterior parts of the thorax, also known as meso- and metaventrites. Because of its large size, this species is commonly traded by collectors and its conservation status is not well known. The larva of the related species *O. mucronatus* is known as a specialized predator of termites of the genus *Neotermes* in Java.

## RELATED SPECIES

Other species in the genus *Oxynopterus* are broadly distributed in the Malay Archipelago, which comprises Borneo, the Philippines, Sumatra, and other islands nearby. The taxonomy of the genus has not been studied recently, and modern diagnosis and illustrations are lacking. The relationships between the species are not well understood.

Actual size

**Oxynopterus audouini** is a large, robust beetle whose dorsal surface is covered with short, appressed brown setae, and whose integument is dark brown with a polished surface and a few fine punctures. The posterior edges of the pronotum are pointed and its base is as broad as the base of the elytra. The antennae are large and pectinated. The legs are robust and adapted for walking and climbing.

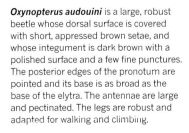

| FAMILY | Elateridae |
|---|---|
| SUBFAMILY | Dendrometrinae |
| DISTRIBUTION | Palearctic: Europe and Asia |
| MACROHABITAT | Loose sandy soils, cliffs, quarries, and open woodlands |
| MICROHABITAT | Adults are usually found on flowers; larvae develop in soil |
| FEEDING HABITS | Adults are phytophagous, consuming plant juices; larvae are thought to feed on the roots of various plants (e.g., *Calluna* spp., *Erica* spp., *Betula* spp., *Salix* spp.) |
| NOTE | Populations of this species are significantly declining in some countries |

ADULT LENGTH
¼–⁹⁄₁₆ in
(7–14 mm)

*ANOSTIRUS CASTANEUS*
# CHESTNUT CLICK BEETLE
(LINNAEUS, 1758)

334

The Chestnut Click Beetle has a characteristic color pattern and is widely distributed in Europe. Males and females can be distinguished by the length of their antennae: in males they extend beyond the base of the pronotum, but in females they are noticeably shorter. The larvae live in the soil and feed on roots of low vegetation. Populations of this species have seen a marked decline in some European countries: in the United Kingdom, for example, it was found on a number of sites 75 years ago but is now limited to a few extremely scattered sites, including on the Isle of Wight.

### RELATED SPECIES

There are several species of *Anostirus* with a similar color pattern but their affinities have not been investigated. Nearly 50 species and subspecies are known in the Palearctic Realm and three species are known from North America. Two subspecies of *A. castaneus* are considered valid: *A. c. japonicus* from the Russian Far East and Japan; and *A. c. castaneus* from Europe east to the Russian Far East but not Japan.

**The Chestnut Click Beetle** has an elongate body and a dark brown to black pronotum covered with golden yellow setae. The elytra are light brown to yellow and have a small black patch at the apex. The head, legs, and antennae are black. The females (pictured here) have distinct triangular antennal segments, while the males have comb-like antennae.

Actual size

| FAMILY | Elateridae |
|---|---|
| SUBFAMILY | Negastriinae |
| DISTRIBUTION | Australian: Australia |
| MACROHABITAT | Riparian habitats |
| MICROHABITAT | On sand or other substrates near water bodies |
| FEEDING HABITS | Presumably feeds on plant juices |
| NOTE | This species is one of two described Negastrinae known to occur in Australia |

ADULT LENGTH
³/₁₆ in
(3.5–4 mm)

*RIVULICOLA VARIEGATUS*

# RIVULICOLA VARIEGATUS
(MACLEAY, 1872)

335

Actual size

*Rivulicola variegatus* is a small Australian click beetle and the only member of the elaterid subfamily Negastriinae to occur in Australia along with the related species *R. dimidiatus*. Morphological characteristics of the group include two sublateral carinae on the base of pronotum. The larva is unknown. This species is riparian, adults living on sandbanks along rivers. Adult individuals can be attracted to artificial lights in habitats close to flowing water and during every month of the year.

## RELATED SPECIES
The small subfamily Negastriinae is generally widely distributed, but more abundant and diverse in the northern hemisphere. As far as is known, the genus *Rivulicola* contains two described and two undescribed species and is endemic to Australia. Adults of *R. dimidiatus* are about the same length as *R. variegatus* but are distributed in Western Australia, whereas *R. variegatus*, originally described from Queensland, occurs broadly along the east coast of Australia.

**Rivulicola variegatus** is covered with black, golden, and silver scales, forming variegated patterns on the pronotum and elytra. The legs are partially covered with white scales. The head is moderately visible in dorsal view and the eyes are large and slightly protuberant. The antennae are rather long and filiform. The elytra have several noticeable longitudinal striae.

| FAMILY | Elateridae |
|---|---|
| SUBFAMILY | Elaterinae |
| DISTRIBUTION | Australian: coastal New South Wales and Queensland |
| MACROHABITAT | Coastal rainforest and heathland |
| MICROHABITAT | Adults are found on blooming flowers; larval habits are unknown |
| FEEDING HABITS | Adults feed on flower nectar |
| NOTE | This uncommon species may have been extirpated in parts of its range |

**ADULT LENGTH**
⁹⁄₁₆–⁷⁄₈ in
(15–22 mm)

336

*OPHIDIUS HISTRIO*
# OPHIDIUS HISTRIO
(BOISDUVAL, 1835)

The distinctively marked *Ophidius histrio* is one of the most attractive click beetles in Australia. It is active during the months of November through February, and has been found feeding on the nectar produced by the small white flowers of *Baeckea frutescens*. Mating usually takes place among the leaves or branches, as well as on the flowers. This uncommon species is sporadically distributed along the east coast and may have been extirpated in locations where commercial developments have removed most of the native vegetation.

### RELATED SPECIES

The four species of *Ophidius* (*O. dracunculus*, *O. elegans*, *O. histrio*, and *O. vericulatus*) are all restricted to New South Wales and Queensland, and are characterized by having a vertically raised scutellum and four distinctly padded tarsomeres on all legs, and they lack a ridge around the front of the head. *Ophidius histrio* has a distinctive pattern of black and cream lines on its pronotum and elytra.

**Ophidius histrio** has a convex black head and serrate antennae. The broad, evenly rounded pronotum is finely pubescent and dark cream with three dark stripes. The elytra have a distinctly wavy pattern of black and orange-brown curving lines on a cream background. The tarsomeres on the short legs become progressively shorter toward the claws, and each has a distinctly rounded pad.

Actual size

| FAMILY | Elateridae |
|---|---|
| SUBFAMILY | Cardiophorinae |
| DISTRIBUTION | Oriental: India, Sri Lanka, Bangladesh |
| MACROHABITAT | Tropical forest |
| MICROHABITAT | Tree trunks and lower vegetation |
| FEEDING HABITS | Adults feed on flowers and young leaves; larval feeding habits uncertain |
| NOTE | *Cardiophorus* is the most diverse genus in the family Elateridae |

ADULT LENGTH
¼–⁵⁄₁₆ in
(7–8 mm)

*CARDIOPHORUS NOTATUS*

# CARDIOPHORUS NOTATUS

(FABRICIUS, 1781)

337

The click beetle subfamily Cardiophorinae is thought to be closely related to the subfamily Negastriinae. The genus *Cardiophorus*, with approximately 600 species classified in several subgenera, is the most speciose genera of Elateridae. Its species are widely distributed throughout the world, except for South America and Australia. The larvae of these beetles are predators in soil or rotten wood. *Cardiophorus notatus* was originally described in the genus *Elater* by the eminent Danish zoologist Johan Christian Fabricius (1745–1808) in his classical entomological book *Species Insectorum*.

## RELATED SPECIES

Several species in *Cardiophorus* occur in South Asia, some of which remain undescribed. Adult *Cardiophorus* are characterized by their heart-shaped scutellum. Most of the species are very similar in general aspects and a study of their relationships based on modern techniques is badly needed. Adults of *C. notatus*, however, have a unique color pattern that will distinguish this species from others.

Actual size

*Cardiophorus notatus* is a very attractive click beetle with the dorsal surface covered by pubescence and setae forming different patterns. The pronotum has a pair of black spots anteriorly and the elytra have a pair of white spots near the middle. The elytra also have a white transverse band close to the apex. The antennae are filiform and relatively long. The prothorax is broader apically and its base is as broad as the base of the elytra.

| FAMILY | Elateridae |
|---|---|
| SUBFAMILY | Hemiopinae |
| DISTRIBUTION | Palearctic and Oriental: China, Taiwan, Southeast Asia |
| MACROHABITAT | Tropical forests |
| MICROHABITAT | Lower vegetation and tree trunks |
| FEEDING HABITS | Adults are presumably phytophagous, feeding on plant juices; larval feeding habits are unknown |
| NOTE | This species represents a group of click beetles with poorly known relationships |

ADULT LENGTH
½–¹¹⁄₁₆ in
(12.4–17 mm)

338

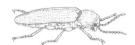

*HEMIOPS FLAVA*
# HEMIOPS FLAVA
LAPORTE DE CASTELNAU, 1836

The genus *Hemiops* occurs mostly in continental Asia, although one species (*H. ireii*) was described from the Japanese island of Okinawa in 2007. *Hemiops*, *Parhemiops*, and other related genera comprise the Hemiopinae, a subfamily restricted to the eastern hemisphere that has uncertain relationships with other click beetles. *Hemiops flava* is widespread in Asia and has been recorded along with other click beetles as being economically important in China. The larvae of this species and other members of the subfamily are unknown.

RELATED SPECIES

The subfamily Hemiopinae includes *Hemiops*, *Parhemiops*, *Plectrosternum*, and several other related genera. The species in this group are characterized by several morphological characters, including the shape of the pronotum and a pair of short longitudinal ridges near the base of the pronotum. *Hemiops* includes eight species, of which *H. substriata* and *H. ireii* are the closest known species to *H. flava*. These species can be separated by differences in color, in the length of antennal segments, and in the male genitalia.

Actual size

**Hemiops flava** has yellow coloration on most of the body. The elytra have distinct punctate longitudinal striae, which are darker in color. The whole body is covered with short setae. The apices of the tibiae, the tarsi, and the antennae are dark brown. The antennae are filiform to slightly serrated. The legs are long.

| FAMILY | Elateridae |
|---|---|
| SUBFAMILY | Physodactylinae |
| DISTRIBUTION | Neotropical: Brazil |
| MACROHABITAT | Forested areas |
| MICROHABITAT | Foliage and tree trunks |
| FEEDING HABITS | Phytophagous, presumably feeding on plant juices; larvae are unknown |
| NOTE | This species represents a very particular and poorly studied group of beetles whose classification currently remains unclear |

ADULT LENGTH
⁹⁄₁₆–⅝ in
(13.5–15.5 mm)

*PHYSODACTYLUS OBERTHURI*

# PHYSODACTYLUS OBERTHURI

FLEUTIAUX, 1892

339

The genus *Physodactylus* belongs to the subfamily Physodactylinae, which includes seven genera: *Dactylophysus*, *Physodactylus*, *Teslasena*, *Margogastrius*, *Oligosthetius*, *Idiotropia*, and *Toxognathus*, from South America, North Africa, central and southern Africa, India, and Southeast Asia. These beetles are characterized by the falciform shape of the mandibles, but their status as a monophyletic group is still open to question. The genus *Physodactylus* comprises about six species, of which *P. oberthuri* was described from a male specimen collected in Brazil.

## RELATED SPECIES

*Physodactylus oberthuri* is a close relative of *P. testaceus* and *P. fleutiauxi*. It can be distinguished externally from the first by the brown to black color, the shape of the frons, and the short antenna; and from *P. fleutiauxi* by the absence of spiniform setae on the maxilla, the pronotum being strongly produced over head and the abdomen being concave laterally.

Actual size

**Physodactylus oberthuri** has a brown dorsal surface covered with short, sparse setae. The paler pronotum is distinctly densely punctured and the elytra are striated. The filiform antennae are long, reaching the anterior margin of the prothorax. The setose legs are robust, probably an adaptation for walking, and the tarsi are particularly long.

| | |
|---|---|
| FAMILY | Plastoceridae |
| SUBFAMILY | |
| DISTRIBUTION | Palearctic: Turkey (Anatolia) |
| MACROHABITAT | Unknown |
| MICROHABITAT | Unknown |
| FEEDING HABITS | Unknown |
| NOTE | Nothing is known about the ecology or biology of this small and enigmatic family, and females and immature stages also remain unknown |

ADULT LENGTH
⅜–⁷⁄₁₆ in
(9.5–10.5 mm)

*PLASTOCERUS ANGULOSUS*
# PLASTOCERUS ANGULOSUS
(GERMAR, 1845)

This beetle belongs to the rare family Plastoceridae, which contains a single genus and two described species: *Plastocerus angulosus* from Anatolia in Turkey; and *P. thoracicus* from Southeast Asia. The placement of this family in the classification scheme of Coleoptera is uncertain. Detailed studies of their morphology and biology will be necessary to address this problem. Morphological characteristics of these beetles include a reduced maxilla and the presence of seven abdominal ventrites, the first three of which are connate (not freely movable). Females and larvae are unknown for this family.

RELATED SPECIES

*Plastocerus thoracicus* is one of two species currently included in the genus *Plastocerus*, and was originally described from a single male specimen. *Plastocerus thoracicus* can be differentiated from *P. angulosus* by using morphological characters such as features of the body surface and color. The distribution of *P. thoracicus* also differs, with the species being restricted to Southeast Asia.

Actual size

**Plastocerus angulosus** males are densely covered with fine setae. They have long and pectinated antennae. The pronotum is dark brown, the elytra are brownish yellow, and the legs are yellow. The body shape resembles that of a click beetle. The tarsi are long and the legs are adapted for climbing and walking.

| FAMILY | Drilidae |
|---|---|
| SUBFAMILY | Drilinae |
| DISTRIBUTION | Palearctic: Europe |
| MACROHABITAT | Lower mountain forest |
| MICROHABITAT | Lower vegetation |
| FEEDING HABITS | Larvae and females feed on terrestrial mollusks; feeding habits of adult males are unknown |
| NOTE | *Drilus flavescens* belongs to a poorly studied group of beetles with fully winged males and wingless, larviform females |

*DRILUS FLAVESCENS*

# DRILUS FLAVESCENS

OLIVIER, 1790

ADULT MALE LENGTH
¼–⅜ in
(7–10 mm)

ADULT FEMALE LENGTH
⅜ in
(9.5 mm)

341

*Drilus flavescens* belongs to the small family Drilidae, which contains about 100 species in six genera. Species in this family are distributed primarily in the Mediterranean region and Afrotropical Realm. The relationships of these beetles within the superfamily Elateroidea remains uncertain. Extreme sexual dimorphism occurs among adults of *D. flavescens*. The wingless females are larviform and live on the soil surface together with larvae, where both life stages appear to feed on snails. The feeding habit of the males is still unknown, although they are encountered on flowers.

## RELATED SPECIES

The genus *Drilus* contains more than 25 species, found mostly in the Mediterranean and Caucasus regions. The relationships between those species remain uncertain. Historically, the restricted information published about these beetles was primarily based on brief descriptions without illustrations, but modern studies are starting to clarify species concepts. The distribution of *D. flavescens* overlaps with that of *D. concolor*, but this species has noticeably darker elytra.

Actual size

**Drilus flavescens** males have long, pectinated antennae that can extend posteriorly to reach the basal fourth of the elytra. The head and pronotum are dark brown, while the elytra are brownish yellow. The pronotum and elytra are covered with long setae, The apex of the abdomen is exposed beyond the elytra in dorsal view.

| FAMILY | Lycidae |
|---|---|
| SUBFAMILY | Lyropaeinae |
| DISTRIBUTION | Oriental: Malaysia |
| MACROHABITAT | Tropical forest |
| MICROHABITAT | Rotting logs |
| FEEDING HABITS | Predaceous |
| NOTE | Females of this beetle are large and larviform, resembling trilobites, and do not pupate before sexual maturation |

**ADULT MALE LENGTH**
¼ in
(6.6 mm)

**ADULT FEMALE LENGTH**
1⁷⁄₁₆–2⅜ in
(37–60 mm)

342

*PLATERODRILUS KORINCHIANUS*
# PLATERODRILUS KORINCHIANUS
BLAIR, 1928

Actual size

*Platerodrilus* is a genus of soft-bodied beetles in the family Lycidae, whose members display neoteny. The females are larviform and resemble extinct marine arthropods of the class Trilobita, hence their common name, trilobite beetles or trilobite larvae. These larviform females intrigued entomologists until the 1925 publication of Swedish zoologist Eric Mjöberg, who during an expedition to Borneo established that they are an example of neoteny. The fully winged males are usually much smaller than the larviform females. Kenneth Blair described *P. korinchianus* based on the larviform female.

### RELATED SPECIES

Based on a taxonomic study published in 2009, *Platerodrilus* includes 25 species and subspecies. Females in this genus can be up to 15 times longer than males. Males in this genus are separated by their color pattern and by differences in their genitalic structures. Males and larviform females are known in two other genera (*Macrolibnetis, Lyropaeus*) while larviform females are expected in other genera (e.g., *Scarelus, Leptolycus*) but are still unknown.

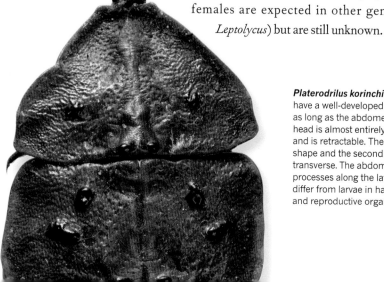

**Platerodrilus korinchianus** larviform females have a well-developed thorax, which is about as long as the abdomen, and are flightless. The head is almost entirely covered by the prothorax and is retractable. The prothorax is triangular in shape and the second and third segments are transverse. The abdomen has well-developed processes along the lateral margins. The females differ from larvae in having well-developed eyes and reproductive organs.

| FAMILY | Lycidae |
|---|---|
| SUBFAMILY | Lycinae |
| DISTRIBUTION | Afrotropical: tropical Africa, South Africa |
| MACROHABITAT | Forest, savanna, grassland |
| MICROHABITAT | Lower vegetation |
| FEEDING HABITS | Larvae are presumably predators; feeding habits of adults are uncertain |
| NOTE | The genus *Lycus* contains species that show striking color patterns and body shapes |

ADULT LENGTH
⁷⁄₁₆–1 in
(11–25 mm)

*LYCUS MELANURUS*

# LYCUS MELANURUS

DALMAN, 1817

343

*Lycus* is a large and diverse genus divided in several subgenera. Adults of this mostly Afrotropical group are known to aggregate in high numbers in flowering trees. Their aposematic coloration warns potential predators that they are protected by chemicals (such as an acetylenic acid appropriately named lycidic acid) and distasteful. These beetles are also commonly involved in mimicry complexes that sometimes include other beetles as well as butterflies and true bugs. Adults are distinctive beetles and, as is the case for many other species of Lycidae, the head is developed into an elongate rostrum and the elytra are colorful.

## RELATED SPECIES

A relatively large number of species belongs to the genus *Lycus*, but their affinities remain poorly known to this day. Species are generally separated based on differences of the pronotum, elytra, and color patterns. It has been reported that *L. melanurus* could be closely related to *L. latissimus*, although a more definitive consensus on relationships will require a detailed study of all the species of the genus with comparative descriptions and illustrations of external and internal morphological structures.

**Lycus melanurus** adults are soft-bodied beetles. The dorsal surface is mostly yellowish orange although there is a dark longitudinal, median band on the pronotum and the apices of the elytra are black. The antennae are long, black, and moderately serrated. The flattened elytra are very wide medially and have reticulate leaf-vein patterns and longitudinal carina. The elytra each have a sharply pointed projection near the anterior corners.

Actual size

| FAMILY | Lycidae |
| --- | --- |
| SUBFAMILY | Lycinae |
| DISTRIBUTION | Palearctic: Russian Far East, Japan, Mongolia, Korea, China (Heilongjiang), Taiwan |
| MACROHABITAT | Forests |
| MICROHABITAT | Adults favor moist, shaded lower vegetation; larvae live inside decomposing wood |
| FEEDING HABITS | The feeding habits of adults are uncertain; larvae in this genus feed on, or in, decomposing wood |
| NOTE | *Macrolycus flabellatus* is a characteristic net-winged beetle that is broadly distributed in northern Asia |

ADULT LENGTH
⁹⁄₁₆ in
(13.5–14.5 mm)

*MACROLYCUS FLABELLATUS*
# MACROLYCUS FLABELLATUS
(MOTSCHULKSY, 1860)

*Macrolycus*, which occurs from lowlands to high mountainous areas in the Palearctic and Oriental realms, is the sole genus in the lycid tribe Macrolycini. The adults in this genus typically prefer moist and shaded areas with rotten logs or trunks in close contact with the soil, and are most active in the morning. As for other species in the family, adults of *M. flabellatus* have a slow, cumbersome flight and are not attracted to artificial lights as many other beetles are. Although this is a widespread species in Asia, little is known about its biology.

### RELATED SPECIES

Species of *Macrolycus* and the distantly related genus *Dilophotes* differ from other Lycidae species in having tarsal claws that are forked at their apex. *Macrolycus* adults, however, are unique in having a pronotum with prominent posterior angles and a single longitudinal ridge medially. The relationships of the approximately 50 species in the genus *Macrolycus* are not well studied. Species are generally separated by differences in color patterns as well as in male genital structures.

**Macrolycus flabellatus** is a soft-bodied beetle whose dorsal surface is covered with short setae. The antennae are black, very long, and deeply pectinated, and they extend posteriorly approximately to the middle of the elytra. The elytra are reddish and are covered with irregular punctures. The pronotum is black and has an uneven surface. The flattened black legs are adapted for walking.

Actual size

| FAMILY | Telegeusidae |
|---|---|
| SUBFAMILY | |
| DISTRIBUTION | Nearctic and Neotropical: southern USA, northern Mexico, Panama |
| MACROHABITAT | Tropical dry forest |
| MICROHABITAT | Unknown |
| FEEDING HABITS | Unknown |
| NOTE | Species in this small family are appropriately referred to as "long-lipped beetles" |

ADULT LENGTH
³⁄₁₆–¼ in
(5–6.2 mm)

*TELEGEUSIS ORIENTALIS*

# TELEGEUSIS ORIENTALIS

ZARAGOZA CABALLERO, 1990

345

Actual size

Beetles of this family are distributed from the southwestern USA, south to Trinidad and Ecuador. They are usually very rare and poorly studied, and in fact the females and larvae remain completely unknown to this day. Males have generally been found at artificial lights at night or collected using flight-intercept traps, but have never been found in their natural microhabitat. *Telegeusis orientalis* and other species within the genus are characterized by their very long maxillary and labial palpomeres, which are flattened and clothed with complex setae. Based on knowledge from related families, it has been hypothesized that females of this and other telegeusid species are either flightless or larviform.

### RELATED SPECIES

The genus *Telegeusis* contains 12 species (including five described in 2011) that occur in Central America north to the southwestern United States. *Telegeusis orientalis* and *T. granulatus* share several morphological attributes, such as a similar body color (black to brownish red or yellow) and a similar length and shape of the elytra, but the two species can be separated by differences in structures on their heads.

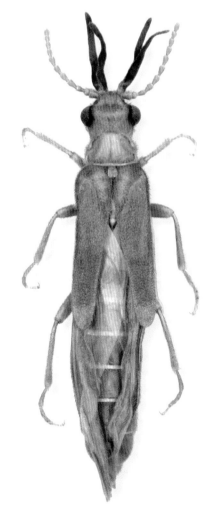

**Telegeusis orientalis** adults have the same general appearance as some soldier beetles (family Cantharidae) or rove beetles (family Staphylinidae) because of the soft, pale-colored body and short elytra exposing most of the abdomen. The dorsal surface is covered with fine setae and the antennae are rather long and filiform. The eyes are large and protuberant. The legs are covered by setae and adapted for walking.

| FAMILY | Phengodidae |
|---|---|
| SUBFAMILY | Phengodinae |
| DISTRIBUTION | Nearctic and Neatropical: Pacific Coast states to Nevada, southwestern Arizona, and northern Baja California, Mexico. |
| MACROHABITAT | Desert, chaparral, oak woodland, pinyon–juniper woodland |
| MICROHABITAT | Larvae and females hide in litter or under debris on the ground |
| FEEDING HABITS | Adults do not feed; larvae prey on millipedes |
| NOTE | Adult females lack wings and resemble larvae with compound eyes |

ADULT MALE LENGTH
½–⅞ in
(12–23 mm)

ADULT FEMALE LENGTH
1³⁄₁₆–2⅝ in
(30–65 mm)

*ZARHIPIS INTEGRIPENNIS*
# WESTERN BANDED GLOWWORM
(LECONTE, 1874)

The Western Banded Glowworm's eggs, larvae, and pupae are bioluminescent. The soft-bodied adult males lose their glow after they emerge from the pupa, but the larviform adult females continue to glow. The larva preys on millipedes by running alongside them before throwing a coil of its body around the millipede's head and biting it under the neck. Fluids delivered through the larva's sickle-like mandibles paralyze the millipede. The larva then forces its way into the victim's body cavity to feed. Females probably release pheromones to attract males. Once in the immediate vicinity, the males locate the female by her lights.

## RELATED SPECIES

The genus *Zarhipis* is restricted to western North America and contains three species. Males are distinguished from the other North American phengodid genera by their large size, bipectinate antennae, and elytra that nearly cover the entire abdomen. *Zarhipis integripennis* males have concave head surfaces, distinct lobes on the third and fourth tarsal segments, and elytra about the same width along their entire length.

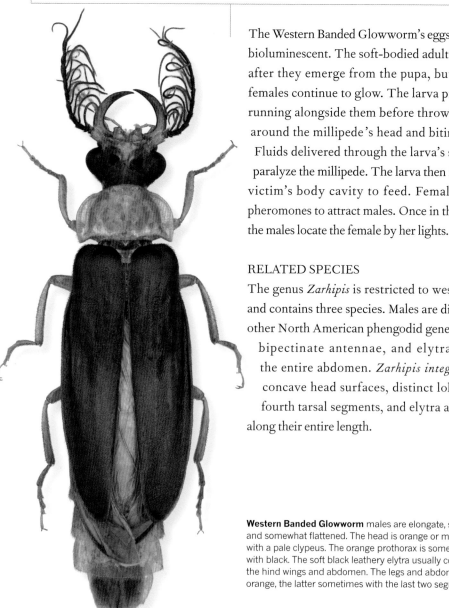

**Western Banded Glowworm** males are elongate, soft bodied, and somewhat flattened. The head is orange or mostly dark with a pale clypeus. The orange prothorax is sometimes tinged with black. The soft black leathery elytra usually cover most of the hind wings and abdomen. The legs and abdomen are orange, the latter sometimes with the last two segments black.

Actual size

| FAMILY | Rhagophthalmidae |
| --- | --- |
| SUBFAMILY | |
| DISTRIBUTION | Oriental: Sri Lanka |
| MACROHABITAT | Tropical forest |
| MICROHABITAT | Lower vegetation |
| FEEDING HABITS | Adult feeding habits uncertain; larvae are predaceous |
| NOTE | Beetles in this family are rare and their biology is not well known. The placement of Rhagophthalmidae among other beetle families is also poorly understood |

ADULT LENGTH
7/16 in
(11 mm)

*RHAGOPHTHALMUS CONFUSUS*

# RHAGOPHTHALMUS CONFUSUS

OLIVIER, 1911

347

The genus *Rhagophthalmus* contains 35 Asian species, all of which are rare and have poorly known biology. The larvae are predaceous and adult females are apterous (lacking wings) but with developed eyes, a rare phenomenon known as incompletely larviform. Bioluminescence is known to occur in both females and larvae. A notable characteristic of these beetles is the extraordinary adaptation of the eyes to their nocturnal activities. *Rhagophthalmus confusus* is rare and was described from a single specimen.

## RELATED SPECIES

The high number of species in *Rhagophthalmus* and the lack of global studies of the genus have complicated the distinction between related species. It is known that *R. confusus* has black elytra, as do *R. gibbosulus*, *R. tonkineus*, and *R. scutellatus*, but in *R. confusus* the prothorax is not entirely black as in the other species.

Actual size

**Rhagophthalmus confusus** is a soft-bodied beetle with a dark head and a brownish body covered with short, fine setae. The large eyes are a common feature for members of this family. The antennae are short, and when extended reach the middle area of the prothorax. The legs are long and adapted for walking on foliage.

| FAMILY | Lampyridae |
|---|---|
| SUBFAMILY | Lampyrinae |
| DISTRIBUTION | Nearctic and Neotropical: USA (southernmost Florida and Texas), Mexico, Cuba, Hispaniola, Puerto Rico, several of the Lesser Antilles, Venezuela, Colombia, Brazil |
| MACROHABITAT | Open areas and woodlands |
| MICROHABITAT | Lower vegetation |
| FEEDING HABITS | Adults are not known to feed; larvae are predaceous |
| NOTE | *Aspisoma* are bioluminescent beetles. The males are winged but females are larviform with well-developed compound eyes |

ADULT LENGTH
½–⁹⁄₁₆ in
(11.5–15 mm)

348

*ASPISOMA IGNITUM*
# ASPISOMA IGNITUM
(LINNAEUS, 1767)

Bioluminescence in adults of the family Lampyridae is typically used in sexual signaling to communicate species identity and facilitate mating. In *Aspisoma ignitum*, flashing typically starts at least 30 minutes after sunset and goes on for up to three hours. Individuals tend to fly slowly within 10 ft (3 m) of the surface of the ground. Males fly around in order to find the stationary females. During the day, individuals can be found hiding or mating in the upper part of bushes.

## RELATED SPECIES

The tribe Cratomorphini, which includes *Aspisoma*, is characterized by having small mandibles with narrow, glabrous apices. *Aspisoma* is a relatively diverse genus with approximately 80 described species in the Neotropical Realm. Several species remain to be described. The only known lampyrid with a conspicuous uniform green pigmentation is *A. physonotum*.

Actual size

**Aspisoma ignitum** adults have a broadly oval, brownish-yellow body covered with fine yellow setae dorsally and with the head hidden under the pronotum. The pronotum is lighter in color anteriorly, while the elytra have a paler spot laterally anterior of the middle and a small number of paler longitudinal lines. Males have bright yellow abdominal segments near the apex ventrally, as opposed to brown and yellow in females.

| | |
|---|---|
| FAMILY | Lampyridae |
| SUBFAMILY | Lampyrinae |
| DISTRIBUTION | Palearctic and Oriental: Europe, Russia and Mongolia |
| MACROHABITAT | Open woodlands and areas of human habitation |
| MICROHABITAT | Grass and low vegetation |
| FEEDING HABITS | Larvae are predators; adults rarely feed |
| NOTE | *Lampyris noctiluca* is a widespread and relatively common firefly. The females are larviform and the males are winged |

ADULT MALE LENGTH
⅜–½ in
(10–12 mm)

ADULT FEMALE LENGTH
⁹⁄₁₆–¾ in
(15–20 mm)

*LAMPYRIS NOCTILUCA*
# COMMON GLOWWORM
(LINNAEUS, 1767)

349

*Lampyris noctiluca* is a common beetle in European and Asian regions, and presents noticeable sexual dimorphism. The males are winged, with brown elytra, a clearer pronotum, and a large median brown spot; the females are larviform and popular for their glow—they are capable of glowing during all stages of their life cycle and are often twice the size of the males. These beetles use their bioluminescence to attract mates, emitting a yellowish-green light from the translucent underside of their last three abdominal segments.

RELATED SPECIES

*Lampyris* is a large genus with poorly studied taxonomy. For example, *L. noctiluca* was previously recorded as the only species of the genus in Portugal, but a 2008 study identified that the specimens from the region belonged to a new species, *L. iberica*, which differs in body color, presence of transparent spots, body size, length of the antennae, and male genitalia.

Actual size

**Common Glowworm** males have a soft body with a brownish color. The dorsal surface is covered with small, dense setae. The antennae are filiform and moderately long. The prothorax covers the head, and the elytra have a reticulated surface. The legs are adapted for walking on vegetation. The female is larviform and lacks developed elytra (see top right).

| FAMILY | Lampyridae |
|---|---|
| SUBFAMILY | Photurinae |
| DISTRIBUTION | Nearctic: southern Canada and northeastern USA |
| MACROHABITAT | Open woodlands |
| MICROHABITAT | Grass and low vegetation |
| FEEDING HABITS | Predaceous |
| NOTE | This species is the state insect of Pennsylvania; females in the genus are regarded as "femmes fatales" |

ADULT LENGTH
¼–1¹⁵⁄₁₆ in
(20–50 mm)

*PHOTURIS PENSYLVANICA*
# PENNSYLVANIA FIREFLY
(DE GEER, 1774)

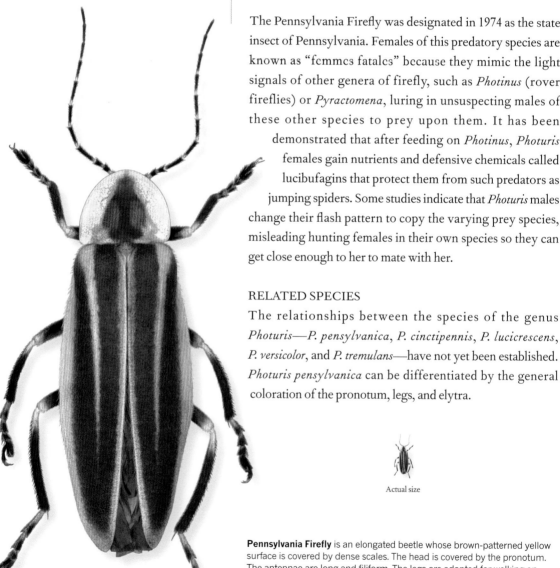

The Pennsylvania Firefly was designated in 1974 as the state insect of Pennsylvania. Females of this predatory species are known as "femmes fatales" because they mimic the light signals of other genera of firefly, such as *Photinus* (rover fireflies) or *Pyractomena*, luring in unsuspecting males of these other species to prey upon them. It has been demonstrated that after feeding on *Photinus*, *Photuris* females gain nutrients and defensive chemicals called lucibufagins that protect them from such predators as jumping spiders. Some studies indicate that *Photuris* males change their flash pattern to copy the varying prey species, misleading hunting females in their own species so they can get close enough to her to mate with her.

### RELATED SPECIES
The relationships between the species of the genus *Photuris*—*P. pensylvanica*, *P. cinctipennis*, *P. lucicrescens*, *P. versicolor*, and *P. tremulans*—have not yet been established. *Photuris pensylvanica* can be differentiated by the general coloration of the pronotum, legs, and elytra.

Actual size

**Pennsylvania Firefly** is an elongated beetle whose brown-patterned yellow surface is covered by dense scales. The head is covered by the pronotum. The antennae are long and filiform. The legs are adapted for walking on foliage. The base of the tibia and apex of the femur are yellow, while the rest of the leg is brown.

| FAMILY | Omethidae |
|---|---|
| SUBFAMILY | Omethinae |
| DISTRIBUTION | Nearctic: eastern North America |
| MACROHABITAT | Temperate deciduous forests |
| MICROHABITAT | Adults are found on herbaceous undergrowth |
| FEEDING HABITS | The feeding habits of both adults and larvae are unknown |
| NOTE | This species is rarely encountered |

ADULT LENGTH
⁵⁄₁₆ in
(4–5 mm)

*OMETHES MARGINATUS*
# OMETHES MARGINATUS
LECONTE, 1861

351

The family Omethidae consists of eight genera and 33 species distributed in eastern Asia and North America. Larval omethids are entirely unknown, as are the feeding habits of the adults. The scant published information on North American omethids suggests they emerge in spring and early summer, are predominately diurnal, and are short-lived. Although the taxa from North America are taxonomically well known, the world omethid fauna lacks a catalogue and species are difficult to identify.

### RELATED SPECIES

The monotypic *Blatchleya* and *Omethes* are the only species of Omethidae found east of the Mississippi River. Antennomeres 4 and 5 of *Blatchleya* are enlarged and excavated, while those of *Omethes* are filiform, or threadlike, and lack such modifications. The genus *Omethes* contains two species worldwide, *O. rugiceps* from Japan and *O. marginatus* from eastern North America, from Connecticut to Georgia, west Indiana, and Arkansas.

Actual size

**Omethes marginatus** is elongate, parallel-sided, and clothed in long, reclining yellowish setae. The head, antennomeres, and elytra are mostly dark brown, while the antennal bases, pronotum, and elytral margins are reddish brown. The top of the head is rough, is not deeply excavated, and is partly covered by the pronotum. The coarsely punctured elytra have fine, indistinct ridges.

| FAMILY | Omethidae |
|---|---|
| SUBFAMILY | Matheteinae |
| DISTRIBUTION | Nearctic: USA (Oregon, California) |
| MACROHABITAT | Temperate forest |
| MICROHABITAT | Lower vegetation |
| FEEDING HABITS | Unknown |
| NOTE | The entire subfamily Matheteinae is endemic to California and Oregon, USA, and contains only three species whose biology is unknown |

ADULT LENGTH
⅜ – ½ in
(10–11.5 mm)

352

*MATHETEUS THEVENETI*
# MATHETEUS THEVENETI
LECONTE, 1874

This species belongs to the obscure and poorly studied Omethidae, a small family of eight genera and approximately 30 species. Matheteinae contains two genera that are both endemic to Oregon and California, USA. Specimens of *Matheteus theveneti* are not common in collections, although several individuals have occasionally been observed in close proximity. The species resembles a firefly beetle in its general body shape, and in its natural habitat looks like roseate petals of the Salmonberry (*Rubus spectabilis*). Its biology and larvae are unknown.

## RELATED SPECIES

The only other species in the subfamily Matheteinae are *Ginglymocladus discoidea*, which occurs in coastal northern California, and *G. luteicollis*, which is only known from Sequoia National Park, also in California. The elytra of species in *Ginglymocladus* are black or black with pale margins compared to red in *Matheteus*. *Matheteus theveneti* is so far the only species described in this genus.

Actual size

**Matheteus theveneti** is very similar to a firefly beetle but is reddish in color, has a black disk on the pronotum, and has very long, pectinated antennae. The body surface is covered with short, fine setae. The elytra are long and wide, with well-defined longitudinal striae. The legs are black and adapted for climbing and walking on vegetation.

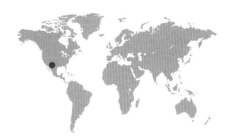

| FAMILY | Cantharidae |
|---|---|
| SUBFAMILY | Chauliognathinae |
| DISTRIBUTION | Nearctic: Arizona and New Mexico |
| MACROHABITAT | Riparian habitats and surrounding areas |
| MICROHABITAT | On flowers of shrubs and trees |
| FEEDING HABITS | Adults feed on pollen; larvae probably prey on small insects |
| NOTE | Species of *Chauliognathus* north of Mexico were last revised in 1964 |

ADULT LENGTH
⁹⁄₁₆–¹¹⁄₁₆ in
(14–17 mm)

*CHAULIOGNATHUS PROFUNDUS*
# CHAULIOGNATHUS PROFUNDUS
LECONTE, 1858

353

Adult *Chauliognathus* are commonly found on flowers and are among the most frequently encountered cantharid beetles in North America. *Chauliognathus profundus* adults are sometimes found in large numbers feeding on a variety of flowers on herbaceous plants, trees, and shrubs, especially those growing along stream-lined canyon bottoms. They are sometimes found on the same plants as the red and black *C. lecontei*.

## RELATED SPECIES
Nearly 350 species of *Chauliognathus* occur in the Neotropics, with additional species in Australia and Papua New Guinea, and it is the only genus representing the tribe Chauliognathini in North America. *Chauliognathus profundus* is distinguished from the other 19 species known north of Mexico by its orange or reddish-orange color, black head and apical third of the elytra, and mostly black legs.

Actual size

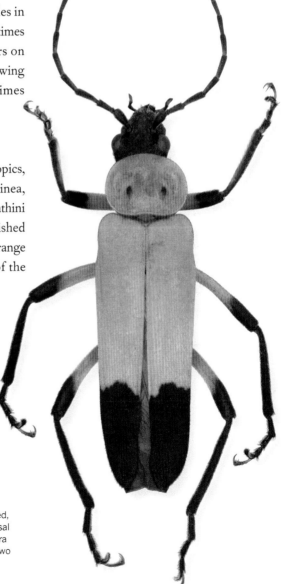

**Chauliognathus profundus** is soft bodied, elongate, somewhat flattened, parallel-sided, and mostly orange or reddish orange. The head, the basal antennal segments, most of the legs, and the apical portion of the elytra are black. Females are similar to males, but the abdomen has one or two pairs of black spots on the sides and a black apex.

| FAMILY | Cantharidae |
|---|---|
| SUBFAMILY | Chauliognathinae |
| DISTRIBUTION | Palearctic: eastern Siberia |
| MACROHABITAT | Temperate forest |
| MICROHABITAT | Lower vegetation |
| FEEDING HABITS | Predaceous; they supplement their diet with nectar and pollen |
| NOTE | *Trypherus rossicus* is a soldier beetle, exuding fluids to repel aggressors when disturbed |

**ADULT LENGTH**
³⁄₁₆–³⁄₈ in
(5.2–9.5 mm)

354

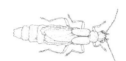

*TRYPHERUS ROSSICUS*
# TRYPHERUS ROSSICUS
(BAROVSKY, 1922)

Actual size

*Trypherus rossicus* is a typical soldier beetle, with a relatively soft body and straight sides. These beetles are effective control agents of a number of pest insects, in general consuming grasshopper eggs, aphids, caterpillars, and other soft-bodied insects. Adults are especially important predators of aphids. They supplement their diet with nectar and pollen, and consequently can act as minor pollinators. This species and its relatives were redescribed in detail by Michel Brancucci in 1985.

## RELATED SPECIES

The genus *Trypherus* contains approximately 30 species distributed in the Palearctic, Oriental, and Nearctic realms. Along with the Japanese *T. babai*, *T. rossicus* can be diagnosed from other species in the genus by the middle tibiae of males, which are slightly expanded near their apex. *Trypherus babai* and *T. rossicus* can be differentiated by the shape of the male genitalia.

**Trypherus rossicus** resembles a rove beetle, with short elytra and freely moving abdominal segments. The dorsal surface is covered with short, dense setae. The flight wings are well developed and clearly visible below the elytra. The sides of the pronotum are dark or with only a narrow yellow-brown border. The elytra are mostly black but with yellow coloring in the external and apical margins.

| FAMILY | Cantharidae |
|---|---|
| SUBFAMILY | Silinae |
| DISTRIBUTION | Nearctic: eastern USA |
| MACROHABITAT | Temperate forest and shrubland |
| MICROHABITAT | Lower vegetation and flowers |
| FEEDING HABITS | Predaceous |
| NOTE | *Silis bidentata* is a soldier beetle encountered in the eastern United States |

ADULT LENGTH
$\frac{1}{8}-\frac{3}{16}$ in
(3–4 mm)

*SILIS BIDENTATA*
# SILIS BIDENTATA
(SAY, 1825)

355

Actual size

*Silis* occurs worldwide and contains about 68 species, many of them in North America, particularly in California. Several morphological characteristics are diagnostic of *Silis* adults, such as the lamellate prothorax, simple tarsal claws, and last abdominal segment, which is divided in the male. *Silis bidentata* is a common species with a wide distribution, and there appears to be variation in the color of the head in the northern and southern limits of its distribution. As with many other members in this family, this species is a predator.

RELATED SPECIES
*Silis bidentata* differs from other species in the genus in that the surface of the pronotum has shallow impressions, the antennae are slightly serrated, and the tarsi are of similar length. It is similar to *S. latiloba*, but in *S. bidentata* the posterior corners of the pronotum are projected and rectangular, while in *S. latiloba* they are rounded and indistinct.

**Silis bidentata** is a small, soft-bodied beetle with a pale pronotum and dark elytra (appearing light brown in recently emerged adults). The dorsal surface of the pronotum is polished and rugose on the elytra. The pronotum has a pair of laterally projecting teeth on each side. The elytra do not cover the entire abdomen, leaving at least the last two segments uncovered in live individuals. The antennae are long, robust, and saw-toothed.

| FAMILY | Derodontidae |
|---|---|
| SUBFAMILY | Peltasticinae |
| DISTRIBUTION | Palearctic: east Siberia, Japan |
| MACROHABITAT | Temperate forest |
| MICROHABITAT | Under bark |
| FEEDING HABITS | Mycophagous |
| NOTE | *Peltastica* is the only known genus of the subfamily Peltasticinae; several aspects of the biology of its species are unknown |

ADULT LENGTH
³⁄₁₆ in
(3.8–4.2 mm)

356

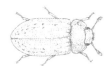

*PELTASTICA AMURENSIS*
# PELTASTICA AMURENSIS
REITTER, 1879

Actual size

*Peltastica* is one of the few members of the family Derodontidae and the only known member of the subfamily Peltasticinae. It includes two species, *P. tuberculata* in North America, and *P. amurensis* in east Siberia and Japan. Species of this genus have been found in association with fermenting sap under bark, where they feed on fungi. The beetles have ocelli between the eyes and, unlike other members of the family, the sides of the prothorax are explanate and flattened. The biology of this species remains largely unknown.

### RELATED SPECIES

This species is related to the North American *Peltastica tuberculata*, but it can be distinguished from it by the length and width of the elytra, the shape of the lateral pronotal margins, and the characteristics of the surface of the pronotum. A phylogenetic analysis published in 2007 suggested that *Peltastica* is a sister taxon to the remainder of the species in the family Derodontidae.

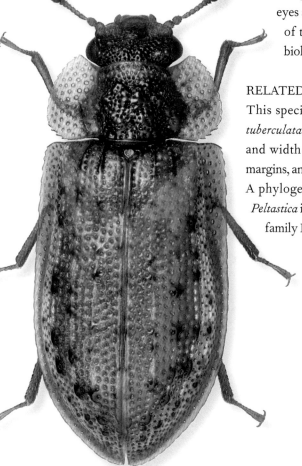

**Peltastica amurensis** is a small beetle with explanate prothorax and elytra. It is light brown overall with a black head and a dark pronotal disk. The antennae are moderately long with a well-defined antennal club. The sides of the prothorax and elytra are finely crenulated. The legs are brown and adapted for walking.

| | |
|---|---|
| FAMILY | Derodontidae |
| SUBFAMILY | Derodontinae |
| DISTRIBUTION | Palearctic: Europe |
| MACROHABITAT | Temperate forests |
| MICROHABITAT | Dead wood |
| FEEDING HABITS | Mycophagous |
| NOTE | As with other Derodontidae, this species has two ocelli on the frons |

ADULT LENGTH
⅛ in
(2.5–3 mm)

*DERODONTUS MACULARIS*
# DERODONTUS MACULARIS
(FUSS, 1850)

357

Actual size

*Derodontus* includes eight species spread across three continents and is the only member of Derodontinae. Its species can be abundant, but this isn't the case with *D. macularis*, which has been listed as rare. These beetles are easy to distinguish by the two lateral triangular ocelli on the head and the presence of small spines along the sides of the prothorax. This beetle feeds on fungi and the larvae have been found on the Basydiomycota *Ischnoderma resinosum*.

## RELATED SPECIES

*Derodontus macularis* is similar to *D. maculatus* and *D. esotericus*; they all share common elytral patterns but differ in details of the apical region. *Derodontus macularis* also shares similarities in the shape of the pronotum with *D. trisignatus* and *D. japonicus*.

**Derodontus maculatus** is a small beetle whose dorsal surface varies from yellow to brown in color with dark brown patterns. The head vertex has two ocelli and a deep central furrow. The eyes are prominent and globose. The sides of the pronotum typically have six sharp teeth along the sides and the elytra have distinctly punctate rows of striae.

| FAMILY | Nosodendridae |
|---|---|
| SUBFAMILY | |
| DISTRIBUTION | Palearctic: Europe |
| MACROHABITAT | Temperate forest |
| MICROHABITAT | Dead wood |
| FEEDING HABITS | Mycophagous |
| NOTE | Members of this family are very similar in general form; most are distinguished by characters on the underside of the body or general sculpture of the prothorax and elytra |

ADULT LENGTH
³/₁₆ in
(4–4.6 mm)

358

*NOSODENDRON FASCICULARE*
# TUFFED NOSODENDRON
(OLIVIER, 1790)

*Nosodendron fasciculare* was the first species in this family to be described—originally as *Sphaeridium fasciculare*—and until now it is the only known member of this family present in Europe. Nosodendridae only includes the genus *Nosodendron* with about 60 species worldwide, all very similar in general form. Beetles in this family probably feed on bacteria, fungi, and products of fermentation. The Tuffed Nosodendron has been included in lists of threatened species by some countries in Europe.

## RELATED SPECIES

Adults of *Nosodendron* are capable of folding their legs into cavities on their ventral surface as in the distantly related beetles in the family Byrrhidae. However, they differ from the Byrrhidae in having a prognathous head as well as other important differences. The closest species to *N. fasciculare* are probably the Holarctic species *N. asiaticum* and *N. coenosum* from Japan, and *N. californicum* and *N. unicolor* from the United States.

Actual size

**The Tuffed Nosodendron** is a small black to dark brown beetle with a very convex, oval body. Its surface is coarsely punctured, and the elytra are covered with scattered patches of yellow setae. The antennae are capitate, with the club formed by the last three segments. The legs are robust and apparently adapted for burrowing.

| FAMILY | Jacobsoniidae |
|---|---|
| SUBFAMILY | |
| DISTRIBUTION | Australian: northeast Australia |
| MACROHABITAT | Temperate and subtropical forest |
| MICROHABITAT | Under bark of dead wood |
| FEEDING HABITS | Probably mycophagous |
| NOTE | The systematic position of this small beetle is not clear, and its characteristic external morphology indicates an unusual biology |

ADULT LENGTH
¹⁄₁₆ in
(1.7–2.1 mm)

*SAROTHRIAS LAWRENCEI*

# SAROTHRIAS LAWRENCEI

LÖBL & BURCKHARDT, 1988

359

Actual size

Jacobsoniidae is a small and enigmatic family with 21 species in three genera of uncertain affinities with other beetles. The larvae and adults of these beetles live under bark, and in plant litter, fungi, bat guano, and rotten wood. Species of this family are poorly represented in collections and little is known about their biology. *Sarothrias lawrencei* was described from a small number of individuals from the Australian wet tropics area in northeastern Queensland and is generally encountered in leaf litter. The species is wingless and its larvae are unknown.

RELATED SPECIES

*Sarothrias lawrencei* is closely related to *S. papuanus*, distributed in Papua New Guinea. The species can be distinguished by their distribution, the number of longitudinal striae on the elytra and the distance between them, as well as the density of punctures on the elytral interstriae; additional distinguishing characters include the shape of the male genitalia.

**Sarothrias lawrencei** is a minute, dark brown beetle with the head mostly hidden in the prothorax and the base of the prothorax nearly as wide as the elytra. The antennae have rather broad antennomeres and are covered with disperse scalelike setae. The dorsal surface is mostly glabrous with a few scattered clusters of setae. The legs are relatively long and robust, most probably adapted for burrowing.

| | |
|---|---|
| FAMILY | Dermestidae |
| SUBFAMILY | Orphilinae |
| DISTRIBUTION | Nearctic: western North America, from British Columbia to Montana, east to Nebraska and south to California and New Mexico |
| MACROHABITAT | Temperate forests to scrub |
| MICROHABITAT | Larvae occur in dead, dry, fungus-infested wood |
| FEEDING HABITS | Adults feed on pollen |
| NOTE | Widespread, seldom encountered, with poorly known biology |

ADULT LENGTH
⅛–³/₁₆ in
(2.5–4 mm)

*ORPHILUS SUBNITIDUS*
# ORPHILUS SUBNITIDUS
LECONTE, 1861

Like many members of the family, this species has a median ocellus on the head, a rare feature in beetles, but present in other insects. The ocellus does not occur in all dermestids (e.g., it is absent in members of the genus *Dermestes*), but having this structure is generally diagnostic for the family. *Orphilus*, like many of its relatives, has adults that feed on flowers, but unlike other dermestids, the larvae lack the fantastic and specialized needle-like setae seen in other carpet beetles, and also, instead of feeding in carrion, these larvae feed in dry fungus-infected wood.

## RELATED SPECIES

There are six species of *Orphilus*, two in North America and the remaining in Eurasia (central and southern Europe, the Mediterranean region, Asia Minor, and central Asia). The genus also includes one fossil from the Early Oligocene Florissant fossil beds, Colorado, but the generic assignment of this species requires confirmation. The only other member of the subfamily Orphilinae is the genus *Orphilodes*, which occurs in Australia, the Malay Peninsula, and Borneo.

Actual size

**Orphilus subnitidus** is unicolorous black and generally shiny. The antennae, mouthparts, and tarsi are lighter colored. The body is highly compact and similar to that of members of black species of Phalacridae, but can be distinguished easily from them by the presence of the median ocellus.

| | |
|---|---|
| FAMILY | Dermestidae |
| SUBFAMILY | Trinodinae |
| DISTRIBUTION | Cosmopolitan: native to central Asia |
| MACROHABITAT | Temperate forests |
| MICROHABITAT | Dry habitats |
| FEEDING HABITS | Dry animal matter |
| NOTE | Widespread, encountered in museums and elsewhere as a pest |

ADULT LENGTH
$\frac{1}{16}$–$\frac{1}{8}$ in
(2–3 mm)

*THYLODRIAS CONTRACTUS*
# ODD BEETLE
MOTSCHULSKY, 1839

361

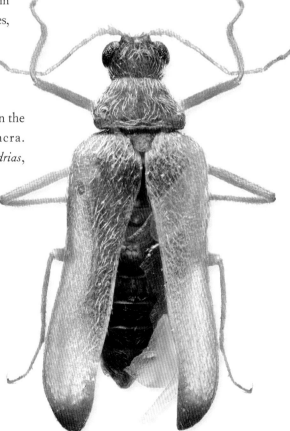

Actual size

Living up to its common name, *Thylodrias contractus* is an odd beetle indeed. Males are rather leggy and females are neotenic (retain larval features) and lack elytra, scutellum, and hind wings, but both have the characteristic ocellus on the frons. The larvae, with their modified setae, are similar to those of other dermestids. The Odd Beetle is often encountered in dry conditions where desiccated animal matter accumulates, and the species is considered a serious pest in museums, where it ruins specimens.

## RELATED SPECIES

The genus *Thylodrias* is monotypic and is contained in the subfamily Trinodinae, which includes seven genera. *Thylodrias* is in the tribe Thylodrini along with *Trichodrias*, also a monotypic genus, which is found in Java, Borneo, Malaysia, and the Philippines.

**The Odd Beetle** is unicolorous tan or pale and setose, but the sexes differ drastically in form and do not appear similar to other commonly collected dermestids. The adult male is soft bodied, lightly sclerotized (hardened with sclerotin), leggy, and not as compact as other members of the family. The female is larviform (see top right).

| | |
|---|---|
| FAMILY | Dermestidae |
| SUBFAMILY | Megatominae |
| DISTRIBUTION | Cosmopolitan: native to Central Asia |
| MACROHABITAT | Temperate forest |
| MICROHABITAT | Dry habitats |
| FEEDING HABITS | Dry animal matter |
| NOTE | Widespread, encountered in buildings as a pest |

ADULT LENGTH
$\frac{1}{16}$–$\frac{1}{16}$ in
(2.2–3.6 mm)

362

*ANTHRENUS MUSEORUM*
# MUSEUM BEETLE
(LINNAEUS, 1761)

Actual size

The Museum Beetle belongs to one of the most diverse genera of dermestids, which are as colorful as they are annoying, especially to those who maintain animal collections. This common species eats almost everything, mainly as larvae, including fur, carpets, wool, silk, feathers, skins, stored grain, stuffed animals, and dead insects. Outside human habitats, the adults may be found during the day feeding on pollen. Their larvae are distinct, like most larvae of the family, having modified needle-like setae, which detach when touched.

### RELATED SPECIES

The genus *Anthrenus* contains about 130 species. *Anthrenus museorum* is very similar to the Varied Carpet Beetle (*A. verbasci*), which is more abundant in homes. Taxonomy of the genus *Anthrenus* is complicated, and many species are very similar—historically, *A. museorum* has been described more than 14 times.

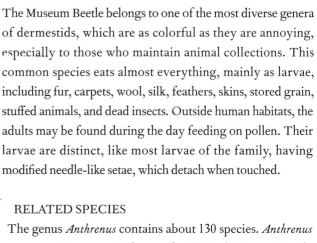

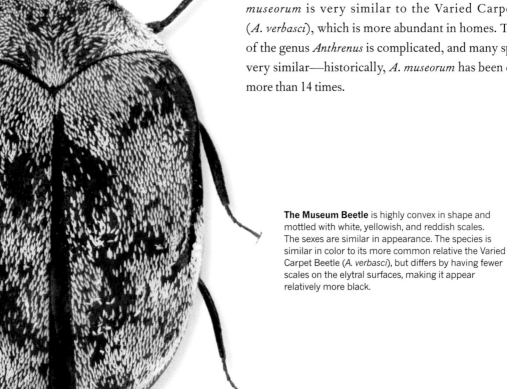

**The Museum Beetle** is highly convex in shape and mottled with white, yellowish, and reddish scales. The sexes are similar in appearance. The species is similar in color to its more common relative the Varied Carpet Beetle (*A. verbasci*), but differs by having fewer scales on the elytral surfaces, making it appear relatively more black.

| FAMILY | Endecatomidae |
|---|---|
| SUBFAMILY | |
| DISTRIBUTION | Nearctic: southeastern United Sates, including Missouri, southern Illinois, Oklahoma, Alabama, Texas |
| MACROHABITAT | Temperate forests |
| MICROHABITAT | Deciduous fungi |
| FEEDING HABITS | Woody fungi |
| NOTE | Common on certain species of fungi |

ADULT LENGTH
³/₁₆–¼ in
(4.5–5.5 mm)

*ENDECATOMUS DORSALIS*
# ENDECATOMUS DORSALIS
MELLIÉ, 1848

363

Members of *Endecatomus* are fuzzy little beetles that are easily found boring within their hosts, which tend to be woody polyporoid fungi. The larvae are scarabaeiform (grub-like) and are found together with adults. The small family was once included in the family Bostrichidae; it has uncertain phylogenetic relationships, but is thought to be a very primitive member of the superfamily Bostrichoidea. *Endecatomus dorsalis* is the least common of the species found in the southeastern United States, but the distribution of this overlooked beetle requires confirmation. To find the species, one must look inside its fungal host.

Actual size

## RELATED SPECIES

Endecotomidae is a small, underrated family, with four species in the Holarctic Realm, stretching from Japan and the Russian Far East all the way to Oklahoma, but absent from western North America. They appear, for all intents and purposes, like setose bostrichids. The late great father of modern beetle classification, Roy Crowson, provided two hypotheses about their basal relationships to other bostrichoids back in 1961.

**Endecatomus dorsalis** is a small cylindrical beetle that is uniformly reddish to dark brown with a covering of tightly curled setae. The head is ventrally directed (hypognathous), like most members of the superfamily Bostrichoidea, and the legs are clearly visible in lateral view. The sexes are similar.

| FAMILY | Bostrichidae |
|---|---|
| SUBFAMILY | Bostrichinae |
| DISTRIBUTION | Nearctic: Mexico (northern Baja California) and USA (southern California) |
| MACROHABITAT | Desert |
| MICROHABITAT | California Fan Palm (*Washingtonia filifera*) |
| FEEDING HABITS | Feeds on plants |
| NOTE | The largest bostrichid in the world |

ADULT LENGTH
1³⁄₁₆–2 in
(30–52 mm)

364

*DINAPATE WRIGHTII*
# GIANT PALM BORER
HORN, 1886

The Giant Palm Borer is the largest bostrichid in the world. Its host use is restricted to large palms, including *Phoenix* species. and the California Fan Palm (*Washingtonia filifera*), found in desert oases of North America. Larvae and adults are found feeding at the trunks, though adults can be seen flying in midsummer. Larvae live up to several years, and both life stages can be heard feeding from several feet away. The species was once a rarity but is now considered a pest where the California Fan Palm is grown as an ornamental tree, especially in Arizona and California, because tunnels excavated during extensive feeding can weaken trees and cause them to fall over in high winds.

RELATED SPECIES

Members of Bostrichinae are found worldwide, and the subfamily consists of 60 genera in five tribes. Dinapatini is monogeneric, and *Dinapate* includes only two species, *D. wrightii* and *D. hughleechi*, which also feeds on palms in Mexico.

**The Giant Palm Borer** is a large cylindrical species that is uniformly dark brown with a ventral covering of golden setae. The head is ventrally directed (hypognathous) due to the orientation of the prothorax, and has an asymmetrical antennal club. The elytra have raised costae (ridges) that are confluent and terminate apically into spine-like projections. Larvae are grub-like.

Actual size

| FAMILY | Bostrichidae |
|---|---|
| SUBFAMILY | Psoinae |
| DISTRIBUTION | Palearctic: southern Europe, western Asia, northern Africa |
| MACROHABITAT | Forests and open woodlands |
| MICROHABITAT | Understory vegetation and vines |
| FEEDING HABITS | Phytophagous |
| NOTE | Though normally associated with woody plants, this species has been implicated as a pest of library books |

ADULT LENGTH
¼–⁹⁄₁₆ in
(6–14 mm)

*PSOA DUBIA*
# PSOA DUBIA
(ROSSI, 1792)

365

Members of the family Bostrichidae are almost exclusively wood-borers as larvae. Members of the genus *Psoa* are associated with woody vines, including grapes (*Vitis* spp.). Several older writings on pests of libraries in Europe have mentioned *P. dubia* as a pest of old books and other manuscripts ("bibliophagous"), but noted that the species is too rare in libraries to be considered a serious threat. The wide range of adult size of this species is typical of wood-boring insects due to the variation in nutritional quality of the food source.

RELATED SPECIES
Psoinae is a small subfamily with five genera distributed mainly in the Old World. *Psoa* includes two species in the Mediterranean region and three in western North America. The two Mediterranean species are similar in overall appearance, but differ in the color and texture of elytral pubescence. *Psoa* species bear a superficial resemblance to some clerid beetles due to their bright coloration and cylindrical body shape.

Actual size

**Psoa dubia** is an elongate, subcylindrical species that is covered in setae. It has a black body with rusty brown to strikingly red elytra. The head is slightly hypognathous, the antennal club is symmetrical, and the elytra have confused punctation with rounded apices. Members of the genus are unusual among bostrichids in being relatively brightly colored.

| FAMILY | Bostrichidae |
|---|---|
| SUBFAMILY | Dinoderinae |
| DISTRIBUTION | Cosmopolitan: originates from tropical America and southern USA, introduced in other warmer parts of the world |
| MACROHABITAT | Warmer regions |
| MICROHABITAT | Stored products |
| FEEDING HABITS | Larvae and adults feed on stored products |
| NOTE | Adults bore into grains making neat round holes |

**ADULT LENGTH**
⅛–³⁄₁₆ in
(3–4.5 mm)

*PROSTEPHANUS TRUNCATUS*
# LARGER GRAIN BORER
(HORN, 1878)

366

Actual size

The Larger Grain Borer is originally from tropical Central and South America, where its principal host, Maize (*Zea mays*), originated. It has spread throughout the world via commerce and can be a serious pest of stored foods, especially Maize, but also Cassava (*Manihot esculenta*) and other products. Small, neat pinholes in the stored grain and a pile of dust is a sure indication that the Larger Grain Borer is present. There are several methods to control further spread, good hygiene being the most economical, simplest, and safest for the environment.

RELATED SPECIES

The genus contains five species, mostly endemic to North America, with one species in Chile. There are other bostrichids that also feed on stored grain, including the Lesser Grain Borer (*Rhyzopertha dominica*), which is smaller in size and more elongate in appearance.

**The Larger Grain Borer** is a small tubular species that is uniformly dark to reddish brown with a sparse covering of setae. The head is ventrally directed (hypognathous) and held beneath the prothorax, while the anterior portion of the pronotum has a field of well-developed spine-like denticles that are used to bore into stored maize and other foodstuffs.

| FAMILY | Bostrichidae |
|---|---|
| SUBFAMILY | Lyctinae |
| DISTRIBUTION | Circumtropical |
| MACROHABITAT | Humid forests |
| MICROHABITAT | Dry sapwood of fallen trees |
| FEEDING HABITS | Both adults and larvae feed on wood |
| NOTE | Originally described from specimens collected in Ceylon (Sri Lanka) in 1858, then redescribed under different names from Indonesia (1866), Dominican Republic (1879), and Hawaii (1879) |

ADULT LENGTH
¹⁄₁₆–¹⁄₈ in
(2–3 mm)

*MINTHEA RUGICOLLIS*
# HAIRY POWDER POST BEETLE
(WALKER, 1858)

367

Actual size

The Hairy Powder Post Beetle is a cosmopolitan tropical pest of dry seasoned wood. Thought by some forest entomologists to be increasing in number, the species may affect the economies of some tropical countries and has been rated among one of the most destructive pests in Nigeria, portions of India, and the United States. This may be due, in part, to its life history, as it thrives year-round in tropical conditions. These beetles can develop from egg to adult in two to six months, depending on the starch and moisture contents of the wood, as well as the temperature.

RELATED SPECIES
*Minthea* is a circumtropical genus of eight species, and is one of the more attractive members of Lyctinae. This group, collectively called powder post beetles, includes other pestiferous species, but these commonly encountered beetles lack the scales that are so distinctive of the genus *Minthea*.

**The Hairy Powder Post Beetle** is an elongate and somewhat flattened species with a uniform brown to reddish-brown color. It is covered with distinctive scales that form neat rows on the elytra. The antennal club has two segments and the pronotum has a distinctive median impression.

| FAMILY | Bostrichidae |
|---|---|
| SUBFAMILY | Euderiinae |
| DISTRIBUTION | Australian: New Zealand |
| MACROHABITAT | Temperate forest |
| MICROHABITAT | Southern beeches (*Nothofagus* spp.) and podocarp trees |
| FEEDING HABITS | Larvae feed in galleries of live and dead or injured trees |
| NOTE | Categorized as "Naturally Uncommon" in a 2012 publication |

ADULT LENGTH
³⁄₁₆–¼ in
(4.4–5.3 mm)

*EUDERIA SQUAMOSA*
# EUDERIA SQUAMOSA
BROUN, 1880

Actual size

*Euderia squamosa* is a strange, undercollected species of bostrichid, with uncertain phylogenetic relationships to other members of the family. It was originally described as a member of Ptinidae but then transferred to Bostrichidae, despite having characters more in common with the former. Specimens are relatively rare in collections, though host-use patterns seem to indicate it feeds on several temperate trees.

### RELATED SPECIES

*Euderia squamosa* is the only member of the genus *Euderia*, itself the only member of the subfamily *Euderiinae*, which is restricted to New Zealand. Its phylogenetic relationships remain uncertain, and it does not look similar to other bostrichids or ptinids. *Euderia* tends to be considered alongside another unusual bostrichoid, *Endecatomus*, and together they provide a conundrum for beetle systematists.

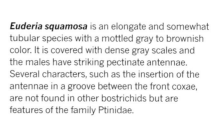

**Euderia squamosa** is an elongate and somewhat tubular species with a mottled gray to brownish color. It is covered with dense gray scales and the males have striking pectinate antennae. Several characters, such as the insertion of the antennae in a groove between the front coxae, are not found in other bostrichids but are features of the family Ptinidae.

| FAMILY | Ptinidae |
| --- | --- |
| SUBFAMILY | Ptininae |
| DISTRIBUTION | Cosmopolitan |
| MACROHABITAT | Forests |
| MICROHABITAT | Accumulated dried animal or plant matter |
| FEEDING HABITS | Stored products |
| NOTE | Fused elytra conceal the spiracles to minimize water loss |

ADULT LENGTH
¹⁄₁₆–¹⁄₈ in
(1.7–3.2 mm)

*GIBBIUM AEQUINOCTIALE*
# SMOOTH SPIDER BEETLE
BOIELDIEU, 1854

369

Species of *Gibbium* are detritivores, feeding on all sorts of animal products, from dog biscuits and opium cakes to leather and wool. They can be common where food is plentiful, but are rare otherwise, especially in nature, where they may have originally been associated with rodent middens. The common Smooth Spider Beetle is flightless, but the miracle of its widespread distribution is linked to its ability to aestivate (become dormant), tolerate cool conditions, and live without water for long periods.

### RELATED SPECIES

The genus *Gibbium* consists of two species. *Gibbium aequinoctiale* is often confused with the Old World *G. psylloides*; they can be separated only with difficulty by the shape of the antennal fossae and genitalia. These species also resemble the genus *Mezium*, but they have fewer abdominal ventrites and the head and pronotum lack setae.

**The Smooth Spider Beetle** has a mite-like appearance. It is highly convex, compact, and globular, and the pronotum and elytra lack setae and punctation. It ranges in color from red to black, and has dense, short golden setae ventrally that perfectly match the color of the antennae and long spider-like legs.

Actual size

| FAMILY | Ptinidae |
|---|---|
| SUBFAMILY | Ernobiinae |
| DISTRIBUTION | Nearctic and Neotropical: native to Mexico and California; introduced to southern Europe and North Africa (Madeira archipelago, Malta, Spain, Tunisia) |
| MACROHABITAT | Temperate forests |
| MICROHABITAT | Mostly in dead wood, flowers, and dry plant matter |
| FEEDING HABITS | Fruits, stems, oak galls, pine tree blossoms |
| NOTE | Records of introductions to New Zealand require confirmation |

**ADULT LENGTH**
¹⁄₁₆–¹⁄₈ in
(1.5–2.5 mm)

*OZOGNATHUS CORNUTUS*
# OZOGNATHUS CORNUTUS
(LECONTE, 1859)

Actual size

*Ozognathus cornutus* originated from the western portions of North America, but has spread and is now established in southern Europe and North Africa. Horns, like those seen in many species of scarab beetles, are rare in ptinid beetles, but occur on a few species feeding in dead wood, and the males of *O. cornutus* have remarkable tusks that arise from the base of the mandible and extend over the head. Though the biology of this species is poorly known, it is likely that the males—like other male beetles with horns—may compete for females for mating.

RELATED SPECIES

There are many genera in the Ernobiinae, all or most of which are wood-boring beetles and can be commonly encountered by beating dead wood or by rearing from enclosed host trees and waiting for the beetles to come out naturally. The genus *Ozognathus* contains three species from North America and can be distinguished from most of its relatives by the presence of tusks on the male mandibles.

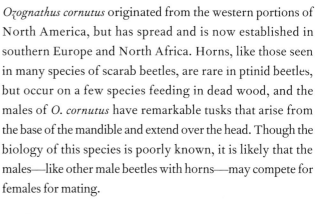

**Ozognathus cornutus** is a small, dark brown ptinid that is oblong and convex, and is covered with elongate setae over its body. The head is ventrally directed (hypognathus) and the males have large tusks arising from the base of the mandibles. Males also have an elongate antennal club. Females are much harder to distinguish, having features much like those of other ernobiines and lacking peculiar sexual dimorphisms.

| | |
|---|---|
| FAMILY | Ptinidae |
| SUBFAMILY | Ernobiinae |
| DISTRIBUTION | Palearctic and Oriental: widespread in Europe and Asia |
| MACROHABITAT | Temperate forests |
| MICROHABITAT | Hardwoods |
| FEEDING HABITS | Larvae feed in wood that has been decayed by fungi |
| NOTE | When tapping, the beetle lifts its body on all legs, orients the flattened vertex of the head to the woody substrate, and propels itself forward |

ADULT LENGTH
³/₁₆–³/₈ in
(4–9 mm)

*XESTOBIUM RUFOVILLOSUM*

# DEATH WATCH BEETLE

(DE GEER, 1774)

371

The superstition that the Death Watch Beetle portends death arose from the eerie tapping of both sexes on wood, especially when the species occurs at night on exposed oak rafters. The ritual is initiated by drumming males looking for a mate; stationary females respond by tapping in turn. Eventually the female is located and the male mates with her, but it is the female that chooses her partner based on his knocking. It has been reported that nearly all pre-nineteenth century buildings containing oak timbers in England have previously been, or currently are, infested with these beetles.

### RELATED SPECIES

Ernobiine ptinids are a taxonomically neglected group worldwide, as is the case with many other groups of small beetles. The genus *Xestobium* contains 17 species, mainly from Europe and North America, all of which attack hardwoods like other members of the group. *Xestobium rufovillosum* is most similar to *X. elegans* from the Russian Far East.

Actual size

**The Death Watch Beetle** is a moderate-size, oblong, convex wood-borer that is red to dark brown or even black in color. It is covered with elongate pale or yellowish hairlike setae.

| | |
|---|---|
| FAMILY | Ptinidae |
| SUBFAMILY | Xyletininae |
| DISTRIBUTION | Mainly circumtropical |
| MACROHABITAT | Human habitation |
| MICROHABITAT | Stored products |
| FEEDING HABITS | Feeds on a wide range of stored plant products |
| NOTE | One of the most damaging pests of tobacco |

ADULT LENGTH
¹⁄₁₆–¹⁄₈ in
(2–3 mm)

372

*LASIODERMA SERRICORNE*
# CIGARETTE BEETLE
(FABRICIUS, 1792)

Actual size

**The Cigarette Beetle** is small, reddish brown, compact, oval, and convex, and its body is covered with setae. The head is held beneath the prothorax in repose, and the beetle will sit motionless upon disturbance with its legs retracted beneath the body. The antennae are serrated and not clubbed, and the elytra are smooth and lack distinct striations.

The Cigarette Beetle has long been associated with man, specimens having been found in dried resin in the tomb of the Egyptian pharaoh Tutankhamun, who died more than 3,300 years ago. They reach high numbers in disorganized cabinets, the setose grub-like larvae undergoing development in about 26 days. A symbiotic yeast held in the midgut assists in digestion, and also supplies vitamins, sterols, and resistance to toxins. The yeast is held in specialized organs called mycetomes, and in the female it is deposited onto the surface of the egg as it passes through the oviduct; the hatchlings feed on the eggshell and ingest the yeast.

RELATED SPECIES
Xyletininae is a taxonomically diverse group of more than 30 genera and about 150 species. The genus *Lasioderma* contains about 40 species, mostly from the Palearctic. *Lasioderma serricorne* is often confused with the Drugstore Beetle (*Stegobium paniceum*), an anobiine, which has similar habits. *Stegobium*, however, have deep elytral striae that are absent in the Cigarette Beetle.

| FAMILY | Ptinidae |
|---|---|
| SUBFAMILY | Dorcatominae |
| DISTRIBUTION | Nearctic: southeastern North America, from Texas northeast to New Jersey and south to Florida |
| MACROHABITAT | Temperate forest |
| MICROHABITAT | Fungi |
| FEEDING HABITS | Both adults and larvae feed on puffballs |
| NOTE | Adults are rarely encountered |

ADULT LENGTH
¹⁄₁₆–¹⁄₈ in
(2–2.5 mm)

*CAENOCARA INEPTUM*
# PUFFBALL BEETLE
FALL, 1905

373

Actual size

Though belonging to a group primarily associated with dead wood, many dorcatomines are mycophagous, feeding on wood-rotting fungi. Puffball beetles of the genus *Caenocara* are found on many species of puffball and puffball-like fungi. This is a unique association that has evolved repeatedly in beetles, but it is not especially common across all mycophages. Puffball beetles are found rarely as adults, typically when they are mating and ovipositioning on the host. The grub-like larvae feed on the developing fungal stroma, and can spoil a good puffball for mushroom collectors.

RELATED SPECIES

Dorcatominae is a taxonomically diverse subfamily of 50 genera and about 150 species, but it is a neglected group taxonomically with many undescribed species, especially in tropical regions. *Caeonocara* contains about 16 species, mostly from the Holarctic, and it is the only genus that has been reported to feed on puffballs in North America.

**The Puffball Beetle** is a small, round, convex black beetle that is covered in setae and has a shiny cuticle. When the beetle is disturbed, the head is tucked beneath the prothorax and the appendages are held tightly so that the beetle rolls off the puffball into the forest litter. The segments of the antennal club are enlarged, and the elytra have distinctive lateral grooves.

| FAMILY | Lymexylidae |
|---|---|
| SUBFAMILY | Hylecoetinae |
| DISTRIBUTION | Cosmopolitan: native to northern Scandinavia, west to Siberia, and south to the Caucasus Mountains; now spread worldwide |
| MACROHABITAT | Temperate forests |
| MICROHABITAT | Coniferous and deciduous trees |
| FEEDING HABITS | Larvae bore into wood and feed on symbiotic fungi |
| NOTE | Larvae are tidy, keeping the galleries free of frass (excreta) |

ADULT LENGTH
¼–¹¹⁄₁₆ in
(6–18 mm)

374

*ELATEROIDES DERMESTOIDES*
# LARGE TIMBERWORM BEETLE
(LINNAEUS, 1761)

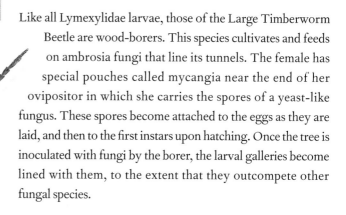

Like all Lymexylidae larvae, those of the Large Timberworm Beetle are wood-borers. This species cultivates and feeds on ambrosia fungi that line its tunnels. The female has special pouches called mycangia near the end of her ovipositor in which she carries the spores of a yeast-like fungus. These spores become attached to the eggs as they are laid, and then to the first instars upon hatching. Once the tree is inoculated with fungi by the borer, the larval galleries become lined with them, to the extent that they outcompete other fungal species.

RELATED SPECIES

The subfamily Hylecoetinae contains a single genus with six species distributed in the Holarctic Realm. All have elongate elytra, but are distinguished from all other lymexylonids by the presence of an epicranial pit. *Elateroides dermestoides* is very similar to the North American *E. lugubris*, but only the former species is of economic importance.

**The Large Timberworm Beetle** is an elongate species that is light brown to tan in color, sometimes with a darker head, and covered with setae. The body is soft and the elytra have thin, widely spaced costae. Males have an extravagant organ on the maxillary palps and the antennae are fan-shaped (flabellate) while the females (shown in the photograph) have serrate antennae.

Actual size

| FAMILY | Lymexylidae |
|---|---|
| SUBFAMILY | Atractocerinae |
| DISTRIBUTION | Afrotropical: widespread in west Africa and Madagascar |
| MACROHABITAT | Tropical forests |
| MICROHABITAT | Tree species including mahogany (*Swietenia* spp.), Teak (*Tectona grandis*), and Cashew (*Anacardium occidentale*) |
| FEEDING HABITS | Larvae bore into wood |
| NOTE | Specimens are most commonly collected at night with black lights and in Malaise traps |

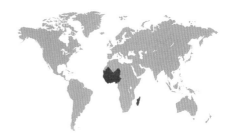

ADULT LENGTH
⁹⁄₁₆–2³⁄₈ in
(15–60 mm)

*ATRACTOCERUS BREVICORNIS*

# ATRACTOCERUS BREVICORNIS

(LINNAEUS, 1766)

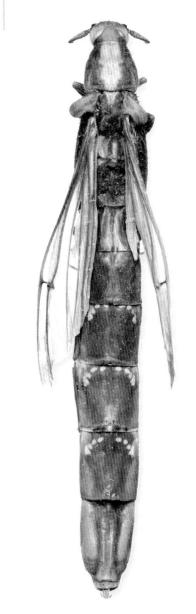

375

All members of *Atractocerus* are strange-looking beetles, and to the novice entomologist they appear more like flying worms than beetles. Some species of the genus are brightly colored and are thought by some naturalists to be wasp mimics. The big eyes of this species and the fact that specimens are most often collected at night suggest that it is nocturnal. Larvae are wood-boring, and the tail end of first instars has a heavily sclerotized flat or concave plate, which serves to block their tunnels from potential predators or parasites.

RELATED SPECIES

The subfamily Atractocerinae now contains six genera. In 1985, *Atractocerus* was split into five genera and a sixth genus from southeastern Europe was added in 2004. Species can be distinguished from other brachypterous lymexylonids by their large eyes and a head that is narrower than the width of the pronotum.

**Atractocerus brevicornis** is vermiform (worm-like) and has very reduced elytra, with exposed wings that fold lengthwise at rest (as opposed to staphylinids, which have more complex folding). The pronotum has a broad median stripe that is typically light tan, and the elongate tarsi, which are also tan-colored, contrast with the darker portions of the remaining body. Males have a complex multipronged organ on the maxillary palps.

Actual size

| FAMILY | Phloiophilidae |
| --- | --- |
| SUBFAMILY | |
| DISTRIBUTION | Palearctic: Europe |
| MACROHABITAT | Temperate forest |
| MICROHABITAT | Lower vegetation and dead wood |
| FEEDING HABITS | Mycophagous |
| NOTE | The family Phloiophilidae contains only one species, restricted to Europe, and appears to have affinities with the family Melyridae |

ADULT LENGTH
⅛ in
(2.5–3.3 mm)

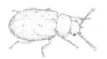

*PHLOIOPHILUS EDWARDSII*
# PHLOIOPHILUS EDWARDSII
STEPHENS, 1830

Actual size

Phloiophilidae contains the single genus *Phloiophilus* with the single species *P. edwardsi*. The family seems to be closely related to Melyridae, but recent studies have suggested a placement in the family Trogossitidae. This beetle can be found on living vegetation and on lichens or associated with fungi. Both the adults and larvae can be abundant and have been associated with fruiting bodies of the fungus *Phlebia merismoides* on oaks (*Quercus* spp.) in northern England; the pupae can be found in the soil. The larvae are apparently active in the winter.

RELATED SPECIES

The relationships of the families within the superfamily Cleroidea are uncertain. Some cleroid groups are difficult to distinguish from members of the superfamily Cucujoidea. An extensive phylogenetic study based on the morphology of adult and larval characters among most Coleoptera groups published in 2011 unfortunately did not include the family Phloiophilidae. *Phloiophilus edwardsii* is the only species in this family.

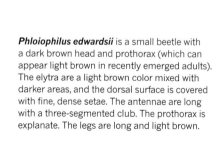

**Phloiophilus edwardsii** is a small beetle with a dark brown head and prothorax (which can appear light brown in recently emerged adults). The elytra are a light brown color mixed with darker areas, and the dorsal surface is covered with fine, dense setae. The antennae are long with a three-segmented club. The prothorax is explanate. The legs are long and light brown.

| FAMILY | Trogossitidae |
|---|---|
| SUBFAMILY | Peltinae |
| DISTRIBUTION | Nearctic: present from Manitoba east to Nova Scotia in Canada; in the USA it is known from Massachusetts, Maine, New Hampshire, New York, and Vermont |
| MACROHABITAT | Temperate forest |
| MICROHABITAT | Under bark of dead wood |
| FEEDING HABITS | Mycophagous |
| NOTE | The family Trogossitidae contains a diverse range of species, some of which are rare and poorly known |

ADULT LENGTH
³/₁₆–³/₈ in
(4.9–10.4 mm)

*GRYNOCHARIS QUADRILINEATA*
# FOUR-LINED BARK-GNAWING BEETLE
(MELSHEIMER, 1844)

377

Actual size

The genus *Grynocharis* occurs in the Northern Hemisphere and contains the European species *G. oblonga*, which was included in the IUCN Red List of Threatened Species because of habitat degradation. A study published in 2013 reviewed the classification and relationships of *Grynocharis* and related genera. *G. quadrilineata* was described based on specimens from Pennsylvania and is distributed in the northeastern USA, Ontario, Quebec, and surrounding regions. It is currently placed in the tribe Lophocaterini. Adults can be found under bark and in the rotten wood of deciduous and coniferous trees between February and April.

### RELATES SPECIES

*Grynocharis oregonensis* is similar to *G. quadrilineata* but differs in that the elytral carina are more prominent and the sides of the elytra are explanate. Other diagnostic characteristics of *G. quadrilineata* are the single spur at the apex of the front tibia, and the fact that the last three segments of the antennae, also known as the antennal club, are asymmetrical.

**The Four-lined Bark-gnawing Beetle** is a small dark brown to black beetle with a shiny dorsal surface. The pronotum is finely punctured and the elytra are coarsely striated. The prothorax is transverse with the anterior angles slightly projected. The antennae are relatively long, with the last three segments larger. The legs are robust, adapted for moving under bark.

| FAMILY | Trogossitidae |
|---|---|
| SUBFAMILY | Peltinae |
| DISTRIBUTION | Nearctic: western North America |
| MACROHABITAT | Montane coniferous forests |
| MICROHABITAT | Adults and larvae live under the bark of dead conifers |
| FEEDING HABITS | Adults and larvae probably eat wood-rotting fungi |
| NOTE | This species was previously placed in the genus *Ostoma* |

ADULT LENGTH
³/₁₆–⁷/₁₆ in
(5–11 mm)

378

*PELTIS PIPPINGSKOELDI*
# PELTIS PIPPINGSKOELDI
(MANNERHEIM, 1852)

Both the adults and larvae of *Peltis pippingskoeldi* are associated with the polypore fungi that attack mostly conifers, that is, *Fomitopsis pinicola*, *Oligoporus leucospongia*, and *Pycnosporellus alboluteus*. The flat adults are adapted to living under the bark of snags and logs of pine (*Pinus* spp.), fir (*Abies* spp.), Douglas-fir (*Pseudotsuga menziesii*), and hemlock (*Tsuga* spp.), while the larvae feed and develop within the rotting wood. In North America, this species occurs primarily in coniferous forests.

### RELATED SPECIES

There are nine species of *Peltis* distributed across northern and western North America and Eurasia. The tuberculate ridges and reddish-yellow spots on the elytra distinguish *P. pippingskoeldi* from other species in the genus. It superficially resembles similarly flattened sap beetles, such as the North American genera *Amphotis*, *Lobiopa*, and *Prometopia*, all of which are much smaller and more elongate than *Peltis*, and have antennae with compact clubs.

Actual size

**Peltis pippingskoeldi** is flat, dull reddish brown, and relatively short-legged. The last three antennomeres form a loose club. The margins of the pronotum and elytra are broad and flattened. The six elytral ridges are studded with bumps, or tubercles; the surfaces in between have several reddish-yellow patches on each elytron.

| FAMILY | Trogossitidae |
|---|---|
| SUBFAMILY | Trogossitinae |
| DISTRIBUTION | Holarctic: North America and Europe |
| MACROHABITAT | Coniferous forests |
| MICROHABITAT | Adults and larvae live under the bark of dead pine |
| FEEDING HABITS | Larvae and probably adults eat fungus |
| NOTE | This species is perfectly shaped for living in tight microhabitats |

ADULT LENGTH
¼–½ in
(6–12 mm)

*CALITYS SCABRA*

# CALITYS SCABRA

(THUNBERG, 1784)

379

The adults of *Calitys scabra* are found under the loose bark of snags and logs of large pines (*Pinus* spp.), spruces (*Picea* spp.), and firs (*Abies* spp.). The larvae feed in the fruiting bodies of polypore fungi, including *Fomitopsis pinicola*. This species is considered endangered in some European countries where old-growth conifer forests are rapidly disappearing. In North America, this species is found across the forested regions of Canada and the northern United States.

## RELATED SPECIES

There are two species of *Calitys* in North America and Europe. The only other species in the genus, the North American *C. minor*, is generally slightly smaller (¼–⁵⁄₁₆ in/6 8 mm), reddish brown, with less prominent sculpturing on the pronotum and elytra. The sides of the pronotum and elytra are lighter and somewhat translucent. It occurs across Canada and the western United States to central California and Nevada.

Actual size

**Calitys scabra** is parallel-sided, somewhat flat, and dark brown to black. Its rough surfaces have tubercles with short, curved setae. The broad pronotum and elytra have prominent raised areas and tuberculate ridges, respectively, and their sides are saw-toothed. The elytra each have the second and third ridges merging at the tips, and a fifth ridge along the side.

| FAMILY | Trogossitidae |
|---|---|
| SUBFAMILY | Trogossitinae |
| DISTRIBUTION | Australian: eastern Australia |
| MACROHABITAT | Forest |
| MICROHABITAT | Dead wood |
| FEEDING HABITS | Predaceous |
| NOTE | The genus *Leperina* belongs to the tribe Gymnochilini, a diverse group with scattered distribution in several regions of the world |

ADULT LENGTH
¼–⁷⁄₁₆ in
(6.6–10.5 mm)

*LEPERINA CIRROSA*
# LEPERINA CIRROSA
PASCOE, 1860

The nomenclatural history of the genus *Leperina* is filled with several names, often synonymized or invalid. The genus belongs in the tribe Gymnochilini, which is distributed in Australasia, Africa, and the southern Pacific. *Leperina* is distributed in Australia, Papua New Guinea, New Caledonia, and adjacent regions, and so far most of the species found are present in Australia. *Leperina cirrosa* occurs in eastern Australia, and the adults and larvae are predators that live under bark or in tunnels of wood-boring beetles of *Eucalyptus*, *Acacia*, and other trees.

### RELATED SPECIES

As most recently defined, *Leperina* is a genus of 18 species. In a phylogenetic analysis of the closely related genus *Phanodesta*, *L. cirrosa* was placed as sister of a clade that includes *L. decorata* and *L. moniliata*. A broader analysis will be necessary to identify the relationships of these species. *Kolibacia*, a related genus described for the first time in 2013, differs in the punctation between ridges on the elytra.

Actual size

**Leperina cirrosa** is densely covered with white and black scales. The anterior angles of the prothorax project anteriorly. The antennae are short and have a three-segmented apical club. The legs are robust and probably adapted for moving under bark. The elytra have longitudinal coarse punctures that form striae, these are usually covered by setae.

| FAMILY | Trogossitidae |
|---|---|
| SUBFAMILY | Trogossitinae |
| DISTRIBUTION | Nearctic: western North America |
| MACROHABITAT | Coniferous forests, oak and riparian woodlands, deserts |
| MICROHABITAT | Under the bark of dead limbs and trees |
| FEEDING HABITS | Adults and larvae prey on all stages of wood-boring insects |
| NOTE | Genus is often misspelled *Temnocheila* |

ADULT LENGTH
⁵⁄₁₆–¾ in
(8–20 mm)

*TEMNOSCHEILA CHLORODIA*
# GREEN BARK BEETLE
(MANNERHEIM, 1843)

381

*Temnoscheila chlorodia* is widely distributed west of the Great Plains and occurs in montane forests, valleys, and deserts. Both the adults and larvae are important predators of bark beetles and are generally found on conifers and other trees, searching under the bark of dead branches and trees for prey in the galleries of wood-boring insects. The larvae consume all life stages of bark beetles, including the eggs, larvae, pupae, and newly emerged adults, and pupate under bark. Adults have powerful jaws and can deliver a painful nip when handled. Efforts to use species of this genus to control bark beetle populations have proven unsuccessful.

RELATED SPECIES

There are about 150 species of *Temnoscheila* distributed throughout the Northern Hemisphere and Neotropical Realm, with most species occurring in South America. *Temnoscheila chlorodia* is similar to two other metallic green species occurring in North America, *T. acuta* and *T. virescens*, both of which occur only east of the Great Plains.

Actual size

**The Green Bark Beetle** is elongate, not quite cylindrical in cross section, parallel-sided, and with a somewhat convex pronotum and elytra; it is uniformly brilliant metallic green, blue-green, or rarely purplish. The eyes are not as prominent as the pointed front angles of the pronotum. The long elytra have rows of fine and shallow punctures.

| FAMILY | Trogossitidae |
|---|---|
| SUBFAMILY | Trogossitinae |
| DISTRIBUTION | Cosmopolitan |
| MACROHABITAT | Food-storage facilities |
| MICROHABITAT | Stored-grain containers |
| FEEDING HABITS | Adults and larvae eat plant and animal materials |
| NOTE | A pest of stored food-products worldwide |

ADULT LENGTH
¼–⅜ in
(6–10 mm)

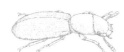

*TENEBROIDES MAURITANICUS*
# CADELLE
(LINNAEUS, 1758)

382

The Cadelle is a serious pest of stored foods. Adults and larvae eat grains, cereal products, nuts, dried fruits, potatoes, and other stored plant-based foods, as well as other stored-product pests. They live in granaries, grain elevators, warehouses, and mills. The larvae cause additional damage by chewing into woodwork of grain bins to pupate. A single female will scatter up to 1,000 eggs in foodstuffs, and the eggs soon hatch into fleshy, black-headed larvae each with a pair of black projections on the tip of the abdomen. The life cycle may take as little as 70 days, but longer under less favorable conditions.

## RELATED SPECIES

There are about 150 species of *Tenebroides* distributed throughout the Northern Hemisphere and Neotropical Realm, with most species occurring in South America. Although challenging to distinguish from other species in the genus, the size, color, and body form of *T. mauritanicus* is sufficient to distinguish it from other pest beetles that infest stored grains and other plant-based stored foods.

Actual size

**The Cadelle** is elongate, somewhat convex, and shiny dark brown to black. Antennomeres 8–11 are all similar in shape and increase in size toward the tip. The pronotum gradually narrows from the front to the rear and its base is well separated from the base of the elytra. The elytra are slightly flattened, with shallow rows of deep, oblong punctures.

| FAMILY | Chaetosomatidae |
| --- | --- |
| SUBFAMILY | |
| DISTRIBUTION | Australian: New Zealand |
| MACROHABITAT | Subtemperate forest |
| MICROHABITAT | Under bark |
| FEEDING HABITS | Apparently predaceous |
| NOTE | *Chaetosoma scaritides* is endemic to New Zealand, and members of the family Chaetosomatidae occur only in New Zealand and Madagascar |

ADULT LENGTH
¼–½ in
(6–12 mm)

*CHAETOSOMA SCARITIDES*

# CHAETOSOMA SCARITIDES

WESTWOOD, 1851

383

Members of the enigmatic Chaetosomatidae are thought to be closely related to the cleroid families Trogossitidae and Cleridae. *Chaetosoma scaritides* seems to be very variable in color, body size, sculpture, number of tibial spines, and wing venation. This is the only described species in the genus, but apparently there are two additional undescribed species. Some evidence has indicated that these beetles have predatory feeding habits. Larvae of this species have been encountered in burrows of several trees, including *Nothofagus*.

## RELATED SPECIES

Chaetosomatidae is a rare small family of beetles with three genera, *Chaetosoma*, *Chaetosomodes*, and *Malgassochaetus*, distributed in New Zealand and Madagascar. Phylogenetic relationships among the genera and species of this family have not been published. *Chaetosoma scaritides* is the only species in the genus *Chaetosoma*, but there are apparently a further two species yet to be described.

Actual size

**Chaetosoma scaritides** is a small beetle, dark brown in color but with a yellowish to pale brown base to the elytra. The pronotum has some coarse punctures and the elytra have coarsely punctured striae. The dorsal surface is scattered with long, erect setae. The mandibles are well developed and the antennae are filiform. The legs are pale brown.

| FAMILY | Thanerocleridae |
| --- | --- |
| SUBFAMILY | Zenodosinae |
| DISTRIBUTION | Nearctic: east of the Rocky Mountains in Canada and USA |
| MACROHABITAT | Temperate forest and shrubland |
| MICROHABITAT | Under bark |
| FEEDING HABITS | Predaceous |
| NOTE | *Zenodosus sanguineus* is a colorful beetle and the only member of the genus |

ADULT LENGTH
³⁄₁₆–¼ in
(4.1–6.5 mm)

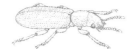

384

*ZENODOSUS SANGUINEUS*
# ZENODOSUS SANGUINEUS
(SAY, 1835)

*Zenodosus sanguineus* is an isolated genus with one species defined by a series of unique morphological characteristics and mentioned as the most ancestral member of the family Thanerocleridae. Particular characteristics include open front coxal cavities and intercoxal processes that are not carinate. Adults of this species are diurnal and occur beneath bark and moss where boring insects are abundant. Its larvae have been described and have similarities with larvae of the genus *Thaneroclerus*.

## RELATED SPECIES
The small family Thanerocleridae includes approximately 30 species, which are distributed throughout the world. *Zenodosus sanguineus* is the sole member of the genus *Zenodosus*. The bright red color of the elytra and the front coxal cavities that are open behind will readily separate this species from those of the related genera *Thaneroclerus* and *Ababa*, which also occur in North America.

Actual size

**Zenodosus sanguineus** is a colorful beetle. Its integument is dark brown but its elytra are reddish in live individuals and the whole dorsal surface and legs are covered with dense, fine setae. The antennae are robust and the last three segments are larger. The punctures of the elytra form an irregular pattern. The legs are robust.

| FAMILY | Thanerocleridae |
|---|---|
| SUBFAMILY | Thaneroclerinae |
| DISTRIBUTION | Cosmopolitan |
| MACROHABITAT | Forested areas |
| MICROHABITAT | Tree branches, stored products |
| FEEDING HABITS | Predaceous |
| NOTE | The larvae and adults are predators of wood-boring or mycophagous beetles |

ADULT LENGTH
³⁄₁₆–¼ in
(4.7–6.5 mm)

*THANEROCLERUS BUQUET*

# THANEROCLERUS BUQUET
(LEFEBVRE, 1835)

385

Species of this genus differ from the closely related *Zenodosus* in the close front coxal cavities and longer first abdominal ventrite. The larvae and adults of *Thaneroclerus buquet* are diurnal predators of wood-boring or mycophagous beetles, and have been reported as predators of insects found in groceries, spices, drugs, and tobacco. This species, which is thought to have originated from India, has a cosmopolitan distribution and is the only species from this family found in Europe. The elongate larva can measure up to ⁷⁄₁₆ in (11 mm) when mature and is characterized by the presence of a well-sclerotized dorsal plate on the ninth abdominal segment, which bears a pair of rudimentary urogomphi.

RELATED SPECIES

*Thaneroclerus buquet* resembles *T. impressus*, *T. aino*, and *T. termitincola*, but in *T. buquet* there is a central depression on the prothorax that is short, broad, and variable in depth, and there is also a depression along the elytral suture. The species can further be distinguished by the setae on its dorsal surface.

Actual size

**Thaneroclerus buquet** is a small beetle whose body is covered by dense setae, and that has a reddish or brown integument. The antennae are long with the last three segments larger. The prothorax is very narrow at the base compared with the elytral bases. The eyes are not protuberant but are visible from above. The legs are rather long and are brown.

| FAMILY | Cleridae |
|---|---|
| SUBFAMILY | Tillinae |
| DISTRIBUTION | Nearctic: Arizona, USA |
| MACROHABITAT | Temperate forest |
| MICROHABITAT | Lower vegetation |
| FEEDING HABITS | Predaceous |
| NOTE | The large genus *Cymatodera* has a neglected taxonomy that requires systematic studies in order to diagnose its species |

ADULT LENGTH
approximately ⁷⁄₁₆ in
(11 mm)

386

*CYMATODERA TRICOLOR*
# CYMATODERA TRICOLOR
SKINNER, 1905

*Cymatodera tricolor* belongs to the subfamily Tillinae, one of the biggest subfamilies in the family Cleridae, with 543 species in 67 genera distributed worldwide. This subfamily is especially species-rich in Africa, Madagascar and the Oriental Realm. *Cymatodera* is largely distributed in the New World. The taxonomy of the group is not clear since extreme variation in color and form in the same species is frequent. *Cymatodera tricolor* is a predator and may be found on trees infested with bark beetles. Research from 2006 indicated that members of Tillinae are capable of producing stridulations.

RELATED SPECIES

This genus contains dozens of species that have been described at intervals by different authors over several years. In North America there are about 60 species and the relationships between them are poorly known. When *Cymatodera tricolor* was described it was said to be related to *C. belfragei* and very distinct from several other species.

Actual size

**Cymatodera tricolor** is a small, colorful beetle. Its integument is dark brown with half of the pronotum reddish. The base of the elytra is also reddish, with a medium transverse white band and black to the apex. The antennae are long and filiform. The body is covered by short, dense pubescence. The legs are long and are adapted for running.

| FAMILY | Cleridae |
|---|---|
| SUBFAMILY | Hydnocerinae |
| DISTRIBUTION | Nearctic: Canada and the United States |
| MACROHABITAT | Subtropical and temperate forest |
| MICROHABITAT | On foliage and flowers of shrubland |
| FEEDING HABITS | Predator |
| NOTE | A small, soft-bodied Cleridae that may resemble several other beetles that frequent flowers (e.g., Melyridae species). It has also been mentioned as a beneficial predator of the larvae of some pests |

ADULT LENGTH
⁵⁄₁₆ in
(3.5–5 mm)

*PHYLLOBAENUS PALLIPENNIS*
# PHYLLOBAENUS PALLIPENNIS
(SAY, 1825)

387

*Phyllobaenus pallipennis* belongs to a particular group of checkered beetles that have a more elongated body, enormous eyes, a narrow pronotum, and often colorful patterns. In this species the elytra are shorter than the hind wings and the abdomen and widest at the base, and the pronotum is widest at the middle. It can be found on a range of vegetation and preys on small wood-borers, immature weevils, hymenopterous larvae, and aphids. It has been indicated as a predator of the larvae of the Cotton Boll Weevil (*Anthonomus grandis*) in Texas, USA.

## RELATED SPECIES

*Phyllobaenus pallipennis* may resemble the variable *P. verticalis*. Even though great variability in *P. pallipennis* has been noted, the species seems to have a clearly characteristic color pattern with four distinct, although occasionally adjacent, elytral maculae, and no yellowish markings on the pronotum or head.

Actual size

**Phyllobaenus pallipennis** is a small beetle with a soft body and short elytra, and whose surface is covered with short setae. The eyes are conspicuous and clearly visible. The antennae are short. The elytra have brown and yellow patterns with rounded elytral apices. The legs are long and light brown, slightly darker at the end of the femur, and are adapted for walking or running on foliage.

| FAMILY | Cleridae |
|---|---|
| SUBFAMILY | Clerinae |
| DISTRIBUTION | Palearctic: Europe |
| MACROHABITAT | Temperate forest |
| MICROHABITAT | Dead wood, especially oak (*Quercus* spp.) |
| FEEDING HABITS | Predator |
| NOTE | *Clerus mutillarius mutillarius* has been classified as endangered in several areas of Europe; it mimics some ant wasps |

ADULT LENGTH
⅜–⁹⁄₁₆ in
(9–15 mm)

388

*CLERUS MUTILLARIUS MUTILLARIUS*
# CLERUS MUTILLARIUS MUTILLARIUS
FABRICIUS, 1775

*Clerus mutillarius mutillarius* is a checkered beetle that used to be common in central Europe but today has been listed as rare to very rare. In the Invertebrate Red List of Germany, it is classified as "critically endangered" and in similar regional lists of some countries it is considered extinct. The species is similar to female wasps of the family Mutilidae, and during the day it preys on a variety of arthropods. It can be found on logs and on dead tree stumps. An illustration of this beetle was featured on a former German Democratic Republic postage stamp in 1968.

## RELATED SPECIES

Ten species and two subspecies are recognized in the genus *Clerus* across the Palearctic Realm, the subspecies being *C. mutillarius mutillarius* and *C. m. africanus* from northern Africa. Despite the recent publication of identification keys, no phylogenetic or taxonomic studies have been carried out to determine the relationships between the species.

Actual size

**Clerus mutillarius mutillarius** is a colorful beetle. The integument is black overall, with the base of the elytra reddish and a transverse white band near the apex of the elytra. The eyes are large and conspicuous but not prominent. Most of the body is covered by black and white setae. The legs are long and are adapted for running or walking on vegetation.

| FAMILY | Cleridae |
|---|---|
| SUBFAMILY | Clerinae |
| DISTRIBUTION | Nearctic: eastern North America |
| MACROHABITAT | Forests and woodlands |
| MICROHABITAT | Branches and trunks infested with bark beetles |
| FEEDING HABITS | Adults and larvae prey on bark beetles |
| NOTE | This species strongly resembles female Mutillidae, wingless wasps known as velvet ants |

ADULT LENGTH
⁵⁄₁₆–⁷⁄₁₆ in
(8–11 mm)

*ENOCLERUS ICHNEUMONEUS*
# ENOCLERUS ICHNEUMONEUS
(FABRICIUS, 1776)

389

*Enoclerus ichneumoneus* adults and larvae are found on conifers and hardwoods infested with bark beetles, especially in the genera *Phloeosinus*, *Pityophthorus*, and *Scolytus*, as well as longhorn beetles (Cerambycidae). The larvae hunt for the brood of these wood-boring beetles in their mines and galleries. The adults are frequently found on the trunks and branches of infested trees during the summer on bright sunny days. They move in a quick and sometimes jerky fashion, just like a velvet ant, as they search for prey. Overwintering beetles are sometimes encountered wedged into deep cracks on tree trunks or under loose tree bark.

## RELATED SPECIES

The large and complex New World genus *Enoclerus* includes many species that mimic velvet ants, ants, flies, and leaf beetles. The broad orange band across the middle of the elytra and distinctly long, triangular scutellum distinguishes *E. ichneumoneus* from the other 35 species inhabiting America north of Mexico. The similar *E. muttkowski*, from eastern North America, has a broader, more rounded scutellum and basal elytral tubercles.

**Enoclerus ichneumoneus** is a large, reddish velvet ant (Mutillidae) mimic. In life, it has a red head, pronotum, and abdomen. The elytra are coarsely punctured at the base, each has a basal tubercle; the basal quarter is reddish and margined by an incomplete narrow black band, followed by a broad orange band, then broad black and narrower white bands, and tipped in black.

Actual size

| FAMILY | Cleridae |
|---|---|
| SUBFAMILY | Clerinae |
| DISTRIBUTION | Palearctic and Nearctic: native to Palearctic; introduced to North America |
| MACROHABITAT | Temperate forest |
| MICROHABITAT | On bark |
| FEEDING HABITS | Predator |
| NOTE | A colorful beetle that mimics velvet ants and is a predator of the larvae of several bark beetles; it was introduced to North America in biological control programs |

ADULT LENGTH
¼–⅜ in
(7–10 mm)

390

*THANASIMUS FORMICARIUS*
# EUROPEAN
# RED-BELLIED CLERID
(LINNAEUS, 1758)

*Thanasimus formicarius* is a medium-size soft-bodied beetle, and a predator of the larvae of several species of bark beetles, including *Tomicus piniperda*, *Tomicus minor*, and *Ips typographus*. The adults overwinter at the base of conifers and are often seen awaiting their prey on the bark of fallen pine (*Pinus* spp.) or spruce (*Picea* spp.) trees. The larvae grow slowly, spend two years in the larval stage, and then pupate in the fall. Aposematism is common in these beetles—their body shape and coloration resembles that of velvet ants, famous for their painful sting. This species was introduced to North America in 1892 and again in 1980 to control the Southern Pine Beetle (*Dendroctonus frontalis*).

## RELATED SPECIES

The relationships between the species of the genus *Thanasimus* are not clear. Most of the species can be differentiated by the color of the prothorax, the punctures of the elytra, and the morphology of the male genitalia.

Actual size

**The European Red-bellied Clerid** is a colorful beetle—its integument is black, and most of the pronotum and the base of the elytra is a reddish color. The remainder of the elytra is black with two transverse bands of white scales, and the whole body is covered with dense, fine setae. The legs are long and black. The antennae are long and light brown with a three-segmented club at the apex.

| FAMILY | Cleridae |
|---|---|
| SUBFAMILY | Clerinae |
| DISTRIBUTION | Palearctic: Europe, Asia, North Africa |
| MACROHABITAT | Temperate forest |
| MICROHABITAT | Flowers |
| FEEDING HABITS | Predator |
| NOTE | The larvae of this particularly colorful beetle parasitize the larvae of solitary bees and honeybees (hence the species name *apiarius*) |

ADULT LENGTH
⅜–⅝ in
(9–16 mm)

*TRICHODES APIARIUS*
# TRICHODES APIARIUS
(LINNAEUS, 1758)

391

*Trichodes apiarius* is a small, setose beetle. The species of this genus have a peculiar biology—their larvae are parasites of solitary bees of the genera *Osmia* and *Megachile*, or of honeybees (*Apis* spp.). The adults lay eggs in the nests of those bees, and the larvae that hatch then feed on the host larvae and nymphs. Adults feed on the pollen of several different species of flowers and their diet is complemented by insects.

## RELATED SPECIES

The genus *Trichodes* is very large and widely distributed in the Nearctic, Afrotropical, and Palearctic realms—at least 70 species have been described from the Palearctic alone. With such a vast distribution and number of species, there are not the comprehensive taxonomical studies available to determine the closest relatives and diagnosis of *T. apiarius*.

Actual size

**Trichodes apiarius** is a colorful beetle with a shining blue integument. The dorsal surface is covered with dense, fine setae. The antennae are large and capitated, with the last three segments larger. The elytra have three transverse, bright orange or red bands and are constricted at the base. The legs are long and robust, adapted for walking and running.

| FAMILY | Cleridae |
|---|---|
| SUBFAMILY | Clerinae |
| DISTRIBUTION | Australian: coastal eastern Australia and South Australia |
| MACROHABITAT | Open vegetation |
| MICROHABITAT | Termite nests |
| FEEDING HABITS | Predator |
| NOTE | This genus is endemic to Australia; the larvae prey on wood-nesting termites of the genus *Mastotermes* |

ADULT LENGTH
⅜ in
(9.3–9.7 mm)

392

*ZENITHICOLA CRASSUS*
# ZENITHICOLA CRASSUS
(NEWMAN, 1840)

The genus *Zenithicola* is endemic to Australia. *Z. crassus* is widely distributed and commonly found on flowers of *Acacia* and *Eucalyptus* species on the east coast and in South Australia. So far, it is the only checkered beetle whose larvae have been reported to inhabit the burrows of the wood-nesting termite *Mastotermes darwiniensis*, which is almost certainly their prey. The larvae have particularly long setae covering the body, possibly as a protection from their prey.

## RELATED SPECIES

The genus *Zenithicola* is characterized by having its metaventrite on a different plane to the mesoventrite. Related species include *Z. australis*, *Z. cribricollis*, *Z. funestus*, and *Z. scrobiculatus*. All except for *Z. cribricollis* were described in the nineteenth century. The phylogenetic relationships between species of *Zenithicola* have not been investigated to date.

Actual size

**Zenithicola crassus** has a mostly metallic black to dark blue integument, except on the prothorax, where it is reddish. The body is covered by setae that are very dense and long on the prothorax and much more dispersed on the elytra. The elytra have a few short transverse bands of white setae and are coarsely punctured in the basal half. The legs are long and black. The antennae are short and noticeably enlarged toward the apex.

| | |
|---|---|
| FAMILY | Cleridae |
| SUBFAMILY | Korynetinae |
| DISTRIBUTION | Nearctic: from British Columbia in Canada south to California and Texas |
| MACROHABITAT | Forested areas |
| MICROHABITAT | Lower vegetation |
| FEEDING HABITS | Predator |
| NOTE | This species has been recorded as a predator of the adults and larvae of wood-boring beetles |

ADULT LENGTH
¼–⁹⁄₁₆ in
(7–14.5 mm)

*CHARIESSA ELEGANS*

# CHARIESSA ELEGANS

HORN, 1870

393

The genus *Chariessa* is widely distributed in North America, and its members are large with bright or attractive colors. Several morphological characteristics can help to distinguish this genus, particularly the shape of the eyes, the shape of labial and maxillary palpomeres, and the elytral punctation. The larvae of *C. elegans* are known to be predators of the larvae and adults of longhorn beetles such as the Western Ash Borer (*Neoclytus conjunctus*) and *Schizax senex*.

## RELATED SPECIES

There are four species of *Chariessa* described from North America. *Chariessa elegans* can be differentiated from the other species by the color of the abdomen, the depressed thorax with sides narrowing anteriorly, and the shape of the elytra. *Chariessa dichroa* has been indicated as a close relative of *C. elegans*, it differs slightly in its color, the punctures of the pronotum, and its larger size.

Actual size

**Chariessa elegans** is a clearly distinctive species, having blue elytra, a reddish pronotum, and legs with black tarsi. The dorsal surface of the body is covered with fine, dense setae. The last three segments of the antennae are large and asymmetrical. The head is partially hidden under the prothorax. The large eyes are visible dorsally.

| FAMILY | Cleridae |
|---|---|
| SUBFAMILY | Korynetinae |
| DISTRIBUTION | Neotropical: Brazil, Argentina |
| MACROHABITAT | Subtropical forest |
| MICROHABITAT | Lower vegetation |
| FEEDING HABITS | Predator |
| NOTE | As the species epithet suggests, the legs of this species are noticeably reddish |

ADULT LENGTH
½–¹¹⁄₁₆ in
(11.6–17.6 mm)

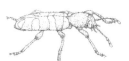

LASIODERA RUFIPES

# LASIODERA RUFIPES

(KLUG, 1842)

The genus *Lasiodera* is distributed in South America. A 1996 study based on male morphological characters clarified the definition of the genus and its species. *Lasiodera rufipes* is a typical checkered beetle with a soft body and bright colors. It was described originally as *Enoplium rufipes*, but the Irish entomologist Charles Joseph Gahan recognized its placement in 1910 when he revalidated the genus *Lasiodera*. The first two antennomeres of males in the related genus *Philhyra* (which is sometimes treated as a synonym of *Lasiodera*) have a lateral, finger-like projection that is longer than the antennal segment itself. This structure, of uncertain function, is not present in females.

## RELATED SPECIES

The genus *Lasiodera* includes seven species, mostly characterized by the color of certain structures. *Lasiodera rufipes* is similar to *L. zonata* and distributed in the same area. They share a reddish leg color and black prothorax, but *L. rufipes* can be distinguished by the longitudinal depression on its pronotum, the shallow punctures on its elytra, and its black tarsi.

**Lasiodera rufipes** is a colorful beetle. The head and pronotum are black while the elytra have whitish-yellow and dark blue transverse bands and patches. The whole dorsal surface is covered with fine, erect setae. The punctures on the head and pronotum are coarse but finer on the elytra. The legs are robust and reddish.

Actual size

| | |
|---|---|
| FAMILY | Cleridae |
| SUBFAMILY | Korynetinae |
| DISTRIBUTION | Originally from the Palearctic, now cosmopolitan |
| MACROHABITAT | Various, especially in or near human habitations |
| MICROHABITAT | Carrion, dried meats, bones, and hides |
| FEEDING HABITS | Adults and larvae scavenge animal tissues and prey on fly larvae |
| NOTE | The species is also known as the Ham or Red-necked Bacon Beetle |

ADULT LENGTH
³⁄₁₆–¼ in
(4–7 mm)

*NECROBIA RUFICOLLIS*
# RED-SHOULDERED
# HAM BEETLE
(FABRICIUS, 1775)

395

Actual size

Both larvae and adults of the Red-shouldered Ham Beetle scavenge carrion and dead insects. They also infest ancient Egyptian mummies, dried and smoked meats and fish, moldy cheese, and shipments of bone meal. Individual beetles associated with human remains during the latter stages of decomposition may provide information to forensic entomologists attempting to determine cause of death. Mature larvae seek shelter within existing cavities and abandoned fly puparia in which to pupate, or will construct their own pupal cells in other substrates and line them with secretions.

### RELATED SPECIES

*Necrobia* contains nine species, six of which occur in Europe (*N. kelecsenyi* and *N. konowi*), Argentina (*N. fusca*), and South Africa (*N. aenescens*, *N. atra*, and *N. tibialis*). The remaining three cosmopolitan species (*N. ruficollis*, *N. rufipes*, and *N. violacea*) are all of economic importance and are associated with animal products. The Red-shouldered Ham Beetle is easily recognized among these pest species by its distinctive coloration.

**The Red-Shouldered Ham Beetle** is somewhat oval and distinctly bicolored, with the front of the head and apical three-quarters of the elytra shiny black or deep metallic blue. The remainder of the body is brownish red, while the antennae and underside of the abdomen are dark brown. The head and pronotum are convex. The elytral surface has widely separated rows of fine punctures.

| FAMILY | Cleridae |
|---|---|
| SUBFAMILY | Korynetinae |
| DISTRIBUTION | Nearctic: USA, District of Columbia to Florida, Ohio, Illinois, Missouri, Kansas, Texas, and southern California |
| MACROHABITAT | Temperate forest |
| MICROHABITAT | Lower vegetation and logs |
| FEEDING HABITS | Predator |
| NOTE | A small, soft-bodied checkered beetle with mixed color patterns giving the appearance of lichens |

ADULT LENGTH
¼–⁷⁄₁₆ in
(6–11 mm)

396

### PELONIUM LEUCOPHAEUM
# PELONIUM LEUCOPHAEUM
(KLUG, 1842)

Actual size

*Pelonium* is a large genus of checkered beetles broadly distributed in the Americas, from Argentina to the United States, with species also in the Caribbean and the Galápagos Islands. The body color of *P. leucophaeum* adults is thought to resemble lichens growing on trees on which they are found. The fully winged adults are sometimes attracted by artificial lights. Larvae of *P. leucophaeum* develop in branches and small trees (e.g., *Taxodium* and *Juniperus*) where they feed on larvae of longhorn beetles in the family Cerambycidae.

RELATED SPECIES

The genus *Pelonium* includes four species spread across North America. The relationships between the species are poorly known and identification of the species relies mostly on data published with original descriptions. Most of the species share similar coloration patterns, but a more comprehensive study based on comparative internal morphology of males and females, and of male genitalia, may support better diagnosis and understanding of relationships between these species.

**Pelonium leucophaeum** is a small, soft-bodied brownish beetle with noticeably paler transverse bands in the middle of and at the apex of the elytra. The dorsal surface is covered by dense, fine setae and the legs are light brown. The coloration pattern is reminiscent of mossy dead wood. The last antennal segments are elongated and asymmetrical.

| FAMILY | Acanthocnemidae |
|---|---|
| SUBFAMILY | |
| DISTRIBUTION | Australian, Palearctic, Afrotropical, and Oriental: native to Australia; accidentally introduced to various forested parts of the world, including southern Europe, Africa, India, Thailand, Burma, New Caledonia |
| MACROHABITAT | Forests |
| MICROHABITAT | On bark |
| FEEDING HABITS | Predator |
| NOTE | Adults have highly sensitive infrared receptor organs on their prothorax to guide them toward recent fires |

ADULT LENGTH
⅛–¼ in
(3–6 mm)

*ACANTHOCNEMUS NIGRICANS*
# LITTLE ASH BEETLE
(HOPE, 1845)

397

Adult Little Ash Beetles are considered to be pyrophilous (associated with fire) since they are known to congregate on the bark of freshly burned trees shortly after bush fires. After mating, the females deposit their eggs into the ash or under the bark of burnt trees. The larvae, which can reach more than ⅜ in (10 mm) in length, are elongate and more or less parallel-sided, have scattered setae, and are generally lightly pigmented except for the more heavily sclerotized head and apical abdominal segment. The adults sometimes fly to artificial lights at night. Although this species is native to Australia, populations have been transported elsewhere in the world, presumably through commerce.

## RELATED SPECIES

*Acanthocnemus nigricans* is the only known species in the genus and family. Its overall body shape and the presence of erect setae on its dorsal surface give the beetle the same general appearance as members of the melyrid subfamily Dasytinae, but they differ in having a distinct antennal club and specialized organs on the ventral surface of their prothorax.

Actual size

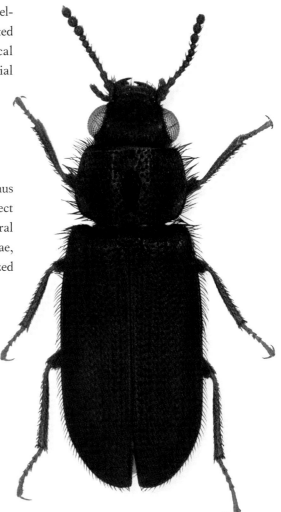

**The Little Ash Beetle** is an elongate, flattened, dark brown to black beetle whose dorsal surface is covered with rather long, stiff, erect, dark setae. The legs are usually light brown and the elongate antennae end with a three-segmented club. Two conspicuous, circular, specialized thermal imaging sensors are located on the ventral side of the prothorax.

| FAMILY | Phycosecidae |
|---|---|
| SUBFAMILY | |
| DISTRIBUTION | Australian: New Zealand |
| MACROHABITAT | Coastal areas |
| MICROHABITAT | Sand |
| FEEDING HABITS | Predator |
| NOTE | This species is unpopular with beach visitors because it inflicts an itchy bite |

ADULT LENGTH
⅛ in
(2.5–2.8 mm)

398

*PHYCOSECIS LIMBATA*
# PHYCOSECIS LIMBATA
(FABRICIUS, 1781)

Actual size

The relationship of this beetle family to others is still the subject of controversy. Phycosecidae occurs in Australia, New Zealand, Vanuatu, and New Caledonia. *Phycosecis limbata* is endemic to New Zealand and the only member of the family to occur there. It lives in coastal sandy areas, and the adults and larvae are active during the day and feed on a variety of decaying animal parts (e.g., dead fish or birds). The beetle is known locally particularly for the bites given by the larvae to beach visitors—but this has never been proven.

## RELATED SPECIES

The genus includes the following additional species: *Phycosecis algarum*, *P. ammophilus*, *P. atomaria*, *P. discoidea*, *P. hilli*, and *P. litoralis*. *Phycosecis limbata* can be distinguished from these species by its body color and dorsal covering of short, erect scales.

**Phycosecis limbata** is a small, convex beetle whose dorsal surface is covered with short, whitish scales. The body color is mostly dull black but can appear paler in recently emerged adults. The antennae are clubbed and the head is capable of some retraction into the prothorax. The prothorax is somewhat rounded, with slightly projected anterior angles. The elytra are rounded, with irregular, coarse punctures. The legs are robust and adapted for digging into sand.

| FAMILY | Prionoceridae |
| --- | --- |
| SUBFAMILY | |
| DISTRIBUTION | Oriental and Australian: Asia to New Guinea |
| MACROHABITAT | Tropical forest |
| MICROHABITAT | Foliage of forested areas |
| FEEDING HABITS | Probably a pollen-feeder or predacious |
| NOTE | The genus *Prionocerus* contains eight species distributed in the Oriental and Australian realms |

ADULT LENGTH
⁵⁄₁₆–½ in
(8.3–13.3 mm)

*PRIONOCERUS BICOLOR*

# PRIONOCERUS BICOLOR

REDTENBACHER, 1868

The family Prionoceridae is related to Melyridae and contains three genera and several species, most of which are pollen-feeders. *Prionocerus* is closely related to *Idgia* and can be distinguished from that genus by the flattened and more or less strongly serrate antennae—the genus was the subject of a revision published in 2010 that expanded the number of species from four to eight. *Prionocerus bicolor* is one of the most common and widespread species of the family. The coloration of its last antennal segments and the maxillary palpi and scutellum can be very variable.

RELATED SPECIES

*Prionocerus bicolor* clearly differs from other species in its coloration, the shape of the male genitalia, and also the shape of the last abdominal segments in males. This species is very similar to *P. coeruleipennis*, but is easily recognized by the yellow or brownish elytra, and by the shape of the male genitalia.

Actual size

**Prionocerus bicolor** is a medium-size soft-bodied beetle with a bright reddish-orange prothorax and elytra. The dorsal surface is covered with fine, dense setae. The head, antennae, and legs are a metallic blue color. The antennae are long and well developed. The prothorax is usually narrower than the elytra and its surface is slightly depressed. The legs are long and are adapted for walking.

| FAMILY | Mauroniscidae |
|---|---|
| SUBFAMILY | |
| DISTRIBUTION | Neotropical: Argentina |
| MACROHABITAT | Temperate and tropical areas |
| MICROHABITAT | Unknown |
| FEEDING HABITS | Unknown |
| NOTE | *Mauroniscus maculatus* is a member of a family of beetles described in 1994, the biology of which remains largely unknown |

**ADULT LENGTH**
¹⁄₁₆–¹⁄₈ in
(2.2–3.3 mm)

400

# MAURONISCUS MACULATUS

PIC, 1927

Actual size

The family Mauroniscidae was described by the Czech entomologist Karl Majer in 1994. Based on a range of characteristics, the relationships of this family seem to place it near Melyridae, and it comprises five genera in total: *Amecomycter*, *Mectemycor*, *Mecomycter*, *Scuromanius*, and *Mauroniscus*. The biology of this group is very poorly known. There are nine species of the genus *Mauroniscus*, all of them restricted to the Andes in South America. *Mauroniscus maculatus* is restricted to the provinces of Catamarca, Salta, and Tucumán in Argentina.

## RELATED SPECIES

*Mauroniscus maculatus* can be differentiated from other species in the genus by the general shape of the prothorax and by the pronotum, whose transverse and lateral sides are not crenulated and whose basal angles are not projected. It seems to be related to *M. boliviensis*, but can be differentiated by its variegated color and distribution.

**Mauroniscus maculatus** is a small beetle with a dark integument, and a covering of short, dense setae on its dorsal surface. The elytra have dense and irregular punctation, not forming a pattern. The legs are light brown. The antennae are moderately long and the segments are larger toward the apex. The eyes are large and protuberant.

| FAMILY | Melyridae |
|---|---|
| SUBFAMILY | Melyrinae |
| DISTRIBUTION | Neotropical and Afrotropical: native to South America; accidentally introduced to South Africa |
| MACROHABITAT | Vegetation |
| MICROHABITAT | Flowers |
| FEEDING HABITS | Polyphagous |
| NOTE | This species is a pest in certain crops such as Maize (*Zea mays*) and Sorghum (*Sorghum bicolor*), especially during its larval stages |

ADULT LENGTH
³/₈ –⁷/₁₆ in
(8.7–10.5 mm)

*ASTYLUS ATROMACULATUS*
# SPOTTED MAIZE BEETLE
(BLANCHARD, 1843)

401

Actual size

Spotted Maize Beetle adults are opportunistic pollen-feeders, notably on crops such as rice (*Oryza* spp.), Sorghum (*Sorghum bicolor*), and cotton (*Gossypium* spp.) in Brazil and Argentina. The species can be very abundant and it has been considered a pest, especially at the larval stage, causing economic losses on Maize (*Zea mays*) and Sorghum. This species was introduced accidentally to South Africa in 1916 and is now considered a major pest of crops and gardens there, with reports of cattle dying after ingesting the species.

## RELATED SPECIES

The genus *Astylus* is a member of the tribe Astylini, one of four tribes in the subfamily Melyrinae. This tribe contains several species in South America, which are largely differentiated based on superficial characters as no illustrative keys are available to aid identification. The relationship between the species has not yet been established.

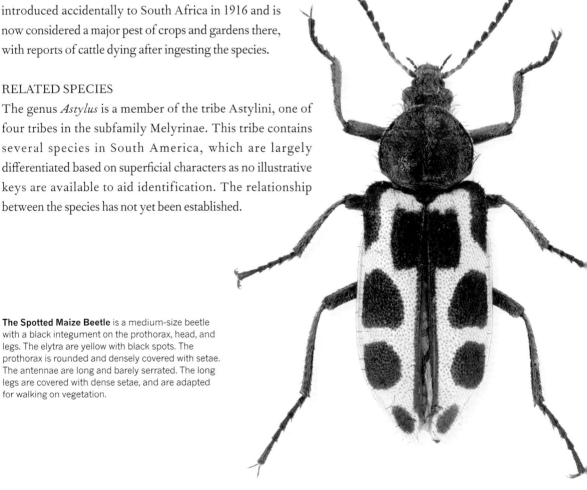

**The Spotted Maize Beetle** is a medium-size beetle with a black integument on the prothorax, head, and legs. The elytra are yellow with black spots. The prothorax is rounded and densely covered with setae. The antennae are long and barely serrated. The long legs are covered with dense setae, and are adapted for walking on vegetation.

| FAMILY | Melyridae |
|---|---|
| SUBFAMILY | Melyrinae |
| DISTRIBUTION | Nearctic: USA |
| MACROHABITAT | Vegetation |
| MICROHABITAT | Flowers |
| FEEDING HABITS | Pollen-feeder |
| NOTE | *Melyrodes* represents the only native American genus of Melyrinae; other members of this subfamily occur in Europe, Asia, and Africa |

ADULT LENGTH
⅛–³⁄₁₆ in
(3–4 mm)

402

# MELYRODES BASALIS

(LECONTE, 1852)

Actual size

*Melyrodes* is the only Melyrinae that is native to America; other genera such as *Melyris* have been intercepted in major ports of entry and apparently some populations of these non-native species have become established (e.g., *Melyris oblonga* in New Jersey). *Melyrodes* can be distinguished by its elytral epipleura, which are almost equal in width. The genus contains a small number of species, with poorly known biology, from Bolivia north to the United States. In general, species of Melyrinae can be found on flowers feeding on pollen, but the larvae may be predacious. *Melyrodes basalis* was originally described as *Dasytes*, from specimens from Georgia, the United States.

## RELATED SPECIES

There are about eight species of *Melyrodes* described from different areas of America, the most similar to *M. basalis* being *M. cribatus* and *M. floridiana*. *Melyrodes basalis* can be differentiated from these species by its small size, characteristic elytral color pattern and punctures, and the serrated lateral margins of the prothorax.

**Melyrodes basalis** is a small brown beetle with a reddish base to the elytra, and a couple of yellow spots at the apex of the elytra. The prothorax is transverse and the surface of the pronotum coarsely punctured with the sides slightly serrated. The antennae are short and also slightly serrated. The legs are brown and rather long.

| FAMILY | Melyridae |
|---|---|
| SUBFAMILY | Dasytinae |
| DISTRIBUTION | Palearctic: Europe, North Africa, and Iran |
| MACROHABITAT | Temperate forest |
| MICROHABITAT | Foliage and lower vegetation, as well as on flowers |
| FEEDING HABITS | Adults feed on pollen; larvae are unknown |
| NOTE | The genus *Dasytes* contains many species spread across several regions; they are often found on shrubland flowers |

ADULT LENGTH
³/₁₆–¼ in
(5–5.5 mm)

*DASYTES VIRENS*
# DASYTES VIRENS
(MARSHAM, 1802)

403

Actual size

The genus *Dasytes* is commonly found on flowers feeding on pollen and its species are usually unicolor and iridescent. The definition of the genus is not clear and requires further taxonomic and phylogenetic studies, which will be a difficult task because the genus currently includes hundreds of described species and probably several that are as yet undescribed. *Dasytes virens* is distributed in the western, southern, and central parts of Europe. Details on the biology of this species are not known. This species appears to be declining in abundance in some areas.

RELATED SPECIES

The large number of species in the genus *Dasytes* and the lack of modern studies makes it difficult to determine the related species of *D. virens*, most of which have been described across several years without illustrations or keys to separate them. Diagnostic characteristics of the species present in the male genitalia have not been always been illustrated and compared.

**Dasytes virens** is a small, elongated beetle with a shiny, dark brown integument, densely covered with decumbent and erect setae. The filiform antennae are long, and when extended reach the bases of the elytra. The tibiae are light brown, and the legs are long and adapted for walking on foliage.

| | |
|---|---|
| FAMILY | Melyridae |
| SUBFAMILY | Malachiinae |
| DISTRIBUTION | Nearctic: USA |
| MACROHABITAT | Temperate forest and shrubland |
| MICROHABITAT | Flowers |
| FEEDING HABITS | Predator; adults are also pollen-feeders |
| NOTE | This popular beetle has colorful elytral patterns and is an important predator of other insects |

**ADULT LENGTH**
¼—⁵⁄₁₆ in
(6–8 mm)

*COLLOPS BALTEATUS*
# RED CROSS BEETLE
LECONTE, 1852

Species in the genus *Collops* are important in agro-ecosystems as they are predators of the adults and larvae of agricultural pests. *Collops balteatus* adults evidently feed on flower-visiting insects and pollen, while the larvae live under bark and are primarily predators of other insects. The species displays sexual dimorphism—males have a notably developed second antennal segment in comparison with females. The common name Red Cross Beetle is due to the cross pattern on the elytra.

RELATED SPECIES

The genus *Collops* was studied early in the twentieth century and divided into informal groups, *C. balteatus* being included in group C with species such as *C. punctulatus* and *C. versatilis*. It can be differentiated from those species by the coarsely punctated elytra. This species superficially resembles *C. quadrimaculatus* but is bigger and has dark markings on the pronotum.

Actual size

**The Red Cross Beetle** is a small, colorful beetle with a metallic blue integument and yellowish to reddish margins on the prothorax. The elytra have a broad, transverse yellowish to reddish band as well as a similarly colored longitudinal band along the midline. The long antennae are paler towards the base and the second antennal segment of the male is highly modified.

| FAMILY | Melyridae |
|---|---|
| SUBFAMILY | Malachiinae |
| DISTRIBUTION | Palearctic and Nearctic: Europe, northern North America, Asia |
| MACROHABITAT | Temperate forest and shrubland |
| MICROHABITAT | Flowers and foliage |
| FEEDING HABITS | Predator; probably also eats pollen |
| NOTE | This species is known as one of the most beautiful insects in England and also as a very rare one—its populations are actively being monitored |

ADULT LENGTH
³/₁₆–⁵/₁₆ in
(5–8 mm)

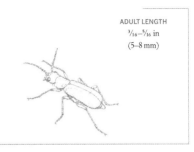

*MALACHIUS AENEUS*

# SCARLET MALACHITE BEETLE

(LINNAEUS, 1758)

405

The Scarlet Malachite Beetle is one of the UK's rarest and most beautiful insects. Adults appear during April and May, and feed on the flowers of shrubs. The species' distribution area has been in decline, thought to be the result of general habitat loss and intensive farming practices. Several conservation programs across England have been monitoring specimens of this beetle and it has been classified as an endangered invertebrate. The beetles probably complement their diet with pollen. Their larvae have been found under bark.

RELATED SPECIES

The genus *Malachius* contains several species described over a long time period without major attention to the illustration of critical diagnostic characters that will help to understand the relationships between them. Recent papers are placing more focus on regional studies and have disputed the internal generic arrangements described by previous authors.

Actual size

**The Scarlet Malachite Beetle** is a small beetle with a metallic green integument and reddish anterior corners of the prothorax. The elytra are broad and expose the abdomen, and their apex is broadly rounded. The antennae are filiform and long. The legs are long and black.

| FAMILY | Boganiidae |
|---|---|
| SUBFAMILY | Paracucujinae |
| DISTRIBUTION | Australian: southern Western Australia |
| MACROHABITAT | Forest and dry scrub |
| MICROHABITAT | *Macrozamia* cycads |
| FEEDING HABITS | Adults and larvae feed on pollen |
| NOTE | The specific epithet, *rostratum*, meaning "beaked," refers to the beetle's extended labrum and mandibles |

**ADULT LENGTH**
⅛ –³⁄₁₆ in
(3–3.6 mm)

406

# PARACUCUJUS ROSTRATUS
SEN GUPTA & CROWSON, 1966

Actual size

**Paracucujus rostratus** is a glabrous brown species that is dorsoventrally flattened; it lacks setae dorsally but is setose below. The head has a median sulcus (groove), the long beaded antennae reach beyond the posterior edge of the pronotum, and the labrum is remarkably long and the mandibles protracted.

All Boganiidae are pollen-feeders; *Paracucujus rostratus* is found exclusively on the male inflorescence of cycads, an uncommon and yet poorly studied association. *Paracucujus rostratus* was one of the first species to be named when Boganiidae was recognized by Roy Crowson and Tapan Sen Gupta. Although no Boganiidae species are known from the Americas, historical and current environmental conditions suggest that the presence of this family in South America can be expected. In the Sixties, Roy Crowson was busy developing a new beetle classification that remains the foundation of beetle systematics and spurred a modern synthesis that continues, mostly led by preeminent coleopterist John Lawrence and his colleagues.

## RELATED SPECIES

The family Boganiidae is a small group of beetles containing 11 species, with more being described at the time of writing. They have setose mandibular cavities, which Crowson thought could be used to carry pollen, but this assertion requires further study. The host-plant associations vary, with members of the African genus *Metacucujus* and genus *Paracucujus* feeding principally on cycads.

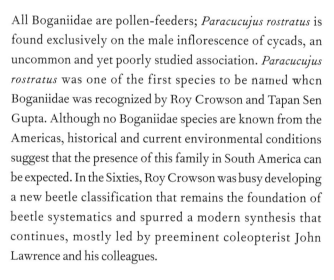

| FAMILY | Byturidae |
|---|---|
| SUBFAMILY | Byturinae |
| DISTRIBUTION | Palearctic and Oriental: Europe to northeast Asia; more common in central Europe. |
| MACROHABITAT | Forest fringes |
| MICROHABITAT | Flowers and fruits, mainly *Rubus* spp. |
| FEEDING HABITS | Larvae feed on fruits and seeds; adults feed on developing leaves and flowers, especially pollen once available |
| NOTE | Pest on raspberries, blackberries, loganberries, and other fruits |

ADULT LENGTH
⅛–³⁄₁₆ in
(3.5–4.5 mm)

*BYTURUS TOMENTOSUS*
# RASPBERRY BEETLE
(DE GEER, 1774)

407

Actual size

The Raspberry Beetle is commonly collected as an adult on a variety of flowers, but it is a fruit pest—mainly of *Rubus* species, especially cultivated raspberries, but also affecting others, including blueberries. Females lay eggs on the flowers, and larvae develop within, and feed on, the fruit, making the fruit appear small and shriveled, and eventually causing them to rot. There are various control measures that may decrease numbers, including turning the soil around the bushes and plowing along the row. Other byturids are less harmful, including the palm-associated subfamily Platydascillinae.

**The Raspberry Beetle** is a somewhat elongate, convex, light to dark brown beetle; some darker specimens have lighter antennae and appendages. It is heavily setose, with decumbent long setae that give it a silky appearance, and its antennae have a three-segmented club.

### RELATED SPECIES
*Byturus* consists of five species that occur in the Holarctic (from Europe to Japan and North America) and Argentina. The related North American species, the Raspberry Fruitworm (*B. unicolor*), has a similar life cycle to *B. tomentosus*. The large eyes and the presence of a prominent tooth on the front tibia in males can be used to distinguish *Byturus* from other byturid genera.

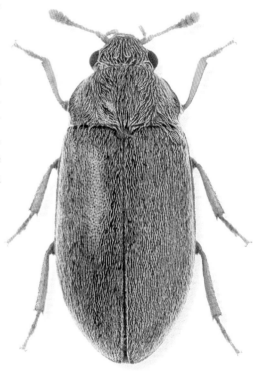

| FAMILY | Helotidae |
|---|---|
| SUBFAMILY | |
| DISTRIBUTION | Palearctic and Oriental: Far East Russia, China (Hubei, Liaoning), Japan, South Korea |
| MACROHABITAT | Forests |
| MICROHABITAT | Presumably associated with decaying and fermenting plant tissue |
| FEEDING HABITS | Adult and larval feeding habits are unknown |
| NOTE | Known pupae in this enigmatic family have a pair of anteriorly projecting processes on the pronotum, and their dorsal surface is covered with seta-bearing tubercles |

ADULT LENGTH
⁵⁄₁₆–½ in
(8.5–12 mm)

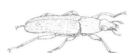

408

*HELOTA FULVIVENTRIS*
# HELOTA FULVIVENTRIS
KOLBE, 1886

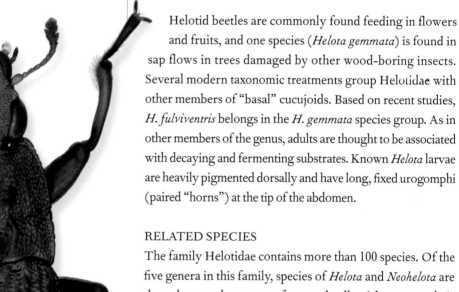

Helotid beetles are commonly found feeding in flowers and fruits, and one species (*Helota gemmata*) is found in sap flows in trees damaged by other wood-boring insects. Several modern taxonomic treatments group Helotidae with other members of "basal" cucujoids. Based on recent studies, *H. fulviventris* belongs in the *H. gemmata* species group. As in other members of the genus, adults are thought to be associated with decaying and fermenting substrates. Known *Helota* larvae are heavily pigmented dorsally and have long, fixed urogomphi (paired "horns") at the tip of the abdomen.

RELATED SPECIES

The family Helotidae contains more than 100 species. Of the five genera in this family, species of *Helota* and *Neohelota* are the only ones that possess four oval yellowish areas on their elytra. *Helota* species can be separated from those in *Neohelota* by the presence of raised patches on the pronotum. *Helota fulviventris* is most similar to *H. gorhami* but differs in having oval elytral tubercles as well as diagnostic genitalic structures.

Actual size

**Helota fulviventris** adults are elongate, flattened and lack setae dorsally. Like many other species in the genus, it is dark olive-green and has four white to yellow spots on the elytra. The elytral striae 2 to 4 are sinuate, the punctures on the elytra are variable. The fifth abdominal ventrite has a semicircular patch of setae medially near the apex. The apex of the elytra differs slightly between the sexes.

| FAMILY | Protocucujidae |
|---|---|
| SUBFAMILY | |
| DISTRIBUTION | Neotropical: southwestern Argentina and Chile |
| MACROHABITAT | Temperate forest |
| MICROHABITAT | Southern beeches (*Nothofagus* spp.) |
| FEEDING HABITS | Unknown |
| NOTE | Very little is known about the life history of members of the family |

ADULT LENGTH
³⁄₁₆–¼ in
(4.5–6 mm)

*ERICMODES FUSCITARSIS*
# ERICMODES FUSCITARSIS
REITTER, 1878

409

Actual size

This family contains one genus of seven species distributed in southern South America and Australia, with a biogeographic range referred to as Gondwanan. Biologists propose that Protocucujidae and other Gondwanan families represent lineages that have geological histories dating back to times before the ancient supercontinent Gondwana drifted apart via plate tectonics 180 million years ago. Fragmented distributions cause some problems with this theory, however. Adaptations in the adult (e.g., lobed tarsomeres) and putative larva of *Ericmodes* suggest that these species are equipped to walk on foliage and may feed on rust fungi there. However gut-content analyses have not revealed any spores or other fungal material to confirm this yet.

## RELATED SPECIES
*Ericmodes* all look very similar to one another but can be distinguished by body-surface structures (e.g., the absence or presence of elytral costae), number of elytral striae, and shape of the pronotum. *Ericmodes fuscitarsis* is most similar to *E. nigris*, which is restricted to Bosque Fray Jorge National Park, a coastal forest fragment in dry north-central Chile that derives most, if not all, of its moisture from westerly fogs.

**Ericmodes fuscitarsis** is elongate, flattened, and setose, and ranges in color from light to dark brown. The outline of the pronotum is almost evenly rounded, and the dorsal surfaces of the pronotum and the elytra are uneven, with weak impressions, a feature common to many Gondwanan and other beetle groups.

| FAMILY | Sphindidae |
|---|---|
| SUBFAMILY | Protosphindinae |
| DISTRIBUTION | Neotropical: Chile |
| MACROHABITAT | Temperate forest |
| MICROHABITAT | Slime mold |
| FEEDING HABITS | Larvae and adults feed on slime molds |
| NOTE | Although species in many families of beetles feed on slime molds, Sphindidae is the only family in which all species feed exclusively on these molds in both larval and adult stages |

ADULT LENGTH
⅛ – ³⁄₁₆ in
(3–4.2 mm)

*PROTOSPHINDUS CHILENSIS*
# PROTOSPHINDUS CHILENSIS
SEN GUPTA & CROWSON 1977

Actual size

Slime molds, Myxomycetes, are strange amoeboid organisms that crawl along the surface of logs and leaf litter seeking food. There are not many groups of beetles that feed exclusively on slime molds, and sphindids are the only family that is exclusive to them. Other groups include some very special staphylinids (including many members of Scaphidiinae), two unrelated groups of Leiodidae beetles (including the entire tribe Agathidiini), and the latridiid genus *Enicmus*. When traced in phylogenies, most of the ancestors of these slime-mold specialists evolved from fungus-feeders. Sphindid larvae mature through four instars and the mature larva uses an anal secretion to secure itself to its substrate before pupation. A typical life cycle for a sphindid lasts between 20 and 30 days.

## RELATED SPECIES

The family contains nine genera and about 60 species, and is found worldwide, exclusive of New Zealand. *Protosphindus* has two species restricted to south temperate South America, and is the only genus with species that have ornate sculpturing and ridges on the pronotum and elytra. The two species can be distinguished easily by the form of the elytral carinae, and *P. bellus* is also shorter than *P. chilensis*.

**Protosphindus chilensis** is a highly sculptured, glabrous, mottled dark brown and yellow beetle. The antennae have a three-segmented club. The pronotum has laterally dentate margins and the disk is vaulted. The elytra are punctured and have distinctive thin, ornate carinae (raised ridges). As in other adult sphindids, the mandibles have pouches that serve as mycangia to carry slime-mold spores to new microhabitats.

| FAMILY | Biphyllidae |
|---|---|
| SUBFAMILY | |
| DISTRIBUTION | Nearctic: Indiana eastward, south to Florida, and southwest to eastern Texas |
| MACROHABITAT | Temperate forest |
| MICROHABITAT | Under bark |
| FEEDING HABITS | Larvae and adults feed on fungi |
| NOTE | The function of deep setose pits below the eyes of adults is completely unknown |

ADULT LENGTH
¹⁄₁₆–¹⁄₈ in
(2–3 mm)

### DIPLOCOELUS RUDIS
# DIPLOCOELUS RUDIS
(LECONTE, 1863)

411

Actual size

Biphyllidae are common under bark, and/or fermenting conditions, especially in tropical areas, and in rotting vegetation. *Diplocoelus rudis* has been found under bark of hickory (*Carya* spp.), oak (*Quercus* spp.), and pine (*Pinus* spp.) trees, especially where there is moisture. All biphyllids may be fungus-feeders, with some collected from specific fungi, including ascomycetes and basidiomycetes. The heads of the adult beetles have extraordinary invaginations, but there is no evidence (so far) that these serve as true mycangia (fungus-holding organs), which are present in other groups of beetles.

RELATED SPECIES

The family contains six genera and about 200 species, and is found worldwide, exclusive of New Zealand. However, the taxonomy of the group is so poor that some of the genera are superficially constructed and the family is in dire need of revision. There are many species of *Diplocoelus*; aside from *D. rudis*, *D. brunneus* also occurs in North America and is widely sympatric with the former. *Diplocoelus rudis* is, however, easily distinguished from *D. brunneus* by the absence of sublateral ridges on the pronotum.

**Diplocoelus rudis** is uniformly light reddish to dark brown, glabrous, very setose, and dorsoventrally compressed. The antennae have a three-segmented club. The pronotum lacks sublateral carinae (or ridges), which are distinctive in many other species. As in most biphyllids, the lateral carina of the prothorax has a serrate or crenulate margin and there are distinct subcoxal lines on the first abdominal segment.

| FAMILY | Erotylidae |
|---|---|
| SUBFAMILY | Xenoscelinae |
| DISTRIBUTION | Australian: New Zealand |
| MACROHABITAT | Montane and high latitudes |
| MICROHABITAT | Flowers |
| FEEDING HABITS | Adults feed on pollen |
| NOTE | *Loberonotha olivascens* is the only species in the genus |

**ADULT LENGTH**
¹⁄₆–¹⁄₈ in
(2.6–3.1 mm)

412

# LOBERONOTHA OLIVASCENS
(BROUN, 1893)

**Actual size**

Erotylidae is a diverse group that has undergone a classificatory restructuring over recent years following several phylogenetic studies examining morphological and molecular characters. Though many erotylids are fungus-feeders, there are numerous groups that feed on plants. The latter include the large subfamily Languriinae, which was long considered a separate family, and *Loberonotha olivascens*, which as an adult feeds on the pollen of many shrubs that occur in alpine and subalpine areas, and at lower altitudes, in the southern portion of New Zealand. *Loberonotha* is the only member of the Xenoscelinae in New Zealand, and may be one of the primitive members of the Erotylidae family.

## RELATED SPECIES

The subfamily Xenoscelinae is widespread and contains eight genera with ten species. *Loberonotha* is monotypic and can be distinguished from all other xenoscelines by having an incomplete epipleuron (most erotylids have a complete epipleuron that extends to the apex of the elytra) and lacking lateral carinae (raised ridges) on the pronotum. The elytral character also separates the genus from similar-looking members of the Eurasian genus *Macrophagus*.

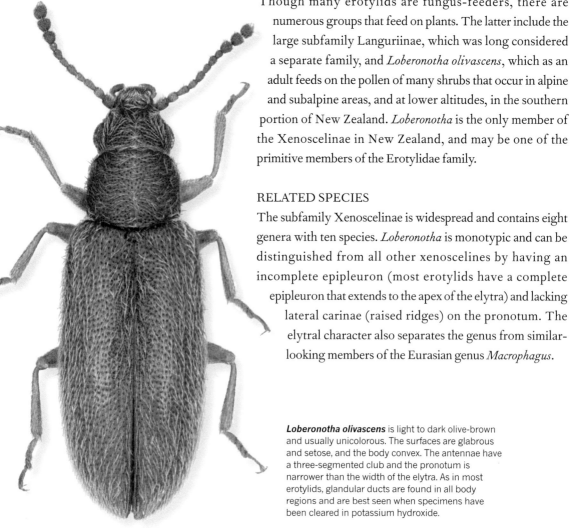

**Loberonotha olivascens** is light to dark olive-brown and usually unicolorous. The surfaces are glabrous and setose, and the body convex. The antennae have a three-segmented club and the pronotum is narrower than the width of the elytra. As in most erotylids, glandular ducts are found in all body regions and are best seen when specimens have been cleared in potassium hydroxide.

| FAMILY | Erotylidae |
|---|---|
| SUBFAMILY | Cryptophilinae |
| DISTRIBUTION | Neotropical: Costa Rica |
| MACROHABITAT | Montane areas |
| MICROHABITAT | Nests of the Chiriqui Brown Mouse (*Scotinomys xerampelinus*) |
| FEEDING HABITS | Scavenger |
| NOTE | Restricted to Cerro de la Muerte in Costa Rica's Cordillera de Talamanca |

ADULT LENGTH
⅛ in
(2.53–2.94 mm)

*LOBEROPSYLLUS EXPLANATUS*
# NEOTROPICAL MOUSE BEETLE
LESCHEN & ASHE, 1999

413

Actual size

While a number of beetle species are associated with mammal nests, few have been collected or shown to live on the animals themselves. *Loberopsyllus* contains three species that have been associated with rats and mice, including *L. explanatus*, and a fourth, free-living species in montane Oaxaca, Mexico. All adults in the genus are wingless. Like the other two mammal inquilines, the Neotropical Mouse Beetle lacks eyes and is phoretic, having been observed clinging to the hindquarters of its rodent host, the Chiriqui Brown Mouse (*Scotinomys xerampelinus*). It does not harm its host, but is a friendly symbiont that grooms the mouse and feeds on its dead skin and other organic debris.

## RELATED SPECIES

The genus *Loberopsyllus* is found from southern Mexico to Costa Rica, but with more study, other species are likely to be found. *Loberopsyllus explanatus*, *L. halffteri*, and *L. traubi* are all eyeless and found with rodents. *Loberopsyllus oculatus* has well-developed eyes and is free-living.

**The Neotropical Mouse Beetle** is red-brown with paler legs, antennae, and mouthparts. The surfaces are glabrous to subglabrous and microsetose. The body is somewhat rigid and dorsoventrally flattened. The lack of eyes and absence of wings are thought to be adaptations to phoresy. The specific epithet refers to the sides of the elytra, which are more explanate compared with those of other members of the genus.

| FAMILY | Erotylidae |
| --- | --- |
| SUBFAMILY | Erotylinae |
| DISTRIBUTION | Neotropical: Costa Rica to Ecuador |
| MACROHABITAT | Montane rainforest |
| MICROHABITAT | On basidiomycete fungi |
| FEEDING HABITS | Adults and larvae feed on fungi |
| NOTE | The toxicity of the foul-tasting chemicals released by the beetle is unknown |

ADULT LENGTH
¾–⅞ in
(19.5–20.5 mm)

*EROTYLUS ONAGGA*
# EROTYLUS ONAGGA
LACORDAIRE, 1842

414

The tribe Erotylini (subfamily Erotylinae) has an exclusively New World distribution. Most members have gaudy coloration, which functions as a warning signal to potential predators that they are loaded with foul-tasting chemicals. These chemicals are stored within the body and released through pores or joints, from where they travel along grooves on the body, especially on the pronotum and elytra, and can be seen with a hand lens. A photograph of the attractive *Erotylus onagga* was depicted on a stamp in Ecuador in 1993.

## RELATED SPECIES

There are many species of *Erotylus*, all of which tend to be brightly colored and, like other erotylines, have larvae that are ornate, with spines and processes over the dorsal portions of the body. The body color of adults and the armature of larvae are effective against predators—essential defense mechanisms, as the predators are active on the surfaces of the basidiomycete fungi upon which the *Erotylus* feed.

Actual size

**Erotylus onagga** is black with distinctive transverse yellow stripes on its elytra. The body lacks setae and is highly convex. The antennae are clubbed, but the segments are flattened, unlike those of other members of Erotylidae. The body of many erotylines is not well hardened like that of other beetles such as members of the family Tenebrionidae, which may also be gaudily colored species that are active in the open air.

| FAMILY | Monotomidae |
|---|---|
| SUBFAMILY | Rhizophaginae |
| DISTRIBUTION | Neotropical: Costa Rica |
| MACROHABITAT | Tropical rainforest |
| MICROHABITAT | Nests of stingless bees |
| FEEDING HABITS | Scavenger |
| NOTE | These beetles are nearly blind |

ADULT LENGTH
⅛–³⁄₁₆ in
(2.8–3.7 mm)

*CROWSONIUS MELIPONAE*

# CROWSONIUS MELIPONAE

PAKALUK & ŚLIPIŃSKI, 1993

415

Actual size

Not many beetles are associated with stingless bees (Meliponinae), but *Crowsonius meliponae* is one of them. Members of the genus are virtually blind (having an eye consisting of a single facet), wingless, and can be found in large numbers within a bee nest. It is thought that the species may be phoretic (transported by another organism) like some other highly adapted inquilines (guests in the nests of other insects)—including members of Scotocryptini (Leiodidae) that have been observed being carried around by stingless bees. Like other scavenging bee inquilines, the guts of specimens of *C. meliponae* have been found to be packed with pollen, and it is thought the beetle feeds on pollen contained in refuse piles in bee nests.

## RELATED SPECIES

There are three species of the Neotropical genus *Crowsonius*: two from Brazil and one from Costa Rica. They are unlike any other members of the family in that they have reduced eyes and compact antennae, and, of course, their presence in the nests of stingless bees is unique. The species are distinguished by the shape of the frons, pronotal characters (such as shape and sculpturing), and surface details of the elytra.

**Crowsonius meliponae** is dorsoventrally flattened and light to dark reddish brown, and has a covering of setae. The head is constricted posteriorly, the eyes are reduced and not visible in dorsal view, and the pronotum and elytra are sculptured. The antennae are compact and the club has one segment. The elytra are abbreviated, exposing the pygidium.

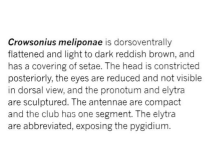

| FAMILY | Monotomidae |
|---|---|
| SUBFAMILY | Monotominae |
| DISTRIBUTION | Australian: widespread in New Zealand |
| MACROHABITAT | Podocarp–broadleaf and beech forests |
| MICROHABITAT | Under bark and rotten wood |
| FEEDING HABITS | Adults and larvae may feed on fungi, but their behavior is poorly known |
| NOTE | This is the only native species of Monotomidae in New Zealand |

**ADULT LENGTH**
³⁄₁₆ in
(4.3–4.7 mm)

416

*LENAX MIRANDUS*
# LENAX MIRANDUS
SHARP, 1877

Monotomidae are generally found under wood or in decaying vegetable matter, although the group is diverse and poorly known. *Lenax mirandus* is the sole member of its genus, and is quite unlike other monotomids. While the thorax and abdomen are not strikingly different from those of other members of the family, the compact structuring of the head capsule is distinctive. The antennae fit into a large ventral cavity, and behind the eyes is a deep groove extending along the margin of the vertex that is often filled with a waxy substance, the purpose of which is unknown.

RELATED SPECIES
While many monotomids may be fungus-feeders, some species may be found on flowers, one species (*Phyconomus marinus*) has been found in the intertidal zone, and the Graveyard Beetle (*Rhizophagus parallelocollis*) is found commonly in coffins in European cemeteries. Other species are predatory, feeding on bark beetles, such as some members of *Rhizophagus*.

Actual size

**Lenax mirandus** is a solidly constructed elongate beetle that is glabrous, reddish to dark brown, and has very fine setae that are visible only under high magnifications (apart from those at the apex of the abdomen). The body is deeply punctured, especially the elytral striae and the abdominal ventrites. The antennae have 11 segments, although the last two are fused into a club.

| FAMILY | Hobartiidae |
|---|---|
| SUBFAMILY | |
| DISTRIBUTION | Neotropical: Chile and Argentina |
| MACROHABITAT | Temperate forests |
| MICROHABITAT | Fungi |
| FEEDING HABITS | Adults and larvae may be fungus-feeders |
| NOTE | The only South American species of this otherwise Australian genus |

ADULT LENGTH
⅛ in
(2.6–2.9 mm)

*HOBARTIUS CHILENSIS*
# HOBARTIUS CHILENSIS
TOMASZEWSKA & ŚLIPIŃSKI, 1995

417

The small family Hobartiidae is distributed in temperate areas of Australia and South America. The biology of its members is poorly known, but records from Australian species indicate that adults and larvae are fungus-feeders. The exact biology of *Hobartius chilensis* is unknown, though specimens are frequently collected in leaf litter in *Nothofagus*, *Araucaria*, and other forest types. They are also commonly collected with various trapping techniques, especially flight-intercept traps, which are effective for flight-capable beetles, especially little-studied microcoleoptera whose habits are poorly known.

RELATED SPECIES
Hobartiidae contains two genera: *Hobartius*, with four species; and *Hydnobioides*, with two species. The genera can be distinguished by antennomere 7, which is enlarged in *Hydnobioides*. The form of the body setae are important characters for separating the *Hobartius* species.

Actual size

**Hobartius chilensis** is similar to a cryptophagid, but it has a dorsal tubercle on the mandible and the pronotal sides are explanate. The body is elongate and convex, and the color ranges from dark to light brown, though there is a broad darkened area in the middle of the elytra in most specimens. It has a frontoclypeal suture and the punctation of the elytra is confused.

| FAMILY | Cryptophagidae |
|---|---|
| SUBFAMILY | Cryptophaginae |
| DISTRIBUTION | Nearctic: northeastern North America |
| MACROHABITAT | Temperate forest |
| MICROHABITAT | Bumblebee nests |
| FEEDING HABITS | Adults and larvae feed on nest detritus, especially pollen collected from bees |
| NOTE | Adults wait on flowers and crawl on bumblebees to be carried back to their nest |

ADULT LENGTH
⅛–³⁄₁₆ in
(3–5 mm)

418

# ANTHEROPHAGUS CONVEXULUS
LECONTE, 1863

Actual size

*Antherophagus* species are associated specifically with *Bombus* bees, and are distributed in the Nearctic, Palearctic, and Oriental realms. Adult beetles are found on flowers, where they wait for a visiting bumblebee. The beetle attaches itself to the bee's mouthparts or a leg and is carried back to the nest, where presumably it mates and/or lays eggs. While most species of *Antherophagus* have wings, others are completely wingless and have reduced eyes. Individuals of *A. convexulus* were recently recorded from flowers of White Meadowsweet (*Spiraea alba*) in a red oak forest.

## RELATED SPECIES

Currently, *Antherophagus* consists of 13 species, but a revision is needed to determine their taxonomic status and to describe new species, especially those collected in Costa Rica, Colombia, and Venezuela. General body shape may be of help to diagnose the species, as well as setation and color, but as coleopterist Yves Bousquet stated in a review of North American Cryptophaginae, "members of this group are rather difficult to identify."

**Antherophagus convexulus** is golden tan to reddish brown in color. It is dorsoventrally compressed and has a covering of recumbent setae, which is more developed dorsally. The sexes are dimorphic: males have a notch in the clypeus and the antennomeres are more compact compared with those of females.

| FAMILY | Agapythidae |
|---|---|
| SUBFAMILY | |
| DISTRIBUTION | Australian: New Zealand, southern North Island and South Island |
| MACROHABITAT | Mainly southern beech (*Nothofagus* spp.) forests |
| MICROHABITAT | Sooty molds |
| FEEDING HABITS | Adults and larvae may feed on sooty molds |
| NOTE | *Agapytho foveicollis* is the sole representative of the family Agapythidae in the world |

ADULT LENGTH
¹⁄₁₆–¹⁄₈ in
(2.3–3 mm)

*AGAPYTHO FOVEICOLLIS*
# AGAPYTHO FOVEICOLLIS
BROUN, 1921

419

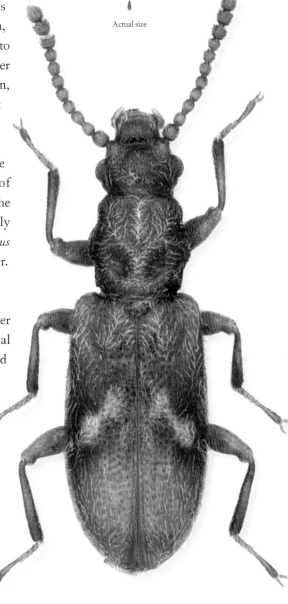

Actual size

Within the last decades, the superfamily Cucujoidea has undergone a major restructuring of family-level classification, and Agaypthidae, consisting of a single species, was elevated to family status. The family was originally described as a member of Salpingidae by New Zealand coleopterist Thomas Broun, then was recognized as a subfamily of Phloeostichidae. It wasn't until 2005 that Phloeostichidae was formally shown by phylogenetic analysis to be polyphyletic (consisting of unrelated groups), at which point it was divided into separate families, including Agapythidae. Adults and larvae of *Agapytho foveicollis* live in black sooty mold that grows on the honeydew excreted by scale insects (bugs in the superfamily Coccoidea) on the trunks of southern beech trees (*Nothofagus* spp.). Individuals have also been recorded in moss or leaf litter.

RELATED SPECIES

The family Agapythidae is an enigmatic member of the "lower Cucujoidea." *Agapytho* can be distinguished by several characters, including the incomplete lateral carina (raised ridge) of the prothorax.

**Agapytho foveicollis** is a setose, light to dark brown beetle with distinctive elytral maculas. It can be separated from other members of the superfamily and similar-looking beetles based on the following characters in combination: antennae that have a weak antennal club, a head constricted behind the eyes, the pronotal lateral carina of pronotum weakly developed, the elytra with confused punctation and with the epipleuron incomplete, and the abdominal ventrite 1 not longer than ventrite 2. A photograph is the best way to identify the species.

| FAMILY | Priasilphidae |
|---|---|
| SUBFAMILY | |
| DISTRIBUTION | Australian: New Zealand—Westland, South Island |
| MACROHABITAT | Podocarp–broadleaf forest |
| MICROHABITAT | Leaf litter and slime flux |
| FEEDING HABITS | Adults and larvae may feed on fungi |
| NOTE | All known species in the genus *Priasilpha* are restricted to New Zealand; the egg and pupal stages of *P. angulata* are unknown |

ADULT LENGTH
³⁄₁₆–¼ in
(4.5–6 mm)

420

*PRIASILPHA ANGULATA*

# PRIASILPHA ANGULATA

LESCHEN, LAWRENCE, & ŚLIPIŃSKI, 2005

Actual size

Priasilphidae is restricted to the Southern Hemisphere, a distribution referred to as Gondwanan by biogeographers. The New Zealand genus *Priasilpha* consists of seven species, and apart from one widespread and flight-capable species, the others have restricted distributions and are completely flightless. *Priasilpha angulata* is found only in what has been referred to as the Westland "beech gap," where trees of the genus *Nothofagus* are completely absent, possibly owing to repeated glaciation during the Pleistocene epoch. The presence of endemic species like *P. angulata* within the beech gap suggests that there may have been small refugia where populations survived during major glacial advances. A small number of adults and a larva have been reported feeding on slime flux oozing from a tree wound.

RELATED SPECIES

The phylogenetic relationships among the species of *Priasilpha* were reconstructed by Leschen and Michaux in 2005. Results indicated that *P. angulata* belongs to a group of five closely related species that are restricted to the west of the Alpine Fault in the South Island of New Zealand. The distribution of all these species, west of the Alpine Fault, suggests that the lineage is relatively ancient. *Priasilpha angulata* can be distinguished from the others by the angulate form of the pronotum.

**Priasilpha angulata**, like other members of the genus, is often covered in debris, but once this is removed the dark reddish-brown coloration is exposed, as are the decumbent setae, which may form distinct clusters on the body. All *Priasilpha* are dorsoventrally compressed, and many of the wingless forms, like *P. angulata*, have raised and laterally notched edges to the pronotum.

| FAMILY | Priasilphidae |
|---|---|
| SUBFAMILY | |
| DISTRIBUTION | Australian: Tasmania |
| MACROHABITAT | *Eucalyptus* forest |
| MICROHABITAT | Under bark |
| FEEDING HABITS | Adults and larvae may feed on fungi |
| NOTE | The dorsal surface of adult *Priastichus* species are often covered by debris and exudate (discharge from the body through pores), which are held in place by scalelike setae |

ADULT LENGTH
³⁄₁₆ in
(4.1–4.9 mm)

*PRIASTICHUS TASMANICUS*

# PRIASTICHUS TASMANICUS

CROWSON, 1973

421

Actual size

*Priastichus* looks similar to, and may be the sister group of, New Zealand's endemic genus *Priasilpha*. Together with the Chilean *Chileosilpha*, the genera make up the family Priasilphidae, which currently remains relatively poorly known and rarely collected. Many species of the family are known from only a handful of specimens. Individuals of *P. tasmanicus* occur in montane forests up to 5,000 ft (1,524 m) in elevation. The first specimens ever encountered were collected by the coleopterist Philip Darlington from Harvard University's Museum of Comparative Zoology in the 1950s. Dr. Darlington, who made a significant contribution to the knowledge of beetles from Australasia, became one of the twentieth-century's best-known zoogeographers.

RELATED SPECIES

There are three species of *Priastichus*, all of which are found only in Tasmania. *Priastichus tasmanicus* occurs in northern Tasmania, whereas the other two species are generally found in the south, though there may be some overlap in their distributions. The different body shapes and elytral elevations help distinguish the three species.

**Priastichus tasmanicus** is a dorsoventrally compressed beetle. Specimens may be covered by debris, but once this is removed the cuticle is seen to be dark reddish brown to black with a covering of short decumbent or recumbent setae. The sides of the pronotum are broadly undulate and the elytra have weak elongate ridges. It lacks hind wings and is flightless.

| | |
|---|---|
| FAMILY | Silvanidae |
| SUBFAMILY | Silvaninae |
| DISTRIBUTION | Cosmopolitan |
| MACROHABITAT | Human habitation |
| MICROHABITAT | Stored products |
| FEEDING HABITS | Adults and larvae feed on cereals and grains |
| NOTE | A worldwide pest of stored products |

**ADULT LENGTH**
¹⁄₁₆–⅛ in
(2.4–3 mm)

*ORYZAEPHILUS MERCATOR*
# MERCHANT GRAIN BEETLE
(FAUVEL, 1889)

Actual size

Carl Linnaeus, the eighteenth-century Swedish father of taxonomic nomenclature, coined the Latin genus name *Oryzaephilus*, meaning "rice-lover." *Oryzaephilus mercator*, the Merchant Grain Beetle, is a stored-product pest and can be found in any situation where grains are kept, especially grains of high oil content, like oatmeal, bran, rolled oats, and, of course, brown rice. These beetles are most common in households. Females can lay up to 200–300 eggs over a three-month period, and populations can consequently build up rather rapidly.

### RELATED SPECIES

*Oryzaephilus mercator* is a relative of the more common Sawtoothed Grain Beetle, *O. surinamensis*. There are 16 species of *Oryzaephilus*, found mainly in the Old World, with *O. surinamensis* and *O. mercator* now widespread pests of stored products. Some new and exciting species are being discovered in unusual locations such as the island of Socotra off the Horn of Africa, where active entomological surveys are taking place.

**The Merchant Grain Beetle** is more or less dorsoventrally compressed, dark reddish brown to black and punctured, and has a covering of setae. The sides of the pronotum are serrate or toothed, and the elytra have distinct seriate punctation. There are slightly elongate setae on the pronotum and elytra perched on distinctive longitudinal carinae.

| FAMILY | Cucujidae |
|---|---|
| SUBFAMILY | |
| DISTRIBUTION | Australian: New Zealand, Manawatawhi/Three Kings Islands |
| MACROHABITAT | Podocarp–broadleaf forest |
| MICROHABITAT | Under bark |
| FEEDING HABITS | Adults and larvae may be predacious |
| NOTE | The tip of the abdomen of the larva of *Platisus zelandicus* consists of a hardened plate that extends posteriorly to form a spectacular, large, forked median process with upturned spines. |

ADULT LENGTH
½–¹¹⁄₁₆ in
(12–17 mm)

*PLATISUS ZELANDICUS*
# PLATISUS ZELANDICUS
MARRIS & KLIMASZEWSKI, 2001

423

The relict species *Platisus zelandicus* provides a wonderful glimpse into New Zealand's ancient biological and geological history. It was described from Manawatawhi/Three Kings Islands, which are located 35 miles (55 km) off the northern tip of North Island and are part of what was once a ridge that connected New Zealand with New Caledonia. The islands are home to many other plants and animals that, like *P. zelandicus*, appear to be biological remnants of a vast fauna that may once have been more widespread throughout the world, but is noticeably absent from mainland New Zealand.

## RELATED SPECIES

The family Cucujidae, once including members of the families Silvanidae and Laemophloeidae, currently consists of four genera and about 50 species. Some species of *Cucujus*, *Palaestes*, and *Platisus* may be strikingly colored metallic blue, bright red, or yellow, but there are also several unicolorous black or brown species like *P. zelandicus*. There are five described species of *Platisus*, but more are unnamed from Australia and the Neotropics. The fourth genus *Pediacus* includes 22 species with a primarily Holarctic distribution and its species are usually light brown.

**Platisus zelandicus** is a flattened, dark reddish-brown to black beetle with a covering of short setae. The head is transverse and the antennae are filiform, while the mandibles are visible in dorsal view, indicating that this species may be a predator. The larvae are also flattened and the abdomen ends in an extravagant sclerotized plate (tergum 9) that is hinged.

Actual size

| | |
|---|---|
| FAMILY | Myraboliidae |
| SUBFAMILY | |
| DISTRIBUTION | Australian: eastern Australia and Tasmania |
| MACROHABITAT | *Eucalyptus* forests |
| MICROHABITAT | Under bark of living trees |
| FEEDING HABITS | Unknown |
| NOTE | All known species in this family are restricted to Australia |

ADULT LENGTH
¹/₈ –³/₁₆ in
(2.85–3.65 mm)

424

*MYRABOLIA BREVICORNIS*
# MYRABOLIA BREVICORNIS
(ERICHSON, 1842)

Actual size

While many biologists tend to overlook the tiniest brown beetle species, there are plenty of discoveries to be made about microcoleoptera. *Myrabolia brevicornis* was described by the German scientist Wilhelm Ferdinand Erichson in 1842, in what was the first major entomological work describing the insects of Tasmania (known as Van Diemen's Land at the time). Erichson went on to publish several significant entomological works, including some on African beetles, before his death at the young age of 40. The fact that early entomologists could describe very small species such as *M. brevicollis* with what could be called primitive optical instruments, and without even the benefit of electric light, is a wonder.

### RELATED SPECIES

The 13 species of *Myrabolia* in the family Myraboliidae are all endemic to Australia. *Myrabolia brevicornis* is the most widespread species in Australia and can be differentiated from others by careful scrutiny of several external characters (such as those relating to the antennae and prosternum) and internal female and male characters.

**Myrabolia brevicornis** is a dorsoventrally flattened, dark brown beetle with a covering of setae. The elytra are serially punctate and also have serially arranged rows of setae. The antennae are three-segmented, but the last segment is small with respect to antennomere 10. Males have a glabrous, circular, slightly concave area on the ventral side of the abdomen, with numerous pores in the center.

| FAMILY | Cavognathidae |
|---|---|
| SUBFAMILY | |
| DISTRIBUTION | Australian: eastern Australia |
| MACROHABITAT | *Eucalyptus* forests |
| MICROHABITAT | Birds' nests |
| FEEDING HABITS | Scavenger |
| NOTE | The scientific name for this species means "eating bird chicks" |

ADULT LENGTH
¹⁄₈ in
(2.5–3.3 mm)

*TAPHROPIESTES PULLIVORA*
# TAPHROPIESTES PULLIVORA
(CROWSON, 1964)

425

Actual size

The family Cavognathidae consists of the single genus *Taphropiestes* containing nine species, all of which have a Gondwanan distribution (Australia, New Zealand, and southern South America). Based on observations and collections of some Australian and New Zealand species, most appear to be associated with active birds' nests. Adults and larvae do not attack the nestlings directly, despite reports to the contrary in the literature, and may instead scavenge in the nests for food. Some specimens have been found outside nests, suggesting that at least some species are free-living. Adults and larvae of *T. pullivora* have been recorded in association with nestlings of the Australian Magpie (*Cracticus tibicen*).

### RELATED SPECIES
Two of the nine species of *Taphropiestes* are found in Australia, four occur in New Zealand and three are from South America. *Taphropiestes pullivora* can be distinguished by the presence of frontal pits on the head connected by a groove, while the genal projections are distinct.

**Taphropiestes pullivora** is a more or less dorsoventrally flattened, dark brown beetle with a covering of setae. The antennal club is three-segmented, with the last antennomere elongate, and the pronotum is transverse, not elongate as in some other species. The frons has a U-shaped groove, whereas in other species there may be two pits or the groove may be absent.

| FAMILY | Lamingtoniidae |
|---|---|
| SUBFAMILY | |
| DISTRIBUTION | Australian: Tasmania and Victoria |
| MACROHABITAT | *Eucalyptus* and southern beech (*Nothofagus* spp.) forests |
| MICROHABITAT | Leaf litter |
| FEEDING HABITS | Feeds on fungi |
| NOTE | The three known species in this family occur in eastern Australia |

ADULT LENGTH
¹⁄₁₆–¹⁄₈ in
(2.5–3.2 mm)

*LAMINGTONIUM LOEBLI*
# LAMINGTONIUM LOEBLI
LAWRENCE & LESCHEN, 2003

Actual size

*Lamingtonium loebli* was described from a small number of individuals that were all obtained using two methods commonly used to sample beetles in forested areas: window traps and a small-scale pyrethrum knockdown technique. The vertically placed window traps are typically left in forests for several days at a time, and the beetles encountering the window fall into a receptacle filled with preserving fluid. The knockdown technique involves spraying a small amount of pyrethrum on a tree riddled with holes or with fungi and moss to flush beetles out of their hiding places and onto a collecting sheet.

## RELATED SPECIES

The three species of Lamingtoniidae, endemic to Australia, may all be fungus-feeders, as indicated by host records from two species. Coloration and punctation characters are used to separate the species, and *Lamingtonium loebli* has two maculae (pigmented spots) on the elytra and widely distributed pronotal punctures on the disk.

**Lamingtonium loebli** is a dorsoventrally flattened, glabrous, usually tricolored beetle, mainly reddish orange to yellow, with two maculae on the black elytra, one basal and the other present as a zigzag to transverse form just beyond the midline. The antennal club is three-segmented, the pronotum is distinctly punctured, and the elytra lack a scutellary striole (rudimentary stria).

| FAMILY | Passandridae |
|---|---|
| SUBFAMILY | |
| DISTRIBUTION | Afrotropical: south of the Sahara (Cameroon, Ghana, Ivory Coast, Kenya, South Africa, Tanzania, Zaire, Zimbabwe) |
| MACROHABITAT | *Eucalyptus* and southern beech (*Nothofagus* spp.) forests |
| MICROHABITAT | Rotten and sound wood |
| FEEDING HABITS | Larvae are ectoparasites of wood-boring larvae |
| NOTE | The head of many adult passandrids have well-developed grooves where powerful mandibular muscles attach |

ADULT LENGTH
¼–½ in
(7–13 mm)

*PASSANDRA SIMPLEX*

# PASSANDRA SIMPLEX

(MURRAY, 1867)

427

Passandridae is a small group of beetles found worldwide (except from New Zealand and the Pacific). Larval passandrids are ectoparasites of larvae and pupae of various wood-boring beetles (bostrichids, weevils, longhorn beetles, bark beetles, and ambrosia beetles) and braconid wasps. Adult size varies depending on larval nutrition. Not much is known about the adults, but the head of many species has large dorsal sulci (grooves) associated with well-developed mandibular muscles. What they do with these powerful mandibles remains a mystery, but perhaps adults also feed on wood-boring insects.

### RELATED SPECIES

There are about 30 species of *Passandra*, found mainly throughout tropical regions but absent from the Pacific. The species can easily be distinguished by the surface structure of the head, pronotum, and elytra, as well as the form of the antennae and, in some cases, color of the body.

Actual size

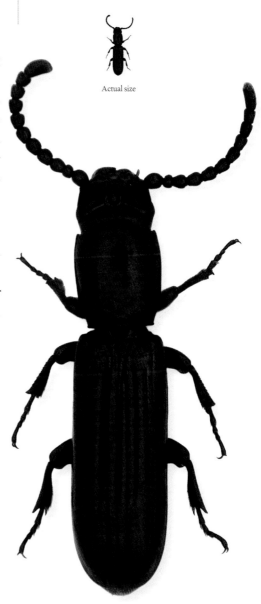

**Passandra simplex** is a rigid, well-sclerotized subcylindrical black beetle. It is glabrous and lacks setae. The head has paired median sulci and the antennomeres are quite compact, with the last one sulcate. The marginal groove of the pronotum has a simple medial notch, a key character shared with another African species, *P. oblongicollis*.

| FAMILY | Phalacridae |
|---|---|
| SUBFAMILY | Phalacrinae |
| DISTRIBUTION | Australian: southwest Western Australia |
| MACROHABITAT | *Eucalyptus* forests |
| MICROHABITAT | Male cones of *Macrozamia* cycads |
| FEEDING HABITS | Adults probably feed on pollen |
| NOTE | New species of beetles are discovered and described every year, including this species described in 2013; it is estimated only one quarter of all species of beetles that occur in Australia have been described to date |

428

ADULT LENGTH
⅛ in
(2.7–2.9 mm)

*PLATYPHALACRUS LAWRENCEI*
# PLATYPHALACRUS LAWRENCEI
GIMMEL, 2013

Actual size

The diversity of Phalacridae is extraordinary, with the form of the larval mouthparts varying depending on its diet. Most species feed on a wide variety of fungi (mostly smuts and other molds growing on herbaceous plants and dead leaves), while others may feed on the flowerheads of Asteraceae. *Platyphalacrus lawrencei* is the only species found on cycads, and has been collected only from male cones. Other beetle cycad specialists include members of the families Curculionidae, Erotylidae, Boganiidae, and, to a lesser extent, other groups such as Nitidulidae and Tenebrionidae.

## RELATED SPECIES

*Platyphalacrus* is monotypic but is classed within the *Olibroporus* group, consisting of four widespread genera, including the predominantly Australian genus *Austroporus*, which contains 30 species. Because exact phylogenetic relationships among the genera are uncertain and life-history information is lacking, the exact ancestral diet that led to the evolutionary switch to cycad association in *Platyphalacrus* remains ambiguous.

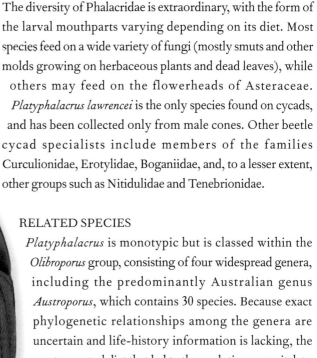

**Platyphalacrus lawrencei** is an oval, light red-brown beetle that lacks dorsal setae, although a medially setose prosternum is diagnostic for the genus. Unlike most members of Phalacridae, *P. lawrencei* is flattened and not highly convex. The elytron lacks a scutellary striole (rudimentary stria), but has well-developed seriate punctures, while the epipleuron is not visible in lateral view. The legs of these and related beetles are often concealed underneath the body.

| FAMILY | Propalticidae |
| --- | --- |
| SUBFAMILY | |
| DISTRIBUTION | Pacific: Hawaii (Kauai, Maui, Oahu), Guam, Northern Mariana Islands (Saipan, Tinian), Samoa |
| MACROHABITAT | Tropical forest |
| MICROHABITAT | Adults found on tree surfaces |
| FEEDING HABITS | Adults probably feed on lichen or fungi |
| NOTE | The front legs of these beetles, with long tibiae armed with a large apical spur, are used for jumping |

ADULT LENGTH
¹/₃₂ in
(1.1–1.4 mm)

*PROPALTICUS OCULATUS*

# PROPALTICUS OCULATUS

SHARP, 1879

429

Actual size

There are two genera of Propalticidae—*Propalticus*, which has 32 species, and *Slipinskogenia*, with 11 species—distributed in tropical areas around the Pacific and Indian oceans. When describing *P. oculatus*, David Sharp mentioned "I am sorry I am unable to see accurately the structure of the tarsi of this minute insect." This exemplifies the technological challenges faced by entomologists in the nineteenth century when trying to adequately classify tiny beetles such as this. Adults from this family have been collected from the surface of dead trees and, oddly, jump using the front legs like some anthribids.

**Propalticus oculatus** is an oval species that is light to dark brown with light spots, or maculae, on the elytra. The surface is covered in tiny setae that give it a silky appearance. The antennal club is not compact, but rather loosely joined, and each elytron bears three distinctive striae.

RELATED SPECIES

The poorly studied Propalticidae may be related to the family Laemophloeidae. The more widespread genus *Propalticus* can be separated from the African genus *Slipinskogenia* by the eyes, which are posteriorly convergent. There is no full revision of *Propalticus*, but *P. oculatus* can be differentiated from most other species by the faint maculae (pigmented spots) on the elytra.

| FAMILY | Laemophloeidae |
|---|---|
| SUBFAMILY | |
| DISTRIBUTION | Palearctic: widespread across Europe except the far north |
| MACROHABITAT | Temperate forest |
| MICROHABITAT | Bark beetle galleries |
| FEEDING HABITS | Adults and larvae are both probably predatory |
| NOTE | The elongate and narrow shape of this beetle enables it to crawl in bark beetle galleries |

**ADULT LENGTH**
1/16 in
(1.9–2.4 mm)

*LEPTOPHLOEUS CLEMATIDIS*
# LEPTOPHLOEUS CLEMATIDIS
(ERICHSON, 1846)

Actual size

Laemophloeids are thought to be either fungus-feeders or predacious, and larvae and adults are often found together under bark. The body forms also vary from completely flat species to those that are cylindrical or subcylindrical in cross section. Members of *Leptophloeus* and the genus *Dysmerus* are usually associated with wood-boring scolytine weevils. *Leptophloeus clematidis* is part of an excellent example of what ecologists call a tritrophic relationship: it occurs in the galleries of the Clematis Bark Beetle (*Xylocleptes bispinus*), which feeds on Old Man's Beard (*Clematis vitalba*).

RELATED SPECIES

*Leptophloeus* contains 27 species worldwide, eight occurring in Europe. The species are distinguished by particular features of the pronotum and elytra, as well as color and size of the eyes. Male genitalia and the form of the female spermatheca are also used in laemophloeid species taxonomy.

**Leptophloeus clematidis** is an elongate subcylindrical species that is light to dark brown in color. The pronotum has distinct sublateral lines or carinae (raised ridges), and the elytra have deep longitudinal striae that are characteristic of the family. The antennal insertions are concealed in dorsal view and the antennae have a weak antennal club.

| FAMILY | Laemophloeidae |
| --- | --- |
| SUBFAMILY | |
| DISTRIBUTION | Nearctic: USA (Texas) |
| MACROHABITAT | Forests |
| MICROHABITAT | Under bark |
| FEEDING HABITS | Unknown |
| NOTE | One of the few rostrate beetles in the family Laemophloeidae |

ADULT LENGTH
¹⁄₁₆ in
(2.2 mm)

*METAXYPHLOEUS TEXANUS*

# METAXYPHLOEUS TEXANUS
(SCHAEFFER, 1904)

431

Actual size

Having a rostrum is not unique to weevil families, and the feature occurs throughout the Coleoptera, in such groups as Archostemata, Staphylinidae, Lycidae, Tenebrionidae, Salpingidae, Chrysomelidae, and Cerambycidae. Few members of the superfamily Cucujoidea have an elongate preocular region of the head, and *Metaxyphloeus texanus* is one of a few rostrate genera in the Laemophloeidae family. In weevils the rostrum is used by females as an ovipositor, but its function remains mysterious for many other groups because of their cryptic behavior. It is likely that head prolongation may be associated with a specialized diet.

## RELATED SPECIES

The five species that make up the New World genus *Metaxyphloeus* can be distinguished from other rostrate laemophloeids by having a six-segmented antennal club, complete sublateral pronotal lines, and spotted elytra. *Metaxyphloeus texanus* is very similar to *M. signatus* and can be distinguished from it only by genitalic dissection.

**Metaxyphloeus texanus** is elongate and dorsoventrally flattened, with subparallel-sided, maculate elytra. It is generally dark brown in color and glabrous, and has very weak punctation and pale antennae. The rostrum is flattened, the antennae are inserted on the side and base of the frons, and there are distinctive lateral and sublateral carinae on the pronotum and elytra.

| FAMILY | Tasmosalpingidae |
| --- | --- |
| SUBFAMILY | |
| DISTRIBUTION | Australian: Tasmania |
| MACROHABITAT | *Eucalyptus* forests |
| MICROHABITAT | Unknown |
| FEEDING HABITS | Adults are fungus-feeders |
| NOTE | Both known species in this small family occur in Tasmania, although evidence suggests that *Tasmosalpingus* also occurs on the mainland of Australia |

ADULT LENGTH
¹⁄₃₂–¹⁄₁₆ in
(1.2–2.2 mm)

432

# TASMOSALPINGUS QUADRISPILOTUS
LEA,1919

Actual size

The family Tasmosalpingidae contains a single genus with two species. Only a single putative larva of *Tasmosalpingus* has been collected, from the bark of the podocarp tree *Phyllocladus aspleniifolius*, and adults have been collected from Malaise traps. Males have a setose patch in the gular (throat) area, while both sexes have setose foveae at the base of the pronotum. Gut preparations made from specimens have been found to be packed with fungal hyphae.

RELATED SPECIES
The phylogenetic relationships of this group are poorly known, though it was once treated as a member of the Phloeostichidae. In the only phylogenetic study of the group where both larval and adult characters were analyzed, tasmosalpingids were resolved as sister taxon to the New Zealand family Cyclaxyridae. The two described species can be distinguished from each other based on color and different punctation of the elytra.

**Tasmosalpingus quadrispilotus** is a somewhat elongate species that is convex, glabrous, setose and chocolate-brown in color, with lighter maculae (pigmented spots) on the elytra. The cuticle is punctured and elytral punctation is seriate. The antennal insertions are not visible in dorsal view, and the setose foveae at the lateral margins of the pronotum are distinctive for the family.

| | |
|---|---|
| FAMILY | Cyclaxyridae |
| SUBFAMILY | |
| DISTRIBUTION | Australian: northeastern South Island of New Zealand |
| MACROHABITAT | Podocarp–broadleaf and southern beech (*Nothofagus* spp.) forests |
| MICROHABITAT | Tree trunks infected with sooty molds |
| FEEDING HABITS | Adults and larvae are fungus-feeders |
| NOTE | This entire family of beetles is restricted to New Zealand |

ADULT LENGTH
¹⁄₁₆–¹⁄₈ in
(2–2.6 mm)

*CYCLAXYRA JELINEKI*

# CYCLAXYRA JELINEKI

GIMMEL, LESCHEN, & ŚLIPIŃSKI, 2009

433

Actual size

The Cyclaxyridae family contains only two species, both of which are endemic to New Zealand. The beetles can easily be spotted at night feeding on sooty molds, while larvae are well hidden in the masses of the same molds. Few groups of beetles worldwide specialize on sooty molds, and yet there is a significant diversity of beetles and other insects associated with them. A few sooty-mold specialists have a Southern Hemisphere, or Gondwanan, distribution, but many groups are unique to New Zealand: not only species or genera, but also three families, Metaxinidae, Agapythidae, and Cyclaxyridae.

RELATED SPECIES

Taxonomists are still unsure about the relationships of Cyclaxyridae to other cucujoid beetles, though tasmosalpingids from Australia may be their closest relatives. The more restricted species *Cyclaxyra jelineki* can be differentiated from the more widespread species *C. politula* easily by genitalic differences and by the high density of punctures on the frons.

**Cyclaxyra jelineki** is convex and black, though can be reddish or pale-colored when not fully hardened. The antennae are three-segmented and the insertions are visible in dorsal view. The front coxal cavities are broadly open behind, and there are remarkable fovea in the epipleuron, which are lined with setae and often filled with wax.

| FAMILY | Kateretidae |
| --- | --- |
| SUBFAMILY | |
| DISTRIBUTION | Palearctic: south-central Europe, from Austria south to Greece and Israel and east to Iraq |
| MACROHABITAT | Podocarp–broadleaf and southern beech (*Nothofagus* spp.) forests |
| MICROHABITAT | Mediterranean steppes and scrublands |
| FEEDING HABITS | Adults and larvae are associated with angiosperms, mainly Papaveraceae |
| NOTE | Species in this family occur in temperate and subtropical zones of the world but are completely absent in New Zealand |

ADULT LENGTH
³⁄₁₆–¼ in
(4–6 mm)

*BRACHYLEPTUS QUADRATUS*
# BRACHYLEPTUS QUADRATUS
(STURM, 1844)

Actual size

Kateretidae are nitidulid-like beetles that feed on plants. While adults may be found on several unrelated host plants, larval associations are more restricted. Kateretidae genera tend to develop on one plant family: *Anthoneus* on Agavaceae; *Brachypterolus* on Scrophulariaceae; *Amartus*, *Anamartus*, *Brachyleptus* on Papaveraceae; *Brachypterus* on Urticaceae; *Heterhelus* on Caprifoliacea; and *Kateretes* on Cyperaceae and Juncaceae. Larvae and adults of *Brachyleptus quadratus* are mostly found on fruits and flowers of poppies (*Papaver* spp.). Female ovipositors in this species are distinctly long and narrow (at least five times as long as wide) and are forked at their apex.

## RELATED SPECIES

There are 14 genera and about 100 species of Kateretidae worldwide. *Brachyleptus* is Holarctic in its distribution, with some species occurring in the Afrotropical and Oriental realms; *B. quadratus* is one of the more wide-ranging species in Europe and central Asia. Species identification is based mainly on tarsal structure, shape of the pronotum, and punctation; genitalic examination may be needed.

**Brachyleptus quadratus** is a somewhat oblong, convex species. It is black to brown in color, often with lighter-toned appendages, and the surfaces are setose and densely punctured. The pronotum is transverse and the sides are evenly arcuate. The elytra are brachyeptrous, exposing the last abdominal segments. The tarsi are expanded and have dense setose pads, especially in males.

| FAMILY | Nitidulidae |
|---|---|
| SUBFAMILY | Nitidulinae |
| DISTRIBUTION | Neotropical: southern Mexico |
| MACROHABITAT | Tropical rainforest |
| MICROHABITAT | Possibly palm tree flowers |
| FEEDING HABITS | Presumably on pollen or flowers |
| NOTE | Adults and larvae may be important palm pollinators |

*CYCHROCEPHALUS CORVINUS*

# CYCHROCEPHALUS CORVINUS

REITTER, 1873

435

Many species of beetle occur on palms, including weevils, nitidulids, and some Old World tropical groups of byturids. While there are several groups of nitidulids that are strictly flower-feeders, the tribe Mystropini, which contains the genus *Cychrocephalus*, has several members in Central and South America that feed on palms. Large palm inflorescences may yield hundreds of beetle specimens, but *Cychrocephalus* is elusive: it is poorly collected and definitive host associations have not been reported in the literature. The rostrum of *C. corvinus* indicates that this nitidulid may be a special pollinator, but diligent collecting and observation is necessary to learn more about the species.

Actual size

### RELATED SPECIES

There are two described and several undescribed species of *Cychrocephalus*. Color is the most distinguishable characteristic, with some species black with an almost bluish tinge and others brown to black. Details in punctation and type of setation are also important, especially on the head, pronotum, and elytra. *Cychrocephalus corvinus* is slightly larger than its similarly colored Colombian relative *C. luctuosus*.

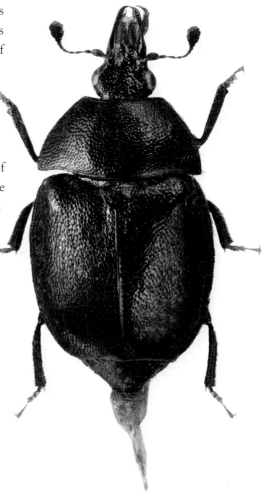

**Cychrocephalus corvinus** has a distinct rostrum, is dorsoventrally flattened, and is mostly very dark brown apart from the extreme parts of the legs and the mouthparts. The antennae are 11-segmented with a flattened three-segmented club, and the insertions are visible in dorsal view. The pygidium (tip of the abdomen) is exposed and the elytra are explanate.

| | |
|---|---|
| FAMILY | Nitidulidae |
| SUBFAMILY | Nitidulinae |
| DISTRIBUTION | Palearctic: Russian Far East, Japan, Korea |
| MACROHABITAT | Temperate forests |
| MICROHABITAT | Puffball fungi |
| FEEDING HABITS | Adults and larvae are mycophagous |
| NOTE | *Pocadius* species feed on various puffball fungi worldwide |

ADULT LENGTH
⅛ –³⁄₁₆ in
(3–4 mm)

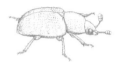

436

*POCADIUS NOBILIS*
# ASIAN HAIRY
# PUFFBALL BEETLE
REITTER, 1873

Actual size

Nitidulid beetles are a rich group whose members have diverse diets: they feed on fungi, plants, and carrion, and in some cases are predatory. The majority of species, however, are associated with fungi—members of the genus *Pocadius*, for example, are strictly associated with puffballs and puffball-like fungi. Adults tend to be found on fresh puffballs, where they mate and deposit their eggs. They may leave the larvae to feed on the fungal hyphae and, eventually, the spore masses (the gleba), or the adults remain to feed alongside the larvae. *Pocadius* is exceptional in that it has a nearly worldwide range yet the genus has maintained its special association with puffballs.

RELATED SPECIES

There are nearly 50 species of *Pocadius*. The genus has been revised recently, so the species can now be recognized; differentiation between them may be difficult and require genitalic dissection, so geography is a very important criterion for identifying species. There are few species known from east Asia, and only two described from Japan, one the more widespread *P. nobilis* and another known only from Okinawa.

**The Asian Hairy Puffball Beetle** is a convex reddish-tan species whose head, antennal club, and much of the elytra are darker. The surfaces are glabrous and have large ovate punctures, and the body is setose, with the elytral setae forming distinctive rows. The elytra are elongate and the apex of the abdomen is exposed in dorsal view; in males, the tip of tergite 8 is visible.

| FAMILY | Nitidulidae |
|---|---|
| SUBFAMILY | Cryptarchinae |
| DISTRIBUTION | Neotropical: southern Chile |
| MACROHABITAT | Temperate forests |
| MICROHABITAT | Sap flows and slime fluxes |
| FEEDING HABITS | Adults and larvae feed on sap |
| NOTE | Adults are aposematically colored to warn off predators |

ADULT LENGTH
½ in
(11.5–12.5 mm)

LIOSCHEMA XACARILLA

# LIOSCHEMA XACARILLA
(THOMSON, 1856)

437

Members of Cryptarchinae are diverse, but most species are found in association with sap flows and slime fluxes, where they may imbibe the fluids but more than likely derive nourishment from suspended yeasts and other organisms. Many cryptarchines, like members of *Lioschema*, are aposematically colored to warn off predators, though it is not known if these species are actually protected chemically. Many cryptarchine species also have a stridulatory file on the vertex of the head in both sexes. The file (or pars stridens) is struck by a ridge (or plectrum) under the edge of the pronotum.

### RELATED SPECIES
Cryptarchinae is a moderately sized group containing 22 genera and about 300 species worldwide. There are four cryptarchine genera in Chile, three of which are endemic to temperate South America. Members of the genera *Lioschema* and *Paromia* are the most colorful and among the largest species of the group, and are sometimes classified under a single genus (as *Paromia*).

Actual size

**Lioschema xacarilla** is a large, convex, glabrous species, black in color with orange to red basal and subapical transverse stripes on the elytra. The antennae are hidden in dorsal view and the labrum and clypeus are fused. An orange area on the vertex of the head indicates the stridulatory file, and the pronotum has a large lateral bead.

| FAMILY | Smicripidae |
|---|---|
| SUBFAMILY | |
| DISTRIBUTION | Nearctic and Neotropical: Cuba, Puerto Rico, United States Gulf Coast, California |
| MACROHABITAT | Coastal forests |
| MICROHABITAT | Adults are found on the inflorescences of Cabbage Palmetto (*Sabal palmetto*) and larvae in leaf litter |
| FEEDING HABITS | Unknown |
| NOTE | This family contains only one genus, *Smicrips*, which includes six described species |

ADULT LENGTH
¹⁄₃₂–¹⁄₁₆ in
(1–1.6 mm)

438

*SMICRIPS PALMICOLA*
# PALMETTO BEETLE
LECONTE, 1878

Actual size

Smicripidae are tiny nitidulid-like beetles that are restricted to the New World and are mainly tropical. The group has been little studied and there are new species requiring taxonomic names in addition to the six already described. The family has been referred to by the common name palmetto beetles, but not all species are associated with the family Arecaceae, to which the Cabbage Palmetto (*Sabal palmetto*) belongs. Though palm associations dominate, specimens have been collected in decaying matter, under bark, and in flowers of various trees. Adults of the Palmetto Beetle are often found in great abundance on the flowers of Cabbage Palmetto. Another efficient way to obtain adults is by using passive traps such as barrier pitfalls or flight-intercept traps.

## RELATED SPECIES

The members of Smicripidae are fairly uniform in structure, looking somewhat like a cross between Monotomidae and Nitidulidae species, though clearly sharing characters with the latter, including the absence of a galea. Most Coleoptera have a galea, including the nitidulid relative Kateretidae, but the presence of this feature is otherwise rare in Cucujoidea.

**The Palmetto Beetle** is light to dark brown, elongate, parallel-sided, and dorsoventrally flattened. It has shortened elytra, exposing the last abdominal segment. The antennae have a three-segmented club and the insertions are exposed in dorsal view. Under high magnification, one can see the 4-4-4 tarsomeres, and with even higher magnification and careful dissection, the absence of a galea can be seen.

| FAMILY | Bothrideridae |
|---|---|
| SUBFAMILY | Bothriderinae |
| DISTRIBUTION | Afrotropical: Tanzania, Malawi, Kenya, Zambia, Zimbabwe, Democratic Republic of Congo, South Africa |
| MACROHABITAT | Tropical forests |
| MICROHABITAT | Dead wood; associated with wood-boring insects |
| FEEDING HABITS | Adults are saproxylic; larvae may be parasitic on wood-boring insects |
| NOTE | The deep channels that form an "island" in the middle of the pronotum in species of *Pseudobothrideres* are unique among beetles |

ADULT LENGTH
³⁄₁₆ in
(3.7–5 mm)

*PSEUDOBOTHRIDERES CONRADSI*

# PSEUDOBOTHRIDERES CONRADSI

POPE, 1959

439

Actual size

Members of the subfamily Bothriderinae are poorly known biologically, and we know almost nothing about *Pseudobothrideres*, apart from the fact that adults are saproxylic and associated with dead wood, and larvae are parasitic. The larvae are hypermetamorphic, with an active triungulin that attaches itself to the host, which may be a hymenopteran or a beetle. The triungulin molts in a grub stage, which continues feeding on the host until the pupal stage, when a cell may be constructed out of wax or other substrate. Some specimens of *P. conradsi* were collected near artificial lights at night.

## RELATED SPECIES

There are 19 known species of *Pseudobothrideres*, found in tropical regions of the Old World, including Australia and New Caledonia. There has not been a full worldwide revision of the genus, but its members can be distinguished from other bothriderines by the presence of femoral lines on the metaventrite, the distinctive shape and form of the pronotum, and a length exceeding ³⁄₁₆ in (4 mm).

**Pseudobothrideres conradsi** is dorsoventrally compressed and dark red in color. The antennae are inserted under the frons and are two-segmented. The pronotum has a distinct ovate groove and its posteriolateral margins are acute. Deep, broad furrows are present among the elytral carinae. The front tarsi are apically toothed and the tarsal formula is 4-4-4.

| FAMILY | Bothrideridae |
|---|---|
| SUBFAMILY | Teredinae |
| DISTRIBUTION | Afrotropical: tropical West Africa |
| MACROHABITAT | Tropical forests |
| MICROHABITAT | Ambrosia beetle galleries |
| FEEDING HABITS | Adults and larvae are predators and parasites on platypodine weevils (pinhole bark borers) |
| NOTE | The first-instar larva of this species has long legs and actively seeks pupae of pinhole bark borers, on which they eventually feed |

ADULT LENGTH
³⁄₁₆–¼ in
(4.5–6 mm)

*SOSYLUS SPECTABILIS*
# SOSYLUS SPECTABILIS
GROUVELLE, 1914

Actual size

Many bothriderids are parasitic on wood-inhabiting insects; members of *Sosylus* are associated with ambrosia beetles (platypodine weevils). Adult *Sosylus* enter ambrosia beetle galleries, and after mating, the female kills the male and then lays her eggs. Larvae are free-living and attach themselves to young platypodine pupae, after which they undergo hypermetamorphosis. The ambulatory larvae do not feed until after they have molted into a grub-like larva that embeds its head into the pupa to feed. Feeding on the pupa lasts for two to three days until a pre-pupal phase occurs, and the last instar spins a web inside the host chamber.

## RELATED SPECIES

There are more than 50 species of *Sosylus*, whose members are distributed throughout much of the world's tropical regions; about one-third of the described species are Afrotropical. The family has been poorly studied, and while *Sosylus* is distinctive (it has an elongate and somewhat tubulate body), it is a genus that requires full worldwide revision.

**Sosylus spectabilis** is an elongate, tubulate, glabrous, dark reddish-brown to black beetle. The antennae are 11-segmented with a compact two-segmented club, and the insertions are visible in dorsal view. The elytra are distinctly grooved and there is an apical declivity. The head has antennal grooves and the front coxal cavities are closed behind.

| FAMILY | Cerylonidae |
|---|---|
| SUBFAMILY | Ceryloninae |
| DISTRIBUTION | Neotropical: Napo province, Ecuador |
| MACROHABITAT | Tropical forests |
| MICROHABITAT | Rotten wood and leaf litter |
| FEEDING HABITS | Adults and larvae are probably fungus-feeders |
| NOTE | This genus was named in honor of coleopterist James Pakaluk |

ADULT LENGTH
⅛ – ³⁄₁₆ in
(2.6–3.5 mm)

*PAKALUKIA NAPO*

# PAKALUKIA NAPO

ŚLIPIŃSKI, 1991

441

Actual size

Cerylonidae is a worldwide group of 52 genera and about 450 species. Many cerylonids have piercing and sucking mouthparts (present in both larvae and adults of Ceryloninae), but most, if not all, are fungus-feeders, dispelling a myth that adults with modified mouthparts are predatory. There are also species that are found in the galleries of wood-boring beetles, some found with ants and termites, and even some found in mammal nests (one species with a modified larva has been found with Naked Mole Rats, *Heterocephalus glaber*). Adults of *Pakalukia* have been found in leaf and log litter, in association with rotten palms, and have been extracted from fermenting tree-stump pulp using a Berlese funnel technique.

## RELATED SPECIES

Cerylonines are distinctive in that they have a crenulate abdominal apex that fits into corresponding grooves on the apex of the elytra, and appears to be a mechanism for locking the elytra into the abdomen. *Pakalukia* is one of the few cerylonine genera with a three-segmented club, present also in one other Neotropical genus, *Glyptolopus*. *Pakalukia* ranges from Central to South America, and one species has been described.

**Pakalukia napo** is convex, dark brown, and clothed with long setae. The maxillary palpi are marked with fine, irregular scratches. The pronotum has shallow sublateral furrows connected to a deeper basal impression and there is a median transverse carina just behind the midline. The punctation of the elytra is confused and covers the entire abdomen, such that the abdominal crenulations are difficult to observe without dissection.

| FAMILY | Alexiidae |
| --- | --- |
| SUBFAMILY | |
| DISTRIBUTION | Palearctic: Bulgaria, Hungary, Poland, and Slovakia |
| MACROHABITAT | Montane temperate forests |
| MICROHABITAT | Rotten wood and leaf litter |
| FEEDING HABITS | Adults and larvae are fungus-feeders |
| NOTE | The affinities of this family of minute beetles to other beetles are still unresolved |

ADULT LENGTH
¹⁄₃₂–¹⁄₁₆ in
(1.2–2.1 mm)

442

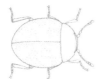

*SPHAEROSOMA CARPATHICUM*
# SPHAEROSOMA CARPATHICUM
(REITTER, 1883)

Actual size

Alexiidae contains the single genus *Sphaerosoma*, which in turn includes about 50 species ranging from central and southern Europe to Asia Minor and North Africa. The group is a member of the cerylonid series and has been variously treated as a separate family or grouped within the Endomychidae. Adults and larvae may feed on fungi, and there are records from mushrooms, but the diversity and biology of the group has been little studied, despite the numbers of specimens that have been collected in leaf litter across its range. *Sphaerosoma carpathicum* is a fairly restricted montane species.

### RELATED SPECIES

All the species in *Sphaerosoma* were described before the mid-1930s and there has been no revision of the genus recently, thus little is known about the relationships among the species. Early twentieth-century specialist Viktor Apfelbeck separated species of *Sphaerosoma* into three subgenera based on whether the adults had pubescence on the surface of the cuticle or not, and whether males have expanded tarsi or not. These unreliable subgeneric divisions have not been followed by recent workers.

**Sphaerosoma carpathicum** is a highly convex reddish-brown beetle with a covering of short setae. The antennae have ten segments and a three-segmented club. The pronotum lacks sulci and the tarsal formula is 4-4-4 in both sexes. The short prosternum is carinate medially in front of the front coxae, and the front coxal cavities are wide open behind.

| FAMILY | Discolomatidae |
|---|---|
| SUBFAMILY | Notiophyginae |
| DISTRIBUTION | Afrotropical: Rwanda |
| MACROHABITAT | Rotten wood |
| MICROHABITAT | Possibly fungi |
| FEEDING HABITS | Possibly feeds on fungi |
| NOTE | This family is most diverse in the Afrotropical Realm |

ADULT LENGTH
1/16–1/8 in
(2–2.5 mm)

*PARMASCHEMA BASILEWSKYI*

# PARMASCHEMA BASILEWSKYI

JOHN, 1955

443

Actual size

Discolomatids are found mainly in tropical regions, though some groups extend into temperate areas. They are generally poorly collected, but can often be found in leaf litter and rotten wood. There are several fungal-host records, indicating that many, if not all, members are mycophagous. All adults have glandular pores that are visible along the margins of the pronotum and elytra, and the flattened disk-like larvae also have glandular ducts opening near the spiracles: Presumably these beetles release chemicals as a defense against predation. Adults of *Parmaschema basilewskyi* can sometimes be found in high numbers in the decaying humus of forest patches that occur along rivers.

**Parmaschema basilewskyi** is brown in color, flattened, rugose, and punctate, with a covering of setae. The antennae are nine-segmented and end in a distinctive one-segmented club, with the insertions visible in dorsal view. The prothorax is distinctly transverse and narrower than the elytra, while the elytra are explanate with weakly crenulate margins.

## RELATED SPECIES

Discolomatidae contains 16 genera and about 400 species, but it is in need of major revision. The round to disk-like adults come in a variety of forms, ranging from those with smooth dorsal surfaces to those that are relatively rugose or tuberculate. The genus *Parmaschema* includes more than 15 species that occur mostly in Africa and southeast Asia. The species can be separated from each other by features of the antennae (particularly the shape of the antennal club), the pronotum (the shape and punctation on the surface), the presence or absence of a tooth at the apex of the hind tibia in males, and genitalic differences in males.

| FAMILY | Endomychidae |
| --- | --- |
| SUBFAMILY | Anamorphinae |
| DISTRIBUTION | Nearctic: southeastern United States |
| MACROHABITAT | Deciduous and pine forests |
| MICROHABITAT | Dead wood |
| FEEDING HABITS | Adults and larvae are probably fungus-feeders |
| NOTE | New species of small beetles continue to be described as collecting techniques and imaging technologies improve |

ADULT LENGTH
¹⁄₃₂ in
(1–1.2 mm)

*MICROPSEPHODES LUNDGRENI*
# MINUTE FUNGUS BEETLE
LESCHEN & CARLTON, 2000

•
Actual size

New species of microcoleoptera are still being described throughout the world, including some that are wide-ranging or occur in areas with dense human populations and where there has been relatively thorough collecting, such as the United States. The Minute Fungus Beetle is one such example—it was described relatively recently, first from specimens collected in Florida, Louisiana, and Tennessee, and then later discovered in other areas in the southeastern United States. Adult Minute Fungus Beetles occur under the bark of both dead and live trees where they may aggregate using the pheromone frontalin. Recent studies have shown that these beetles fly in the forest canopy at heights of 50 ft (15 m) or more.

## RELATED SPECIES

Anamorphinae occur worldwide apart from New Zealand and much of the Pacific. There are 34 genera, and most are small and often setose, looking like Cocinellidae, to which they are related. There are three described species of *Micropsephodes*, from the Bahamas, Guatemala, and the United States, and still more that require description.

**The Minute Fungus Beetle** is a convex, shiny black species with a purple or greenish sheen. The setae are sparse and the antennae are eight-segmented with a three-segmented serrate club, and in the males the scape is distally angulate. The heads of males have a setose tumulus and the frons is concave. The tarsi are three-segmented.

| FAMILY | Endomychidae |
|---|---|
| SUBFAMILY | Lycoperdininae |
| DISTRIBUTION | Palearctic, Oriental, and Australian: south Asia, east Asia, Southeast Asia, Papua New Guinea |
| MACROHABITAT | Tropical forests |
| MICROHABITAT | Fungi |
| FEEDING HABITS | Adults and larvae are fungus-feeders |
| NOTE | Several species of fungus-feeding beetles have yellow or orange spots on their elytra, as is the case for this species |

ADULT LENGTH
⁵⁄₁₆–½ in
(7.5–12 mm)

*EUMORPHUS QUADRIGUTTATUS*
# EUMORPHUS QUADRIGUTTATUS
(ILLIGER, 1800)

445

Endomychidae is a diverse family of mycophages with a worldwide distribution. Though many species are small and inconspicuous, others, like *Eumorphus*, are gaudily colored and can be collected easily from large bracket fungi growing on dead and dying trees. When adults are disturbed, they release their grip and drop like falling rain. *Eumorphus quadriguttatus* has been divided into four subspecies across its range, however divisions within the species may change because the morphological variation does not seem to correspond to natural groups or geographic distribution (e.g., one of the subspecies is known principally by its bicolored femora).

RELATED SPECIES

There are about 70 species and subspecies of *Eumorphus*; a key to the genus was written by Henry F. Strohecker, who published papers on endomychids from 1939 to 1986. Characters that are used to separate the species and subspecies include the shape, size, and position of the spots on the elytra, the color of the legs, and the presence and shape of a tooth near the apex of tibiae in males.

Actual size

**Eumorphus quadriguttatus** is a flattened, shiny black beetle, paler below, with four yellow to orange spots on the elytra (these spots can appear pale yellow to white in preserved specimens). The antennae are 11-segmented with a flattened three-segmented club. The pronotum has sublateral sulci at the base, a feature present in many endomychids. The legs can be of various colors, depending on subspecies; in the specimen shown, subspecies *Eumorphus quadriguttatus pulchripes*, the legs are red.

| | |
|---|---|
| FAMILY | Coccinellidae |
| SUBFAMILY | Coccinellinae |
| DISTRIBUTION | Oriental: montane Thailand |
| MACROHABITAT | Forests |
| MICROHABITAT | Leaf litter |
| FEEDING HABITS | Unknown; probably feeds on members of *Sternorrhyncha* (aphids, whiteflies, and scale insects) |
| NOTE | The few known species in the peculiar ladybird beetle tribe Carinodulini are all flightless |

ADULT LENGTH
¹⁄₃₂ in
(0.9 mm)

*CARINODULINA BURAKOWSKII*
# CARINODULINA BURAKOWSKII
ŚLIPIŃSKI & JADWISZCZAK, 1995

446

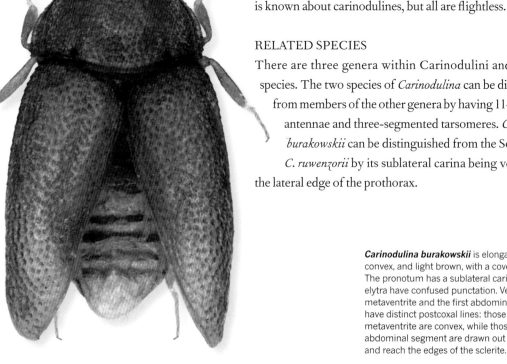

Actual size

Aside from the well-recognized, colorful ladybirds common in gardens, fields, and forests, Coccinellidae also includes some unladybird-like forms that will challenge even the best-trained coleopterist. These oddities include some members of the tribe Carinodulini—strange elongate beetles that could be confused with other cucujoids such as Cryptophagidae. However, careful assessment of characters with a good hand lens or dissecting microscope, especially the enlarged last maxillary palp or the classically modified coccinellid aedeagus, will help to place the odd taxa in the correct family. Not much is known about carinodulines, but all are flightless.

RELATED SPECIES
There are three genera within Carinodulini and only four species. The two species of *Carinodulina* can be distinguished from members of the other genera by having 11-segmented antennae and three-segmented tarsomeres. *Carinodulina burakowskii* can be distinguished from the South Indian *C. ruwenzorii* by its sublateral carina being very close to the lateral edge of the prothorax.

**Carinodulina burakowskii** is elongate-oval, convex, and light brown, with a covering of setae. The pronotum has a sublateral carina and the elytra have confused punctation. Ventrally, the metaventrite and the first abdominal segment have distinct postcoxal lines: those of the metaventrite are convex, while those of the first abdominal segment are drawn out posteriorly and reach the edges of the sclerite.

| FAMILY | Coccinellidae |
|---|---|
| SUBFAMILY | Coccinellinae |
| DISTRIBUTION | Neotropical: central and southern Mexico (possibly introduced to Colombia and Venezuela) |
| MACROHABITAT | Higher altitudes |
| MICROHABITAT | Herbaceous plants |
| FEEDING HABITS | Feeds on plants in the families Cucurbitaceae and Solanaceae |
| NOTE | Highly convex species, typically encountered from approximately 3,280 ft (1,000 m) in elevation |

ADULT LENGTH
⁵/₁₆–⁷/₁₆ in
(7.7–10.6 mm)

*EPILACHNA MEXICANA*

# EPILACHNA MEXICANA
(GUÉRIN-MÉNEVILLE, 1844)

447

Coccinellidae are well known as the ladybird beetles and consist mainly of species that are predators on sternorhyncan Hemiptera, mites, and other arthropods. However, they also include pollen- and fungal-feeders, and phytophagous members of the tribe Epilachnini, to which several genera—including *Epilachna mexicana*—belong. *Epilachna mexicana* has several adaptations associated with phytophagy, including specialized mouthparts, robust multi-pronged mandibles in the larvae, and a lack of waxy exudates and dorsal glands on the body, although these features have also evolved on predatory groups. Some species of epilachnines are destructive pests as well, including the Spotted Potato Ladybird (*E. vigintioctomaculata*) and the Mexican Bean Beetle (*E. varivestis*).

## RELATED SPECIES
Ladybird specialist Robert Gordon revised the New World Epilachnini in 1985, and at that time there were about 200 species. Most species are very colorful and often aposematic, with spots, broad maculae, or stripes. *Epilachna mexicana* is similar to many other species, but can be distinguished by having up to six pale spots on a usually black background.

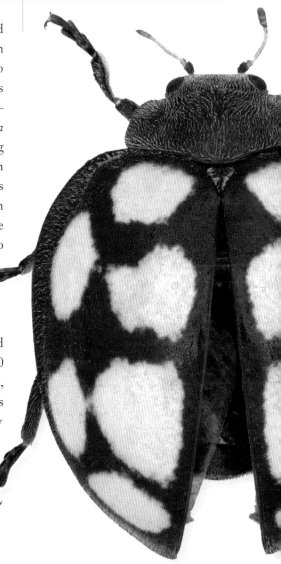

**Epilachna mexicana** is a highly convex species, like most members of Coccinellidae, and black with yellow or pale spots on the elytra that do not meet the lateral margin. Antennomere 1 and usually antennomeres 6–11 are brown, while the remaining antennomeres are yellow. The sides of the elytra are explanate.

Actual size

| FAMILY | Coccinellidae |
|---|---|
| SUBFAMILY | Coccinellinae |
| DISTRIBUTION | Nearctic: North America, south to Mexico |
| MACROHABITAT | Forests and grasslands |
| MICROHABITAT | Trees, shrubs, and grasses |
| FEEDING HABITS | Adults and larvae feed on aphids |
| NOTE | Several species of lady beetles are beneficial to agriculture since individuals can feed on a large number of potentially damaging aphids |

ADULT LENGTH
³/₁₆–⁵/₁₆ in
(4.2–7.6 mm)

448

*HIPPODAMIA CONVERGENS*
# CONVERGENT LADY BEETLE
GUÉRIN-MÉNEVILLE, 1842

Actual size

Like most ladybird beetles, the Convergent Lady Beetle is a predator of stenorrhynchan Hemiptera. Adults and larvae are very common throughout the species' range and can be found feeding on aphids, with mature larvae consuming up to 50 aphids per day. Many ladybird beetles, although not this species, have been actively introduced across the world as biological control agents and, likewise, are good species to have in the home garden to reduce plant pests. The Convergent Lady Beetle also forms impressive aggregations prior to overwintering and can be found by the thousands in forests, and often around homes where temperatures are warmer than the ambient temperature.

### RELATED SPECIES

There are about 35 species of *Hippodamia* in the Holarctic, and some have been introduced elsewhere (such as the nearly cosmopolitan species *H. variegata*). There are 18 species in North America, some of which—including the Convergent Lady Beetle—come in a variety of color forms.

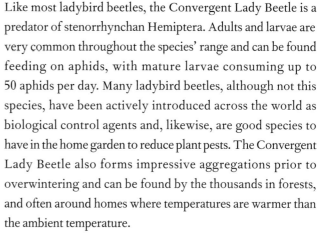

**The Convergent Lady Beetle** is ovoid, convex, and glabrous, and has a black pronotum with white stripes and a white margin. The extreme base of the elytra is also white, but the remaining portion is orange with one to six black spots and a short black stripe along the base of the elytral suture, which may sometimes be elongate and curved laterad.

| FAMILY | Corylophidae |
|---|---|
| SUBFAMILY | Periptyctinae |
| DISTRIBUTION | Australian: southern Victoria |
| MACROHABITAT | *Eucalyptus*, southern beech (*Nothofagus* spp.), and *Acacia* forests |
| MICROHABITAT | Leaf litter |
| FEEDING HABITS | Adults and larvae are assumed to be fungus-feeders |
| NOTE | All species of *Periptychus* occur in eastern Australia from northeastern Queensland south to Tasmania |

ADULT LENGTH
$^{1}/_{16}$–$^{1}/_{8}$ in
(2.3–2.8 mm)

*PERIPTYCTUS VICTORIENSIS*
# PERIPTYCTUS VICTORIENSIS
TOMASZEWSKA & ŚLIPIŃSKI, 2002

449

The subfamily Periptyctinae is restricted to eastern Australia, but the habits of its members are largely unknown. It includes relatively common winged species that are collected in flight-intercept traps, and rare wingless species collected in leaf litter and in pitfall traps. The first member of the genus to be named, *Periptyctus russulus*, may indicate a relationship with fungi (the genus *Russula* is a common group of mushrooms), but most other members of the family Corylophidae are also fungus-feeders, with few records of species feeding on other types of food. Individuals of *P. victoriensis* have been extracted from leaf litter in Snow Gum (*Eucalyptus pauciflora*) woodlands at elevations up to 4,660 ft (1,420 m).

### RELATED SPECIES

There are three genera of Peryptictinae and 23 species of *Periptyctus*. Many are quite distinctive, based on body color, presence or absence of markings on the pronotum and elytra, overall body shape, and the form of the pronotum.

**Periptyctus victoriensis** is a brachypterous species that is oblong, weakly convex, and black and orange in color. It is glabrous but it has a short covering of setae. The head is largely hidden and is inserted into the prothorax, while the pronotum has a well-developed sublateral line or carina. The elytra have weakly prominent humeri.

Actual size

| FAMILY | Corylophidae |
|---|---|
| SUBFAMILY | Corylophinae |
| DISTRIBUTION | Nearctic: southern Canada and some states in the USA |
| MACROHABITAT | Grasslands |
| MICROHABITAT | Soil |
| FEEDING HABITS | Feeds on decomposing plant material and spores of fungi |
| NOTE | Beetles in this family are often referred to as minute hooded beetles since several species, including *Arthrolips decolor*, are physically very small, and the head of the adults can be completely hidden under the hood-like pronotum |

ADULT LENGTH
¹⁄₃₂ in
(0.8–1 mm)

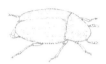

450

*ARTHROLIPS DECOLOR*
# ARTHROLIPS DECOLOR
(LECONTE, 1852)

Actual size

The taxonomy of the Corylophidae, which includes adults generally ¹⁄₃₂–¹⁄₈ in (0.5–2.5 mm), has undergone revision in the last decade, with morphologists and molecular systematists using new tools to generate phylogenetic hypotheses to classify the natural groupings of its members. Although miniaturization, exemplified in this and other groups of beetles, can be a hindrance to performing various types of studies, it is generally considered as a key innovation enabling individuals to access new resources (such as food and niches) and possibly avoiding predation. The biology of *Arthrolips* is largely unknown but adults have been found in association with the sac fungus *Nummulariola* (Ascomycota).

RELATED SPECIES

There are almost 30 species of *Arthrolips* worldwide, with most species being described from the Holarctic Realm, but a revision is needed. The genus is one of two in the tribe Parmulini (*Clypastraea* being the other), a group in which the larval tergite 9 has sclerotized asperities. The anterior margin of the prosternum of *Arthrolips* lacks antennal slots, which are present in *Clypastraea*.

**Arthrolips decolor** is flattened, light brown to tan, and weakly convex, with a very fine covering of setae. The head is covered by the semicircular pronotum, which, like that of many corylophids, has a clear or pale apical area that functions as a window while the beetle is not in flight. The last abdominal segment is exposed.

| | |
|---|---|
| FAMILY | Akalyptoischiidae |
| SUBFAMILY | |
| DISTRIBUTION | Nearctic: South Coast Ranges, Transverse Ranges, Peninsular Ranges, Mojave Desert, eastern Sierra Nevada, and White Mountains, California |
| MACROHABITAT | Oak (*Quercus* spp.) forests |
| MICROHABITAT | Nests of *Neotoma* woodrats and leaf litter |
| FEEDING HABITS | Adults and larvae are probably fungus-feeders |
| NOTE | The genus name is derived from the Greek words *akalyptos* ("open") and *ischion* ("hip") and refers to the unusual "open" procoxal cavities visible from the ventral side on adult individuals |

ADULT LENGTH
$\frac{1}{32}$–$\frac{1}{16}$ in
(1.2–1.5 mm)

*AKALYPTOISCHION ATRICHOS*
# AKALYPTOISCHION ATRICHOS
ANDREWS, 1976

451

Actual size

*Akalyptoischion* is a strange latridiid-like genus and the only member of the family Akalyptoischiidae, endemic to California and Baja California, an area of high endemicity. The biology of the genus is poorly known, but species have been collected from leaf litter of hardwoods (e.g., *Quercus*, *Ilex*, *Rhus* spp.) and conifers (e.g., *Pinus* spp.) as well as in nests (e.g., *Neotoma* woodrats). All species are flightless, and are thought to be restricted in range due to their limited flight capability. *Akalyptoischion atrichos* occurs in a broad range of habitats including moist low-elevation coastal woodland, dry high-elevation pine forests (up to 11,500 ft/3,500 m) as well as dry desert pinyon-pine areas.

## RELATED SPECIES

There are 24 species of *Akalyptoischion*. The genus can be distinguished from similar-looking latridiids by the open procoxal cavities and the pseudosegmentation of the 3-3-3 tarsi in some of the species. *Akalyptoischion atrichos* has a relatively large geographic range and can be distinguished from other members of the genus by the single median puncture on abdominal ventrite 1.

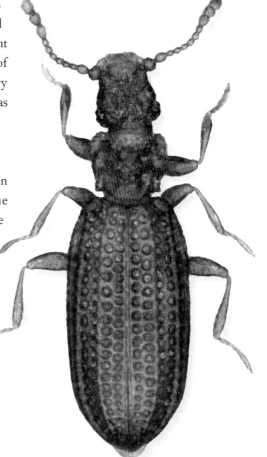

**Akalyptoischion atrichos** is an elongate yellowish to dark brown beetle with a rugose, glabrous cuticle. The head has a distinct neck, the antennal insertions are hidden in dorsal view, and the antenna itself has a three-segmented club. The eyes have four to five facets and the elytra have six punctate striae.

| FAMILY | Latridiidae |
|---|---|
| SUBFAMILY | Latridiinae |
| DISTRIBUTION | Probably native to Europe, but now nearly cosmopolitan |
| MACROHABITAT | Temperate forests and grasslands |
| MICROHABITAT | Leaf litter, dry habitats, and stored products |
| FEEDING HABITS | Adults and larvae are fungus-feeders |
| NOTE | Found commonly in stored products |

ADULT LENGTH
¹/₃₂– ¹/₁₆ in
(1.3–1.5 mm)

*DIENERELLA FILUM*
# MINUTE BROWN
# SCAVENGER BEETLE
(AUBÉ, 1850)

Actual size

Latridiidae are found mainly in drier habitats and are generally associated with decaying vegetation. Latridiinae is the more extravagant subfamily, with most members having grooves, carinae, and foveae on their body. These surface features are associated with waxes that build up on the dorsal and ventral surfaces. Reports in the literature suggest that *Dienerella filum* can feed on spores of *Ustilago* (smut fungi parasitic on grasses) and that at least some of the spores are able to germinate after passing through the digestive system of the beetle. This species has also been found in high numbers in air-conditioning and refrigeration systems, which is an indication that fungus is present in the cooling systems.

RELATED SPECIES

*Dienerella* contains about 40 species worldwide, these split into two subgenera; *D. filum* is placed in the nominate subgenus. Members of *Dienerella* can be distinguished from other highly sculptured genera by their relatively few eye facets (fewer than 20), and by the length of the trochanters, the form of the metaventrite, and details of the antennae.

**The Minute Brown Scavenger Beetle** is an elongate, flattened, rugose, dark to light brown beetle. The antennae are three-segmented and the insertions are visible in dorsal view. The pronotum is widened anteriorly and is notched near the middle. The elytra is about three times longer than the pronotum and has seriate punctation. The tarsal formula is 3-3-3.

| FAMILY | Latridiidae |
|---|---|
| SUBFAMILY | Corticariinae |
| DISTRIBUTION | Cosmopolitan, but may be European in origin |
| MACROHABITAT | Forests, grasslands, human habitats |
| MICROHABITAT | Drier habitats |
| FEEDING HABITS | Adults and larvae are fungus-feeders |
| NOTE | A widespread yet minor pest of stored products |

ADULT LENGTH
$^1/_{32}$–$^1/_{16}$ in
(1.2–2.2 mm)

*CORTICARIA SERRATA*
# COSMOPOLITAN MOLD BEETLE
(PAYKULL, 1798)

453

Actual size

The Cosmopolitan Mold Beetle is one of hundreds of beetle species that are pests of stored products. The adults and larvae feed on fungi that grow in damp conditions and can be transported over great distances; for example, they have been found in cargo ships carrying wheat and barley. In addition to stored products, individuals have been found in moldy plant debris, in dry porcupine dung, and have been reared from dead wood. Although most adults of *Corticaria serrata* are macropterous (with complete flight wings), some individuals have strongly reduced flight wings. Reasons for this reduction in some individuals are still unknown.

## RELATED SPECIES
Corticariines are easily separated from latridiines in that the clypeus and frons are on the same plane, but the genera within the subfamily may be difficult to distinguish. Luckily, *Corticaria* can be recognized by the presence of deep foveae in front of the front coxae, which may be used as mycangia (fungus-holding organs).

**The Cosmopolitan Mold Beetle** is a somewhat elongate, convex, dark to light brown species with a covering of setae. The antennae are three-segmented and the insertions are visible in dorsal view. The pronotum has teeth along the lateral carina, and the elytra, which are slightly wider than the pronotum, have distinct seriate punctation and rows of setae.

| FAMILY | Mycetophagidae |
|---|---|
| SUBFAMILY | Mycetophaginae |
| DISTRIBUTION | Holarctic: northern Europe, North America (has now been found throughout the World in stored agricultural produce) |
| MACROHABITAT | Various |
| MICROHABITAT | Moldy plant/animal materials, including stored food-products |
| FEEDING HABITS | Fungivorous |
| NOTE | Often occurs in synanthropic situations, where it is an indicator of substandard storage conditions |

ADULT LENGTH
⅛–³⁄₁₆ in
(3.3–4 mm)

454

*MYCETOPHAGUS QUADRIGUTTATUS*
# SPOTTED HAIRY FUNGUS BEETLE
MÜLLER, 1821

Actual size

The Spotted Hairy Fungus Beetle is found across a wide swath of the Northern Hemisphere in habitats ranging from forests to grain elevators. The species is common in synanthropic (human-associated) situations. Both adults and larvae feed on fungal spores and hyphae growing on animal and vegetable substrates. They are a common component of the stored-product pest fauna in grain-producing and storage areas. Their presence in stored food-products is an indication of poor hygiene and moisture control since their occurrence is conditional on mold growth. They are capable of transporting spores from contaminated to uncontaminated stored products.

## RELATED SPECIES

Several other similar beetles that occur in the same circumstances may be confused with the Spotted Hairy Fungus Beetle. These include various silken fungus beetles (Cryptophagidae), minute fungus beetles (Latridiidae), and another mycetophagid, the Hairy Fungus Beetle, *Typhaea stercorea*. At least 35 additional Palearctic and 15 Nearctic species are known, and many are difficult to distinguish without specialized literature and/or examination of type specimens in museums.

**The Spotted Hairy Fungus Beetle** is an elongate, oval, finely pubescent brown beetle with four to six yellowish spots on the elytra. The spots are somewhat variable and may coalesce anteriorly into a single irregular spot on each elytron. Adult beetles possess a pair of distinct depressions along the posterior margin of the pronotum.

| FAMILY | Pterogeniidae |
|---|---|
| SUBFAMILY | |
| DISTRIBUTION | Oriental: Malaysia |
| MACROHABITAT | Tropical forests |
| MICROHABITAT | Fungus-infiltrated dead wood |
| FEEDING HABITS | Fungivorous |
| NOTE | The extremely elongate first antennal articles look superficially like greatly enlarged mandibles |

ADULT LENGTH
$\frac{1}{16}$ in
(1.8–2.4 mm)

HISTANOCERUS FLEAGLEI

# HISTANOCERUS FLEAGLEI

LAWRENCE, 1977

455

Actual size

Little is known of the life-history details of this obscure family of beetles. This species is based on adults collected from *Amauroderma* polypore fungi. Larvae of *Histanocerus fleaglei* and other members of the genus have also been recorded from polypores. Many species in the family are known only from adults collected in forest litter. The family is restricted to southern and southeastern Asia. The placement of this and other early described genera varied among several families until the Pterogeniidae was erected. Its relationship to other families in the tenebrionid group is unclear.

## RELATED SPECIES

*Histanocerus* is the largest genus in the Pterogeniidae, with 14 species scattered throughout Southeast Asia. They differ from each other in subtle details of external anatomy, size, and antennal segmentation. Adults are similar to those of *Pterogenius*, but differ in the details of the antennal insertions, shape of antennal articles, and other structures.

**Histanocerus fleaglei** adults are small, short-ovate, setose brown beetles, with the pronotal base being noticeably broader than the shoulders of the elytra. Only the males possess the extremely elongate and hooked scape of the antennae and their function is unknown, but in both males and females the scape extends beyond the base of the pedicel (second article).

| FAMILY | Pterogeniidae |
|---|---|
| SUBFAMILY | |
| DISTRIBUTION | Oriental: Sri Lanka |
| MACROHABITAT | Forests |
| MICROHABITAT | Fungus-infiltrated dead wood |
| FEEDING HABITS | Fungivorous |
| NOTE | This beetle's mandibles have been likened to the teeth of elephants, suited to grinding tough, fibrous food substrates |

ADULT LENGTH
⅛ in
(3–3.3 mm)

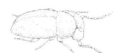

*PTEROGENIUS NIETNERI*
# PTEROGENIUS NIETNERI
CANDÈZE, 1861

Among members of this family, only this species and *Histanocerus pubescens* have been studied in sufficient detail to document life histories and allow descriptions of immature stages. Larvae of *Pterogenius nietneri* were collected in a dark, tough polypore, possibly a species of *Ganoderma*. The structure of the mandibles is suited to grinding and tearing the tough fibrous host tissue sufficient for ingestion, and the author noted structural similarities of the molar surfaces to those of elephants. Gut-content analysis confirmed this feeding strategy. Adults were also sifted from various forest-litter substrates.

RELATED SPECIES

Only two species are included in *Pterogenius*, both occurring in Sri Lanka. *Pterogenius nietneri* differs from *P. besucheti* in that the adult males possess a much more broadly expanded head and in structural differences in the antennae. *Pterogenius nietneri* is the larger of the two species. *Histanocerus* lacks the expanded male head, but possesses modifications of the antennal scapes that are lacking in *Pterogenius*.

Actual size

**Pterogenius nietneri** is unique among almost all beetles in possessing remarkably expanded heads in males. This feature is seen in only a few other beetle species scattered among various families. The heads of large males may exceed the width of the pronotum. The head is not so expanded in females. Otherwise, the beetle has a generalized small, ovate body form

| FAMILY | Ciidae |
|---|---|
| SUBFAMILY | Ciinae |
| DISTRIBUTION | Neotropical: Central America |
| MACROHABITAT | Tropical forests |
| MICROHABITAT | Woody polypore fungi on dead wood |
| FEEDING HABITS | Fungivorous |
| NOTE | Adult males use their long head horn like a crowbar to dislodge opponents during combat |

ADULT LENGTH
¹⁄₁₆ in
(1.5–2 mm)

*CIS TRICORNIS*
# CIS TRICORNIS
(GORHAM, 1883)

457

Actual size

As with most members of the family, *Cis* species feed on woody polypore fungi as both adults and larvae. The genera *Polyporus*, *Trametes*, and *Ganoderma* appear frequently in the lists of known hosts for various members of the genus. Observations of fighting behavior in males of this species confirmed the use of the frontal horn as a pry bar. The beetle pushes it beneath the opponent's body and pries upwards to dislodge it. In other cases of fighting males they simply pushed and shoved their opponent backward.

RELATED SPECIES

*Cis* is an enormous genus containing approximately 350 species among 24 species groups, including the *C. tricornis* group of three North and South American species. Species are largely separated based on the shapes and sizes of body punctures, and length, density, and orientation of pubescence on the dorsal surfaces; these differences can be quite subtle.

**Cis tricornis** is a small, cylindrical beetle with a classically *Triceratops*-like array of horns in adult males. The central head horn is the most obvious, supplemented by two smaller pronotal horns. As in most horn-bearing ciids, major males possess larger horns and minor males have smaller horns, with females lacking horns altogether.

| | |
|---|---|
| FAMILY | Ciidae |
| SUBFAMILY | Ciinae |
| DISTRIBUTION | Palearctic: northern Eurasia |
| MACROHABITAT | Forests |
| MICROHABITAT | Polypore fungi on dead wood |
| FEEDING HABITS | Fungivorous |
| NOTE | Oversize, asymmetrical mandibles are typical of adult males in several species of the genus |

ADULT LENGTH
¹⁄₁₆ in
(2–2.5 mm)

*OCTOTEMNUS MANDIBULARIS*
# OCTOTEMNUS MANDIBULARIS
(GYLLENHAL, 1813)

Actual size

Members of the family feed as both adults and larvae on dense, fibrous, wood-destroying fungi. Larvae bore into the tissues of woody-polypore fruiting bodies of several fungus genera, including *Trametes* and *Ganoderma*, and adults occur on the outer sporulating surfaces. Adults may be reared by harvesting fungal fruiting bodies and holding them in a ventilated container at room temperature. Adult emergence may require many months and may occur during a narrow annual seasonal window. Adults orient to their respective host fungi by following odor trails of volatile chemicals produced by the fungi.

### RELATED SPECIES

About 16 species of *Octotemnus* are known, mostly in Eurasia, with a single described species in the United States. An undescribed species of *Octotemnus* has been introduced to the United States and is an invasive non-native species that may be displacing native polypore-inhabiting ciids. Species are distinguished by sizes and shapes of male secondary sexual characters, differences in surface punctures, and other details.

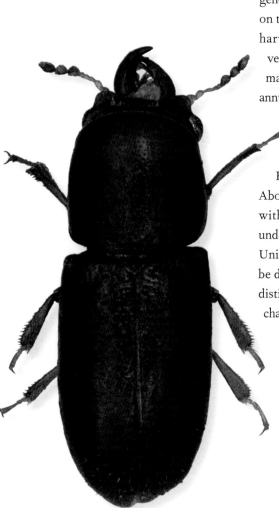

**Octotemnus mandibularis** adults are small, cylindrical brown beetles with eight-segmented antennae. The enlarged mandibles are polymorphic. Males may possess dramatically enlarged mandibles (major males) or somewhat less enlarged mandibles (minor males). Females possess normally proportioned mandibles for their size. The male mandibles are probably used in sexual combat, as in other beetles with forebody horns or enlarged mandibles.

| FAMILY | Tetratomidae |
|---|---|
| SUBFAMILY | Penthinae |
| DISTRIBUTION | Nearctic: eastern North America |
| MACROHABITAT | Forests |
| MICROHABITAT | Fungus-infiltrated dead wood |
| FEEDING HABITS | Fungivorous |
| NOTE | One of the two largest members of the family Tetratomidae in North America |

ADULT LENGTH
½–⁹⁄₁₆ in
(12–15 mm)

*PENTHE OBLIQUATA*
# PENTHE OBLIQUATA
(FABRICIUS, 1801)

459

This species is one of two large tetratomids that occur throughout forested habitats in eastern North America. Both species are typically found under loose bark of large fallen branches, stumps, and logs of deciduous trees. The larvae burrow through, and feed on, fruiting bodies of polypore fungi. Adults may be encountered any time of the year under bark of fungus-infiltrated logs and stumps. Many tetratomids deposit eggs in bark during the fall. The resulting small larvae overwinter, then develop in fungal hosts the following spring and summer.

RELATED SPECIES

The two species of *Penthe* are nearly identical to each other in size, shape, and overall color. Live adults of *P. obliquata* possess an orange scutellum that is immediately obvious when individuals are discovered. *Penthe pimelia* possesses a black scutellum and the remainder of the body is also black. No other members of the family in eastern North America approach the size of these two species.

Actual size

**Penthe obliquata** adults are medium-size, elongate, oval beetles bearing dense coverings of coarse black pubescence that give them a velvety appearance. In fact, the related species, *P. pimelia*, is commonly known as the Velvety Fungus Beetle. The scutellum of *P. obliquata*, although a relatively small structure, stands out from the remainder of the surface due to the bright yellowish-orange pubescence in live specimens.

| FAMILY | Melandryidae |
|---|---|
| SUBFAMILY | Melandryinae |
| DISTRIBUTION | Palearctic: Europe |
| MACROHABITAT | Forests |
| MICROHABITAT | Under bark, and on logs and standing dead trees |
| FEEDING HABITS | Xylophagous on fungus-infiltrated wood |
| NOTE | A familiar and widespread species in European native forests |

ADULT LENGTH
⅜–⅝ in
(9–16 mm)

460

*MELANDRYA CARABOIDES*
# MELANDRYA CARABOIDES
(LINNAEUS, 1760)

Adults of this characteristic European beetle are active throughout the spring and summer months. The adults may be found on or under logs and loose bark, or at large during periods of dispersion. Larvae feed on moist, rotting, fungus-infiltrated wood of various species of deciduous trees. The species is considered an important indicator of mature native forests since the larvae must have relatively large-size woody debris in advanced stages of decay for development. The association with wood-destroying fungi is a common life-history pattern for the majority of melandryid species whose life histories have been studied.

RELATED SPECIES

At least 24 species of the genus occur in various parts of Eurasia, with a single species in North America. *Melandrya caraboides* is one of the largest and most commonly encountered. Other species may be separated on the basis of size, color, nature of external pubescence, and other characters. Distribution is an important guide to determining species. The species may be confused with superficially similar carabid and tenebrionid beetles.

**Melandrya caraboides** adults are elongate, parallel-sided beetles with a bluish-black, metallic dorsal surface, and black to reddish-brown appendages. The large maxillary palpi are prominently visible beneath the antennae. The tarsal segmentation, as in other members of the tenebrionoid group of beetle families, is 5-5-4 front to rear; the large size of these beetles makes this character easy to observe.

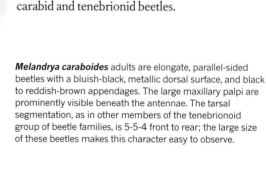

Actual size

| FAMILY | Mordellidae |
|---|---|
| SUBFAMILY | Mordellinae |
| DISTRIBUTION | Nearctic: endemic to Florida |
| MACROHABITAT | In or near forests |
| MICROHABITAT | Adults are found on flowers; larvae live in rotten wood |
| FEEDING HABITS | Adults feed on pollen; larvae develop in rotten logs (e.g., *Quercus* spp.) |
| NOTE | Although their adults are quite different morphologically, members of the families Melandryidae and Mordellidae are considered closely related based on similarities of their larvae |

ADULT LENGTH
⅜–⁷⁄₁₆ in
(10–11.2 mm)

*HOSHIHANANOMIA INFLAMMATA*

# HOSHIHANANOMIA INFLAMMATA
(LECONTE, 1862)

461

*Hoshihananomia* belongs to the diverse tribe Mordellini, which contains approximately 50 genera in all regions of the world. These beetles are characterized by their wedge-shaped body, which is typically widest near the base of the prothorax, and the spine-line extension of the abdomen beyond the apex of the elytra. Adults of *H. inflammata* are fully winged and are most efficiently collected using flight-intercept and Malaise traps, or they can be reared from rotten oak logs. The related *H. octopunctata* have larvae that develop in decaying tissues of American Beech (*Fagus grandifolia*) and oaks (*Quercus* spp.).

Actual size

## RELATED SPECIES
The cosmopolitan genus *Hoshihananomia* includes more than 50 species worldwide, only three of which occur in America. The other species are *H. octopunctata*, broadly distributed in eastern North America from Texas northeast to Quebec and Ontario; and *H. perlineata*, restricted to Arizona and New Mexico. Differences in the color pattern of the elytra are useful to separate the North American species.

**Hoshihananomia inflammata** is an elongate, darkly colored beetle with a broad pronotum and tapering elytra. The pronotum and elytra have distinct patches of yellowish-orange setae that are pressed against the cuticle. The pale setal patches are especially noticeable near the base of the pronotum, and near the apex and base (around the black scutellum) of the elytra. The rather long, posteriorly projecting extension of the abdomen is narrow and pointed apically.

| FAMILY | Mordellidae |
|---|---|
| SUBFAMILY | Mordellinae |
| DISTRIBUTION | Palearctic |
| MACROHABITAT | Forests, including open areas |
| MICROHABITAT | Adults are found on flowers; larvae live in dead wood |
| FEEDING HABITS | Adults feed on pollen; larvae feed on dead wood |
| NOTE | A rare and vulnerable species in parts of its range |

ADULT LENGTH
¼–⁵⁄₁₆ in
(6.5–8 mm)

462

MORDELLA HOLOMELAENA HOLOMELAENA
# MORDELLA HOLOMELAENA HOLOMELAENA
APFELBECK, 1914

Actual size

Mordellidae includes approximately 1,500 species worldwide, classified in about 85 genera. Species in this family are commonly referred to as tumbling flower beetles because the adults typically tumble about by moving their hind legs rapidly when disturbed, and also because they occur mostly on flowers. *Mordella holomelaena holomelaena* has been found in numbers in old thin oak (*Quercus* spp.), birch (*Betula* spp.), and sometimes aspen (*Populus* spp.) logging residues. In a review of threatened beetles in Great Britain published in 2014, it was determined that this beetle occurs in severely fragmented populations and hence it was given the conservation status of "Vulnerable."

## RELATED SPECIES

The genus *Mordella* belongs to the tribe Mordellini and includes in excess of 500 species worldwide, more than 60 of which occur in the Palearctic Realm. In addition to the broadly distributed *Mordella holomelaena holomelaena*, one other subspecies known to occur in east Siberia, the Russian Far East, and Mongolia is recognized as valid: *M. h. sibirica*. Differences in the antennae, eyes, mouthparts, color pattern, and male genitalia are useful to separate the species.

**Mordella holomelaena holomelaena** is an elongate wedge-shaped beetle with a black cuticle covered with short, dark setae pressed against its surface. The tergite of abdominal segment VII is narrowly produced posteriorly beyond the apex of the elytra and ends in a sharp point. The head is abruptly constricted behind the eyes and is strongly bent downward under the prothorax in live individuals, such that it is generally scarcely visible from above. Their tarsal formula is 5-5-4.

| FAMILY | Ripiphoridae |
|---|---|
| SUBFAMILY | Ripiphorinae |
| DISTRIBUTION | Nearctic and Neotropical: Canada (southern Ontario) and USA (New Hampshire and New York south to Florida and west to Iowa, Kansas and Texas); Central America from Mexico south to Panama |
| MACROHABITAT | Open habitats |
| MICROHABITAT | Adults are found on flowers; larvae are parasites of hymenopterans |
| FEEDING HABITS | Adults presumably feed on nectar; larvae feed on hymenopterans |
| NOTE | *Macrosiagon* is the most diverse genus in the family Ripiphoridae |

ADULT LENGTH
³/₁₆–½ in
(5–12 mm)

*MACROSIAGON LIMBATUM*

# MACROSIAGON LIMBATUM

(FABRICIUS, 1781)

463

Actual size

All species in the family Ripiphoridae with known biology are internal parasites of immature stages of other insects in at least part of their life cycle. Known hosts for the species of *Macrosiagon* include several families of aculeate hymenopterans (Scoliidae, Halictidae, Tiphiidae, Vespidae, Crabronidae, Sphecidae, Apidae, and Pompilidae). Adults of *Macrosiagon* have greatly prolonged proboscis-like mouthparts and it is therefore likely that they suck nectar. The adults of *M. limbatum* are active in the summer and visit flowers such as elderberries (*Sambucus* spp.) and goldenrods (*Solidago* spp.). The larva of *M. limbatum* has been reported as a parasite of the wasp family Crabronidae (e.g., *Cerceris*).

## RELATED SPECIES

Two genera are recognized in the tribe Macrosiagonini: *Metoecus*, with five species in the Palearctic and Oriental realms; and *Macrosiagon*. More than 150 species have been described in *Macrosiagon*. Morphological characters such as the insertion of the antennae anterior to the eyes and the presence of a posterior lobe pronotum distinguish *Macrosiagon* from other genera in the Ripiphoridae in North America.

**Macrosiagon limbatum** is a rather narrow and wedge-shaped beetle with a dorsoventrally elongate head. The body has a contrasting black and orange coloration pattern. The antennae have two rows of comb-like projections in males and are serrate in females. The elytra are held together along the midline near the base in live adults but diverge near the apex. The flight wings are fully developed and partially folded apically (although the degree of folding varies in preserved individuals).

| FAMILY | Ripiphoridae |
|---|---|
| SUBFAMILY | Ripiphorinae |
| DISTRIBUTION | Nearctic: southwestern United States |
| MACROHABITAT | Dry habitats |
| MICROHABITAT | Adults occur on vegetation and flowers; larvae live in the colony of their host |
| FEEDING HABITS | Adult feeding habits are uncertain; larvae are presumably parasites of bee colonies but the host is unknown |
| NOTE | The flight wings of species in this genus are not folded beneath the elytra, as in most other beetles |

ADULT LENGTH
³⁄₈–⁷⁄₁₆ in
(9–11 mm)

464

*RIPIPHORUS VIERECKI*
# RIPIPHORUS VIERECKI
(FALL, 1907)

Actual size

**Ripiphorus vierecki** is an unusual-looking beetle with contrasting black and yellowish-orange coloration and elytra that are reduced to short, scalelike plates. The antennae are flabellate and originate near the top of the large eyes. The unfolded flight wings, which have a noticeable darker area, typically rest partially overlapping across the abdomen in live individuals, in a manner similar to that in flies (Diptera). The tarsal claws are pectinate.

The characteristic genus *Ripiphorus* occurs worldwide except for Australia. In North America, it is the second most commonly encountered genus after *Macrosiagon*. The life history of most species in the genus has not been investigated thoroughly, although a few generalities can be gleaned from some of the better-known species. Females lay a small number of eggs in unopened flower buds. The eggs hatch when the buds open and the active first-instar larva then attaches itself to a visiting bee, which carries it to its nest. The larvae are parasites of ground-nesting bees. The adults of *R. vierecki* are thought to have a flight pattern (hovering and bobbing up and down) similar to that of bee flies (Bombyliidae).

RELATED SPECIES
Approximately 70 species are known in *Ripiphorus*, of which about 30 occur in America north of Mexico. The poor state of taxonomy of this group is in need of a thorough review. Characteristics of the tarsus, tarsal claws, coloration pattern, and punctation of the cuticle are generally used to separate the species. Some species, especially those associated with *R. fasciatus*, cannot be identified with confidence based on existing identification keys.

| FAMILY | Zopheridae |
|---|---|
| SUBFAMILY | Colydiinae |
| DISTRIBUTION | Nearctic: southern USA (Alabama, Florida, Georgia, South Carolina, Louisiana, North Carolina, Tennessee) |
| MACROHABITAT | Forests |
| MICROHABITAT | In cylindrical holes under bark |
| FEEDING HABITS | Adults and larvae are predators of wood-boring weevils (Curculionidae, subfamily Platypodinae) |
| NOTE | This species is considered a beneficial insect since it feeds on wood-boring beetles. |

ADULT LENGTH
¼ in
(6.3–7 mm)

*NEMATIDIUM FILIFORME*

# NEMATIDIUM FILIFORME

LECONTE, 1863

465

The majority of species in the subfamily Colydiinae feed on dead plant material and fungi, and are associated with dead logs. However, some groups, such as the tribe Nematidiini, have developed predatory feeding habits. The cylindrical genus *Nematidium* is known to occur in subtropical and tropical regions, where it feeds on the larvae of wood-boring weevils in galleries under bark. Females in *Nematidium* differ slightly from males in having a more elongate labrum. Adults of *N. filiforme* have well-developed flight wings and can be attracted to mercury vapor as well as ultraviolet lights. These beetles are uncommonly encountered.

## RELATED SPECIES

*Nematidium*, which includes more than ten species in the Americas, India, Indonesia, and the Australian Realm, is the only genus in the tribe Nematidiini. *Nematidium filiforme* is the only species in the genus in North America. Its distinctive body shape and the visible base of the mandibles (when the head is observed from the front) will easily distinguish it from other Colydiinae species in the region.

Actual size

**Nematidium filiforme** is a very narrow, cylindrical beetle with a glabrous reddish-brown body and a pronotum that is slightly curved inward near the middle. The antennae have a distinct short, two-segmented club. Grooves beneath the antennae are distinct. The rather large, circular eyes do not protrude from the side of the head. The tarsal formula is 4-4-4.

| FAMILY | Zopheridae |
|---|---|
| SUBFAMILY | Colydiinae |
| DISTRIBUTION | Australian: New Zealand (both main islands) |
| MACROHABITAT | Forests |
| MICROHABITAT | On tree trunks or under bark |
| FEEDING HABITS | Adults and larvae are thought to feed on molds under bark |
| NOTE | Adults of some Australian and Papuan species in the genus *Prisoderus* (e.g., *P. phytophorus*) have a complex dorsal surface that supports a growth of cryptogamic plants, giving the beetles a greenish color |

**ADULT LENGTH**
⁵⁄₁₆ in
(7.8–8 mm)

466

*PRISTODERUS ANTARCTICUS*
# PRISTODERUS ANTARCTICUS
(WHITE, 1846)

Actual size

The feeding habits of species in the tribe Synchitini, to which *Pristoderus* belongs, seem to vary, as some species feed on rotten wood and cambial tissue under bark while others are found in leaf litter and probably feed on decaying vegetation or fungi. Another group, which includes Australian and Papuan species in *Pristoderus*, is thought to contain lichen-feeders. Adults of *P. antarcticus* occur on standing dead tree trunks and have also been found under loose bark. Larvae found in association with some adults have tentatively been assigned to this species but they have not been formally described in the literature.

RELATED SPECIES
*Pristoderus* is one of the largest and most diverse genera within the tribe Synchitini and occurs in Chile, New Zealand, New Caledonia, New Guinea, and Australia. The genera *Syncalus* and *Isotarphius* are very similar but have a broad process between the hind coxae, as opposed to a narrow process with a pointed apex in *Pristoderus*.

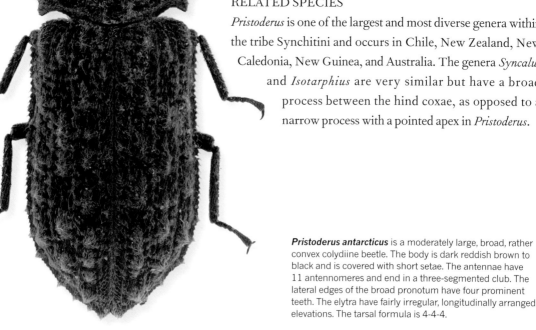

**Pristoderus antarcticus** is a moderately large, broad, rather convex colydiine beetle. The body is dark reddish brown to black and is covered with short setae. The antennae have 11 antennomeres and end in a three-segmented club. The lateral edges of the broad pronotum have four prominent teeth. The elytra have fairly irregular, longitudinally arranged elevations. The tarsal formula is 4-4-4.

| FAMILY | Zopheridae |
|---|---|
| SUBFAMILY | Zopherinae |
| DISTRIBUTION | Nearctic: El Dorado County, California, USA |
| MACROHABITAT | Western North American coniferous forests, at approximately 5,000 ft (1,500 m) altitude |
| MICROHABITAT | Dead wood and associated bracket fungus |
| FEEDING HABITS | Adults apparently feed on decaying bracket fungus such as Sulfur Polypore (*Laetiporus sulphureus*); larvae presumably tunnel in rotting wood |
| NOTE | Has unique grooves on the dorsal surface of the pronotum |

ADULT LENGTH
³⁄₁₆ in
(3.9–5.2 mm)

*USECHIMORPHA MONTANUS*

# USECHIMORPHA MONTANUS

DOYEN & LAWRENCE, 1979

467

Actual size

The tribe Usechini contains only two genera, *Usechimorpha* from western USA and Canada, and *Usechus*, which occurs on the west coast of the United States and in Japan. The males of *Usechimorpha montanus* possess a deep pit filled with setae on their submentum (mouthparts). Such structures are found in males in many beetle groups and can appear on various body parts such as the head, the prothorax, or the abdomen. Although this has not been confirmed in *U. montanus*, these structures may be involved with the production, release, and dissemination of pheromones.

## RELATED SPECIES

Both Usechini genera differ from others in the subfamily Zopherinae in having deep cavities for the reception of the antennae on the dorsal surface of their pronotum near the anterior corners. *Usechimorpha montanus* has regular interstriae on the elytra as opposed to raised, tubercle-bearing interstriae on the elytra as in *U. barberi*.

**Usechimorpha montanus** is a rather elongate reddish-brown beetle that is covered in part by curved golden scalelike setae. The head is deeply inserted within the prothorax and is almost invisible in dorsal view. The pronotum has two deep grooves near the anterior corners for the reception of the antennae. Two additional distinct grooves occur near the posterior corners of the pronotum.

| FAMILY | Zopheridae |
|---|---|
| SUBFAMILY | Zopherinae |
| DISTRIBUTION | Neotropical: southern Mexico south to Venezuela and Colombia |
| MACROHABITAT | Forests |
| MICROHABITAT | On or near dead trees |
| FEEDING HABITS | Adults feed on fungi associated with dead wood (such as *Schizophyllum commune*); larvae develop in dead wood |
| NOTE | Live adults are decorated and worn as live brooches in Mexico |

ADULT LENGTH
1⅝–1¹³⁄₁₆ in
(34–46 mm)

468

*ZOPHERUS CHILENSIS*
# MAQUECH
GRAY, 1832

Species in the tribe Zopherini, which includes *Zopherus*, are commonly referred to as "ironclad" beetles because of their incredibly hard exoskeleton. Adults of *Z. chilensis* are long-lived, flightless and can typically be found on the surface of dead trees, where they feed on fungi. In parts of Mexico, live individuals are decorated with brightly colored glass beads and can be sold as pets in local markets. These jeweled individuals can also be worn as a live brooch after a small gold chain attached to the beetle's body is pinned to a piece of clothing. The Maquech is worn as a reminder of a Mayan legend.

RELATED SPECIES

Members of the tribe Zopherini are widely distributed in the Neotropical Realm but are scattered elsewhere, with one genus each in Southeast Asia (*Zopher*), Australia (*Zopherosis*), and southern Africa (*Scoriaderma*). *Zopherus* species are easily recognized by their nine-segmented antennae, with an apical club composed of three fused segments. *Zopherus chilensis* differs from other species in the genus in that its elytra are abruptly bent inward along the sides.

**The Maquech** is a large elongated beetle, usually dull white dorsally except for a small number of black tubercles throughout. The apex of each elytron bears a prominent rounded tubercle. The body is only slightly constricted between the prothorax and the abdomen when compared with other species in the genus. The size and coloration of adult individuals are highly variable.

Actual size

| FAMILY | Chalcodryidae |
|---|---|
| SUBFAMILY | |
| DISTRIBUTION | Australian: North and South islands, New Zealand |
| MACROHABITAT | Cool, wet forests, especially southern beech (*Nothofagus* spp.) forests |
| MICROHABITAT | Adults are usually found on moss- or lichen-covered branches; larvae occur in galleries in dead twigs and branches |
| FEEDING HABITS | On lichens or vegetation attached to bark or wood surfaces |
| NOTE | All species currently placed in this family are restricted to New Zealand |

ADULT LENGTH
½–¹¹⁄₁₆ in
(12.5–16.5 mm)

*CHALCODRYA VARIEGATA*
# CHALCODRYA VARIEGATA
REDTENBACHER, 1868

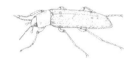

The family Chalcodryidae was created in 1974 to receive enigmatic genera that had previously been treated either as Melandryidae, Zopheridae, or Tenebrionidae. For unknown reasons, individuals of *Chalcodrya* are encountered in nature much more frequently than species in other Chalcodryidae genera. The agile, long-legged larvae of *C. variegata* are known to emerge at night (from the galleries in which they hide during the day) to feed. Although analyses of gut contents of larvae revealed that they primarily eat lichen and moss, they will apparently also feed on other arthropods such as spiders and mites.

### RELATED SPECIES

The family Chalcodryidae includes five species in three genera, *Chalcodrya*, *Philpottia*, and *Onysius*. The genera can be separated by the shape of the eyes (kidney-shaped in *Onysius*, and oval in the other two genera) and by the sculpture on the surface of the elytra (the raised longitudinal costae in *Philpottia* are absent in *Chalcodrya*). The two species of *Chalcodrya* can be separated by the shape of the pronotum and male genitalia.

**Chalcodrya variegata** adults have an elongate, parallel-sided body (more than three times as long as wide). The antennae are relatively short, about as long (or slightly longer) than the combined length of the head and prothorax. Small patches of coarse yellowish pubescence are usually present on the dorsal surface of the head, pronotum, and elytra. The pronotum is noticeably broader than long.

Actual size

| FAMILY | Tenebrionidae |
|---|---|
| SUBFAMILY | Lagriinae |
| DISTRIBUTION | Australian: New Zealand |
| MACROHABITAT | On sandy marine beaches |
| MICROHABITAT | Under washed-up marine algae such as Flapjack (*Carpophyllum aschalocarpum*) |
| FEEDING HABITS | Both adults and larvae feed on marine algae |
| NOTE | The color of adults varies greatly depending on the color of the sand in which they are found |

ADULT LENGTH
¼–⅜ in
(6.5–8.5 mm)

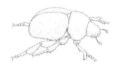

470

*CHAERODES TRACHYSCELIDES*
# CHAERODES TRACHYSCELIDES
WHITE, 1846

Actual size

The small tribe Chaerodini includes *Sphargeris* from Australia and *Chaerodes* from New Zealand. *Chaerodes trachyscelides* is a nocturnal, flightless, sand-burrowing beetle restricted to the intertidal zone of sandy marine beaches in New Zealand. The color of adults, which typically closely matches the sand in which they are found, varies from pale whitish yellow to black. When partially buried pieces of marine algae are pulled out of the sand, adult *C. trachyscelides* beetles fall out with them and quickly burrow into the substrate. Although they have not been described formally, the whitish larvae apparently differ from most other known tenebrionid larvae in having a U-shaped body as opposed to a straight body.

### RELATED SPECIES

With their convex body and legs that are modified to dig into sand, species in the tribe Chaerodini closely resemble those in the distantly related tenebrionid tribe Trachyscelini, which also occur in similar environments. The Australian genus *Sphargeris* includes a single species (*S. physodes*), which is diagnosed by the presence of a five-segmented asymmetrical antennal club as opposed to a three-segmented symmetrical club that can be seen in the two species of *Chaerodes*.

**Chaerodes trachyscelides** has a very convex body, a distinctive three-segmented antennal club, and strongly modified legs for digging in sand. The front tibiae are greatly expanded, have a deep emargination along the outer edge, and are flattened near the apex. The hind femora are greatly expanded and the middle and hind tibiae are distinctly broader at their apex. All legs are covered with stout bristles.

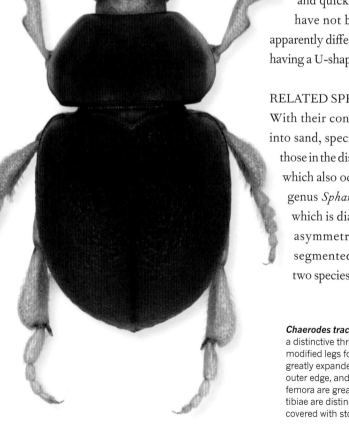

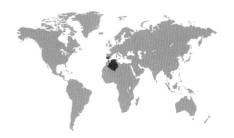

| FAMILY | Tenebrionidae |
|---|---|
| SUBFAMILY | Lagriinae |
| DISTRIBUTION | Palearctic: Portugal, Spain, Corsica, Sardinia, Sicily, Algeria, and Morocco |
| MACROHABITAT | Xeric habitats, from dry forests to sandy areas |
| MICROHABITAT | Under stones, sometimes in close association with ants |
| FEEDING HABITS | Adults probably feed on dead plant matter; larval feeding habits are unknown |
| NOTE | The body shape is thought to mimic seeds that have dropped to the ground |

ADULT LENGTH
⁵⁄₁₆–⁷⁄₁₆ in
(8–11 mm)

*COSSYPHUS HOFFMANNSEGGII*

# COSSYPHUS HOFFMANNSEGGII
HERBST, 1797

471

Actual size

The correct placement of the highly adapted species in the tribe Cossyphini remained enigmatic for a long period; however, recent studies based on internal organs and molecules strongly suggest that they clearly belong to the Lagriinae. The genus *Cossyphus*, which includes more than 30 species and subspecies, occurs in southern Europe and Africa, and extends into India, Southeast Asia, and as far east as Australia. The body shape of these beetles is thought to mimic the winged seeds found on the ground in their habitat. The morphology of *C. hoffmannseggii* is rather variable throughout its range, which has led some coleopterists to recognize different subspecies.

### RELATED SPECIES
*Cossyphus* differs from *Endustomus*, the only other genus in the tribe Cossyphini, by having its head visible in ventral view (in *Endustomus* it is completely concealed). Morphological differences between the two subgenera of *Cossyphus* include whether the elytra have rows of punctures or are smooth, and whether or not the males have a spine on the hind tibia. Males in *Cossyphus* can be separated by characteristics of their last visible abdominal segment.

**Cossyphus hoffmannseggii** adults are light to dark brown, strongly flattened, and oval-shaped. The broad flanges extending outward from the pronotum and elytra can cover the antennae, legs, and head completely. The ventral abdominal segments in this species are not separated by a visible membrane, as is the case for superficially similar beetles such as *Helea spinifer*.

| FAMILY | Tenebrionidae |
|---|---|
| SUBFAMILY | Lagriinae |
| DISTRIBUTION | Oriental: Sri Lanka, India |
| MACROHABITAT | Forests, plantations |
| MICROHABITAT | Usually in dry leaf litter |
| FEEDING HABITS | Adults and larvae feed on fallen leaves |
| NOTE | A significant nuisance pest in and near Rubber Tree (*Hevea brasiliensis*) plantations since adults can aggregate in huge numbers inside and outside buildings |

ADULT LENGTH
¼–⁵⁄₁₆ in
(7–8.5 mm)

472

*LUPROPS TRISTIS*
# RUBBER PLANTATION LITTER BEETLE
(FABRICIUS, 1801)

The life cycle of this nocturnal species takes about 12 months to complete, and includes a nine-month dormant phase. The onset of summer rains, usually in April, triggers huge aggregations of adults before the dormancy phase, especially near plantations of Rubber Trees (*Hevea brasiliensis*). Recent studies report that more than four million individuals can be found on, or in, a single residential building. Adults have fully developed flight wings and are attracted to lights at night. The strongly odorant chemical defense secretions produced by the abdominal glands of adults can also cause discoloration and a slight burn to the skin when the beetles are handled.

## RELATED SPECIES

The tribe Lupropini has a pantropical distribution. *Luprops* includes approximately 80 species that occur from tropical Africa through Asia to Papua New Guinea. A thorough taxonomic revision of this group is needed as there is much morphological variation among species in the genus. *Luprops curticollis* is similar to *L. tristis* but differs in the shape of its eyes, pronotum, and male genitalia.

Actual size

**The Rubber Plantation Litter Beetle** is dark brown to black with the legs and reddish-brown to dark brown antennae. The dorsal surface of the body is covered with short setae. The pronotum is distinctly broader than long, is noticeably narrower than the elytra, and lacks toothlike projections along its lateral edges. The elytra are evenly convex and lack striae.

| FAMILY | Tenebrionidae |
|---|---|
| SUBFAMILY | Nilioninae |
| DISTRIBUTION | Neotropical: Brazil, Ecuador, Paraguay, northern Argentina |
| MACROHABITAT | Forests |
| MICROHABITAT | Usually on tree trunks and branches, occasionally in leaf litter |
| FEEDING HABITS | Fungi and lichens |
| NOTE | The species displays a rare example of chemical defense among beetle pupae |

ADULT LENGTH
¼–⅜ in
(6.5–9 mm)

## NILIO LANATUS

### NILIO LANATUS

GERMAR, 1824

473

Species in the genus *Nilio* are generally referred to as false ladybird beetles. The oval-shaped, long-legged, setose larvae of *N. lanatus* are mostly black in dorsal view, while their head, prothorax, and ventral side are contrastingly orange. The last instar larva attaches itself to the surface of a tree trunk or under a branch, where it develops into a pupa. The pupa possesses unusual mushroom-like lateral tubercles on five of its abdominal segments. The tip of these projections has several pores from which a whitish substance emerges when touched. Although these secretions have not been studied chemically, it is hypothesized that they protect the otherwise defenseless pupae from potential predators.

### RELATED SPECIES

*Nilio*, which is restricted to Central and South America, is the only genus in the subfamily Nilioninae and contains more than 40 species in three subgenera (*Nilio*, *Linio*, and *Microlinio*). The subgenera are separated from each other by details of their elytral punctation. The species can be separated primarily based on differences in color patterns on their elytra.

Actual size

**Nilio lanatus** adults have a circular outline (in dorsal view) and a very convex, nearly hemispherical dorsal surface. The head, appendages, and prothorax are pale, while the elytra are mostly black except for distinctly lighter patches and light margins. The dorsal surface is densely covered with fine setae and the pronotum is much broader than long. The head is almost completely hidden when viewed from above.

| FAMILY | Tenebrionidae |
|---|---|
| SUBFAMILY | Phrenapatinae |
| DISTRIBUTION | Neotropical: Bolivia (Yungas de La Paz), Peru (Marcapata and Madre de Dios), eastern Ecuador (Macas and Jivaria) |
| MACROHABITAT | Tropical forests |
| MICROHABITAT | Under the bark of dead trees |
| FEEDING HABITS | Feeds in rotten wood |
| NOTE | Because of their general appearance, adults of *Phrenapates* are regularly mistaken for beetles belonging to the unrelated family Passalidae |

ADULT LENGTH
1¹⁄₁₆–1¼ in
(27–32 mm)

474

PHRENAPATES DUX
# PHRENAPATES DUX
GEBIEN, 1910

The genus *Phrenapates*, which contains six described species, belongs to the small tribe Phrenapatini along with the genus *Delognatha*. Species in both genera are characterized by robust anteriorly projecting mandibles and are restricted to Central and South America. Published reports suggest that adult *Phrenapates* may feed small wood shavings to their larvae but this behavior needs confirmation. Adults are generally encountered in close proximity to larvae and pupae. The description of the charismatic *P. dux* was based on 24 individuals, but sadly nothing has appeared in the literature about this species since its original description.

### RELATED SPECIES

Among members of Phrenapatini, *Delognatha* species can be distinguished from *Phrenaptes* by their strongly protuberant eyes and the lack of projections on their head. The species of *Phrenapates* can be separated by the shape and size of the horn between their eyes and their mandibles, whether they have strong ridges above their eyes or not, and by features of the male genitalia.

**Phrenapates dux** is an elongated black beetle with a shiny surface. The smooth pronotum is distinctly broader than long. The elytra bear well-defined longitudinal striae. The first antennal segment is as long as the following four segments combined, and the last three antennomeres are widened to form a loose club. The head has a prominent curved projection between the eyes. The front legs have triangular spines along their outer edge.

Actual size

| FAMILY | Tenebrionidae |
|---|---|
| SUBFAMILY | Pimeliinae |
| DISTRIBUTION | Afrotropical: central and southern coasts of northwestern South Africa and Namibia |
| MACROHABITAT | Sandy areas in the Richtersveld desert of South Africa and the Namib Desert |
| MICROHABITAT | Windblown sand and foredunes |
| FEEDING HABITS | Adult individuals have been observed carrying small leaves and seeds into their sand burrows |
| NOTE | The unusually large mandibles of the males of this tenebrionid species resemble those of males in the distantly related family Lucanidae |

ADULT MALE LENGTH
⁹/₁₆–1 in
(14–25 mm)

ADULT FEMALE LENGTH
½–¹¹/₁₆ in
(13–17 mm)

*CALOGNATHUS CHEVROLATI EBERLANZI*

# CALOGNATHUS CHEVROLATI EBERLANZI

KOCH, 1950

475

The tribe Cryptochilini includes five subtribes, 11 genera, and approximately 130 species, all of which occur in southwestern Africa. Adults of *Calognathus chevrolati eberlanzi* are active during the day or crepuscule (twilight) although they usually take cover during the hottest hours. The tarsal "sand shoes" of adults enable them to dig and tunnel in blown sand. The large mandibles of males, which are unique within the Tenebrionidae, are reminiscent of those found in males of several species of Lucanidae. Some adults have been observed running between stones on windblown sand during the midday hours.

## RELATED SPECIES

The genus *Calognathus* differs from other genera in this tribe in having large mandibles in males, a very large head compared with the size of the pronotum and rest of the body, and ten antennal segments (as opposed to nine in other genera such as *Vansonium*). *Calognathus* includes the single species *C. chevrolati*, which is divided into four subspecies, separated mostly by color.

Actual size

**Calognathus chevrolati eberlanzi** adults are black, with pale scalelike setae covering some areas. The pronotum is broader than long and the head is nearly as large as the pronotum. The tarsi are compressed laterally and have long setae forming what are referred to "sand shoes." The females are similar to the males except that they do not have the long, slender, anteriorly projecting mandibles of the males.

| | |
|---|---|
| FAMILY | Tenebrionidae |
| SUBFAMILY | Pimeliinae |
| DISTRIBUTION | Nearctic: coastal California, United States, and northern Baja California, Mexico |
| MACROHABITAT | Foredunes and sand hummocks immediately bordering the Pacific coast |
| MICROHABITAT | Adults are flightless and spend most of the time under the sand, where the larvae also live |
| FEEDING HABITS | Probably decomposing vegetation buried in the sand |
| NOTE | Two of the three species of Tenebrionidae placed on the IUCN Red List of Threatened Species belong to the genus *Coelus* |

ADULT LENGTH
³⁄₁₆–⁵⁄₁₆ in
(5–8 mm)

*COELUS GLOBOSUS*
# GLOBOSE DUNE BEETLE
LECONTE, 1852

Actual size

Darkling beetles (family Tenebrionidae) are a conspicuous faunal component in arid and semiarid environments worldwide. In fact, they often contribute disproportionately high levels of biomass to these ecosystems. The genus *Coelus* is restricted to sand dunes in Pacific coastal North America and all its species are flightless. The Globose Dune Beetle has been given the status of Vulnerable by the International Union for Conservation of Nature because of severe pressures subjected on its fragile habitat by recreational activities. In some areas suitable habitats for this species have been completely destroyed. The congeneric San Joaquin Dune Beetle (*C. gracilis*) is also threatened by similar habitat changes.

### RELATED SPECIES

*Coelus* differs from other genera in the tribe Coniontini by having the first tarsomere of the front legs bearing a long and broadly rounded process. The five species of *Coelus* can be separated from each other based on the number of antennal segments (*C. maritimus* has ten while the other species have 11), the presence and length of setae on the head and front tibiae, as well as shape and density of punctures on the head.

**The Globose Dune Beetle** is a small, dorsally convex, oval-shaped, dark brown to black species. The head is deeply emarginated in the middle anteriorly. The body has long setae around its perimeter in dorsal view and the legs are also covered with long setae. The basal tarsomeres of the front legs have a shovel-shaped process that enables the beetles to dig in the sand.

| FAMILY | Tenebrionidae |
| SUBFAMILY | Pimeliinae |
| DISTRIBUTION | Neotropical: dry Western Cordillera, Peru |
| MACROHABITAT | Semidesert scrub with leguminous shrubs (*Prosopis* and *Acacia* spp.) and cacti (*Opuntia* spp.), approximately 7,500 ft (2,300 m) above sea-level |
| MICROHABITAT | Under rocks near ant nest galleries |
| FEEDING HABITS | Probably on accumulated plant debris near ant nests |
| NOTE | The semicircular head of this beetle is shaped like the blade of a *tumi*, an Incan cutting tool, hence the specific name |

**ADULT LENGTH**
⅛–³⁄₁₆ in
(3–3.7 mm)

*ESEMEPHE TUMI*

# ESEMEPHE TUMI

STEINER, 1980

477

The tenebrionid tribe Cossyphodini includes seven genera that are widely distributed throughout Africa, with some species also occurring in India, the Socotra Archipelago, and the Arabian Peninsula, while the monotypic genus *Esemephe* is the only representative in the Americas. As for all other members of the tribe, *E. tumi* is flightless and mymecophile (found in association with ants)—individuals have been recorded only near nest galleries of the ant *Camponotus renggeri*. When first discovered under rocks, adults remained motionless, but they soon began to run very quickly with their antennae outstretched, a behavior reminiscent of small cockroaches.

Actual size

### RELATED SPECIES

Morphological structures used to separate *Esemephe* from the other genera in Cossyphodini include the number of tarsal segments on the middle legs (four versus five), the number of antennal segments (nine versus 11), and the number of apical antennal segments that are expanded to form a club (from one to three). The presence of three enlarged apical antennal segments is a diagnostic feature for *Esemephe*.

**Esemephe tumi** is flattened dorsoventrally, oval in shape, and has expanded flanges surrounding the entire body, which are thought to protect the appendages (legs and antennae) against attacks from ants. The eyes are small and divided into dorsal and ventral components. The elytra each have five narrow, longitudinal ridges. The scutellum is short but very wide.

| FAMILY | Tenebrionidae |
|---|---|
| SUBFAMILY | Pimeliinae |
| DISTRIBUTION | Neotropical: Argentina (Chubut and Santa Cruz provinces), Chile (General Carrera province) |
| MACROHABITAT | Patagonian desert or steppes |
| MICROHABITAT | On the ground surface, among tufts of vegetation |
| FEEDING HABITS | Feeds on live plants or dead plant matter |
| NOTE | This is arguably the most beautiful species in the genus *Nyctelia* |

ADULT LENGTH
½–⁹⁄₁₆ in
(13–15 mm)

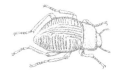

478

*NYCTELIA GEOMETRICA*
# NYCTELIA GEOMETRICA
FAIRMAIRE, 1905

Actual size

The Patagonian steppe, the southernmost desert in the world, is home to a diverse and highly endemic tenebrionid fauna mainly belonging to the tribes Nycteliini, Praociini, and Scotobiini. These beetles have recently been used to delimit areas of endemism within the region in order to understand better the current distributional patterns and historical pressures that may have shaped this fauna over time. *Nyctelia geometrica* is commonly encountered in parts of its range and can typically be found wandering on the ground surface during the daytime, sometimes feeding on live plants, and takes refuge among vegetation.

### RELATED SPECIES
The tribe Nycteliini contains 12 genera and nearly 300 species, which occur from central Peru to southern Argentina and Chile, except for *Entomobalia*, which was described in 2002 from northeastern Brazil. The genus *Nyctelia* is largely restricted to Patagonian steppe in Chile and the Monte Desert in Argentina, and contains 66 species. *Nyctelia geometrica* is most similar to *N. westwoodi* but differs in having three longitudinal grooves near the middle of the elytra and transverse grooves near the sides, while individuals of *N. westwoodi* have five longitudinal grooves near the middle of the elytra and oblique grooves toward the apex.

**Nyctelia geometrica** is an oval, entirely black species with long legs. The elytra bear three longitudinal grooves near the suture (the groove closest to the middle of elytra is complete, the second groove surpasses the midpoint, and the third groove reaches only a third of the length of the elytra) and 18–22 transverse groves near the sides. The tip of the elytra ends in a narrowed process.

| FAMILY | Tenebrionidae |
|---|---|
| SUBFAMILY | Pimeliinae |
| DISTRIBUTION | Afrotropical: southwestern Angola, south to northwestern Namibia |
| MACROHABITAT | Namib Desert |
| MICROHABITAT | Windblown coastal dunes with little or no vegetation |
| FEEDING HABITS | Dead plant matter |
| NOTE | Fog-basking behavior in *Onymacris*, an adaptation not observed in other deserts of the world, seems to have evolved independently in *O. bicolor* (which has white elytra) and *O. unguicularis* (which has black elytra) |

ADULT LENGTH
½–¹⁵⁄₁₆ in
(13–23.5 mm)

*ONYMACRIS BICOLOR*
# WHITE FOG-BASKING BEETLE
(HAAG-RUTENBERG, 1875)

479

In the Namib Desert, darkling beetles form a dominant component of the arthropod fauna and represent approximately 80 percent of the beetle diversity. Tenebrionids in this region have evolved a great number of unique adaptations to survive the challenging conditions. Fog-basking is one example, and sees the beetle climbing to the top of a dune during the early-morning fog and orienting its body with the tip of the abdomen pointed upward and the head angled downward. Water vapor from the fog condenses on the abdomen and runs down the body into the mouth. *Onymacris bicolor*, which is active during the day, has relatively long legs and can move fairly fast.

## RELATED SPECIES

The genus *Onymacris* currently includes 14 valid species that can be separated from one another by characteristics such as the color (from white or yellow to entirely black) and shape of their elytra, and the size and density of punctures on their pronotum. Research based on molecular data published in 2013 suggests that this genus, as currently defined, may not form a natural grouping and needs a thorough systematic revision.

Actual size

**The White Fog-basking Beetle** is black except for the white to ivory elytra, which bear a darker line laterally near the posterior in southern individuals. The pronotum is smooth, with only very fine punctures near the sides. The elytra have a surface sculpture made up of large, flattened tubercles. Males typically have longer middle and hind legs than females.

| FAMILY | Tenebrionidae |
|---|---|
| SUBFAMILY | Pimeliinae |
| DISTRIBUTION | Palearctic: Algeria, Egypt, Libya, Morocco, Tunisia, Israel, Bahrain, Iran, Iraq, Saudi Arabia, Yemen |
| MACROHABITAT | Deserts and sand dunes |
| MICROHABITAT | On the surface of the sand, hiding under vegetation or in small mammal burrows |
| FEEDING HABITS | Dead plant matter |
| NOTE | The common name of this species was coined on the basis of the sun-like appearance of its elytra |

ADULT LENGTH
1–1⁹⁄₁₆ in
(25–40 mm)

480

*PRIONOTHECA CORONATA*
# RADIANT-SUN BEETLE
(OLIVIER, 1795)

The flightless *Prionotheca coronata* is nocturnal and can be encountered wandering on the surface of sand, primarily in summer, sometimes in large numbers. Adults have been found in clay jars in Egyptian tombs dating back more than 5,000 years. Following these findings, some authors have hypothesized that the hollowed-out elytra and abdomen were kept as funerary offerings or were worn as protective amulets. This hypothesis has been disputed more recently, as it seems that the clay jars could have just as well served as unintended pitfall traps.

### RELATED SPECIES

*Prionotheca* belongs to the diverse tribe Pimeliini, which occurs in hot, dry areas of southern Europe, Africa and Asia. The genus includes a single species and can be diagnosed by the distinctive row of sharp spines around its elytra. The three subspecies can be separated by minor differences in the sculpture of the cuticle on the disk of their elytra and their pronotum.

**The Radiant-sun Beetle** is a rather large, dark brown to black species with broad elytra and a pronotum that is much broader than long. The sides of the elytra have a conspicuous row of sharply pointed spines. The middle and hind tibiae also have a row of spines along their inner margin. The dorsal surface of the body is covered with fairly long, erect setae.

Actual size

| FAMILY | Tenebrionidae |
|---|---|
| SUBFAMILY | Pimeliinae |
| DISTRIBUTION | Palearctic: Algeria, Morocco, Tunisia |
| MACROHABITAT | In dry, open areas |
| MICROHABITAT | Under stones, on the ground surface |
| FEEDING HABITS | Detritivorous |
| NOTE | Species in this genus are typically active in the spring or winter |

ADULT LENGTH
½–⁹⁄₁₆ in
(13–15 mm)

*SEPIDIUM VARIEGATUM*

# SEPIDIUM VARIEGATUM
(FABRICIUS, 1792)

481

The tribe Sepidiini is largely restricted to the African continent, except for a small number of species in the genera *Psammophanes*, *Sepidiostenus*, *Sepidium*, *Vieta*, and *Vietomorpha*, which also occur in southern Europe and/or the Middle East. Although little is known about the habits of *Sepidium variegatum*, individuals from this genus are most frequently encountered under stones and adults can also be seen wandering on the ground surface. As its species name suggests (from the Latin *varius*, meaning "varied"), the general appearance of *S. variegatum* is quite variable, especially in its coloration pattern, which has led to multiple descriptions of this beetle by different authors.

RELATED SPECIES

The genus *Sepidium* belongs to the subtribe Sepidiina, tribe Sepidiini, along with a small number of other genera, including the sub-Saharan genus *Vieta* as well as *Echinotus* and *Peringueyia* from southern Africa and Zimbabwe, respectively. The genera in this subtribe are characterized by an anterior process on the pronotum, which can vary in size and shape. Species of *Sepidium* can generally be separated by the shape, sculpture, and patterns of setation on their pronotum and elytra.

Actual size

**Sepidium variegatum** is an elongate black beetle covered with scales over most of its body, these generally varying in color from pale yellow to dark brown. The head is almost entirely concealed in dorsal view by the anteriorly projecting pronotum. The pronotum has a large lateral projection on each side near the anterior corners and three darker longitudinal bands along the midline. Each elytron has a pair of longitudinal ridges that bear large, toothlike projections.

| FAMILY | Tenebrionidae |
|---|---|
| SUBFAMILY | Tenebrioninae |
| DISTRIBUTION | Afrotropical: South Africa (Transvaal), Zimbabwe, Botswana, and Namibia |
| MACROHABITAT | Prefers bush-covered patches of woody savanna in semiarid to moderately mesic habitats; usually absent from deserts and mesic forests |
| MICROHABITAT | In the shade of clumps of bushes |
| FEEDING HABITS | Dead plant material, especially dry fallen leaves |
| NOTE | The complex structures near the apex of the front tibiae of males are unique and described as "monstrous" in the literature |

ADULT LENGTH
1 1⁄16–1 1⁄2 in
(27–38 mm)

482

*ANOMALIPUS ELEPHAS*
# ANOMALIPUS ELEPHAS
FÅHRAEUS, 1870

Species in *Anomalipus* occur widely in Africa south of the Equator but are most diverse in the Transvaal Highveld (inland plateau) in South Africa. *Anomalipus elephas* is the biggest species in this genus, hence it is suitably named. The complex sound production associated with courtship behavior in the beetle consists in part of stridulation (created by rubbing the head against the prosternum) and vibration of the antennae and forebody (resulting in a rustling sound). Female *A. elephas* lay a single large egg in a shallow circular hole in the ground. Adult individuals can live more than five years in captivity.

RELATED SPECIES
The southern African genus *Anomalipus* belongs to the subtribe Platynotina in the tribe Pedinini, which includes about 60 genera from mainly Africa and Asia. *Anomalipus* differs from other genera in the tribe in lacking lateral and basal borders on the pronotum and having a very large mentum. The nearly 70 species and subspecies of *Anomalipus* can be separated mainly by features of the tibiae, pronotum, elytra, and male genitalia.

**Anomalipus elephas** is a flightless black beetle with a very broad pronotum (broader than the elytra in males), and the elytra have several smoothly rounded and equally developed longitudinal ridges. The expanded front tibiae of males have a complex structure near the apex with a deep cavity and a large spine in the middle of it, while females have two triangular spines along the outer edge of their front tibiae.

Actual size

| FAMILY | Tenebrionidae |
|---|---|
| SUBFAMILY | Tenebrioninae |
| DISTRIBUTION | Nearctic: from Nova Scotia west to central Alberta and south at least to Nebraska, northern Mississippi, and central Florida |
| MACROHABITAT | In forests, usually with Paper Birch (*Betula papyrifera*) |
| MICROHABITAT | Decaying tree stumps |
| FEEDING HABITS | Adults feed on, and larvae develop in and feed on, polypore shelf fungi (usually Birch Polypore, *Piptoporus betulinus*) |
| NOTE | This species is arguably one the best-studied fungivore beetles in the Western Hemisphere, with research carried out on its sexual selection, defense behavior, habitat fragmentation, and movement dynamics |

ADULT LENGTH
⅜–½ in
(8.5–13 mm)

*BOLITOTHERUS CORNUTUS*
# FORKED FUNGUS BEETLE
(FABRICIUS, 1801)

483

The clypeal and thoracic projections in males of *Bolitotherus cornutus* occur in a continuous range of sizes, from very small to very large. The courtship ritual begins when the male walks over the female, from the head to the tip of her abdomen, and remains attached to her elytra—often for several hours—until he decides to turn around and attempt copulation. If successful, the male remains on top of the female, guarding her from potential other mates. Males with larger horns have a greater chance of displacing smaller males during the various steps of courtship and reproduction.

### RELATED SPECIES

The monotypic genus *Bolitotherus* belongs to the tenebrionid tribe Bolitophagini, which includes a small number of fungus-feeding species worldwide. In North America, it differs from other genera in this group by having antennae that are not expanded apically (apical antennomeres are comb-like in *Rhipidandrus*) and that have ten segments (11 antennomeres are present in *Eleates*, *Bolitophagus*, and *Megeleates*).

**The Forked Fungus Beetle** is a dark brown to black beetle (light brown in recently emerged specimens) with a roughly sculptured cuticle. The males have a small forked extension of the clypeus and a pair of thoracic horns that project anteriorly over and beyond the head. The horns are covered with yellow setae ventrally. The elytra have rows of elongate, interrupted tubercles in both sexes.

Actual size

| FAMILY | Tenebrionidae |
|---|---|
| SUBFAMILY | Tenebrioninae |
| DISTRIBUTION | Nearctic: southwestern United States |
| MACROHABITAT | Primarily in open arid areas |
| MICROHABITAT | Adults on the surface of the ground, larvae in soil |
| FEEDING HABITS | Mainly scavengers on dead plant tissue but can attack live plants in the larval stage |
| NOTE | Soil-dwelling larvae of the genus *Eleodes* are commonly referred to as false wireworms, because of their general resemblance to wireworm larvae of the beetle family Elateridae |

ADULT LENGTH
⅞–1⅜ in
(21–35 mm)

484

*ELEODES ACUTUS*
# ELEODES ACUTUS
(SAY, 1824)

The flightless genus *Eleodes*, which is a conspicuous faunal element of the dry regions of western North America, contains approximately 235 species and subspecies. Larvae of some species in this genus frequently attack crop seedlings and can cause considerable agricultural damage. Adults of *E. acutus* are most active after dark. A characteristic behavior of species in *Eleodes* is "head standing," during which an individual will raise the tip of its abdomen when approached and spray a defense fluid to dissuade potential predators.

## RELATED SPECIES

The numerous species of *Eleodes* are currently divided into 15 subgenera (e.g., *Blapylis*, *Caverneleodes*, *Melaneleodes*) primarily based on features of the female genitalia. *Eleodes acutus* is one of approximately 40 species classified in the subgenus *Eleodes*, which is typically characterized by the presence of a tooth on the front femur in adult males, and occasionally in females as well. Individuals of *E. acutus* are diagnosed by their large size, the lack of longitudinal ridges on their elytra, and the convex dorsal surface of their pronotum.

**Eleodes acutus** adults are comparatively very large for members of the genus, and are elongate-oblong and somewhat flattened dorsally. Although their body is typically black, the elytra often have a conspicuous longitudinal reddish band along the midline. The lateral margins of the elytra are acute near their anterior corners. The inner side of the front femur bears a tooth in males and occasionally females.

Actual size

| FAMILY | Tenebrionidae |
|---|---|
| SUBFAMILY | Tenebrioninae |
| DISTRIBUTION | Australian: southwestern corner of Western Australia |
| MACROHABITAT | Arid and semiarid open areas |
| MICROHABITAT | Unknown |
| FEEDING HABITS | Adults and larvae probably feed on dried plant matter |
| NOTE | Species of *Helea* can cover ground rapidly on their long legs |

ADULT LENGTH
¾–⅞ in
(19–23 mm)

*HELEA SPINIFER*
# HELEA SPINIFER
(CARTER, 1910)

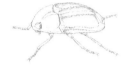

485

This rarely recorded species belongs to a group commonly known as pie-dish beetles, whose combined pronotal and elytral flanges around the body cover all of their appendages, especially their rather long legs. This dorsal shield helps the beetles fend off attacks by predators, such as spiders and scorpions, which are active at night while the beetles forage. The species name *spinifer*, which refers to the longitudinal spine-like ridge in the middle of the pronotum, was given by entomologist Herbert Carter, who described a large number of Australian beetle species in the early 1900s.

### RELATED SPECIES

The genus *Helea* belongs to the tribe Heleini, which is almost exclusively restricted to Australia, although a small number of species also occur in neighboring New Guinea and New Zealand. The 50 or so known species of *Helea* differ from those in related genera by having the anterior corners of the pronotum extending anteriorly and curving inward to approach or meet one another in the middle, either above or in front of the head.

Actual size

**Helea spinifer** is an oval, dorsoventrally flattened, dark brown beetle. The broad lateral extensions of the pronotum project anteriorly and curve inward to meet together over the head, leaving only a small part of the head exposed from above. The elytra each have a strongly raised, continuous ridge extending posteriorly, as well as a row of rounded pustules near the outer raised margin.

| FAMILY | Tenebrionidae |
| --- | --- |
| SUBFAMILY | Tenebrioninae |
| DISTRIBUTION | Neotropical: Chile (Arauco and Aysén provinces), Argentina (western Neuquén province) |
| MACROHABITAT | Southern beech (*Nothofagus* spp.) forests |
| MICROHABITAT | On tree branches and trunks |
| FEEDING HABITS | Adults and larvae probably graze on lichen growing on trees |
| NOTE | The species name *dromedarius* refers to the hump near the base of the adult's elytra in lateral view |

ADULT LENGTH
¾–⅞ in
(19–21 mm)

486

# HOMOCYRTUS DROMEDARIUS
(GUÉRIN-MÉNEVILLE, 1831)

Because of the unique body shape of its species, the genus *Homocyrtus* has been classified in several groups of beetles over time (e.g., in different subfamilies of Tenebrionidae and in the family Chalcodryidae). Recent investigations suggest that it belongs in the small tenebrionid tribe Titaenini along with eight other genera (e.g., *Titaena*, *Callismilax*, and *Artystona*) that occur in Australia, New Zealand, and surrounding islands. *Homocyrtus dromedarius* is frequently encountered within its range and, as for other species in this tribe, the adults and larvae are thought to graze on lichen on the surface of trees and branches.

## RELATED SPECIES

The genus *Homocyrtus* contains three species, two of which (*H. dromedarius* and *H. dives*) occur in both Argentina and Chile, while the other (*H. bonni*) is restricted to Chile. Adults of *H. dives* differ from the other two species by their color pattern and in lacking dorsal tubercles on the elytra. *Homocyrtus dromedarius* has sparse patches of hairlike scales toward the apex of the elytra, while *H. bonni* has distinct longitudinal rows of hairlike scales toward the apex of the elytra.

**Homocyrtus dromedarius** adults are elongated beetles with a somewhat cylindrical prothorax and convex elytra, and are usually dark brown or black, sometimes with a metallic tinge. Longitudinal ridges on the sides of the prothorax are absent (but present in most other tenebrionids). The elytra have a pair of large tubercles near the base and rows of large, irregularly shaped punctures that contain densely packed, hairlike white scales. Each elytron bears a posterior-projecting, sharply pointed spine at its tip.

Actual size

| FAMILY | Tenebrionidae |
|---|---|
| SUBFAMILY | Tenebrioninae |
| DISTRIBUTION | Afrotropical: Ethiopia, Kenya, Tanzania, Zimbabwe, South Africa, Namibia, Zambia, Ivory Coast, Central African Republic, Democratic Republic of Congo, Rwanda, Uganda, and Angola |
| MACROHABITAT | Usually at high elevations, up to 6,500 ft (2,000 m) |
| MICROHABITAT | Unknown; most individuals are attracted to lights at night |
| FEEDING HABITS | Unknown; probably associated with termite nests |
| NOTE | The yellow tufts of setae on antennal segment 6 are thought to produce secretions lapped up by the host termites while the beetles occupy their nest |

ADULT LENGTH
⅛–⁷⁄₁₆ in
(9–11 mm)

*RHYZODINA MNISZECHII*

# RHYZODINA MNISZECHII

CHEVROLAT, 1873

487

The presence of highly modified antennae in *Rhyzodina* species, exemplified by a reduction in the total number of antennomeres and the presence of setal tufts on the sixth segment, suggests that these beetles are associated with live termites. If this is true, they would differ from several other groups of tenebrionids (e.g., the genus *Gonocnemis*) that live in long-abandoned termite nests, where they feed on rotten fungi. A study of *R. mniszechii* encountered in Zambia without setae on the antennae suggests that the putative host termites sometimes chew on the setae in addition to lapping the secretions.

### RELATED SPECIES

The correct placement of *Rhyzodina* within the family Tenebrionidae has been problematic, since it has a number of unique morphological adaptations not encountered in other genera. The six species in the genus can be separated by the shape of their antennal segments, whether or not their head is constricted behind the eyes, and whether or not they have ridges on their pronotum and elytra.

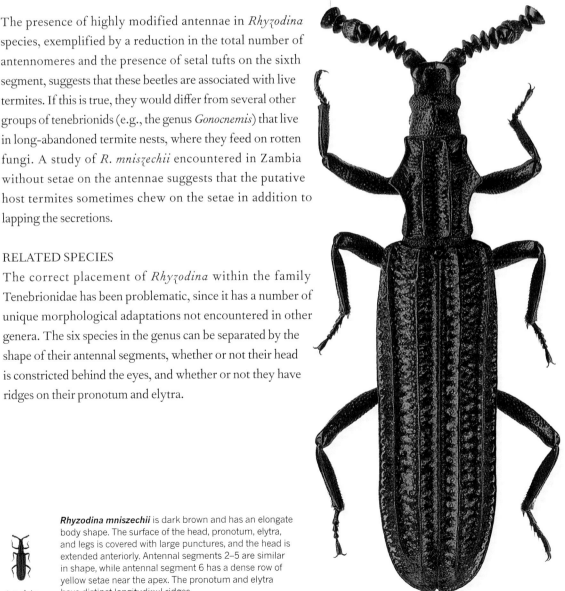

Actual size

**Rhyzodina mniszechii** is dark brown and has an elongate body shape. The surface of the head, pronotum, elytra, and legs is covered with large punctures, and the head is extended anteriorly. Antennal segments 2–5 are similar in shape, while antennal segment 6 has a dense row of yellow setae near the apex. The pronotum and elytra have distinct longitudinal ridges.

| FAMILY | Tenebrionidae |
|---|---|
| SUBFAMILY | Tenebrioninae |
| DISTRIBUTION | Cosmopolitan |
| MACROHABITAT | In rotting tree holes or vertebrate nests in nature; associated with agricultural products around the world |
| MICROHABITAT | Usually in stored products |
| FEEDING HABITS | On a wide variety of dead organic matter but prefers moist, decaying grain and cereal products |
| NOTE | The larvae represent an important source of food for vertebrate pets around the world |

ADULT LENGTH
½–¹¹⁄₁₆ in
(12–18 mm)

488

*TENEBRIO MOLITOR*
# YELLOW MEALWORM
LINNAEUS, 1758

The Yellow Mealworm is commonly encountered in granaries, grain elevators, mills, bakeries, and other food stores. Both the adults and larvae can develop on a wide variety of agricultural plant products (e.g., corn flour, bran, bread, pasta, dried fruit) and occasionally on animal products such as leather. The presence of these beetles spoils the merchandises because of the resulting excreta and cast skins from molting. Because they are easy to rear in great numbers, Yellow Mealworm larvae are often sold as food for a wide variety of vertebrates kept in captivity, including reptiles, amphibians, and birds.

RELATED SPECIES

There are approximately 40 genera in the tribe Tenebrionini worldwide, and in the genus *Tenebrio* there are a small number of species in Europe, Africa, and Asia. *Tenebrio molitor* occurs in similar microhabitats to, and closely resembles, the Dark Mealworm (*T. obscurus*). It differs in having fewer punctures on the head and pronotum, and a shiny appearance overall, instead of the dull body surface of *T. obscurus*.

Actual size

**The Yellow Mealworm** adult is a parallel-sided, rather flat, dark reddish-brown to almost black beetle. The antennae and legs are usually reddish. The longitudinal striae on the elytra are shallowly impressed. Flight wings are fully developed and the adults are strong fliers. As the common name suggests, the active larvae are yellowish in color, with a usually more strongly sclerotized and slightly darker head and abdominal apex.

| FAMILY | Tenebrionidae |
|---|---|
| SUBFAMILY | Tenebrioninae |
| DISTRIBUTION | Cosmopolitan |
| MACROHABITAT | Associated with agricultural products around the world |
| MICROHABITAT | Usually in stored food-products |
| FEEDING HABITS | Both the adults and larvae feed on stored products |
| NOTE | Important for studies in various fields of research, this was the first beetle to have its complete genome sequenced |

ADULT LENGTH
⅛–³⁄₁₆ in
(2.5–4.5 mm)

*TRIBOLIUM CASTANEUM*
# RED FLOUR BEETLE
(HERBST, 1797)

489

Actual size

The small tribe Triboliini includes significant agricultural pests such as *Tribolium castaneum*. This species typically occurs in granaries, flour mills, and other buildings where food is stored, including homes. It can survive in extremely dry environments and has demonstrated resistance to all classes of insecticides used against it. Because of the ease by which it can be reared in laboratory conditions (e.g., short life cycle, high fecundity), this beetle has been used as a model organism in molecular and developmental studies around the world. The complete genome of *T. castaneum*, the first ever assembled for a beetle species, was published in 2008.

RELATED SPECIES
The small tribe Triboliini is distributed worldwide and includes a number of cosmopolitan genera (e.g., *Tribolium, Latheticus, Lyphia*). Species in *Tribolium* can be separated based on the size and shape of their eyes, attributes of their antennae, and the sculpture of the cuticle on their dorsal surface, as well as other characters. Other pest species include the Confused Flour Beetle (*T. confusum*) and Destructive Flour Beetle (*T. destructor*).

**The Red Flour Beetle** is a small, elongate, parallel-sided, rather flattened beetle with a reddish-brown cuticle. The antennae have a loose, three-segmented club. Males have a small circular cavity filled with setae on the inner side of their front femur. The kidney-shaped eyes are rather large ventrally, with their edge reaching the cavity that holds the mouthparts.

| FAMILY | Tenebrionidae |
|---|---|
| SUBFAMILY | Alleculinae |
| DISTRIBUTION | Neotropical: Panama |
| MACROHABITAT | Tropical forests |
| MICROHABITAT | Adults live on vegetation and are attracted to lights at night; larvae live in soil |
| FEEDING HABITS | Unknown |
| NOTE | One of the most colorful Alleculinae |

ADULT LENGTH
½–⁹⁄₁₆ in
(12–14 mm)

490

*ERXIAS BICOLOR*
# ERXIAS BICOLOR
CHAMPION, 1888

The diverse subfamily Alleculinae is unusual among related groups in having a series of comb-like teeth along the inner edge of their tarsal claws. Because of this feature, alleculines used to be classified in their own family, Alleculidae, until recent studies of their internal organs revealed that they in fact belong in the family Tenebrionidae. The rarely collected *Erxias bicolor* was originally described from two female specimens by the British coleopterist George Champion as part of the vast *Biologia Centrali-Americana*, an encyclopedia of Mesoamerican zoology, botany, and archeology. A larva of this species was discovered in dry soil under the edge of a boulder in a montane forest.

## RELATED SPECIES

The subtribe Xystropodina of the tribe Alleculini includes genera such as *Erxias*, *Prostenus*, *Lystronychus*, and *Xystropus*, which are primarily restricted to the Neotropical Realm from the southern United States south to Brazil and Argentina. They are characterized by having tarsi that lack ventral lobes and by the conspicuous, erect black setae on their dorsal surface. *Erxias bicolor* can be separated from *E. violaceipennis* from Nicaragua, the only other species in the genus, mainly by differences of punctation on the dorsal surface.

**Erxias bicolor** is a fairly large alleculine with contrasting coloration and is sparsely covered by erect black setae throughout. The head, pronotum, and ventral surface of the body are pale yellow. The elytra, mouthparts, and antennae are noticeably darker, with a metallic bluish-purple color. The legs are colored as the elytra except for the basal half of the femora, which are pale yellow. The anterior portion of the head is narrowly elongated.

Actual size

| FAMILY | Tenebrionidae |
| --- | --- |
| SUBFAMILY | Diaperinae |
| DISTRIBUTION | Nearctic and Neotropical: North America south to Panama (including the Bahamas, Cuba, Dominican Republic, Jamaica, Puerto Rico) |
| MACROHABITAT | Forest |
| MICROHABITAT | Under bark, on or in fleshy fungi, notably bracket fungi (especially *Polyporus* spp.) |
| FEEDING HABITS | Completes its entire life cycle in fungi |
| NOTE | This subfamily of darkling beetles also includes pests of stored agricultural products (e.g., *Cynaeus*, *Alphitophagus*, and *Gnatocerus* spp.) |

ADULT LENGTH
³⁄₁₆–¹⁄₄ in
(4.5–7 mm)

*DIAPERIS MACULATA*

# DIAPERIS MACULATA

OLIVIER, 1791

491

Actual size

Larvae in *Diaperis* and related genera typically feed in fungal fruiting bodies, in contrast to larvae in other groups of darkling beetles, which either feed in rotten wood or are free-living, detritivorous feeders in the soil. Larvae of *Diaperis* are active tunnel-builders in their hosts, and the solidly built adults can also tunnel. In the northern part of their range, adults of *D. maculata* are known to congregate in large numbers under bark in the fall, where they hibernate. This species is quite abundant throughout its range and adults readily fly to artificial lights at night.

## RELATED SPECIES

*Diaperis* is a small genus but its species are rather broadly distributed, occurring on all continents except for Africa and Australia. The only other species occurring in North America, *D. nigronotata*, can be separated by its red or yellow (as opposed to black) front femora, and by the lack of small, blunt tubercles on the clypeus of the male.

**Diaperis maculata** is a shiny, oval-shaped beetle with a black body except for the elytra, which are mostly red with prominent black patches; the head is also generally reddish behind the eyes. The last eight antennomeres are broadened and form a distinct loose club. Males have two small blunt tubercles on the clypeus and two small rounded tubercles on the anterior edge of the pronotum.

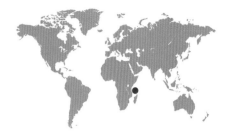

| FAMILY | Tenebrionidae |
| --- | --- |
| SUBFAMILY | Stenochiinae |
| DISTRIBUTION | Afrotropical: Endemic to Frégate Island, Seychelles |
| MACROHABITAT | Tropical forest |
| MICROHABITAT | Adults and larvae are most commonly associated with *Pterocarpus indicus* |
| FEEDING HABITS | Decaying wood and bark |
| NOTE | Known only on Frégate Island, a 0.8 sq miles (2 sq km) island in the Indian Ocean |

ADULT LENGTH
1–1³⁄₁₆ in
(25–30 mm)

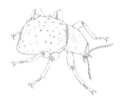

*POLPOSIPUS HERCULEANUS*
# FRÉGATE ISLAND GIANT TENEBRIONID BEETLE
SOLIER, 1848

Actual size

The Frégate Island Giant Tenebrionid Beetle is one of 12 beetle species ranked Critically Endangered on the International Union for Conservation of Nature's Red List of Threatened Species (see also the Delta Ground Beetle, *Elaphrus viridis*, and American Burying Beetle, *Nicrophorus americanus*), and is restricted to Frégate Island in the Seychelles. The accidental introduction of Brown Rats (*Rattus norvegicus*) to the island in 1995 nearly caused the extinction of the flightless beetle, along with the endemic Seychelles Magpie-robin (*Copsychus sechellarum*), before the rodents were eradicated in the early 2000s.

## RELATED SPECIES

Flightless tenebrionid genera were previously grouped together on the basis of the absence of flight wings and their sealed elytra. Recent studies on internal organ systems such as the defense glands and the female genital tube now suggest that the older classification did not reflect natural groupings. Although the monotypic genus *Polposipus* belongs to the diverse subfamily Stenochiinae based on internal characters, its closest relatives have not yet been established.

**Frégate Island Giant Tenebrionid Beetle** adults are pale gray to dark brown and have broadly rounded elytra in dorsal view, which are covered by a small number of apically rounded and shiny tubercles. The elytra are completely fused along the midline, and flight wings are absent. The legs are relatively long and males have curved tibiae.

| FAMILY | Tenebrionidae |
|---|---|
| SUBFAMILY | Stenochiinae |
| DISTRIBUTION | Neotropical: from Mexico south to Bolivia |
| MACROHABITAT | Tropical forests |
| MICROHABITAT | Adults live on the surface of trees or under bark, and larvae in wood |
| FEEDING HABITS | Immature stages probably develop in decaying wood |
| NOTE | One of the most diverse and colorful genera in the family Tenebrionidae |

ADULT LENGTH
½–¾ in
(12–19 mm)

*STRONGYLIUM AURATUM*
# STRONGYLIUM AURATUM
(LAPORTE, 1840)

493

Based on the abundance of darkling beetles in most dry environments on the planet, many people assume that all species in this family are dark brown to black and are ground-dwellers. This is clearly not the case for species in the tribe Stenochiini, which includes the colorful forest-dwelling genera *Stronglyium* and *Cuphotes*. *Strongylium* is certainly one of the most species-rich genera in the family, with nearly 1,000 described species and many more undescribed, especially in tropical areas. *Strongylium auratum* is relatively abundant in Neotropical forests and can be encountered at elevations of 5,000 ft (1,500 m) and more.

### RELATED SPECIES
The overwhelming diversity in *Strongylium*, coupled with an almost complete lack of comparative studies of its species, is a major impediment to taxonomic and biological studies. New species continue to be described every year, however, primarily based on differences in color patterns, sculpture of their cuticle, and sexual characters. Although most species are elongated and have well-developed flight wings, such as *S. auratum*, others are flightless and more convex.

**Strongylium auratum** is an elongated beetle with bright metallic green to reddish-purple reflections on the dorsal surface and legs. Each elytron has nine distinct rows of transverse punctures. Antennae are rather long, reaching beyond the base of the pronotum. Antennomeres are slightly wider at their apex and are speckled with small, circular, white sensory structures. The last two abdominal ventrites are contrasting yellow-reddish in color.

Actual size

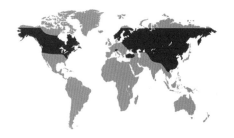

| FAMILY | Tenebrionidae |
|---|---|
| SUBFAMILY | Stenochiinae |
| DISTRIBUTION | Nearctic and Palearctic: from Alaska east to Newfoundland (except Nunavut), and south to Washington, Wyoming, Michigan, and Pennsylvania; and Belarus, Russia, Estonia, Finland, Lithuania, Norway, Poland, Sweden, Switzerland, Ukraine, China, Kazakhstan, Mongolia, Turkey |
| MACROHABITAT | Forests with deciduous trees |
| MICROHABITAT | On tree trunks, under bark, in wood |
| FEEDING HABITS | Larvae develop in rotten wood, especially birch (*Betula* spp.) |
| NOTE | This species is well adapted to survive harsh winters at high latitudes |

ADULT LENGTH
⁹⁄₁₆–¾ in
(14–20 mm)

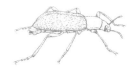

494

*UPIS CERAMBOIDES*
# ROUGHENED DARKLING BEETLE
(LINNAEUS, 1758)

Actual size

Darkling beetles are well known for their ability to survive in some of the hottest deserts on the planet. However their ability to adapt to extreme cold conditions is equally astonishing. Throughout their northern range, adult *Upis ceramboides* can tolerate prolonged freezing down to −76 degrees Fahrenheit (−60 degrees centigrade) in midwinter. Studies on their survival adaptations have led to important discoveries on freeze-tolerant strategies such as a novel non-protein antifreeze molecule and a new sugar alcohol called threitol. Unfortunately, some populations of *U. ceramboides* have become locally extinct over some of its natural range (e.g., southern Sweden) because sustained forestry practices have significantly reduced the amount of dead wood available for their development.

## RELATED SPECIES

*Upis* belongs to the diverse tribe Cnodalonini, which includes species worldwide that develop in dead wood. This tribe is especially diverse in tropical and subtropical habitats. *Upis ceramboides*, the only species in the genus, can be separated from all other Cnodalonini genera in the Nearctic (e.g., *Xylopinus*, *Coelocnemis*) and Palearctic realms (e.g., *Menephilus*, *Coelometopus*) by the characteristic shape of its pronotum and the sculpturing of the cuticle of the elytra.

**The Roughened Darkling Beetle** is a black tenebrionid with a punctate pronotum that is slightly broader than long and noticeably narrower than the elytra. The elytra have irregular, deep depressions and lack distinct longitudinal striae. The flight wings are fully developed and hence the beetle is capable of flight. The male front tibiae curve inward slightly on the apical half and are clothed with dense, pale yellowish setae near the apex.

| | |
|---|---|
| FAMILY | Prostomidae |
| SUBFAMILY | |
| DISTRIBUTION | Palearctic: Europe, Iran, Turkey |
| MACROHABITAT | Forests |
| MICROHABITAT | On or in decaying logs |
| FEEDING HABITS | Adult feeding habits are uncertain; larvae feed on rotting wood |
| NOTE | The function of the long processes beneath the mandibles of both males and females in *Prostomis* species is unknown |

ADULT LENGTH
¼ in
(5.5–6.5 mm)

*PROSTOMIS MANDIBULARIS*

# PROSTOMIS MANDIBULARIS

(FABRICIUS, 1801)

495

Members of the family Prostomidae are referred to as jugular-horned beetles because of the long, narrow, anteriorly projecting hornlike structures carried beneath their mandibles. The classification of this characteristic group of beetles has been the subject of debate. Individuals typically occur in rotten wood with mud-like consistency. Larvae of *Prostomis mandibularis* have a distinct asymmetrical head, are strongly flattened dorsoventrally, and move under bark or in decaying wood by wriggling with the aid of their short legs, which end in strong claws.

Actual size

RELATED SPECIES

The small family Prostomidae includes *Dryocora*, with two species from the Australian Realm, and *Prostomis*, with approximately 30 species distributed in the Holarctic, Oriental, and Australian realms, as well as South Africa. *Prostomis mandibularis* is the only species in the genus that occupies a broad range in Europe, while *P. americanus* is the only member of Prostomidae to occur in North America. The size and shape of the elongated processes beneath the mandibles are usually distinctive for each species, although a study of the male genitalia is often necessary to provide an accurate identification.

**Prostomis mandibularis** is an elongate, parallel-sided reddish-brown beetle with broad, anteriorly projecting mandibles. The small, slightly protruding eyes are circular. The antennae have 11 antennomeres and end with a weakly defined three-segmented club. The elytra have rows of punctate striae and gradually narrow posteriorly. The tarsal formula is 4-4-4.

| FAMILY | Oedemeridae |
|---|---|
| SUBFAMILY | Oedemerinae |
| DISTRIBUTION | Native to the Palearctic Realm but now cosmopolitan |
| MACROHABITAT | Varied habitats, from coastlines to inland cities |
| MICROHABITAT | Near water-saturated wood |
| FEEDING HABITS | Adults do not feed; larvae develop in damp, decaying wood (e.g., oaks, poplars, pines) |
| NOTE | The damaging larval stage of this species tunnels in damp and decaying wood, including old ships and ancient wood remains |

ADULT LENGTH
³⁄₈–⁹⁄₁₆ in
(8.8–14.6 mm)

*NACERDES MELANURA*
# WHARF BORER
(LINNAEUS, 1758)

The adults of the Wharf Borer are short-lived—generally up to two weeks—and are not known to feed. Their longevity decreases with increasing temperatures. The comparatively long-lived larvae typically complete their development in approximately one year. Larvae of the Wharf Borer are known to attack old ships and wharves but have also been found in a variety of other microhabitats, including fences, driftwood, water-saturated wood pilings, and sometimes wood structures in the basement of buildings. Large numbers of adults have been reported in some buildings, where in some cases they were apparently attracted by toilets.

## RELATED SPECIES

This genus belongs to the tribe Nacerdini along with *Anogcodes* and *Opsimea* in the Palearctic Realm. The 60-plus species and subspecies in *Nacerdes* are separated into three subgenera, with *N. brancuccii*, *N. melanura*, and *N. semirufa* being the only representatives of the subgenus *Nacerdes*. Differences in color patterns, the front tibiae, the elytra, and the distance between the eyes are useful to separate the species.

**The Wharf Borer** is an elongate, parallel-sided, mostly yellowish-orange beetle with the apex of the elytra black. The rather long and narrow antennae, which originate slightly below the small, weakly emarginated black eyes, are unusual in having 12 segments. The pronotum is distinctly narrowed on the posterior half. The front tibiae each have a single apical spur.

Actual size

| FAMILY | Oedemeridae |
|---|---|
| SUBFAMILY | Oedemerinae |
| DISTRIBUTION | Palearctic |
| MACROHABITAT | Meadows, gardens, edge of forests |
| MICROHABITAT | Adults are found on flowers and foliage; larvae live in decaying plant tissue |
| FEEDING HABITS | Adults feed on pollen; larvae feed within decaying plant tissue |
| NOTE | The common name for this family is false blister beetles because of their resemblance to blister beetles in the family Meloidae and also because they secrete cantharidins for their defense, which can cause blisters on humans |

ADULT LENGTH
⁵⁄₁₆–½ in
(8–13 mm)

*OEDEMERA PODAGRARIAE PODAGRARIAE*

# OEDEMERA PODAGRARIAE PODAGRARIAE

(LINNAEUS, 1767)

497

The Oedemeridae is a widely distributed family including approximately 1,500 species classified in three subfamilies worldwide. Most larvae within this family develop in decaying wood and can be found in stumps, roots, driftwood, or structural timber, although some species in the genus *Calopus* are known to attack living trees. The contrasting coloration of many species, including *Oedemera podagrariae podagrariae*, is thought to advertise to potential predators that they are distasteful. A study of the chemistry of adults of the closely related subspecies *O. p. ventralis* revealed that females typically have five to six times more cantharidin than males, although both sexes have the ability to produce this defense chemical.

RELATED SPECIES

The genus *Oedemera* belongs to the tribe Oedemerini and contains approximately 100 species or subspecies in the Palearctic Realm. Species in this genus vary in their coloration pattern and attributes of their eyes, although both male and female genitalic structures are also important for accurate identification. Three subspecies are recognized as valid: the widespread *O. podagrariae podagrariae*, *O. p. acutipalpis* from Israel and Turkey, and *O. p. ventralis* from Azerbaijan, Iran, and Turkmenistan.

Actual size

**Oedemera podagrariae podagrariae** is a charismatic elongate beetle with a contrasting color pattern and long, narrow antennae. The head and at least part of the hind legs are black, while the rest of the body is primarily yellowish orange. The pronotum is black in males but orange in females. The hind femora of the male are greatly enlarged when compared with those of the female. The tarsal formula is 5-5-4.

| FAMILY | Meloidae |
|---|---|
| SUBFAMILY | Meloinae |
| DISTRIBUTION | Palearctic: Europe, Turkey |
| MACROHABITAT | Open habitats |
| MICROHABITAT | Adults occur on flowers; eggs in soil; larvae in wasp (Sphecidae) nests |
| FEEDING HABITS | Adults feed on pollen and nectar; larvae feed on host wasp eggs and food stores |
| NOTE | Individuals of *Cerocoma schaefferi* engage in complex sexual behavior associated with modified structures of males (e.g., mouthparts and antennae) |

ADULT LENGTH
⁵⁄₁₆–⁷⁄₁₆ in
(8–11 mm)

498

*CEROCOMA SCHAEFFERI*
# CEROCOMA SCHAEFFERI
(LINNAEUS, 1758)

Actual size

Adults in the genus *Cerocoma* sometimes occur in large numbers and are characterized by metallic aposematic coloration (green, copper, or blue) to advertise to potential predators that they contain toxic defense chemicals (cantharidins). They have modified mouthparts that enable them to feed on the pollen and nectar of herbaceous plants (e.g., Asteraceae and Apiaceae). Before copulation takes place in *C. schaefferi*, the male and female stand in front of each other with the modified portion of the male antennae in contact with the unmodified antennae of the female. The female rubs the sides of the pronotum of the male with the front tarsi at the same time.

### RELATED SPECIES

*Cerocoma*, which was thoroughly revised in 2011 based on morphological and molecular data, ranges from the Iberian Peninsula to western China (with one species in North Africa) and contains approximately 30 species. Species in this genus are characterized by having nine-segmented antennomeres, the first of which forms a dorsal keel in males. *Cerocoma schaefferi* belongs to the subgenus *Cerocoma* with four other species (*C. prochaskana*, *C. simplicicornis*, *C. bernhaueri*, and *C. dahli*). These species can be separated on the basis of differences in their antennae and legs.

**Cerocoma schaefferi** is an elongate, parallel-sided beetle with a metallic green head, prothorax, and elytra. The long, sparse yellowish setae are denser on the head and prothorax. The legs vary from yellow to green, while the antennae and mouthparts are usually pale yellow. The male maxillary palps and antennae are greatly modified compared with those of females.

| FAMILY | Meloidae |
|---|---|
| SUBFAMILY | Meloinae |
| DISTRIBUTION | Nearctic and Neotropical: Canada (Manitoba), eastern USA, northeastern Mexico |
| MACROHABITAT | Open areas |
| MICROHABITAT | On vegetation or in burrows excavated in the soil |
| FEEDING HABITS | Adults most commonly feed on flowers of Asteraceae, Convolvulaceae, and Malvaceae; the predatory larvae feed on the eggs of meloid beetles |
| NOTE | *Epicauta* is one of only five genera (of the approximately 120) in the family Meloidae that occur in both the Eastern and Western Hemispheres; the larval feeding habits of this species are quite unique among beetles |

ADULT LENGTH
¼–½ in
(6–13 mm)

*EPICAUTA ATRATA*
# EPICAUTA ATRATA
(FABRICIUS, 1775)

499

Larvae of species in the genus *Epicauta* are typically predators on acridid grasshopper eggs (e.g., *Melanoplus* spp.), however detailed studies published in 1981 and 1982 revealed a different and unusual type of larval development in *E. atrata*. Larvae of this species develop by feeding exclusively on eggs of other species of *Epicauta*, including eggs of their own species. Laboratory experiments even demonstrated that grasshopper eggs are not attractive as a food source for *E. atrata* first-instar larvae and proved to be toxic if eaten. Adults occur from April to November.

RELATED SPECIES

In North and Central America, close to 200 *Epicauta* species are known and most of the diversity is concentrated in the southwestern United States and in Mexico. *Epicauta atrata* individuals with orange heads cannot be confused with other species, while those with black heads are similar to adults of *E. pennsylvanica* but differ in the width of the eyes.

Actual size

**Epicauta atrata** adults are soft-bodied, rather elongate, dark brown to black beetles with a head ranging in color from almost entirely orange to almost entirely black. The narrow pronotum is narrowest anteriorly. The deflexed head is broad but ends posteriorly in a narrow neck. The front femora have an excavation on the inner surface with a patch of setae that is used for cleaning the antennae.

| FAMILY | Meloidae |
|---|---|
| SUBFAMILY | Meloinae |
| DISTRIBUTION | Palearctic |
| MACROHABITAT | Forests |
| MICROHABITAT | Adults occur on vegetation; larvae develop in bee nests |
| FEEDING HABITS | Adults feed primarily on leaves of European Ash (*Fraxinus excelsior*) and Manna Ash (*F. ornus*), but also on other Oleaceae as well as Caprifoliaceae and Salicaceae; larvae feed on the food stores of bees |
| NOTE | The most commonly studied arthropod with aphrodisiac properties; reported to have been used by historical figures such as the Holy Roman Emperor Henry IV, France's Louis XIV, and the Marquis de Sade |

ADULT LENGTH
½–⅞ in
(12–22 mm)

500

*LYTTA VESICATORIA*
# SPANISH FLY
(LINNAEUS, 1758)

Usage of arthropods and their products as aphrodisiacs has fascinated humans for centuries. Groups that have received particular attention to treat impotence include lobsters, scorpions, spiders, true bugs, and beetles. Aphrodisiac properties of meloid beetles were apparently first reported by the Greek physician Dioscorides in the first century AD. Chemicals in the body fluids of male *Lytta vesicatoria* and related beetles, called cantharidins, have evolved over time as antipredator secretions and therefore these can cause significant harm and even death to humans when ingested in large doses. The stimulating effects reported by men following the ingestion of dried Spanish Fly products have been referred to as unreliable and unsafe.

## RELATED SPECIES

*Lytta* belongs to the tribe Lyttini and its species are usually divided into nine subgenera. This broadly distributed genus occurs across the Nearctic, Neotropical, Palearctic, and Oriental realms. Five subspecies are recognized as valid: *L. vesicatoria vesicatoria*, *L. v. freudei*, *L. v. heydeni*, *L. v. moreana*, and *L. v. togata*.

**The Spanish Fly** is a charismatic medium-size, elongated metallic beetle with elytra that are broadly rounded at their apex. The body color is variable and can have greenish-blue, golden, or coppery reflections. The elytra have faint veinlike longitudinal patterns. The pronotum is narrower than both the head and elytra. Males have two spurs at the apex of their middle tibiae.

Actual size

| | |
|---|---|
| FAMILY | Meloidae |
| SUBFAMILY | Meloinae |
| DISTRIBUTION | Palearctic: Europe, North Africa, and Asia |
| MACROHABITAT | Mesic to arid steppe; montane grasslands associated with woodlands |
| MICROHABITAT | Adults crawl on ground or on plants; larvae develop in nests of mining bees |
| FEEDING HABITS | Adults feed on leaves and flowers, while larvae parasitize bee grubs |
| NOTE | In addition to defending themselves with caustic cantharidin, adults also play dead |

ADULT LENGTH
¾–1¾ in
(20–45 mm)

*MELOE VARIEGATUS*
# SPECKLED OIL BEETLE
DONOVAN, 1793

501

The flightless, diurnal adults emerge in spring and feed on the leaves of many plant species, including Corn Gromwell (*Lithospermum arvense*), False Hellebore (*Veratrum*), Ranunculus (*Ranunculus*), and Tuberous Valerian (*Valeriana tuberosa*), and sometimes attack crops. The first-instar larva, or triungulin, hatches in about a month, climbs up on a flower, uses modified spines on its head to attach itself to the abdomen of a digger bee (*Anthophora*), and hitches a ride back to the bee's subterranean nest to parasitize its brood. This action sometimes injures or kills the carrier bee and the triungulins are occasionally implicated in damaging or destroying European honeybee (*Apis mellifera*) colonies.

RELATED SPECIES

*Meloe* is mostly a Holarctic genus, with more than 100 species in 16 subgenera distributed from western Europe to Japan. The subgenus Lampromeloe contains only two species, *M. variegatus* and *M. cavensis*. The latter species is distinguished by the large and raised polished areas on the elytra.

**The Speckled Oil Beetle** is a soft-bodied, dark metallic blue or green beetle with coppery or violet reflections. The equally broad head and pronotum are both coarsely punctate. The short, overlapping elytra are unevenly sculptured. The abdomen of the female extends well beyond the elytra and is festooned with row of brilliant iridescent patches down the middle.

Actual size

| FAMILY | Meloidae |
|---|---|
| SUBFAMILY | Nemognathinae |
| DISTRIBUTION | Palearctic: Israel, Lebanon, Syria, Turkey |
| MACROHABITAT | Mediterranean habitats |
| MICROHABITAT | Adults occur on Asteraceae (e.g., *Crepis*); eggs on vegetation; larvae in bee (Apoidea) nests |
| FEEDING HABITS | Adults are phytophagous; larvae are parasites of wild bee (Apoidea) nests |
| NOTE | Larvae of *Stenodera* differ from all other known larvae in Nemognathinae in missing adaptations for phoretic behavior, i.e., they do not attach themselves to flower-visiting bees to reach host bees' nests |

ADULT LENGTH
¼–½ in
(7–12 mm)

502

*STENODERA PUNCTICOLLIS*
# STENODERA PUNCTICOLLIS
(CHEVROLAT, 1834)

Actual size

Nemognathinae is the most widespread subfamily of blister beetles and occurs in all major zoographical areas on the planet. It is the only subfamily distributed in the Australian Realm. A study of the first-instar larvae of *Stenodera puncticollis*, described for the first time in 2002, indicates that the genus *Stenodera* represents the most primitive member of Nemognathinae. Adults of this species are typically active in April and May, and copulation is preceded by brief sequences of dorsal courtship.

### RELATED SPECIES

The tribe Stenoderini is restricted to the Palearctic Realm and the genus *Stenodera*, which includes nine species in two subgenera, has one species in Europe (*S. caucasica*) with the other species found in East Asia. The subgenus *Stenoderina*, to which *S. puncticollis* belongs, includes four species with metallic green or blue reflections. The species *Stenodera puncticollis* most closely resembles is *S. palaestina*; they differ primarily in the color pattern of the pronotum and legs.

**Stenodera puncticollis** is an elongate beetle with the head, elytra, and the center of the pronotum metallic blue-green. The apex and base of the femora, and the tibiae, tarsi, antennae, and mouthparts, are black. The outer margin of the pronotum, the middle of the femora, and the last two abdominal ventrites are paler yellowish orange or reddish. The pronotum is narrow, approximately as wide as the head, and is slightly wider posteriorly.

| FAMILY | Mycteridae |
|---|---|
| SUBFAMILY | |
| DISTRIBUTION | Palearctic: Europe, northwest Africa, and western Asia |
| MACROHABITAT | Areas with dry or rocky soils |
| MICROHABITAT | Adults occur on flowers of several groups of plants (e.g., Apiaceae, Asteraceae); larvae are found under bark |
| FEEDING HABITS | Adults feed on pollen; larvae presumably feed on dead wood |
| NOTE | The anterior extension of the head into a distinct rostrum in this species is reminiscent of some species in distantly related weevils in the superfamily Curculionoidea |

ADULT LENGTH
¼–⅜ in
(6–10 mm)

*MYCTERUS CURCULIOIDES*

# MYCTERUS CURCULIOIDES

(FABRICIUS, 1781)

503

The family Mycteridae, which includes approximately 30 genera and more than 150 species, is broadly distributed, although diversity is typically greater in warmer areas. Relatively little is known about the habits of mycterid species. The adults of *Mycterus curculioides* possess well-developed flight wings and are typically active in June and July during the day. They can be abundant at flowers. The elongate, parallel-sided, pale larval stage of this species was described from individuals encountered under the bark of a planted pine (*Pinus*) in Spain.

### RELATED SPECIES

The genus *Mycterus* is more prevalent in temperate areas (primarily in the Holarctic Realm but with species in the Afrotropical, Indian, and Oriental realms) and includes four species in two subgenera in the Palearctic. *Mycterus curculioides* is the only representative of the subgenus *Mycterus*. It can be separated from the other Palearctic species, in part, in having a longer rostrum that is as wide at the apex as it is near the base (as opposed to narrower at the apex in other species).

Actual size

**Mycterus curculioides** is an ovoid black beetle with a long head projecting anteriorly into a distinct flattened rostrum. The dorsal surface is covered with greyish or golden pubescence pressed against the body. The antennae are rather long and narrow, and originate near the middle of the rostrum. The eyes are large and slightly protuberant.

| FAMILY | Trictenotomidae |
|---|---|
| SUBFAMILY | |
| DISTRIBUTION | Oriental: Malaysia, Burma, Indonesia (Borneo, Sumatra, Java), Thailand, Vietnam, Southern China, India (Assam) |
| MACROHABITAT | Forests |
| MICROHABITAT | Associated with dead wood |
| FEEDING HABITS | Larvae are thought to develop in decaying logs |
| NOTE | Adults in this family superficially resemble some members of the distantly related families Lucanidae and Cerambycidae, which has led to confusion regarding their correct placement within the order Coleoptera |

ADULT LENGTH
1⁹⁄₁₆–2¹¹⁄₁₆ in
(40–69 mm)

*TRICTENOTOMA CHILDRENI*

# TRICTENOTOMA CHILDRENI

GRAY, 1832

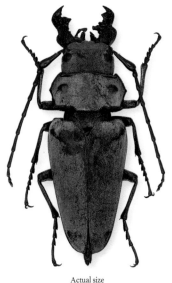

Actual size

The placement of this unique family within the superfamily Tenebrionoidea is based in part on characteristics of the legs of adults (5-5-4 tarsal formula) and features of the larva. The strong-flying trictenotomid adults are commonly encountered around lights at night, although they have also been found on fallen trees and decomposing wood. The larva of *Trictenotoma childreni*, which was described more than 100 years ago, is the only one known in the whole family. It is long (4¾ in / 120 mm), straight, and pale yellowish white, and has well-developed legs and a pair of sharply pointed spines at the end of its abdomen.

## RELATED SPECIES

The small family Trictenotomidae contains only two genera: *Autocrates*, with four species; and *Trictenotoma*, with approximately ten species. All species occur in the southeastern Palearctic and Oriental realms. The sharp, laterally projecting spines on the sides of the pronotum in individuals of *Autocrates* are absent in species of *Trictenotoma*. The short pubescence covering adults of *Trictenotoma* is usually denser than in species of *Autocrates*.

**Trictenotoma childreni** adults are large, robust beetles. Their dorsal and ventral surfaces are distinctly clothed with short setae. The pronotum is distinctly broader than long. The head bears very large, anteriorly projecting mandibles that are usually as long as or longer than the head. The narrow antennae are longer than half the entire body length.

| FAMILY | Pythidae |
|---|---|
| SUBFAMILY | |
| DISTRIBUTION | Palearctic: northeast Europe and Russia |
| MACROHABITAT | Coniferous forest |
| MICROHABITAT | On or under bark of dead trees (e.g., *Picea*) |
| FEEDING HABITS | Adults are presumably predaceous; larvae feed on inner bark of dead coniferous trees |
| NOTE | Copulation typically occurs in May, after which the males die immediately |

ADULT LENGTH
⁷/₁₆–⁵/₈ in
(10.9–15.9 mm)

*PYTHO KOLWENSIS*
# PYTHO KOLWENSIS
SAHLBERG, 1833

505

The small family Pythidae includes approximately 25 described species in seven genera. The nine species of *Pytho* are distributed in the Nearctic and Palearctic realms. The species in this genus typically occur in northern boreal forest or taiga, although some ranges extend southward into areas of higher elevation with conifer forests. Adults of *P. kolwensis* overwinter under bark, inside their pupal cell. Larvae are known to develop over several years. This species, which generally occurs in old-growth forests ranging from 170 to 300 years old, is considered to be endangered in Finland and Sweden.

## RELATED SPECIES

A thorough review of the genus based on adult, larval, and pupal characters, published by D. Pollock in 1991, revealed that *Pytho kolwensis* belongs to a group of species that includes *P. strictus* from eastern North America, and *P. nivalis* from the Russian Far East and Japan. The species in *Pytho* can generally be separated based on characters of the prothorax and elytra, although examination of the male genitalia is sometimes also necessary.

**Pytho kolwensis** is a somewhat flattened reddish-black to black beetle without metallic reflections. The mouthparts, tarsi, and antennae are usually lighter in color. The flattened pronotum is widest near the middle. The pronotal disk has a pair of longitudinal depressions. The elytra, which are convex dorsally, have faintly impressed longitudinal striae.

Actual size

| FAMILY | Pyrochroidae |
|---|---|
| SUBFAMILY | Pyrochroinae |
| DISTRIBUTION | Palearctic: Europe, Turkey |
| MACROHABITAT | Woodlands, hedgerows, parks, gardens |
| MICROHABITAT | Adults are found on flowers and vegetation or under loose bark of deciduous trees; larvae live under bark |
| FEEDING HABITS | Adults are probably omnivorous; larvae feed largely on subcortical woody and fungal tissues |
| NOTE | The common names fire-colored beetles or cardinal beetles have been used for bright orange and red species in the family Pyrochroidae (most of which are European and Asian) |

ADULT LENGTH
³/₈–⁹/₁₆ in
(10–14 mm)

*PYROCHROA SERRATICORNIS*
# COMMON CARDINAL BEETLE
(SCOPOLI, 1763)

Actual size

**The Common Cardinal Beetle** is a medium-size beetle with a bright orange to red pronotum and elytra. The head varies in color from black to orange or red depending on the subspecies. Antennomeres 3–11 have distinct toothlike projections that increase in length toward the apex of the antenna. The head is strongly constricted posteriorly into a distinct neck. The ventral surface of the body, legs, and antennae are black.

Adults of the Common Cardinal Beetle can be very common. They are thought to prey on flower-visiting insects in the summer. The dorsoventrally flattened larvae of this species live mostly under bark (although they are sometimes found deep within soft xylem tissue) and feed largely on fungal hyphae and soft cambium tissue. The generally soft-bodied larvae have a heavily sclerotized apical abdominal segment that ends in a pair of large spines. It has been reported that larvae of the Common Cardinal Beetle can take up to three years to reach the pupal stage.

RELATED SPECIES

The subfamily Pyrochroinae is the most diverse within the family and includes more than 100 species, these primarily distributed in temperate regions of Asia. The genus *Pyrochroa* includes a small number of species in Europe, northern Africa, and Asia.

| FAMILY | Salpingidae |
|---|---|
| SUBFAMILY | Dacoderinae |
| DISTRIBUTION | Australian: Australia (northeastern Queensland) |
| MACROHABITAT | Forest |
| MICROHABITAT | Adults live in nests of ants (*Leptogenys* and *Odontomachus* spp.); larvae are unknown |
| FEEDING HABITS | Unknown |
| NOTE | The genus name is a combination of the Greek *tretos* (meaning "perforated") and "thorax," and refers to the grooved prothorax of this beetle |

ADULT LENGTH
⁵⁄₁₆–½ in
(8.3–11.5 mm)

*TRETOTHORAX CLEISTOSTOMA*

# TRETOTHORAX CLEISTOSTOMA

LEA, 1910

507

The subfamily Dacoderinae contains ten species that each have a rather unusual-looking head and prothorax; five of the species were described in a taxonomic treatment of the group published in 2006. The correct placement of this and related species in the classification of beetles was a subject of debate for many years, until Dacoderinae was placed within the family Salpingidae in 1982 by world Coleoptera expert J. F. Lawrence. Only a small number of adult specimens of this species have been collected, one on a log and others from nests of the ants *Leptogenys excisa* and *Odontomachus ruficeps*.

RELATED SPECIES

The genus *Tretothorax* contains a single species, is the only representative of the subfamily Dacoderinae in the Australian Realm, and is the only genus in the subfamily with an elongated rostrum. The subfamily Dacoderinae includes two other genera (*Dacoderus* and *Myrmecoderus*), distributed from the southwestern United States south to northern South America. The flight wings in *T. cleistostoma* are well developed but are absent in other species of Dacoderinae.

Actual size

**Tretothorax cleistostoma** is an elongate, somewhat flattened black beetle with the anterior portion of the head forming a rostrum that is longer than it is wide. The antennae, which have only ten bead-like segments, are sometimes described as having a one-segmented club. The elongate pronotum is distinctly narrower than the base of the elytra and has three longitudinal grooves.

| FAMILY | Salpingidae |
|---|---|
| SUBFAMILY | Aegialitinae |
| DISTRIBUTION | Nearctic: Canada (Metlakatla in British Columbia) |
| MACROHABITAT | Pacific coast |
| MICROHABITAT | Intertidal rocks |
| FEEDING HABITS | Adults and larvae occur beneath intertidal rocks and feed on algae |
| NOTE | Species in this genus, including *Aegialites canadensis*, are flightless and their range is generally restricted to small geographical areas |

ADULT LENGTH
³⁄₁₆ in
(3.5–4.8 mm)

*AEGIALITES CANADENSIS*
# AEGIALITES CANADENSIS
ZERCHE, 2004

508

Actual size

Individuals of *Aegialites* typically occur halfway between the high- and low-tide marks along the northern Pacific coast. The sharp tarsal claws of these beetles enable them to adhere firmly to the rocks. Adults of *A. canadensis* are reportedly active year-round and occur in crevices or beneath intertidal rocks along the seashore. The immature stages can be found in July and August. The larvae are elongate and parallel-sided, and lack setae on most of their body. This species can occur in large numbers when conditions are favorable.

### RELATED SPECIES

*Aegialites* contains 31 species ranging from the coasts of California, British Columbia, and Alaska (inclusive of the islands), to Japan and 17 islands in the Far East of Russia. The genus *Antarcticodomus*, which occurs on offshore New Zealand islands, is the only other representative genus of the subfamily Aegialitinae. The ratio between the length of the antennae and the width of the head in *Aegialites canadensis* differs from that of other species in British Columbia and Alaska.

**Aegialites canadensis** is an elongate, dark brown to black beetle with a smooth pronotum and an uneven surface on the elytra. The antennae are rather long and end with a loose three-segmented club. The apices of the elytra are broadly rounded. In males the tibiae are broadly curved, whereas in females they are almost straight.

| FAMILY | Anthicidae |
|---|---|
| SUBFAMILY | Eurygeniinae |
| DISTRIBUTION | Nearctic: Canada (British Columbia, Alberta); USA (Idaho, Washington, Oregon, California) |
| MACROHABITAT | Meadows or grasslands near streams |
| MICROHABITAT | Adults are found on flowers or plants; larvae live in bogs |
| FEEDING HABITS | Adults feed on pollen; larval feeding habits are uncertain |
| NOTE | A member of one of the most distinctive subfamilies of Anthicidae, which includes the largest species in the family |

ADULT LENGTH
⁵⁄₁₆–½ in
(8.3–12.2 mm)

*PERGETUS CAMPANULATUS*

# PERGETUS CAMPANULATUS

(LECONTE, 1874)

509

As is the case for the majority of species of Eurygeniinae, adults of *Pergetus campanulatus* are commonly found on flowers. The scoop-like mandibles of these beetles are modified to feed on pollen, and the cutting edge, which is typical of mandibles of other beetles generally, is either reduced or absent. The only known larva for the subfamily Eurygeniinae is a *P. campanulatus* larva that was collected in an old cranberry (*Vaccinium* spp.) bog; it bears a pair of heavily sclerotized, basally branched urogomphi at the apex of the abdomen.

Actual size

### RELATED SPECIES

The cosmopolitan subfamily Eurygeniinae includes approximately 130 described species and is most diverse in the semiarid grasslands of the Nearctic and Australian realms. The genus *Pergetus*, which includes two species restricted to the Pacific Northwest, is diagnosed from related genera in North America (e.g., *Rilettius*, *Qadrius*) in part by the presence of both erect, tactile setae and shorter, suberect setae on the elytra, and the enlarged triangular apical palpomere of the maxillae.

**Pergetus campanulatus** is a rather large, elongate, pale brown to black ant-like flower beetle and is covered with silvery to brown pubescence. The long, narrow antennae do not widen near the apex. The pronotum has a deep longitudinal groove along the middle, and on the anterior margin there is a dorsal flange that broadens evenly to the middle and extends anteriorly over the base of the neck. The punctate, pubescent elytra are parallel-sided and more than twice as long as wide.

| FAMILY | Anthicidae |
|---|---|
| SUBFAMILY | Lemodinae |
| DISTRIBUTION | Australian: Australia (Australian Capital Territory, New South Wales, Queensland, Victoria) |
| MACROHABITAT | Forests |
| MICROHABITAT | On and under logs |
| FEEDING HABITS | Presumably mycophagous |
| NOTE | Several new species in this genus, from Indonesian New Guinea, Papua New Guinea, and the Solomon Islands, have been described in the last ten years |

ADULT LENGTH
¼ in
(5.5–6.5 mm)

*LEMODES COCCINEA*

# LEMODES COCCINEA

BOHEMAN, 1858

Actual size

The small anthicid subfamily Lemodinae contains six genera and approximately 50 species distributed in Australasia, New Zealand, and temperate South America. The elongate, parallel-sided larvae of *Lemodes*, when known, have a dorsal pattern of light and dark colors, suggesting that they feed on exterior surfaces, possibly fungal fruiting bodies. Adults of *L. coccinea* are apparently common under logs in some areas and have been captured crawling over logs with individuals of the related species *L. splendens*.

## RELATED SPECIES

In addition to *Lemodes*, the subfamily Lemodinae also includes the genera *Lemodinus* and *Trichananca* in Australia. Species of *Lemodes* can be recognized in part by the color pattern on their elytra, which can vary from entirely reddish brown to a mixture of reddish brown with blue reflections and/or patches of white setae. *Lemodes elongata* is the only species in the genus with 12 antennomeres instead of 11.

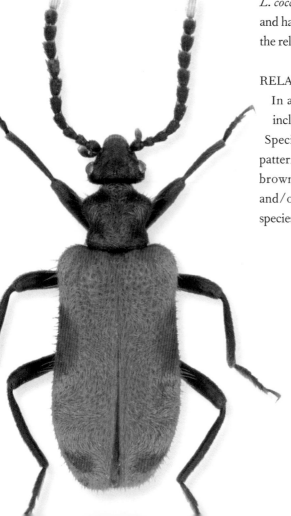

**Lemodes coccinea** is an elongated beetle with rectangular-shaped elytra and relatively long, erect setae on the head, pronotum, and elytra. Antennomeres 9–11, 10–11, or 11 are usually lighter in color. The dorsal surface of the head and pronotum, which are typically covered with pubescence pressed against the body, can vary in color from yellowish orange to reddish or black and lacks a metallic sheen. The legs are noticeable darker than the elytra, which can appear velvety red in some individuals.

| FAMILY | Anthicidae |
|---|---|
| SUBFAMILY | Anthicinae |
| DISTRIBUTION | Neotropical and Nearctic: native to Argentina, Paraguay, Brazil; introduced to southern USA (Florida, Louisiana, Alabama, Georgia, Texas, Mississippi, South Carolina) |
| MACROHABITAT | In or near forests |
| MICROHABITAT | Associated with ants; adults fly to lights at night |
| FEEDING HABITS | Scavengers and opportunistic predators |
| NOTE | Mimics ants in appearance and in their behavior when moving |

ADULT LENGTH
⅛ in
(2.5–3 mm)

*ACANTHINUS ARGENTINUS*

# ACANTHINUS ARGENTINUS

(PIC, 1913)

511

Actual size

Species in the genus *Acanthinus* closely mimic the movements and color of ants as they forage together with them on vegetation. These beetles are sometimes found running in ant columns and the larvae often occur with ants as well. The fast-running adults of *A. argentinus* were recently encountered in the southern United States for the first time, where they seem to be thriving and expanding their distribution. Most adults were encountered near artificial lights at night. Although the pathway of introduction of this species in the southern United States is still unclear, at least some of the individuals were captured near major ports.

## RELATED SPECIES

Along with approximately 30 other genera (e.g., *Amblyderus*, *Anthicus*), *Acanthinus* belongs to the tribe Anthicini, whose members are characterized by the presence of a broadly rounder anterior portion of the pronotum instead of a tubercular projection over the head. It is a relatively diverse genus, with more than 100 species in the Neotropical Realm and a small number of species (e.g., *A. australiensis*) in Australia.

**Acanthinus argentinus** is a small, mostly reddish-brown beetle with a long pronotum that is narrowly constricted behind the middle, giving the beetle an ant-like appearance, especially in lateral view. The basal half of the elytra is a paler reddish brown, while the apical half is dark brown to black, usually with paler markings. The dorsal surface is shiny and glabrous, except for a number of long setae.

| FAMILY | Anthicidae |
|---|---|
| SUBFAMILY | Notoxinae |
| DISTRIBUTION | Nearctic and Neotropical: USA, Mexico |
| MACROHABITAT | Various, including crops, pastures, and orchards |
| MICROHABITAT | On or beneath vegetation; burrows into soil as an adult |
| FEEDING HABITS | Adults are omnivorous; larvae probably feed on roots |
| NOTE | Known as an occasional predator of eggs and small larvae of pests on several crops such as cotton (*Glossopteris* spp.) and Soybean (*Glycine max*). Adults can fly and are attracted to lights at night |

ADULT LENGTH
⅛–³⁄₁₆ in
(2.5–4 mm)

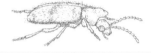

*NOTOXUS CALCARATUS*
# NOTOXUS CALCARATUS
HORN, 1884

512

Actual size

The subfamily Notoxinae includes approximately 400 species worldwide that are characterized by an anteriorly projecting "horn" on the pronotum that covers the head in dorsal view. Adults of some species of *Notoxus*, including *N. calcaratus*, are known to be attracted to cantharidins (antipredator secretions produced by beetles in the families Meloidae and Oedemeridae). Individuals of *N. calcaratus* can be found throughout the year in the southern part of the species' range. Because adults of this species will sometimes feed on eggs and small larvae of known pests, it is considered a low-level biological control agent for many crops.

## RELATED SPECIES

*Notoxus* is a genus distributed worldwide but most diverse in Africa, western North America, and Australasia. Approximately 50 species occur in the United States and Canada, which can primarily be separated based on the color pattern on their elytra, although some require careful examination of their genital structures for accurate identification. *Notoxus calcaratus* and *N. hirsutus* share the presence of a row of pits on the ventral surface of the pronotal horn.

**Notoxus calcaratus** is a small elongated beetle with a reddish-brown body covered in setae. The elytra have an irregular black band near the middle and the apex, as well as a pair of black spots near the base. The pronotum bears a prominent projection along its anterior edge, covering the head in dorsal view. The antennae are long and narrow.

| FAMILY | Aderidae |
| --- | --- |
| SUBFAMILY | |
| DISTRIBUTION | Australian: Australia (northern Queensland) |
| MACROHABITAT | Rainforest |
| MICROHABITAT | Associated with nests of the termite *Microcerotermes turneri* |
| FEEDING HABITS | Adult feeding habits are uncertain; larvae feed on salivary secretions obtained from their termite hosts |
| NOTE | Species of *Megaxenus* are remarkable for their large size when compared with other species in the family, as well as the ability of the larvae to live among, and be fed by, their termite hosts |

ADULT LENGTH
³⁄₁₆–¼ in
(5.2–6.5 mm)

*MEGAXENUS TERMITOPHILUS*

# MEGAXENUS TERMITOPHILUS

LAWRENCE, 1990

513

Species in the unusual aderid genus *Megaxenus* are found in association with nests of termites in the genus *Microcerotermes*. This microhabitat preference differs markedly from that of other aderids, which usually occur in rotten wood, under bark, or in leaf litter. Adults of *Megaxenus termitophilus* can typically be found in web-like cocoons at the periphery of their host termite nests along with late-instar larvae and pupae. Earlier larval instars are found at the center of the nest amongst the termites. The larvae of *M. termitophilus* mimic termite queens in the nests and are, exceptionally, groomed and fed by the termite workers. Adults of this species are not at all integrated into the social system of termites and are readily attacked by termite workers and soldiers.

## RELATED SPECIES

The cosmopolitan family Aderidae, which contains approximately 1,000 species worldwide, is in need of modern taxonomic and phylogenetic study. The genus *Megaxenus* contains *M. termitophilus* from Australia as well as *M. bioculatus* and *M. papuensis* from Papua New Guinea. Species in this genus can be separated based on whether a distinct ridge on the head is present posteriorly or not, as well as on additional differences on the elytra and pronotum.

Actual size

**Megaxenus termitophilus** is an elongate, parallel-sided brown to reddish-brown beetle whose dorsal surface is relatively flattened and covered with fine, short setae pressed against the body. The head, which is as wide as the pronotum, lacks a transverse ridge that is present in other species in the genus. The elytra have vague patterns of darker and lighter areas. The base of the femora is dark brown but the apex is noticeably lighter in color.

| FAMILY | Oxypeltidae |
|---|---|
| SUBFAMILY | |
| DISTRIBUTION | Neotropical: Chile and Argentina |
| MACROHABITAT | Valdivian temperate rainforests in the southern Andes |
| MICROHABITAT | *Nothofagus* (southern beech or coigüe) tree trunks and foliage |
| FEEDING HABITS | Adults may feed on foliage; larvae are xylophagous |
| NOTE | The unusual coloration of this species similar to that of metallic woodboring beetles |

ADULT MALE LENGTH
1–1⁹⁄₁₆ in
(25–40 mm)

ADULT FEMALE LENGTH
1³⁄₁₆–1⁷⁄₈ in
(30–48 mm)

514

*CHELODERUS CHILDRENI*
# COIGÜE
# LONGHORN BORER
GRAY, 1832

This stunning longhorn beetle was named after John Children, the first keeper of the Zoology Department of the Natural History Museum in London. Adults most commonly emerge from their evergreen *Nothofagus* tree hosts (commonly called coigüe or southern beech) in the temperate rainforests of Argentina and Chile from December through March. Adults are diurnal, flying from late morning until the afternoon, during the warmest part of the day. Males are strongly attracted to female pheromones. Currently, the species is placed in the family Oxypeltidae, along with two other species.

RELATED SPECIES

This species is a member of a small family of unusual longhorn woodboring beetles that contains only two genera and three species (the others being *Cheloderus penai* and *Oxypeltus quadrispinosus*). All the related species occur only in Argentina and Chile. They have been treated historically as members of Prioninae or as a separate subfamily of Cerambycidae. Studies of larvae showed some superficial similarities to Vesperidae.

Actual size

**The Coigüe Longhorn Borer** is strikingly colored with metallic blue and green on the head, pronotum, and underside, and red and green on the elytra. The pronotum has large ridges on top, extending to the sides. Pubescence is nearly lacking on the entire body. The antennae are relatively short for longhorn beetles, extending to only about half the length of the body.

| FAMILY | Vesperidae |
|---|---|
| SUBFAMILY | Vesperinae |
| DISTRIBUTION | Palearctic: southern Europe (France, Italy, Croatia) |
| MACROHABITAT | Mixed forest and grassland |
| MICROHABITAT | Grasses, vines |
| FEEDING HABITS | Polyphagous on grasses |
| NOTE | Females and larvae have unusual morphology |

*VESPERUS LURIDUS*
# VESPERUS LURIDUS
(ROSSI, 1794)

ADULT MALE LENGTH
$^9\!/_{16}$–$^{15}\!/_{16}$ in
(15–24 mm)

ADULT FEMALE LENGTH
$^5\!/_8$–$1^1\!/_8$ in
(16–29 mm)

515

Adults of this species are active from April to July in their range through southern Europe. This species exhibits polymorphism: females are larger, with distended abdomens and shortened elytra. The males are nocturnal and attracted to lights, but the females are flightless. The unusually globose and shortened larvae develop in grasses, but may have many unrecorded hosts since other species in the genus are polyphagous. Some related species are known pests of grapevines in vineyards in the Mediterranean region.

RELATED SPECIES
The genus *Vesperus* includes 18 very similar species of southern European and Mediterranean distribution. These have historically been treated within the subfamily Cerambycidae but are now placed in their own family, along with a somewhat disparate collection of genera. Their unusual larval morphology and chromosomes have justified their current placement outside Cerambycidae.

Actual size

**Vesperus luridus** has a very constricted head posteriorly and a narrowed pronotum anteriorly. It superficially resembles beetles of the family Meloidae or primitive species of the Lepturinae subfamily of Cerambycidae. Adults are uniformly pale brown. The females are larger than males and have distended abdomens and shortened elytra. The mature larvae are unusual in that they are globose and shortened.

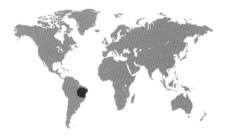

| FAMILY | Vesperidae |
|---|---|
| SUBFAMILY | Anoplodermatinae |
| DISTRIBUTION | Neotropical: east Brazil (Goiás, Bahia, and Minas Gerais) |
| MACROHABITAT | Tropical savanna (*cerrado*) |
| MICROHABITAT | Ground-dwelling |
| FEEDING HABITS | Unknown; probably root-feeders |
| NOTE | Possibly the most bizarre-looking longhorn beetle |

ADULT LENGTH
1⅜–2⅛ in
(35–55 mm)

516

# HYPOCEPHALUS ARMATUS

DESMAREST, 1832

Actual size

This is perhaps the most bizarre-looking longhorn beetle of all. It has so many unusual characteristics that coleopterists have been uncertain of its relationships since its discovery. It is known only from a small area of eastern Brazil (primarily in the state of Minas Gerais), where the flightless adults (primarily males) can be found walking on the ground or burrowing into it from December through January. Females are exceedingly rarely found. Nothing is known of their host plants, but the larvae presumably feed on roots.

RELATED SPECIES

John LeConte, who described thousands of beetles species during his distinguished career, placed *Hypocephalus armatus* in its own family in 1876, saying, "among all Coleoptera known to science, there is none which has provoked more discordant expressions of opinion regarding its position." Its systematic placement has fluctuated ever since. Now it is the only species in the tribe Hypocephalini. Until recently, it had been placed in a separate subfamily of Cerambycidae, the Anoplodermatinae, but is now part of the Vesperidae.

**Hypocephalus armatus** looks, in many ways, more like a mole cricket than a beetle. The head is elongate and deflexed, with very short antennae. The prothorax is very long and as large as the remainder of the body behind. The hind legs are enlarged with curved tibia, and modified for burrowing. The elytra are very hardened and fused.

| FAMILY | Disteniidae |
|---|---|
| SUBFAMILY | Disteniinae |
| DISTRIBUTION | Neotropical: Brazil, Paraguay, northern Argentina |
| MACROHABITAT | Tropical forests |
| MICROHABITAT | Trees |
| FEEDING HABITS | Xylophagous (specific hosts unknown) |
| NOTE | Possesses unusual fringed antennae |

ADULT LENGTH
⁵⁄₁₆–⁷⁄₁₆ in
(8–11 mm)

*COMETES HIRTICORNIS*
# COMETES HIRTICORNIS
LEPELETIER & AUDINET-SERVILLE, 1828

517

This species is widespread throughout Brazil, and in addition it has been collected in Paraguay and Argentina. Further studies may show it to be present also in Bolivia. Nothing is known of its host trees, so this species represents yet another example of how limited our knowledge is for tropical beetles. Adults are usually collected by beating branches and foliage after the beginning of the rainy season from late October through December.

## RELATED SPECIES

Until recently, the genus *Cometes* was moderately large, but many species were removed to other genera by Antonio Santos-Silva and Gérard Tavakilian in 2009. At the time of writing, *Cometes* contains only six species, all restricted to South America. *Cometes hirticornis* is the only member with unicolorous elytra (they are bicolored in all others).

Actual size

**Cometes hirticornis** is a small disteniid recognized by the uniformly blue-gray coloration throughout its body, legs, and antennae. Only the head and part of the prothorax are partially reddish. Like other members of the family, the scape and maxillary palpi are quite long. The antennae are fringed with very long setae on the last four segments.

| FAMILY | Cerambycidae |
|---|---|
| SUBFAMILY | Dorcasominae |
| DISTRIBUTION | Oriental: Borneo |
| MACROHABITAT | Rainforests |
| MICROHABITAT | Tree branches and vines |
| FEEDING HABITS | Larval hosts are unknown but may include *Santalum*, *Pterocarpus*, and *Terminalia*; like most longhorn beetles, adults do little or no feeding |
| NOTE | When resting, holds onto a branch with the front legs and antennae, with the remainder of the body dangling below |

**ADULT LENGTH**
$^{11}/_{16}$–1$^{1}/_{32}$ in
(18–26 mm)

*CAPNOLYMMA STYGIA*
# CAPNOLYMMA STYGIA
PASCOE, 1858

The phylogenetic placement of this enigmatic longhorn species has baffled researchers ever since its description. Little is known of its biology, but adults have been collected flying at dusk in the rainforests of Borneo. Other species in the genus may use *Santalum* (Santalaceae), *Pterocarpus* (Fabaceae), and *Terminalia* (Combretaceae) as hosts. The live resting posture of this species is unique in that the adult holds onto a vine or branch with the two front legs and the antennae together looping over the branch. The rest of the body, with the legs held close, dangles below.

### RELATED SPECIES

Seven species are currently included in *Capnolymma*, of which *C. stygia* is the type species. This enigmatic species was placed in the subfamily Lepturinae until as recently as 2008. Some authors have recently placed it in the subfamily Dorcasominae, but there is no consensus by experts such as Alexander Miroshnikov that this is appropriate.

**Capnolymma stygia** is recognized by its lepturine-like head and pronotum, combined with the very long antennal scape, elytral humeri with a tooth, and outer apex of the elytra with a short spine. The zigzag pattern of white pubescence across the middle of the elytra is distinctive. The unique resting posture described above is also characteristic for this genus.

Actual size

| FAMILY | Cerambycidae |
|---|---|
| SUBFAMILY | Apatophyseinae |
| DISTRIBUTION | Palearctic: western and northern China, Mongolia, eastern Kazakhstan |
| MACROHABITAT | Arid habitats (sandy desert dunes and clay deserts) |
| MICROHABITAT | Trees and shrubs |
| FEEDING HABITS | Larvae are root-borers of desert trees and shrubs; like most longhorn beetles, adults do little or no feeding |
| NOTE | Unusual desert-dwelling cerambycid |

| ADULT MALE LENGTH |
|---|
| $^7/_{16}$–$^{11}/_{16}$ in |
| (11–17 mm) |

| ADULT FEMALE LENGTH |
|---|
| $^9/_{16}$–$^7/_8$ in |
| (15–21 mm) |

*APATOPHYSIS SERRICORNIS*

# APATOPHYSIS SERRICORNIS

(GEBLER, 1843)

519

*Apatophysis serricornis* is a widespread central Asian species known from arid desert and semidesert areas in Kazakhstan, China, and Mongolia. It is the only species of *Apatophysis* with this broad distribution. Adults fly from June through August. The species is probably polyphagous on many desert shrubs and trees, although only one host tree is definitively known, *Haloxylon*, of the family Amaranthaceae. Owing to its similarity to primitive Lepturinae, the species was originally placed in the genus *Pachyta* by Frederic Gebler.

## RELATED SPECIES

There are nearly 30 species in the genus *Apatophysis*, a member of the small subfamily Dorcasominae, which includes many genera that are superficially disparate. Other authors have placed *Apatophysis* in its own subfamily, the Apatophyseinae, but that may render Dorcasominae paraphyletic. Further systematic studies must be carried out to determine its position among the Cerambycidae. Several species, including *A. mongolica*, were synonymized with *A. serricornis* by Mikhail Danilevsky in 2008.

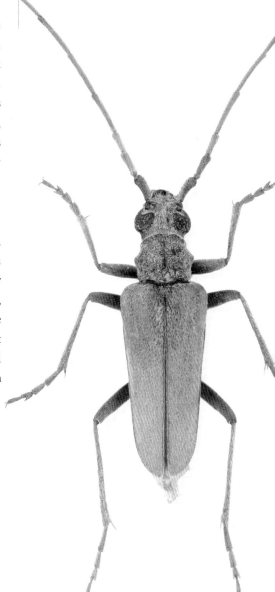

Actual size

**Apatophysis serricornis** is uniformly pale brown in color and superficially resembles primitive members of the subfamily Lepturinae by having an elongate frons on the head and lateral turbercles on the pronotum. However, the antennae are one and a half times the length of the body and have somewhat broad segments, atypical of most lepturines.

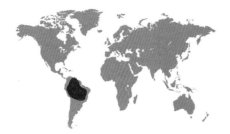

| FAMILY | Cerambycidae |
|---|---|
| SUBFAMILY | Cerambycinae |
| DISTRIBUTION | Neotropical: northern and central South America |
| MACROHABITAT | Tropical rainforests and humid forests |
| MICROHABITAT | Recently dead trees |
| FEEDING HABITS | Unknown, but larvae probably develop in Fabaceae and Lauraceae |
| NOTE | Unique large tufts of pubescence on antennal segments 3–6 |

**ADULT LENGTH**
$^{7}/_{16}$–$^{7}/_{8}$ in
(11–21 mm)

*COSMISOMA AMMIRALIS*
# COSMISOMA AMMIRALIS
(LINNAEUS, 1767)

This is one of the earliest cerambycids classified by Carl Linnaeus, who described it in 1767. Broadly distributed in South America, it is among the most striking longhorn beetles, with black, orange, and yellow markings and distinctive pubescent tufts on antennomeres 3–6. Adults are active primarily from October through January and can be collected on recently dead trees or cut wood, where they congregate in hot afternoons. This species is probably polyphagous, but larval hosts are unknown. Other species are known from *Ocotea* (Lauraceae), and *Parkinsonia* and *Acacia* (Fabaceae).

RELATED SPECIES

The genus *Cosmisoma* is a member of the diverse Nearctic and Neotropical tribe Rhopalophorini and contains 42 species. Although many genera in the tribe have pubescent tufts on the antennae and/or legs, the primary antennal tuft on segment 5 and the lack of pubescent tufts on the hind tibiae characterize most *Cosmisoma* species, including *C. ammiralis*.

Actual size

**Cosmisoma ammiralis** is recognized by having the sides of the pronotum and base and middle of the elytra golden-yellow. The antennae have long tufts at the apex of segments 3 and 4, a very large black tuft on segment 5, and a smaller orange to white or yellow tuft on segment 6.

| FAMILY | Cerambycidae |
|---|---|
| SUBFAMILY | Cerambycinae |
| DISTRIBUTION | Nearctic: eastern United States |
| MACROHABITAT | Deciduous hardwood forests |
| MICROHABITAT | Foliage, branches, and tree trunks |
| FEEDING HABITS | Adults feed on pollen of flowers of *Cornus* and *Prunus* spp.; larvae feed on dead branches of several hosts including *Sapindus*, *Celtis*, *Prosopis*, *Acacia*, and *Zanthoxylum* |
| NOTE | The species is ant-like in appearance and behavior |

ADULT LENGTH
³⁄₁₆–¼ in
(3.5–5.5 mm)

*EUDERCES REICHEI*
# EUDERCES REICHEI
LECONTE, 1873

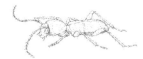

521

This species can be locally common in many parts of its range in the eastern United States. Adults can be collected from March through June on many of their deciduous hardwood host trees. Known larval hosts include persimmon (*Diospyros* spp.), mesquite (*Prosopis* spp.), hawthorn (*Crataegus* spp.), and hackberry (*Celtis* spp.). Adults can be found on the foliage, branches, and trunks of these trees. Unlike most longhorn beetles, adults can also be found feeding on the pollen of flowering trees such as plum and cherry (*Prunus* spp.) and dogwood (*Cornus* spp.).

## RELATED SPECIES

This is a member of the small Neotropical and Nearctic tribe Tillomorphini, which includes 13 genera worldwide, although there are only three in North America: *Euderces*, with four species, and *Tetranodus* and *Pentanodes*, each monotypic. There are two subspecies of *E. reichei* (*E. r. reichei* and *E. r. exilis*), which overlap in their distribution in Texas. The relationships between the Tillomorphini, Anaglyptini, and Clytini, which each contain similar species, needs much further analysis.

Actual size

**Euderces reichei** is recognized by its ant-like appearance—it is small and red and black in color, and has anteriorly constricted elytra and a posteriorly constricted and anteriorly elevated pronotum. It has a transverse ivory-colored callus just in front of the middle of the elytron and a granulate pronotum, which lacks the well-defined wrinkles of other species.

| | |
|---|---|
| FAMILY | Cerambycidae |
| SUBFAMILY | Cerambycinae |
| DISTRIBUTION | Cosmopolitan |
| MACROHABITAT | Coniferous forests |
| MICROHABITAT | Pine and other softwoods, pine flooring in buildings |
| FEEDING HABITS | Adults do not feed |
| NOTE | Adults are known to emerge from wood after 30 years of larval feeding |

ADULT LENGTH
½–1⅛ in
(12–28 mm)

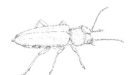

*HYLOTRUPES BAJULUS*
# OLD-HOUSE BORER
(LINNAEUS, 1758)

522

This species is an important structural pest. It has been known to cause significant economic losses by destroying floors, walls, and joists of buildings, but generally does not build up large enough populations to cause total destruction. Because the larvae are potentially so long-lived in pine wood, they have spread worldwide from Europe through commerce and shipping of lumber, and are now cosmopolitan. Larvae are capable of undergoing a very prolonged development if wood becomes very dry, and are known to have emerged from wooden floors in old houses after 30 years, although two to three years is most common.

RELATED SPECIES

The genus *Hylotrupes* includes only this single species. Until recently, it was a member of Callidiini, a large tribe of conifer-feeders in 14 other genera. It is now placed as the only member of its own tribe, Hylotrupini, although the basis for such a treatment may be spurious.

**The Old-house Borer** is recognized by its uniform gray to brownish-black color, with subtle white or gray pubescent markings across the middle of the elytra. The pronotum has a middle ridge with raised knobs on either side. The larvae are unusual in that they have vertical rows of three ocelli on both sides of the head.

Actual size

| FAMILY | Cerambycidae |
|---|---|
| SUBFAMILY | Cerambycinae |
| DISTRIBUTION | Neotropical: eastern and southern Brazil, southern Paraguay, eastern Argentina |
| MACROHABITAT | Tropical moist forests |
| MICROHABITAT | Canopy foliage and flowers |
| FEEDING HABITS | Adults presumably can be attracted to canopy flowers but larval hosts are unknown |
| NOTE | An amazing mimic of wasps in the families Braconidae and Ichneumonidae |

ADULT LENGTH
½–1⅛ in
(12–28 mm)

*ISTHMIADE BRACONIDES*

# ISTHMIADE BRACONIDES
(PERTY, 1832)

523

This species, described nearly 200 years ago, is widespread in eastern South America but most commonly encountered in Brazil. It includes some of the most remarkable mimics of the wasp families Ichneumonidae and Braconidae known in the order Coleoptera. Although hosts are not known for this species, other related species have been collected on flowers of trees in many families, including Sapindaceae, Rhamnaceae, Meliaceae, Rutaceae, and Amaranthaceae, among others. Their perfect wasp mimicry presumably gives them protection from potential predators as they feed beside the wasps and bees.

## RELATED SPECIES

This species is a member of the predominately mimetic tribe Rhinotragini. The genus *Isthmiade* includes 17 species distributed in Central and South America. The type species of this genus is now considered a synonym of *I. braconides*.

**Isthmiade braconides** is among the most spectacular mimics of ichneumonid and braconid wasps known. The morphological features that give it this appearance include the subulate, inconspicuous elytra that are constricted at the middle and diverge at the apex, exposing the prominent hind wings and abdomen. From the lateral view, the abdomen is curved downward and the thorax is reddish at the sides.

Actual size

| FAMILY | Cerambycidae |
|---|---|
| SUBFAMILY | Cerambycinae |
| DISTRIBUTION | Nearctic: west coast of North America, from British Columbia through California |
| MACROHABITAT | Cypress and redwood forests |
| MICROHABITAT | Pinecones of Giant Sequoia (*Sequoiadendron giganteum*) and Coast Redwood (*Sequoia sempervirens*); dead and dying branches of cedar (*Thuja* spp.) and cypress (*Cupressus* spp.) |
| FEEDING HABITS | Adults feed on the flesh of pinecones of Giant Sequoia and Coast Redwood; larvae develop in the pinecones of Giant Sequoia and Coast Redwood, and on branches of cedar and cypress trees |
| NOTE | The species is critical in disseminating seeds of Giant Sequoia and Coast Redwood trees |

**ADULT MALE LENGTH**
³⁄₁₆–⁵⁄₁₆ in
(3.5–7.5 mm)

**ADULT FEMALE LENGTH**
³⁄₁₆–⁷⁄₁₆ in
(4.5–10.5 mm)

*PHYMATODES NITIDUS*
# SEQUOIA CONE BORER
LECONTE, 1874

524

The Sequoia Cone Borer is very interesting since it is critical to the dissemination of seeds of the largest trees in North America, the Giant Sequoia (*Sequoiadendron giganteum*) and Coast Redwood (*Sequoia sempervirens*). Larval hosts include these species as well as others in Cupressaceae, the cypress family. Adults lay their eggs on the surfaces of the pinecones and the larvae burrow inside. Adults also feed on the pinecone flesh, which causes the cones to dry and open, allowing the seeds to disperse. Thus, the species serves as a critical ecological component to the survival of these trees.

### RELATED SPECIES

The Holarctic genus *Phymatodes* includes about 70 species distributed throughout North America, Europe, and Asia. No phylogenetic studies have examined the relationships, but based on morphological characters, *P. nitidus* is most similar to *P. decussatus*, another coastal western North American species.

Actual size

**The Sequoia Cone Borer** is somewhat variable in size and coloration. Like a few other species in the genus, the elytra have two separate, transverse white bands of pubescence. The region between the anterior band and the base of the elytra is usually pale brown. The head and pronotum can be pale to dark reddish brown or nearly black.

| FAMILY | Cerambycidae |
|---|---|
| SUBFAMILY | Cerambycinae |
| DISTRIBUTION | Palearctic: central and southern Europe, west to the Pyrenees Mountains |
| MACROHABITAT | Primary beech (*Fagus* spp.) forests, especially at 2,000–3,280 ft (600–1,000 m) |
| MICROHABITAT | Injured, dying, or dead branches (4–8 in / 10–20 cm diameter) of beech (*Fagus* spp.) and other trees |
| FEEDING HABITS | Adult feeding habits unknown; larvae develop in the European Beech (*Fagus sylvatica*) primarily, but other hosts include *Acer*, *Ulmus*, *Salix*, *Castanea*, *Juglans*, *Tilia*, *Quercus*, *Alnus*, and *Crataegus* |
| NOTE | A widespread but threatened European longhorn beetle |

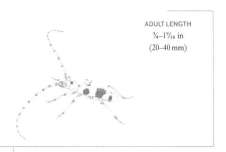

ADULT LENGTH
¾–1⁹⁄₁₆ in
(20–40 mm)

*ROSALIA ALPINA*
# ROSALIA LONGICORN
(LINNAEUS, 1758)

525

This species is one of the most widely recognized species of Cerambycidae in the world because of its beauty. It has been featured on postage stamps in many countries and even a Slovakian coin. Although this species is widespread throughout Europe, it is now becoming locally rare since the beech forests it inhabits are being depleted and "cleaned" of dead wood, killing the larvae before they can complete development. Because of this, it is listed as a threatened species by the International Union for Conservation of Nature (IUCN).

### RELATED SPECIES

Worldwide, there are about 20 different species of *Rosalia*. *Rosalia alpina* is quite distinct from other members of the genus owing to its bluish coloration. Because of the variability of *R. alpina* and its attractiveness to entomologists and laypersons, more than 100 variants and subspecies have been described since Carl Linnaeus proposed this species in 1758. This has created a burdensome taxonomic history.

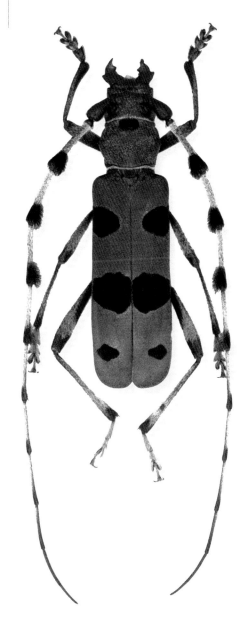

**The Rosalia Longicorn** is distinct, with diffuse blue-white pubescence, black annulate and tufted antennal segments, and bold black markings on the elytra—usually at the middle, base, and apex. The species is variable, however, and some specimens are known to lack black markings on the elytra or have a different pattern, without a middle, transverse black fascia.

Actual size

| FAMILY | Cerambycidae |
|---|---|
| SUBFAMILY | Cerambycinae |
| DISTRIBUTION | Australian: Australia (southeast Queensland and eastern New South Wales) |
| MACROHABITAT | Wild and cultivated *Citrus* trees and orchards |
| MICROHABITAT | Branches of various species of *Citrus* |
| FEEDING HABITS | Adults may feed on pollen and nectar of *Citrus* flowers; larvae develop in the wood of *Citrus* trees |
| NOTE | A serious pest of *Citrus* orchards in Australia |

ADULT MALE LENGTH
¹⁵⁄₁₆–1⁹⁄₁₆ in
(24–39 mm)

ADULT FEMALE LENGTH
¼–1¾ in
(32–44 mm)

526

*URACANTHUS CRYPTOPHAGUS*
# ORANGE-STEM WOOD BORER
OLLIFF, 1892

This species is a pest of many species of *Citrus* trees in the Australian states of Queensland and New South Wales. Adult females lay eggs in crevices in the bark and the larvae then burrow into the wood, tunneling a considerable length along the stem and eventually killing it. In some cases, the larvae will internally girdle the branch so that it may fall off the tree. Injured or weakened trees are more susceptible to attack by this species and *Citrus* orchards can harbor significant populations in as little as two or three years.

RELATED SPECIES

The genus *Uracanthus* includes 39 species, all known only from Australia. In a phylogenetic study by Thongphak and Wang (2008), *U. cryptophagus* was shown to be a member of the largest group of species, the *triangularis* species group, primarily due to characters of the male genitalia.

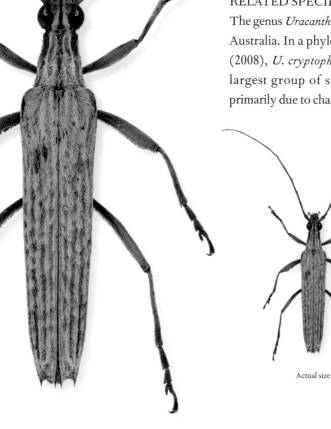

Actual size

**The Orange-stem Wood Borer** is up to 1¾ in (44 mm) in length, but is quite slender. It is distinct, the reddish-brown integument thickly clothed with yellow or golden setae on the sides of the head, prothorax, and venter. The elytra have three raised, longitudinal carinae and rows of pubescence, and are spined apically.

| | |
|---|---|
| FAMILY | Cerambycidae |
| SUBFAMILY | Lamiinae |
| DISTRIBUTION | Neotropical: from central Mexico to north Argentina |
| MACROHABITAT | Tropical forests with Moraceae and Apocynaceae |
| MICROHABITAT | Commonly on trunks of fig (*Ficus* spp.) and fruit (*Atrocarpus* spp.) |
| FEEDING HABITS | Adults feed on sapflows on injured host trees |
| NOTE | Large males have the longest legs of all longhorn beetles |

ADULT LENGTH
1³⁄₁₆–2⁵⁄₁₆ in
(30–78 mm)

*ACROCINUS LONGIMANUS*
# HARLEQUIN BEETLE
(LINNAEUS, 1758)

527

This widespread Neotropical species is well known due to its local abundance, size, and striking coloration. Larvae are borers in Moraceae, primarily. Fig (*Ficus* spp.) trees are the most common host, but the species can also be a major pest of introduced breadfruit trees (*Atrocarpus* spp.) in the Neotropics. The extraordinarily long legs of large males are used in defending mating sites from other males. Males will hold their legs perpendicular to their bodies and headbutt and bite their rivals. This species is also well known for its commensal relationships with pseudoscorpions, which rely on them for dispersal to new feeding and mating sites.

Actual size

## RELATED SPECIES
*Acrocinus longimanus* is the sole member of its own tribe. The genus *Macropophora* (in the tribe Acanthoderini) is similar in that adults of some species are large, have striking patterns (but more subdued), and also have very long front legs that are relatively longer in males than females.

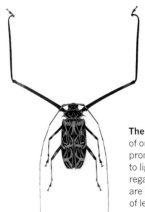

**The Harlequin Beetle** gets its name from the unique pattern of orange, yellow, and black pubescence on the elytra and pronotum. These vibrant colors fade after death, if exposed to light. This is a moderately sexually dimorphic species with regard to the length of the antennae and front legs, which are longer in males than females. In both sexes the front pair of legs is longest, but large males can have the front legs measuring more than 6 in (150 mm) long.

| FAMILY | Cerambycidae |
|---|---|
| SUBFAMILY | Lamiinae |
| DISTRIBUTION | Palearctic and Nearctic: native to China and the Korean Peninsula; introduced and established in the United States, Canada, and Europe |
| MACROHABITAT | Hardwood forests, hardwood trees in urban areas |
| MICROHABITAT | Foliage, branches, trunk of host trees |
| FEEDING HABITS | Larvae develop in many hardwoods (especially *Populus*, *Salix*, *Ulmus*, *Acer*, and *Celtis*) |
| NOTE | In economic terms, this species is the most costly invasive longhorn beetle of all |

ADULT LENGTH
¹¹⁄₁₆–1⁹⁄₁₆ in
(17–39 mm)

*ANOPLOPHORA GLABRIPENNIS*
# ASIAN LONGHORN BEETLE
(MOTSCHULSKY, 1853)

This species is a major pest of poplar trees in China. It was introduced into New York City in the United States in 1996, and is among the most important invasive species ever to become established there. Once in the United States, other trees became targets, expanding the previously known host range for this species. Many thousands of trees had to be removed to try to limit the spread of the species. The Asian Longhorn Beetle has also become established in Canada and parts of Europe, including Austria, France, and Italy.

### RELATED SPECIES

There are now 38 species in the genus *Anoplophora*. All are Asian in distribution, but only a few very closely related species—including *A. freyi* and *A. coeruleoantennata*—have the characteristic black integument with white spots but smooth elytra. *Anoplophora nobilis*, characterized by its yellowish spots, was determined to be a variant and was synonymized in 2002.

**The Asian Longhorn Beetle** is recognized by its shiny black elytra with white spots. The bases of the elytra are smooth, without granules, but with subtle wrinkles. The tarsi of fresh specimens have bright, iridescent bluish pubescence. The otherwise black antennae have blue or white rings at the base of most segments.

Actual size

| FAMILY | Cerambycidae |
|---|---|
| SUBFAMILY | Lamiinae |
| DISTRIBUTION | Palearctic: China, Japan |
| MACROHABITAT | Woodlands of low mountains to plains |
| MICROHABITAT | Tree branches (especially Araliaceae) |
| FEEDING HABITS | Larvae feed in tree branches; like most longhorn beetles, adults do little or no feeding |
| NOTE | Cryptically colored, with an unusual resting posture |

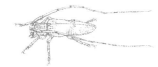

ADULT LENGTH
$^{11}/_{16}$–$^{15}/_{16}$ in
(17–24 mm)

*AULACONOTUS PACHYPEZOIDES*

# AULACONOTUS PACHYPEZOIDES

THOMSON, 1864

529

This species is a member of the worldwide tribe Agapanthiini and known only from China and Japan. Adults have been associated with *Cissus* (Vitaceae) and *Fatsia* (Araliaceae), but it is not known if these are true larval host plants. There is evidence that *Dendropanax* (Araliaceae) is a true larval host. Like other members of Agapanthiini, the adults grip plant stems tightly with a peculiar posture by orienting their antennae straight forward, but keeping them together for half their length and directly on the plant substrate. This provides a form of cryptic mimicry, enabling them to avoid predation.

## RELATED SPECIES

The genus *Aulaconotus* contains only eight species, of which *A. pachypezoides* is the type species. They belong to a tribe of Lamiinae, the Agapanthiini (formerly the Hippopsini), characterized by elongate, narrow bodies and long, sometimes fringed antennae. The relationships among the genera in this tribe have never been examined phylogenetically.

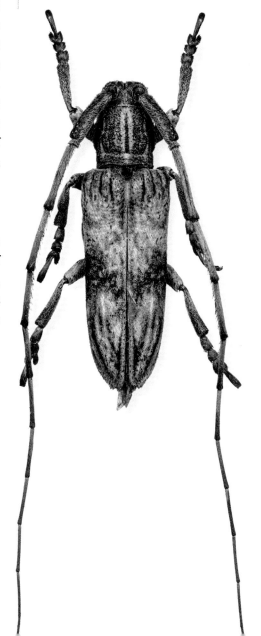

Actual size

**Aulaconotus pachypezoides** is recognized by the mottled brown and pale pubescence covering the body. It is distinguished from other species by the alternating longitudinal stripes of light and dark pubescence on the pronotum, and the base and apex of the elytra. The base of the elytra has a distinctive band of white pubescence posteriorly that is constricted at the suture.

| FAMILY | Cerambycidae |
| --- | --- |
| SUBFAMILY | Lamiinae |
| DISTRIBUTION | Oriental and Australian: Papua New Guinea; Aru Islands, Indonesia; Cape York Peninsula, Australia |
| MACROHABITAT | Tropical rainforests |
| MICROHABITAT | Tree trunks, especially of fig (*Ficus* spp.) trees |
| FEEDING HABITS | Larvae develop in fig trees (*Ficus* spp.); like most longhorn beetles, adults do little or no feeding |
| NOTE | One of the largest beetles in the world; named after Alfred Russel Wallace, who discovered it in the Aru Islands, Indonesia |

ADULT MALE LENGTH
1¹⁵/₁₆–3½ in
(50–88 mm)

ADULT FEMALE LENGTH
1¾–3⅛ in
(45–80 mm)

*BATOCERA WALLACEI*
# WALLACE'S LONGHORN BEETLE
THOMSON, 1858

This striking species is one of the largest beetles in the world. Large specimens can have very long antennae, almost three times their body length. Females are generally smaller, with much shorter antennae. The species was named after the famous naturalist Alfred Russel Wallace, who discovered it in the Aru Islands in 1856. This species ranges throughout Papua New Guinea, and into the Maluku Islands (Moluccas), Indonesia, and the Cape York Peninsula of Queensland, Australia. Adults are often attracted to lights or can be found on the trunks of fig (*Ficus* spp.) trees, their larval host.

### RELATED SPECIES

The genus *Batocera* contains about 60 described species ranging throughout Asia, Australia, and Africa, but none of these has the elytral markings of *B. wallacei*. Only a couple of other species approach *B. wallacei* in size—*B. kibleri* from Papua New Guinea and *B. hercules* from Sulawesi, Ambon, and Java in Indonesia, and the Philippines.

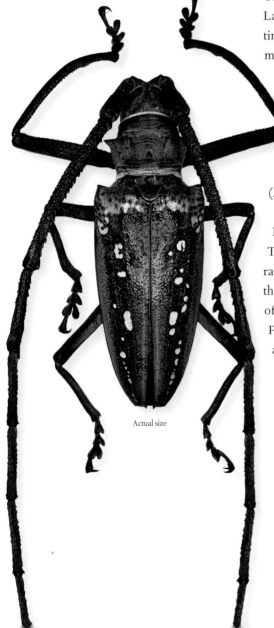

Actual size

**Wallace's Longhorn Beetle** is distinctive by its very large size and extremely long antennae, which can extend more than 9 in (230 mm). The front pair of legs is longest, with very long, bowed tibiae in large males. The elytra are boldly patterned with an irregular longitudinal white pattern of pubescence within a glabrous black background, surrounded by tawny or pale green pubescence.

| FAMILY | Cerambycidae |
|---|---|
| SUBFAMILY | Lamiinae |
| DISTRIBUTION | Nearctic: eastern United States |
| MACROHABITAT | Hardwood forests |
| MICROHABITAT | Foliage and branches |
| FEEDING HABITS | Larvae develop in many hardwood trees, especially oaks (*Quercus* spp.); like most longhorn beetles, adults do little or no feeding |
| NOTE | This is the smallest longhorn beetle in North America |

ADULT LENGTH
¹⁄₁₆–¹⁄₈ in
(2–3 mm)

*CYRTINUS PYGMAEUS*
# PYGMY
# LONGHORN BEETLE
(HALDEMAN, 1847)

531

Actual size

*Cyrtinus pygmaeus* is distributed in the eastern United States. The species can be common in parts of its range, but is probably often overlooked owing to its minute size. Adults are active during the daytime from late spring to midsummer. They can be collected by beating foliage and branches on many species of their hardwood tree larval hosts, especially oaks, birches, and tupelos. The species resembles ants in its size, coloration, and overall morphology, which provides it with some protection from predators.

## RELATED SPECIES

The genus *Cyrtinus* belongs to the lamiine tribe Cyrtinini, which includes five other genera in the Western Hemisphere and many more in Asia and Australia. There are 27 species of *Cyrtinus* in the New World, mostly distributed in Central America and the West Indies. Of these, *C. pygmaeus* is the only species in North America.

**The Pygmy Longhorn Beetle** is the smallest cerambycid in North America and among the smallest in the world. It is very ant-like in appearance, mostly shiny and glabrous, and with red and black coloration. Each elytron at the base has a single long protuberance. The eyes are completely divided, with one lobe above and one below the antennal insertion.

| FAMILY | Cerambycidae |
|---|---|
| SUBFAMILY | Lamiinae |
| DISTRIBUTION | Oriental: Philippines (Luzon, Mindoro, and Mindanao islands) |
| MACROHABITAT | Tropical forests |
| MICROHABITAT | Foliage, branches, the ground |
| FEEDING HABITS | Host plants are unknown for this species |
| NOTE | This longhorn beetle is a perfect Batesian mimic of a weevil |

ADULT LENGTH
³⁄₈–⁹⁄₁₆ in
(9–15 mm)

532

# DOLIOPS DUODECIMPUNCTATA

HELLER, 1923

The diverse and speciose genus *Doliops* is a well-known complex of weevil-mimicking Cerambycidae in the Philippines. For nearly every species of *Doliops*, a comparable model in the weevil genus *Pachyrrhynchus* can be found. *Doliops duodecimpunctata*, with 12 spots on the elytra and pronotum, is most similar to the weevil *P. smaragdinus*. Alfred Russel Wallace expounded upon the aposematic coloration in these weevils, and also noted that their extremely hard integument protected them from predation. This species is a perfect example of Batesian mimicry: it has evolved the same morphology and aposematic coloration of a weevil with which it occurs.

## RELATED SPECIES

*Doliops* has radiated incredibly in the Philippines, with now more than 40 species described. Most are structurally very similar, but vary in the patterns of pubescent markings on the elytra. *Doliops duodecimpunctata* is most similar (and probably most closely related) to *D. curculionoides* and the recently described *D. gutowskii*. A phylogenetic study to understand more clearly their true relationships is needed for this group.

**Doliops decimpunctata** is recognized by the white, yellow, or pink spots on the elytra, pronotum, and head. The spots are arranged in a row of three along the elytral suture, two along the outer margin, one on each side at the base of the pronotum, and another on the vertex of the head.

Actual size

| | |
|---|---|
| FAMILY | Cerambycidae |
| SUBFAMILY | Lamiinae |
| DISTRIBUTION | Palearctic: western and central Europe |
| MACROHABITAT | Pyrenees Mountains |
| MICROHABITAT | Grasslands, especially Meadow Brome (*Bromus erectus*) |
| FEEDING HABITS | Adults feed on grasses such as Meadow Brome; larvae feed on their roots |
| NOTE | Flightless longhorn beetle with unusual body shape and biology |

ADULT LENGTH
⅛–¹¹⁄₁₆ in
(10–17 mm)

*IBERODORCADION FULIGINATOR*
# IBERODORCADION FULIGINATOR
(LINNAEUS, 1758)

533

Over the past 30 years, populations of this flightless species have been declining, and laws are currently in place to protect it in Switzerland and Germany. Note that it has gone under the wrong name, *Dorcadion fulginator*, by many authors. Adults feed on many herbaceous plants, especially the grass *Bromus erectus* in grasslands of warmer parts of western Europe. Females lay eggs in the grass stems in early spring. The larvae hatch after a few weeks and proceed underground, feeding on the roots for approximately a year, then eclose and hibernate for a period, with adults emerging after two years.

## RELATED SPECIES

This species used to be classed within the closely related genus *Dorcadion*, but recent work on taxonomy and systematics has divided that genus into many genera. Consequently, the species is now placed in the genus *Iberodorcadion*, which is treated by some authors as a subgenus of *Dorcadion*. *Iberodorcadion* contains 50 closely related species and subspecies.

**Iberodorcadion fuliginator** is a member of a large tribe of flightless longhorn beetles with mostly fused elytra and ovoid bodies. Adults are quite variable in their elytral pubescence patterns. Some individuals have alternating rows of white or gray and black or tan pubescence, while others are uniformly covered with white, gray, or tan pubescence on the elytra.

Actual size

| FAMILY | Cerambycidae |
|---|---|
| SUBFAMILY | Lamiinae |
| DISTRIBUTION | Nearctic: central, southern, and northwestern USA; south-central Canada |
| MACROHABITAT | Arid areas and deserts |
| MICROHABITAT | Cacti |
| FEEDING HABITS | Feeds on prickly pears (*Opuntia* spp.) |
| NOTE | A flightless, cactus-feeding longhorn beetle |

ADULT MALE LENGTH
⅜–¾ in
(9–19 mm)

ADULT FEMALE LENGTH
⁷⁄₁₆–¹⁵⁄₁₆ in
(11–24 mm)

534

# MONEILEMA ANNULATUM

SAY, 1824

*Moneilema annulatum* is the type species of the genus and was described nearly 200 years ago. It is a member of the small tribe Moneilemini, whose species have evolved a flightless condition with fused elytra. This group is also unusual in that species feed on, and develop as larvae in, prickly pear cacti (*Opuntia* spp.). Although most common in hot, arid deserts, this species also has a cold tolerance and has the most northern distribution of any species in the genus, occurring into Canada in parallel with *Opuntia* species.

## RELATED SPECIES

This species is a member of the Moneilemini, a small tribe of Nearctic and Neotropical longhorn beetles. There is only the single genus in the tribe, and it includes 15 species, mostly in the southern United States and Mexico. The taxonomy of this group is complicated since many species are superficially similar and others are polymorphic. Most species have many synonyms, indicating a tortured taxonomic history.

**Moneilema annulatum**, like most members of the genus, is all black in color. It can be distinguished from the other superficially similar species by the moderate projection at the apex of the antennal scape, small lateral tubercles on the pronotum, and variably wrinkled elytra. The third and fourth antennal segments, at least, are partially annulate (ringed) with white pubescence.

Actual size

| FAMILY | Cerambycidae |
|---|---|
| SUBFAMILY | Lamiinae |
| DISTRIBUTION | Palearctic: China, Taiwan, Vietnam, Japan, North and South Korea |
| MACROHABITAT | Coniferous and mixed forests |
| MICROHABITAT | Trunks and branches of conifers, predominantly on pine trees (*Pinus* spp.) |
| FEEDING HABITS | Adults feed on bark of twigs; larvae develop in many species of pine (*Pinus* spp.), spruce (*Picea* spp.), and fir (*Abies* spp.) |
| NOTE | A pest of pines (*Pinus* spp.) in Asia |

ADULT LENGTH
⁹⁄₁₆–1⅛ in
(15–28 mm)

*MONOCHAMUS ALTERNATUS*
# JAPANESE PINE SAWYER
HOPE, 1842

535

This widespread beetle is a pest of many conifers, particularly pines (*Pinus* spp.). It is also a potential invasive species that has been intercepted many times around the world. However, there are no known instances of establishment of this species outside of its native range. Since the larvae can destroy pine products and lumber, the Japanese Pine Sawyer has the potential to be an economically significant pest. It is also known to be a vector of the Pine Wood Nematode (*Bursaphelenchus xylophilus*), a conifer pathogen.

RELATED SPECIES

The genus *Monochamus* includes 20 species found in coniferous forests throughout the world. There has been much taxonomic confusion in this genus and many species have been described numerous times, creating a convoluted taxonomic history. To date, no phylogenetic study has been made of the group to determine the true relationships of the species.

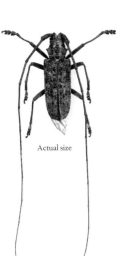

**The Japanese Pine Sawyer** beetle can be recognized by the mottled reddish-brown, black, and white setae covering the dorsum. Some setae are arranged into alternating longitudinal stripes along most of the elytra. The pronotum has two longitudinal stripes, one on either side of the middle callus. The antennae are diffusely and broadly pale annulate (ringed) at the base of most segments.

Actual size

| FAMILY | Cerambycidae |
|---|---|
| SUBFAMILY | Lamiinae |
| DISTRIBUTION | Nearctic: southern, central, and eastern USA |
| MACROHABITAT | Hardwood forests |
| MICROHABITAT | Branches of various trees |
| FEEDING HABITS | Larvae develop in many species of trees, including Pecan (*Carya illinoinensis*), hickories (*Carya* spp.), mesquite (*Prosopis* spp.), Red Oak (*Quercus rubra*), persimmons (*Diospyros* spp.), elms (*Ulmus* spp.), and poplars (*Populus* spp.) |
| NOTE | Adults girdle branches, creating dying twigs for larval feeding and development |

**ADULT LENGTH**
⅜–¹¹⁄₁₆ in
(10–18 mm)

*ONCIDERES CINGULATA*
# TWIG GIRDLER
(SAY, 1826)

This species is a highly polyphagous pest of many different hardwood trees, especially Pecan (*Carya illinoinensis*), hickories (*Carya* spp.), and elms (*Ulmus* spp.). In Texas, it was proposed as a potential biological control agent for mesquite (*Prosopis* spp.) owing to its affinity for these weedy tree species.

Like many species in the tribe Onciderini, adult females will chew a ring around branches and lay eggs at the distal parts. This girdling creates a perfect dying resource for the developing larvae. Often these girdled branches drop off the trees and are easily recognized as the work of the Twig Girdler.

## RELATED SPECIES

*Oncideres cingulata* is a member of the large tribe Onciderini, which includes 79 genera and nearly 500 species in North, Central, and South America. *Oncideres* is among the largest genera in the tribe and contains more than 120 species.

Actual size

**The Twig Girdler** is recognized by its overall reddish-brown color, with a central white band of pubescence on the elytra combined with spots of orange pubescence throughout. The anterior of the head is very flattened (as in most onciderines) and the mandibles are prominent. The antennae are longer than the body and mostly covered in white pubescence.

| FAMILY | Cerambycidae |
|---|---|
| SUBFAMILY | Lamiinae |
| DISTRIBUTION | Neotropical: Brazil, Peru, Bolivia |
| MACROHABITAT | Tropical forests |
| MICROHABITAT | Dead wood |
| FEEDING HABITS | Phytophagous, but host trees unknown |
| NOTE | This is the first known longhorn beetle with a stinger |

ADULT LENGTH
%₁₆–⅞ in
(14–21 mm)

*ONYCHOCERUS ALBITARSIS*
# ONYCHOCERUS ALBITARSIS
PASCOE, 1859

537

This is the only known beetle that has antennae modified with stingers in an interesting case of convergent evolution with scorpions and wasps. Comparative morphological studies (published in 2007) showed remarkable similarities to the telson apparatus of a scorpion, complete with the acute apex, swollen poison receptacle, and paired grooves for delivering the poison. Host trees are unknown for this species, but other species have been reared from trees in the families Anacardiaceae and Euphorbiaceae. These families include toxic plants and this could be the source of the irritants that are injected into the victim when a beetle is defending itself.

### RELATED SPECIES

This species is a member of the Neotropical tribe Anisocerini, which includes 26 genera. The genus *Onychocerus* includes eight species, all South American in distribution except for *O. crassus*, which also occurs in Central America.

**Onychocerus albitarsis** is characterized by its bold black and white pubescence and globose body. Most species in the genus have modified acute terminal antennal segments, but this is the only one that has been shown to have a clear stinger complete with paired delivery grooves and a swollen receptacle for containing the injeclants.

Actual size

| FAMILY | Cerambycidae |
|---|---|
| SUBFAMILY | Lamiinae |
| DISTRIBUTION | Afrotropical: Ethiopia, Somalia, Kenya, Tanzania, Uganda |
| MACROHABITAT | Coastal deciduous forests |
| MICROHABITAT | Branches of the Cashew tree (*Anacardium occidentale*), fig trees (*Ficus* spp.), and Kapok tree (*Ceiba pentandra*) |
| FEEDING HABITS | Adult feeding habits unknown; larvae bore in wood of Cashew, fig, and Kapok trees |
| NOTE | The species is a pest in Cashew plantations in coastal East Africa |

ADULT LENGTH
1–1⁹⁄₁₆ in
(25–40 mm)

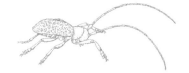

*PARANALEPTES RETICULATA*
# CASHEW STEM GIRDLER
(THOMSON, 1877)

This species can be a pest of Cashew trees (*Anacardium occidentale*) throughout coastal regions of East Africa, especially in Kenya and Tanzania. Other trees attacked include figs (*Ficus* spp.) and Kapok (*Ceiba pentandra*). Adult females will completely girdle branches 1³⁄₁₆–3⅛ in (30–80 mm) in diameter by chewing the circumference with their mandibles. An egg is deposited distal to each girdled branch. As the larvae develop inside, the weakened branches or crowns often break off. Adults emerge after one year of larval development.

### RELATED SPECIES

The genus *Paranaleptes*, containing two species, is a member of the African tribe Ceroplesini. Most species of this tribe are in the genus *Ceroplesis*. There has been no phylogenetic study to determine the generic and species relationships in this enigmatic group of longhorn beetles.

**The Cashew Stem Girdler** is a large and beautifully patterned longhorn beetle. The integument is mostly black but it is partially covered by reddish-brown pubescence. The legs and antennae can be nearly black if the pubescence is sparse. The elytra are covered with a reticulating network of golden-orange pubescence and glabrous black

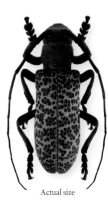

Actual size

| FAMILY | Cerambycidae |
|---|---|
| SUBFAMILY | Lamiinae |
| DISTRIBUTION | Afrotropical: sub-Saharan West and Central Africa |
| MACROHABITAT | Tropical forests |
| MICROHABITAT | Tree bark, root crown, and branches, especially of figs (*Ficus* spp.) |
| FEEDING HABITS | Adult feeding habits unknown; larval tree hosts include *Ficus*, *Ceiba*, *Castilla*, and *Casuarina* spp. |
| NOTE | This is the largest longhorn beetle in Africa and a pest of fig trees |

ADULT LENGTH
1½–2¹⁵⁄₁₆ in
(38–75 mm)

*PETROGNATHA GIGAS*

# GIANT AFRICAN LONGHORN

FABRICIUS, 1792

539

This is one of the largest beetles known from Africa. Adult specimens can be nearly 3 in (76 mm) long and larvae nearly 5 in (127 mm) long. It can become a pest of fig (*Ficus* spp.) plantations and can kill trees within a few years of their infestation. Imported rubber trees (*Castilla* spp.) are also susceptible to infestation. The substantial protein afforded by the gigantic larvae of this species has made them, if not a staple, a delicacy to native West Africans.

## RELATED SPECIES

This species is a member of the small but morphological diverse tribe Petrognathini. This tribe includes ten genera, mostly Afrotropical in distribution, although they probably represent an unnatural assemblage as few characters are shared among them. *Petrognatha* is a monotypic genus. No similar species are known, and there are no closely related species.

Actual size

**The Giant African Longhorn** is immense and can approach 3 in (76 mm) in length. The body coloration and the shape and thickness of the appendages give it a cryptic bark-like and vine-like aspect. The base of the elytra are armed with a spine on each shoulder. This feature, combined with the powerful mandibles, provides this beetle with a defense should a predator discover it.

| FAMILY | Cerambycidae |
|---|---|
| SUBFAMILY | Lamiinae |
| DISTRIBUTION | Nearctic and Neotropical: south Canada, USA, north Mexico |
| MACROHABITAT | Plains, grasslands, riparian areas |
| MICROHABITAT | Milkweed (*Asclepias* spp.) |
| FEEDING HABITS | Adults and larvae feed on and within milkweed (*Asclepias* spp.) stems and roots |
| NOTE | Adults sequester milkweed toxins to provide themselves protection from predators |

ADULT LENGTH
⁵⁄₁₆–³⁄₄ in
(8–20 mm)

540

*TETRAOPES FEMORATUS*
# TETRAOPES FEMORATUS
LECONTE, 1847

This species is a member of the tribe Tetraopini, most members of which are specialized herbivores on milkweeds (*Asclepias* spp.). These plants are toxic to most animals due to the glycosides in their latex secretions. The parallel evolution of *Tetraopes* and *Asclepias* is a classic example both of insect/plant coevolution, and of plant-toxin sequestration in an insect coupled with a bright red warning coloration. *Tetraopes femoratus* is the most widespread of all the species in the genus, occurring throughout the United States and into Canada and Mexico.

RELATED SPECIES

The genus *Tetraopes* is a member of the Nearctic and Neotropical tribe Tetraopini, which includes only two genera. *Tetraopes* contains 22 species distributed from Canada south through to Guatemala, although most are concentrated in the United States. This species is the most widespread and the most variable, and consequently has numerous synonyms.

**Tetraopes femoratus** is the most variable species of the genus, and has the red coloration and black spots characteristic of most species. It can be recognized by the abruptly elevated middle region of the pronotum, distinct punctures at the base of the elytra, and the antennae, which have annulations of gray pubescence at the base and apex of each antennomere.

Actual size

| FAMILY | Cerambycidae |
|---|---|
| SUBFAMILY | Lepturinae |
| DISTRIBUTION | Nearctic: Sacramento Valley, northern California |
| MACROHABITAT | Elderberry plants in riparian valleys and open slopes |
| MICROHABITAT | Roots, branches, and flowers of living Blue Elderberry (*Sambucus cerulea*) |
| FEEDING HABITS | Larvae bore into roots of living Blue Elderberry (*Sambucus cerulea*); like most longhorn beetles, adults do little or no feeding |
| NOTE | Threatened due to its limited distribution and loss of habitat |

ADULT MALE LENGTH
⁹/₁₆–¹¹/₁₆ in
(14–17 mm)

ADULT FEMALE LENGTH
⅝–¹⁵/₁₆ in
(16–24 mm)

*DESMOCERUS CALIFORNICUS DIMORPHUS*

# VALLEY ELDERBERRY LONGHORN BEETLE

FISHER, 1921

541

This subspecies was discovered in Sacramento, California, in 1921. Like other species in the genus, the larvae use *Sambucus* species as their host—in this case, *S. cerulea*, Blue Elderberry. The beetle is considered "threatened" by the United States Fish and Wildlife Service owing to its restricted distribution in the Sacramento Valley of northern California. It exhibits sexual dimorphism with regard to the coloration of the elytra: they are mostly orange in males but orange only on the margins in females. The orange fades after death to a dull yellow.

RELATED SPECIES

The unusual lepturine genus *Desmocerus* contains only three species, all distributed in the United States and Canada. This is one of two subspecies that have been defined for *D. californicus*. It was described originally as a distinct species by Warren Fisher, but subsequent work has shown this (as well as other species in the genus) to be localized variants.

Actual size

**The Valley Elderberry Longhorn Beetle** is recognized by its completely or partially orange elytra, which are coarsely, densely punctate throughout. The name *dimorphus* refers to the fact that the males and females are dimorphic in color: males have mostly orange elytra (except with black spots at the base), while in females the elytra are mostly black (except orange on the margins).

| | |
|---|---|
| FAMILY | Cerambycidae |
| SUBFAMILY | Necydalinae |
| DISTRIBUTION | Nearctic: Pacific coast of North America, from British Columbia to southern California and east to western Idaho |
| MACROHABITAT | Coniferous forests |
| MICROHABITAT | Trunk and stump surfaces of various conifers |
| FEEDING HABITS | Adult feeding habits unknown; larval hosts are primarily Ponderosa Pine (*Pinus ponderosa*) and Douglas-fir (*Pseudotsuga menziesii*). Other hosts include *Abies*, *Picea*, and *Tsuga* spp. |
| NOTE | A bumblebee-mimicking longhorn beetle |

ADULT LENGTH
⁹⁄₁₆–1⅛ in
(15–35 mm)

542

*ULOCHAETES LEONINUS*
# LION BEETLE
LECONTE, 1854

Actual size

**The Lion Beetle** is recognized by its dense golden-yellow pubescence on the pronotum, much like a lion's mane. The black and yellow elytra are very short, extending to only about one-third or one-fourth of the length of the abdomen, exposing the hind wings. The femora, tibial apices, and tarsi are black and the basal two-thirds of the tibiae are yellow.

This peculiar genus is represented by only this species in North America. It is very bumblebee-like in appearance and behavior. Adults will walk erratically on the substrate, flicking their antennae, beating their wings rapidly, and raising the end of the abdomen in a threatening manner. They even make a bee-like buzzing sound when they fly. The very densely pubescent pronotum, like a lion's mane, is the source of its common name, the Lion Beetle. Larvae develop most commonly in standing, dead Ponderosa Pine (*Pinus ponderosa*) and Douglas-fir (*Pseudotsuga menziesii*), and it is on the surfaces of these trees that adults are often seen.

RELATED SPECIES

This species is a member of the small subfamily Necydalinae (formerly included in the Lepturinae), which includes 12 genera. Only three species of *Ulochaetes* are known; the other two occur in Asia, one in Bhutan and one in China. They are morphologically very similar and presumably closely related, but no phylogenetic study has been made of this group of enigmatic longhorn beetles.

| FAMILY | Cerambycidae |
|---|---|
| SUBFAMILY | Parandrinae |
| DISTRIBUTION | Nearctic: eastern half of the United States and southeast Canada |
| MACROHABITAT | Deciduous and coniferous forests |
| MICROHABITAT | Rotting stumps, cavities, and fallen trees |
| FEEDING HABITS | Adults and larvae will feed in nearly all species of dead trees in eastern North America |
| NOTE | Among the most polyphagous longhorn beetles known |

ADULT LENGTH
⅜–1 in
(10–25 mm)

*NEANDRA BRUNNEA*
# NEANDRA BRUNNEA
(FABRICIUS, 1798)

543

*Neandra brunnea* is a member of the "atypical" longhorn beetle subfamily Parandrinae owing to its morphology and biology. This group has habits more similar to passalids in that they develop in moist, rotting wood. Most longhorn beetles will develop in host trees that are recently dead or injured. This species may be the most polyphagous longhorn beetle in North America—the taxon of the host is far less important than the condition of the wood, and any rotting wood, whether coniferous or deciduous, is susceptible to infestation. This species is very important to the decomposition of woody material and production of soil.

## RELATED SPECIES
The subfamily Parandrinae is represented by only three species in North America. These were historically all placed in the genus Parandra, with two subgenera: *Archandra* and *Neandra*. In 2002, *Neandra* was elevated to generic status. Only one other species of *Neandra* occurs in North America, the southwestern US species *N. marginicollis*.

**Neandra brunnea** is recognized by its overall non-cerambycid-like appearance; rather, it looks more like a tenebrionid. It is reddish brown and glabrous dorsally, has very short antennae, tarsi lacking the typical hidden fourth segment, and large mandibles, particularly in males. It differs from the only other eastern North American parandrine in that the tarsi lack a seta-bearing pad- between the claws.

Actual size

| FAMILY | Cerambycidae |
|---|---|
| SUBFAMILY | Prioninae |
| DISTRIBUTION | Neotropical: northern half of South America |
| MACROHABITAT | Tropical rainforest |
| MICROHABITAT | Often found on Maripa Palm (*Attalea maripa*) trees |
| FEEDING HABITS | Adults do not feed at all |
| NOTE | Including the mandibles, these are among the longest beetles in the world |

ADULT MALE LENGTH
2⁵⁄₁₆–6¼ in
(59–160 mm)

ADULT FEMALE LENGTH
2³⁄₈–4½ in
(60–115 mm)

*MACRODONTIA CERVICORNIS*
# GIANT JAWED SAWYER
(LINNAEUS, 1758)

544

Actual size

*Macrodontia cervicornis* is the largest and most common member of the genus. Adults are nocturnal and sometimes come to light. Specimens are often found on Maripa Palm (*Attalea maripa*) trees, which are a food plant. The larvae have a unique morphology, with thoracic and abdominal segments covered with velvet-like setae. They create extensive galleries in the heart of dead and dying softwood trees such as the Coconut Palm (*Cocos nucifera*), but also on *Attalea*, *Ceiba*, and *Jessenia*. Larvae can reach up to 8¼ in (210 mm) in length and are a source of food for the native people of Brazil.

RELATED SPECIES

*Macrodontia* is restricted to the Neotropical Realm and includes 11 species. *Macrodontia zischkai*, *M. jolyi*, *M. itayensis*, *M. dejeani*, *M. mathani*, *M. marechali*, *M. crenata*, and *M. flavipennis* are restricted to South America, while *M. batesi* and the recently described *M. castroi* occur in Central America. Some species have broad geographic ranges, while others are known from only one country.

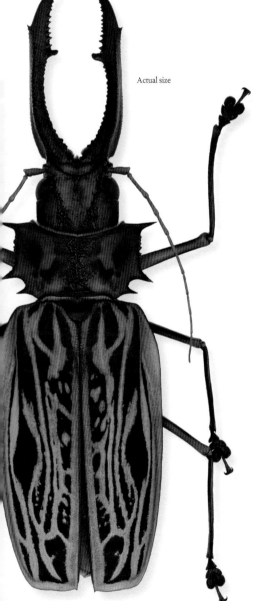

**The Giant Jawed Sawyer** is a very large beetle with a patterned brown and black prothorax. The head, legs, and mandibles are very irregular and the incurved mandibles possess internal teeth. The body of this species is flattened. Specimens show a large variety of size and some are considered giants of the subfamily Prioninae. Large specimens have huge dentate mandibles.

| FAMILY | Cerambycidae |
|---|---|
| SUBFAMILY | Prioninae |
| DISTRIBUTION | Neotropical: northern half of South America |
| MACROHABITAT | Tropical rainforest |
| MICROHABITAT | Base and root crowns of very large trees |
| FEEDING HABITS | Adults do not feed |
| NOTE | The Titan Beetle is among the largest beetles in the world |

*TITANUS GIGANTEUS*
# TITAN BEETLE
(LINNAEUS, 1771)

ADULT MALE LENGTH
3¼–6⁹⁄₁₆ in
(95–167 mm)

ADULT FEMALE LENGTH
4⅞–6¼ in
(124–160 mm)

545

This species has the reputation of being the largest insect in the world. Although specimens perhaps as long as 8–9 in (200–230 mm) have been reported, this is thought to be a myth, since the largest known specimen measures 6⁹⁄₁₆ in (167 mm). For a long time, *Titanus giganteus* was also considered to be one of the rarest beetles. Recently, however, male specimens have been collected in relatively large numbers in French Guiana, attracted by bright artificial lights. Females are not attracted to lights. Larvae probably develop in very large, dying or dead trees and presumably require several years to reach the adult stage. The host tree for this species remains unknown.

Actual size

## RELATED SPECIES

The genus *Titanus* formerly included two subgenera, *Titanus* and *Braderochus*, but *Braderochus* is now recognized as a separate genus of nine species within the tribe Prionini, leaving *Titanus* with just one species, *T. giganteus*. Specimens of *Braderochus* are quite rare and females are difficult to identify. *Ctenoscelis* is a similar genus of large prionines from South America and includes eight species and subspecies.

**The Titan Beetle** is a large, dark brown to black beetle. The elytra are lightly ridged longitudinally. It is easy to differentiate the females from the males because the former have no denticulations on the tibia, their antennae are shorter, and the scape is less globular. The adults defend themselves by hissing in warning, and have sharp spines on their pronotum as well as strong jaws.

| FAMILY | Cerambycidae |
|---|---|
| SUBFAMILY | Spondylidinae |
| DISTRIBUTION | Palearctic: across Europe and into northern Asia, Korea, and Japan |
| MACROHABITAT | Coniferous forests |
| MICROHABITAT | Bark and stumps of dead and living pine trees (*Pinus* spp.) |
| FEEDING HABITS | Adult feeding habits unknown; larvae develop primarily in *Pinus* spp. |
| NOTE | An important decomposer of dead pine in the Palearctic Realm |

ADULT LENGTH
³/₈–1 in
(10–25 mm)

546

*SPONDYLIS BUPRESTOIDES*
# FIREWOOD LONGHORN BEETLE
(LINNAEUS, 1758)

This is one of the earliest longhorn beetles described, by Carl Linnaeus in 1758, more than 250 years ago. It is a widespread European and north Asian species, and the only member of the monotypic genus *Spondylis*. It is unlike a typical longhorn beetle given its morphology and overall trogossitid-like head and pronotum. The informal common name Firewood Longhorn Beetle was given to this primarily nocturnal species because specimens often emerge from pine firewood in and around homes. Like members of Parandrinae, it plays an important ecological role in decomposing old, rotten wood.

## RELATED SPECIES

The most closely related species is *Neospondylis upiformis*, a North American species that was, until recently, included in the now monotypic genus *Spondylis*. Other members of the subfamily Spondylidinae include *Arhopalus*, *Asemum*, and *Tetropium* species. Characters of the larvae are quite similar among all the species and confirm their relationship.

**The Firewood Longhorn Beetle** is recognized by its glabrous black integument and non-cerambycid-like appearance. The antennae and legs are short and stout. The mandibles are pronounced and acute at the apices. The pronotum is large and evenly rounded at the sides. The pronotum and elytra are heavily, closely punctate, with the latter having two raised costae on each side.

Actual size

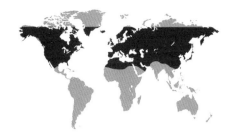

| FAMILY | Megalopodidae |
|---|---|
| SUBFAMILY | Zeugophorinae |
| DISTRIBUTION | Most of the Palearctic, Nearctic |
| MACROHABITAT | Various temperate forests, urban landscapes |
| MICROHABITAT | Adults are found on leaves of woody plants, mostly in the family Salicaceae; larvae mine leaves |
| FEEDING HABITS | Foliage, mostly of plants in the family Salicaceae |
| NOTE | This is another example of a leaf beetle that has migrated from its native Palearctic to North America |

ADULT LENGTH
³⁄₁₆ in
(3.8–4.7 mm)

*ZEUGOPHORA SCUTELLARIS*
# POPLAR BLACKMINE BEETLE
SUFFRIAN, 1840

547

The Poplar Blackmine Beetle belongs to a relatively small group of beetles whose larvae mine inside the leaves of their host plants. The larvae have flat bodies and lack legs, allowing them to live inside the tight space between the leaf surfaces. Once fully developed, the larvae fall to the ground and burrow into the soil, where they pupate. In temperate regions, the adults emerge from May to June. They feed mostly on the underside of the leaves, producing so-called skeletonizing marks.

Actual size

## RELATED SPECIES
Fifteen closely related species of the subgenus *Zeugophora sensu stricto* are known to occur in the Palearctic, and only nine species of the entire genus *Zeugophora* in the Nearctic. Among the Palearctic species, *Z. scutellaris* is similar to *Z. subspinosa*, which has almost the same geographic distribution but is absent from North America, and which feeds on species of *Salix* and *Populus*.

**The Poplar Blackmine Beetle** has a relatively small body with a yellowish head, pronotum, and legs. The antennae are bicolored, with yellowish basal antennomeres and dark brown apical antennomeres. The abdomen and elytra are dark brown. An interesting characteristic of the species is that the sides of the pronotum are expanded into two triangular projections.

| FAMILY | Orsodacnidae |
|---|---|
| SUBFAMILY | Aulacoscelidinae |
| DISTRIBUTION | Neotropical: Panama |
| MACROHABITAT | Tropical forests |
| MICROHABITAT | Altitudes of 330–4,000 ft (100–1,230 m) |
| FEEDING HABITS | Fully expanded leaves of *Zamia fairchildiana* |
| NOTE | One of the most primitive leaf beetles |

ADULT LENGTH
¼–⁵⁄₁₆ in
(6.2–8.2 mm)

548

*AULACOSCELIS APPENDICULATA*
# AULACOSCELIS APPENDICULATA
COX & WINDSOR, 1999

Aulacoscelidinae is one of the groups of leaf beetles important for understanding the evolution of this hyperdiverse taxon. However, their larvae remained unknown until *Aulacoscelis appendiculata* was described in 1999 when only six larvae emerged from about 40 eggs laid by adults kept in a terrarium. Adults are known to exhibit defensive reflex bleeding if disturbed: the beetles secrete droplets of a toxic substance made from the host plant, *Zamia fairchildiana*, from the joint between the tibia and the femur.

### RELATED SPECIES

Aulacoscelidinae is a small group of beetles containing approximately 20 known species in two genera, *Aulacoscelis* and *Janbechynea*. They feed mostly on leaves of Cycadophyta species and often visit flowers (sometimes Bromeliaceae). Among Aulacoscelidinae, *A. melanocera* is most similar to *A. appendiculata*. As currently understood, *A. melanocera* is the most widespread species in the genus and has been reported feeding on Sago Palm (*Cycas revoluta*) in Honduras.

Actual size

**Aulacoscelis appendiculata** is entirely reddish orange with black legs, antennae, and mouthparts. The elytra are flat, much longer than the pronotum, and sparsely covered with short, erect yellowish setae. The base of the pronotum has two very short, longitudinal impressions.

| FAMILY | Chrysomelidae |
|---|---|
| SUBFAMILY | Bruchinae |
| DISTRIBUTION | Cosmopolitan |
| MACROHABITAT | In agro-ecosystems |
| MICROHABITAT | Variety of microhabitats, including stored products |
| FEEDING HABITS | Adults do not feed; larvae feed mostly inside seeds of legumes, particularly *Phaseolus* spp. |
| NOTE | A serious pest of stored products, primarily of Kidney Beans (*Phaseolus vulgaris*) |

ADULT LENGTH
⅛ in
(2.8–3.2 mm)

*ACANTHOSCELIDES OBTECTUS*
# BEAN WEEVIL
(SAY, 1831)

549

Actual size

The Bean Weevil was originally described from Louisiana in the United States but is thought to originate from Central America and is now distributed worldwide. Adults do not feed, so all the resources that are needed to sustain the adult's life are accumulated during the larval stage. Virgin females produce mature eggs complete with a chorion at the beginning of their life, and egg development then continues only in the presence of a host plant (legumes, Fabaceae) or mating. The larvae bore into legume seeds and complete their development inside, with several larvae sometimes living in one bean.

RELATED SPECIES
*Acanthoscelides* is one of the most speciose bruchine genera in the world, with about 54 species in the United States. Among them, *A. rufovittatus* is the most similar to *A. obtectus* but can be separated by the fine details of the body coloration and shape, and by the shape of the male genitalia. It is known to occur in Arizona and Texas, and from Mexico to Venezuela.

**The Bean Weevil** has a black body that is densely covered with pale scales. The legs range in color from reddish brown to black. The hind femora are greatly swollen, with the inner side bearing a short comb of sharp teeth. The apical segment of the antennae is red, and antennomeres 8–10 are broader than they are long.

| FAMILY | Chrysomelidae |
|---|---|
| SUBFAMILY | Bruchinae |
| DISTRIBUTION | Afrotropical, Palearctic, Oriental, Nearctic, and Neotropical: Africa, the Middle East, Asia; introduced to Europe, USA (Florida, Hawaii), West Indies, Colombia, Guyana, Mexico, Venezuela |
| MACROHABITAT | Xeric environments, stored products |
| MICROHABITAT | A variety of habitats; the main hosts are *Tamarindus* and *Acacia* spp. |
| FEEDING HABITS | Larvae feed in seedpods of various species of Fabaceae; adults are short-lived and not known to feed |
| NOTE | An invasive pest of Tamarind (*Tamarindus indica*) and stored Groundnuts (*Arachis hypogaea*) |

**ADULT LENGTH**
³/₁₆–¼ in
(3.5–6.8 mm)

550

*CARYEDON SERRATUS*
# CARYEDON SERRATUS
(OLIVIER, 1790)

*Caryedon serratus* was first described from Senegal, and is considered a tropicopolitan species of possible African and Asian origin. It has been introduced to Europe, Florida and Hawaii, the West Indies, and some Central and northern South American countries. It feeds on a variety of Fabaceae plants, with larvae developing inside the seedpods. Host plants for this species include Tamarind (*Tamarindus indica*), Groundnut (*Arachis hypogaea*), *Acacia* spp., *Bauhinia tomentosa*, Poinciana (*Caesalpinia pulcherrima*), Golden Shower Tree (*Cassia fistula*), Pink Shower Tree (*C. grandis*), and *Prosopis pallida*. In experimental conditions, the pre-adult stage is relatively long, lasting from 60 to 95 days.

## RELATED SPECIES

*Caryedon* contains more than 30 species, mostly distributed in southern and eastern parts of the Mediterranean, tropical Africa, Madagascar, and Asia. At least 28 species are known to occur in the Palearctic. They feed on various Fabaceae, Apiaceae, and Combretaceae species. *Caryedon abdominalis*, a species closely related to *C. serratus*, is distinguished by having a paler integument, slimmer antennal segments, and a shorter pygidium, among other characters.

Actual size

**Caryedon serratus** is light to dark brown in color and densely covered with short, mostly yellowish setae. The head is narrow and the eyes large. The hind femur is hugely expanded and almost disk-like, with a row of numerous sharp teeth. The hind tibia is convex, following the curvature of the inner side of the hind femur.

| FAMILY | Chrysomelidae |
|---|---|
| SUBFAMILY | Bruchinae |
| DISTRIBUTION | Palearctic: southwestern Russia, Turkey, Iran, Kazakhstan, Mongolia |
| MACROHABITAT | Southern Palearctic steppes, semideserts and deserts, often shores of saline ponds and lakes |
| MICROHABITAT | Plants of *Nitraria schoberi* |
| FEEDING HABITS | Adults feed on the leaves and flowers of *Nitraria schoberi*, and larvae feed inside their fruits |
| NOTE | One of the most taxonomically puzzling seed beetles |

ADULT LENGTH
³⁄₁₆ in
(3.5–4.3 mm)

*RHAEBUS MANNERHEIMI*
# RHAEBUS MANNERHEIMI
MOTSCHULSKY, 1845

551

The biology of this *Rhaebus* species is well known, unlike that of the other species of the genus. The Russian entomologist F. K. Lukjanovich studied it in 1937 and 1938 in Kazakhstan. He discovered that adults feed on various parts of the flowers of *Nitraria schoberi* while larvae live and develop inside the fruits of the same plant. Late-instar larvae bore an escape tunnel for the adult that is significantly narrower than the adult, leading scientists to believe that the adults leave the larval chamber after pupation but before their body hardens, which is unlike other bruchines.

## RELATED SPECIES
*Rhaebus* includes only six species, all of which occur in the southern Palearctic. The genus is so morphologically and biologically different from the rest of Bruchinae that it is separated into its own tribe, Rhaebini. The most recently discovered species is *R. amnoni*, which was found in Israel and formally described in 2000.

Actual size

**Rhaebus mannerheimi** is a brilliant metallic green beetle, sometimes with a bluish or purplish tint. The body is narrow and nearly parallel-sided to slightly narrowing from the middle of the elytra, through the pronotum to the end of the head. The hind tarsomeres 1, 2, and 4 are very long and narrow. The males have greatly enlarged hind femora and curved hind tibiae covered with long white setae.

| FAMILY | Chrysomelidae |
|---|---|
| SUBFAMILY | Cassidinae |
| DISTRIBUTION | Neotropical: from Mexico to Brazil |
| MACROHABITAT | Tropical forests |
| MICROHABITAT | Hogvine (*Merremia umbellata*) plants |
| FEEDING HABITS | Adults and larvae feed on Hogvine |
| NOTE | Females exhibit maternal care |

ADULT LENGTH
³⁄₈–⁹⁄₁₆ in
(10–15 mm)

552

# ACROMIS SPARSA
(BOHEMAN, 1854)

*Acromis sparsa* is unique among leaf beetles in having a complex behavior comprising intense male competition and female maternal care. Males commonly antennate (touch with their antennae) one another and often clasp elytra and tug against the other while competing for females. Elytral holes observed in many males are thought to be results of this male combat. Females guard larvae by staying with a grazing larval group and sometimes are observed standing on the backs of larvae, which lack many defensive adaptations displayed by Cassidinae larvae that lack maternal care. This behavior is known to reduce larval mortality.

## RELATED SPECIES

The genus *Acromis* comprises three species that occur in South America. Aside from *A. sparsa* there are no reports of maternal care among these species. The host plant of *A. spinifex* is Sweet Potato (*Ipomoea batatas*), while the host of *A. venosa* is not known.

Actual size

**Acromis sparsa** is straw-yellow in color, with small black spots on the elytra. The pronotum is slightly darker than the elytra, with two narrow longitudinal black lines close to the middle. In the male, the elytra have long, pointed corners.

| FAMILY | Chrysomelidae |
|---|---|
| SUBFAMILY | Cassidinae |
| DISTRIBUTION | Oriental and Australian: Southeast Asia, Australia |
| MACROHABITAT | A variety of forests with palms |
| MICROHABITAT | Palm trees |
| FEEDING HABITS | Feeds on about 20 palm species, including Coconut Palm (*Cocos nucifera*) |
| NOTE | One of the most devastating invasive pests of palms in Asia and Australia |

ADULT LENGTH
¼–⅜ in
(7.3–9.8 mm)

*BRONTISPA LONGISSIMA*
# COCONUT HISPINE BEETLE
(GESTRO, 1885)

553

The Coconut Hispine Beetle is native to Indonesia, and has a current range that includes Australia, China, Laos, Malaysia, Burma, the Philippines, Thailand, and Vietnam. Its entire life cycle, from egg to adult, usually takes five to nine weeks. It is reported that the females cover each egg with excreta. Both adults and larvae tend to avoid light and are nocturnal. They feed on palm leaflets, causing visible damage that may result in the death of damaged plants.

RELATED SPECIES

There are about 20 species of *Brontispa*, all of them from Southeast Asia. They feed on plants in the families Araceae, Arecaceae, Pandanaceae, Poaceae, and Zingiberaceae. Among 17 species of *Brontispa* housed at the Smithsonian Institution's National Museum of Natural History, *B. simonthomasi* is the most similar to *B. longissima*. It was discovered in 1958 in New Guinea and described by J. L. Gressitt in 1960.

Actual size

**The Coconut Hispine Beetle** has a slender, dorsoventrally flattened body. Its main color varies from straw-yellow to dark brown. The head bears a long appendage protruding between the antennae. The legs are short and wide, with slightly curved femora.

| FAMILY | Chrysomelidae |
|---|---|
| SUBFAMILY | Cassidinae |
| DISTRIBUTION | Oriental and Australian: southern Asia |
| MACROHABITAT | Grasslands, rice fields |
| MICROHABITAT | Adults and larvae are found on various grasses |
| FEEDING HABITS | Adults scrape the leaves of their host plants; larvae mine inside the leaves |
| NOTE | A major pest of rice (*Oryza* spp.) in southern Asia, particularly in India, Nepal, and Bangladesh |

ADULT LENGTH
³/₁₆–¼ in
(5–7 mm)

*DICLADISPA ARMIGERA*
# RICE HISPA
(OLIVIER, 1808)

554

The Rice Hispa—also known as the Paddy Hispa—is one of the most damaging pests of rice (*Oryza* spp.) in many countries of southern Asia. The adults feed by scraping the leaf surface and larvae mine the leaves, living in leaf parenchyma. Because of the species' pest status, the biology of the Rice Hispa is relatively well studied. The female usually lays about 80 eggs, which hatch in about five days. Adult females live longer than males. There are four larval instars and the larval development lasts about two weeks. In rice-growing countries the Rice Hispa is usually controlled by pesticides. Biological control methods are not well studied, but it is known that the beetle is parasitized by various wasps and attacked by spiders.

### RELATED SPECIES

In India, the Rice Hispa is most similar to *Dicladispa birendra*. This species was described in 1919 by famous Indian beetle specialist Samarendra Maulik based on three specimens collected in Assam, but its biology remains poorly known. The species are distinguished by the shape of the pronotal spines, which are straight in the Rice Hispa and curved in *D. birendra*.

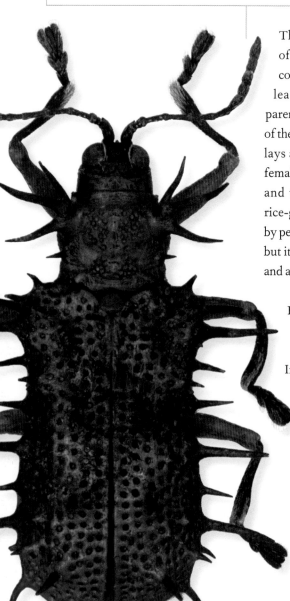

Actual size

**The Rice Hispa** has a relatively flat body covered by long, sharp spines, as do most hispines. It is shiny and black with a light bluish or greenish tint. The legs are black or dark reddish brown.

| FAMILY | Chrysomelidae |
|---|---|
| SUBFAMILY | Cassidinae |
| DISTRIBUTION | Nearctic: southern North America |
| MACROHABITAT | Forests with various palms (e.g., *Serenoa repens*, *Sabal* spp.) |
| MICROHABITAT | Palm trees |
| FEEDING HABITS | Adults and larvae have been recorded on about ten species of palms |
| NOTE | One of only a few leaf beetles that feed on palms |

ADULT LENGTH
³⁄₁₆ in
(4.5–5.3 mm)

*HEMISPHAEROTA CYANEA*
# FLORIDA TORTOISE BEETLE
(SAY, 1824)

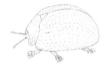

555

The Florida Tortoise beetle is one of a few leaf beetles whose larvae use their own feces to defend against predators and parasites. The adult females cover their eggs with fecal pellets once they are laid. Immediately after hatching and as soon as feeding begins, the larvae excrete feces in the shape of strands, which they build up over the entire larval stage. The strands curl, forming a loose, constantly growing thatch-like shield that hides the larval body and protects the larva from predators and parasites. Pupation occurs on leaves of the host plants under this fecal shield.

Actual size

### RELATED SPECIES
*Hemisphaerota cyanea* belongs to a genus of only nine species. Five of these species occur in Cuba, one in the Dominican Republic, and two are known only from the type locality, which in the original publication is given as "Brasilia." The biology of the species is poorly known.

**The Florida Tortoise Beetle** is dark metallic blue with bright yellow antennae. The body is wide, covering all legs, although the head is visible in between the lobes of the pronotum, which is uncommon among Cassidinae.

| FAMILY | Chrysomelidae |
|---|---|
| SUBFAMILY | Chrysomelinae |
| DISTRIBUTION | Neotropical and Holarctic: Mexico, USA, Europe, Russia (including Caucasus and Far East), China |
| MACROHABITAT | Open habitats |
| MICROHABITAT | Plants of the genus *Solanum* |
| FEEDING HABITS | Adults and larvae feed on leaves of *Solanum* spp. |
| NOTE | The most invasive leaf beetle species in the world |

ADULT LENGTH
⁵⁄₁₆–⁷⁄₁₆ in
(10–11 mm)

556

*LEPTINOTARSA DECEMLINEATA*
# COLORADO POTATO BEETLE
SAY, 1824

The Colorado Potato Beetle is the most widespread species of the genus *Leptinotarsa* and one of the most devastating leaf beetle pests in the word. Adults overwinter in the soil, emerging in the early spring. Oviposition lasts up to one month and a single female may lay up to 500 eggs. Emerging larvae are dark reddish with black spots. Pupation occurs in the soil. In addition to the Potato (*Solanum tuberosum*), other plants in the genus *Solanum* are recorded as hosts for this species, e.g., *S. sisymbriifolium*.

RELATED SPECIES

There are about 40 *Leptinotarsa* species in the world, with a native range in North and Central America. Twelve *Leptinotarsa* species occur in the US; among them, *L. juncta* is the only species that coexists with the Colorado Potato Beetle in the eastern US. It can be differentiated from the Colorado Potato Beetle in that its elytral punctation is arranged in regular rows and it has a black spot on the outer margin of the femur.

Actual size

**The Colorado Potato Beetle** is large, with a body that appears oval and convex in lateral view. Its basic color varies from pale yellow to yellow, including most of the legs. The head and pronotum have black spots and each elytron has five black vittae. The elytral punctation is arranged in irregular rows.

| FAMILY | Chrysomelidae |
|---|---|
| SUBFAMILY | Chrysomelinae |
| DISTRIBUTION | Northern Palearctic: from Scandinavia to Siberia, south to Austria, Germany, and northern and western Scotland |
| MACROHABITAT | Northern forest and southern tundra |
| MICROHABITAT | Mountain forest, forest sides, wet depressions in tundra |
| FEEDING HABITS | Leaves of dwarf willows (*Salix* spp.) and birches (*Betula* spp.) |
| NOTE | One of the few subarctic species of leaf beetle |

ADULT LENGTH
³/₁₆ in
(3.6 – 4.7 mm)

*PHRATORA POLARIS*
# PHRATORA POLARIS
(SCHNEIDER, 1886)

557

*Phratora polaris* is one of a few leaf beetles that have a geographic range extending far north into the tundra and that are adapted to the harsh northern environment. Due to the short vegetation period at such latitudes, the life cycle of *P. polaris* is significantly shorter than that of relatives living further south. The remnants of these beetles are known from the Holocene in southeast Greenland. The larvae live on a leaf surface and when they are approached by a possible enemy release a repelling secretion from eversible glands on the thorax and abdomen.

### RELATED SPECIES

*Phratora polaris* belongs to the subgenus *Phyllodecta*, which is represented by 35 species and subspecies in the Palearctic. In the Nearctic, there are only ten species and subspecies of *Phratora*. Among them, *P. polaris* is very similar to *P. hudsonica* and *P. frosti*, and may be even conspecific with them. *Phratora hudsonica* is known to feed on various willows (*Salix* spp.) and *P. frosti* on birches (*Betula* spp.).

Actual size

**Phratora polaris** has a relatively narrow, almost parallel-sided body, with the strongly convex pronotum almost as wide as the elytra. The body and appendages are black with a light copper, bluish, or greenish tint. Each tarsal claw bears a basal tooth. Antennomeres 2–11 increase slightly in size to the apex.

| FAMILY | Chrysomelidae |
|---|---|
| SUBFAMILY | Chrysomelinae |
| DISTRIBUTION | Palearctic: Europe |
| MACROHABITAT | Broadleaf forests |
| MICROHABITAT | Forest clearings and edges |
| FEEDING HABITS | Adults and larvae feed on leaves of *Galium verum* and *G. mollugo* |
| NOTE | One of the most charismatic European leaf beetles |

**ADULT LENGTH**
⁹⁄₁₆–¹¹⁄₁₆ in
(14–18 mm)

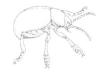

*TIMARCHA TENEBRICOSA*
# BLOODY-NOSED BEETLE
(FABRICIUS, 1775)

The Bloody-nosed Beetle belongs to the tribe Timarchini, which differs from the rest of the chrysomelines in its morphology in that many structures are relatively primitive for leaf beetles, particularly those of female genitalia. The species has one of the largest geographical ranges in Europe and has attracted a lot of public attention from both scientists and amateurs. Its large, hard-bodied, brightly colored larvae are well known and their behavior is documented in various short film-clips on YouTube.

## RELATED SPECIES

The genus *Timarcha* contains about 240 species distributed mostly in southern Europe, the Caucasus, and North Africa (only two are found in the United States), with many having a very narrow geographic range. Many species are flightless and occur at relatively high altitudes in various European and Caucasian mountains. Classification of the genus is not well known and in need of further study. The Bloody-nosed Beetle belongs to a group of five species that occur in Portugal, Spain, France, and Italy.

**The Bloody-nosed Beetle** is black with a light metallic blue, green, or purple tint. Its antennae are short. The pronotum and elytra are covered with relatively small but dense punctation and the spaces between punctures are densely reticulated, so that the entire surface appears dull. The male tarsomeres are much wider than long, which is uncommon among leaf beetles.

Actual size

| | |
|---|---|
| FAMILY | Chrysomelidae |
| SUBFAMILY | Criocerinae |
| DISTRIBUTION | Palearctic and Oriental: China, India, Laos, Nepal |
| MACROHABITAT | Forest |
| MICROHABITAT | Forest margins, roadsides |
| FEEDING HABITS | Adults and larvae feed on leaves of the Air Potato (*Dioscorea bulbifera*) |
| NOTE | Currently being used as a biological control agent of the invasive Air Potato (*Dioscorea bulbifera*) weed |

ADULT LENGTH
¼–⅜ in
(7–9 mm)

*LILIOCERIS CHENI*
# AIR POTATO LEAF BEETLE
GRESSIT & KIMOTO, 1961

559

The Air Potato Leaf Beetle has very narrow host specialization, feeding only on foliage of the Air Potato (*Dioscorea bulbifera*). This invasive weed of Asian origin was introduced to Florida as a medicinal plant in 1905, and since then has become one of the most aggressive weeds ever introduced to the United States. The Air Potato Leaf Beetle was found to cause significant damage to Air Potato plants in Nepal and China, and after extensive studies is being used to control the weed. The larvae feed gregariously on the underside of leaves and a development of four larval instars requires about eight days. After that, larvae descend from the plants and enter the substrate to complete their life cycle.

RELATED SPECIES
There are about 110 species of *Lilioceris* in Asia. Among them, eight species, including *L. cheni*, form a tight group based on shared character states of the pubescence of the scutellum, shape of the basal antennomeres, and structure of the sclerites of the internal sac of male genitalia. The latter characters are used to separate a species most similar to *L. cheni*, *L. egena*. A study of its biology revealed that it lives on the same Air Potato plants as *L. cheni*, but feeds on bulbils rather than foliage.

Actual size

**The Air Potato Leaf Beetle** has reddish-brown elytra and a black or dark brown head, pronotum, legs, and antennae. Antennomere 5 is much wider than antennomere 4, dull, and covered with numerous short white setae. The pronotum is strongly narrowed in the middle, and is much narrower than the elytra.

| FAMILY | Chrysomelidae |
|---|---|
| SUBFAMILY | Cryptocephalinae |
| DISTRIBUTION | Most of the Palearctic Realm |
| MACROHABITAT | Variety of woodlands, meadows, roadsides |
| MICROHABITAT | Adults are found on woody and herbaceous plants; larvae live in ant nests |
| FEEDING HABITS | Adults are phytophagous, feeding on a variety of woody and herbaceous plants; larvae feed on debris in ant nests |
| NOTE | One of only a few leaf beetles whose larvae live in ant nests |

**ADULT LENGTH**
5/16–3/8 in
(7.6–9.8 mm)

560

*CLYTRA QUADRIPUNCTATA*
# CLYTRA QUADRIPUNCTATA
(LINNAEUS, 1758)

The biology of *Clytra quadripunctata* is uncommon among leaf beetles. Females oviposit by dropping eggs from low-hanging vegetation onto the ground near an ant nest, and the ants then carry them into the nest. Before dropping an egg, the female places fecal pellets onto the egg surface while holding the egg in her hind legs. The larvae use these pellets to start building a case, which they then complete using their own feces. The larva develops inside the case, which is usually covered with ridges similar to those many other myrmecophilous beetles have on their bodies.

## RELATED SPECIES

There are about 40 species and subspecies of *Clytra* in the Palearctic Realm. The most similar 14 species are combined into a nominotypical subgenus *Clytra*. Among these, *C. aliena* is most similar to *C. quadripunctata*. To separate the two species reliably, the male genitalia must be dissected. Feeding habits of other *Clytra* species are similar to those of *C. quadripunctata*.

Actual size

**Clytra quadripunctata** has relatively long cylindrical body with relatively short legs and antennae, and bright reddish-orange elytra with black spots. The rest of the body is black, sometimes with a bluish or greenish metallic tint. The antennae are short, with antennomeres shaped like saw teeth.

| | |
|---|---|
| FAMILY | Chrysomelidae |
| SUBFAMILY | Cryptocephalinae |
| DISTRIBUTION | Most of the Palearctic, from Spain to northwest China |
| MACROHABITAT | Mixed and broadleaf forests, meadows |
| MICROHABITAT | Flowerheads of various herbaceous plants |
| FEEDING HABITS | Adults are found on flowers of *Hieracium*, *Knautia*, and *Scabiosa* spp.; larvae occur in leaf litter |
| NOTE | This is one of the most attractive and common leaf beetles in the western Palearctic |

ADULT LENGTH
¼ in
(6–7.1 mm)

*CRYPTOCEPHALUS SERICEUS*
# CRYPTOCEPHALUS SERICEUS
(LINNAEUS, 1758)

561

*Cryptocephalus sericeus* is one of the most common species of *Cryptocephalus* in the western part of the Palearctic. The taxonomy and phylogeny of *C. sericeus* is well known and was inferred by comparative morphological methods, as well as by studying molecular data. The larvae live inside cases that they build from their own feces.

Actual size

## RELATED SPECIES
*Cryptocephalus sericeus* belongs to a species group containing four other species distributed in Europe. Its closest relative is *C. zambanellus*, but the geographic ranges of the two are separated by the Alps, so that *C. zambanellus* occurs only in Italy and the Dalmatian coast south of Istria. The most useful morphological features for separating these species are the shape of the anal (abdominal) ventrite and the male genitalia.

**Cryptocephalus sericeus** is a brilliant metallic green or blue beetle, which sometimes has a purple tint. It has a robust, nearly cylindrical body with relatively short legs and antennae. The head is inserted into a large, convex pronotum, making it barely visible from above.

| FAMILY | Chrysomelidae |
|---|---|
| SUBFAMILY | Cryptocephalinae |
| DISTRIBUTION | Neotropical: Brazil, Guyana |
| MACROHABITAT | Tropical forest |
| MICROHABITAT | Forest margins, coastal dunes |
| FEEDING HABITS | Adults and larvae feed on stems and foliage of *Byrsonima sericea* |
| NOTE | One of the most exotic-looking leaf beetles |

**ADULT MALE LENGTH**
⁵⁄₁₆–³⁄₈ in
(8–10 mm)

**ADULT FEMALE LENGTH**
³⁄₈–¹⁄₂ in
(9–12 mm)

562

*FULCIDAX MONSTROSA*
# FULCIDAX MONSTROSA
(FABRICIUS, 1798)

Actual size

The life cycle of *Fulcidax monstrosa* is well studied in the field and laboratory. The female lays a single egg on the stem of the host plant. The larva hatches about ten days after and goes through four instars (which may take about four months) during which it constantly adds to its elaborately constructed case. By the end of development, the prepupa seals the case and remains attached to a stem for a maximum of another four months. This prepupal diapause is rare among leaf beetles. After emerging, the adults immediately start feeding and mating.

RELATED SPECIES
Seven species are currently known in the genus *Fulcidax*. They are distributed in the Neotropics and are among the largest Fulcidacini in the world. They are bright metallic in color and share a unique natural history, the eggs being covered with fecal plates that are retained during the entire larval development. The larvae live inside cases, where pupation takes place.

**Fulcidax monstrosa** is one of the largest species of the tribe Fulcidacini, with bright blue metallic coloration. The pronotum and elytra are covered with long appendages and ridges, and the surface between them is usually smooth and shiny. The top of pronotum is covered with deep, closely placed punctures. The antennae and legs fit in variously shaped grooves on the ventral side of the body.

| FAMILY | Chrysomelidae |
| --- | --- |
| SUBFAMILY | Donaciinae |
| DISTRIBUTION | Palearctic |
| MACROHABITAT | Rivers, lakes, ponds |
| MICROHABITAT | Leaves of water lilies |
| FEEDING HABITS | Adults feed on the leaves and larvae the roots of water lilies (*Nuphar* spp. and *Nymphaea* spp.) |
| NOTE | One of the prettiest donaciines in eastern Europe |

ADULT LENGTH
⁵⁄₁₆–½ in
(8–12 mm)

*DONACIA CRASSIPES*

# DONACIA CRASSIPES

FABRICIUS, 1775

563

Adults of *Donacia crassipes* live on flat leaf surfaces of water lilies, while larvae develop underwater and feed on roots of the same plants. Observations made in midsummer in central Russia revealed a unique kind of aggressive male behavior. While competing for females, males engage in direct confrontation, swinging and pushing each other away from the female with their large hind legs, which are armed with two sharp teeth. In addition, they push each other with the raised tips of their abdomens while leaning all their legs on the leaf surface.

Actual size

## RELATED SPECIES

There are 70 species and subspecies of the genus *Donacia* within the Palearctic Realm alone. *Donacia crassipes* is one of the most common species in eastern Europe and central Russia. Members of the genus are differentiated from one another by the color and sculpture of the surface of the head, pronotum, and elytra, and the relative size and armament of the hind legs. However, the most reliable characters are those of the male genitalia.

**Donacia crassipes** varies in color from metallic green to blue and violet, with dark orange legs that have metallic green stripes on the upper surface of the tibiae. The hind legs are long, with the femora projecting beyond the elytra. The hind femora are armed with two sharp teeth in males and one tooth in females. The inner corner of the tips of elytra have short, sharp projections.

| FAMILY | Chrysomelidae |
|---|---|
| SUBFAMILY | Eumolpinae |
| DISTRIBUTION | Nearctic: transcontinental in the USA; Canadian southern territories from British Columbia to Nova Scotia |
| MACROHABITAT | Forest, clearings, meadows, agricultural fields, roadsides |
| MICROHABITAT | Plants of *Apocynum* spp. |
| FEEDING HABITS | Adults feed on the leaves, and larvae on the roots, of Dogbane (*Apocynum cannabinum*) and Fly-trap Dogbane (*A. androsaemifolium*) |
| NOTE | One of the most colorful leaf beetles in North America |

ADULT LENGTH
¼–⁷⁄₁₆ in
(6.8–11 mm)

564

*CHRYSOCHUS AURATUS*
# DOGBANE BEETLE
(FABRICIUS, 1775)

The Dogbane Beetle has a life cycle common to many leaf beetles. Females lay eggs from which the first-instar larvae appear. They then borrow into the soil and feed externally on host-plant roots. Adults emerge from the soil after brief development inside the pupa. The species is adapted to ingest and sequester the toxic cardenolides that its host plants contain in their leaves and roots. Both adults and larvae have also adapted to use these toxins to protect themselves from predators by releasing them through glands on the prothorax and elytra when disturbed.

## RELATED SPECIES

There are only two species of the genus *Chrysochus* in North America: *C. auratus* and *C. cobaltinus*. At the western part of its range *C. auratus* interbreeds with *C. cobaltinus*, which occurs mostly in the western United States. As its common name suggests, *C. cobaltinus* is usually cobalt blue, rarely with a greenish tinge or black color. Both species can be separated accurately by differences in the shape of their male genitalia.

Actual size

**The Dogbane Beetle** is iridescent bluish green with a metallic copper, golden, or crimson tint. The ventral side of the body is most commonly metallic green. The pronotum is much narrower than the elytra, and the head can barely be seen in dorsal view. The antennae are fairly long and narrow.

| FAMILY | Chrysomelidae |
|---|---|
| SUBFAMILY | Eumolpinae |
| DISTRIBUTION | Palearctic: Europe, North Africa, Asia |
| MACROHABITAT | Broadleaf forests, steppes, semideserts |
| MICROHABITAT | Sandy, at times xeric, habitats |
| FEEDING HABITS | Adults and larvae feed on various Asteraceae and Poaceae, including thistles (*Cirsium* spp.), wheat (*Triticum* spp.), and Sunflower (*Helianthus annuus*); larvae feed on roots of wheat (*Triticum* spp.) |
| NOTE | At times occurs on slightly saline soils |

ADULT LENGTH
⅛ in
(2.5–3.3 mm)

*PACHNEPHORUS TESSELLATUS*
# PACHNEPHORUS TESSELLATUS
(DUFTSCHMID, 1825)

565

*Actual size*

*Pachnephorus tessellatus* larvae live in the soil on roots of their host plants. They are slightly different from larvae of other soil-dwelling Eumolpinae such as *Chloropterus* in having an only slightly C-shaped body, ¼ in (7 mm) long, with poorly developed folds and a covering of longer, sparse setae. Due to their color and the pale scales that cover the pronotum and elytra, adults of *P. tessellatus* are barely visible in their native sandy habitats when they fall off leaves if disturbed. In western Siberia, larvae of *P. tessellatus* have been considered a serious pest of wheat.

## RELATED SPECIES

There are 25 species of the genus *Pachnephorus* in the Palearctic Realm. *Pachnephorus tessellatus* belongs to a subgenus of 24 species. Among them, it is most similar to species with well-developed humeral calli and to *P. canus* in particular, which is distributed in the Balkans, the southern part of European Russia, and the Near East. Among other characters, members of the genus *Pachnephorus* can generally be differentiated by the presence or absence of scales on various structures, differences in the male tarsal claws and their color patterns.

**Pachnephorus tessellatus** is entirely dark brown with lighter antennae and legs. Its whole body is covered with slightly elongate scales (narrower on the legs than on the elytra), these sometimes being notched at the top. The scales vary from white to a pale, milky coffee color, and are darker at the top of the elytra and pronotum.

| FAMILY | Chrysomelidae |
|---|---|
| SUBFAMILY | Galerucinae |
| DISTRIBUTION | Neotropical, Nearctic, and Palearctic: Mexico, USA, Canada, Europe |
| MACROHABITAT | Mostly open habitats, including fields and meadows |
| MICROHABITAT | Maize (*Zea mays*) plants |
| FEEDING HABITS | Adults have been observed on flowers of Asteraceae and mainly on leaves of Brassicaceae; larvae feed on roots of Maize (*Zea mays*) |
| NOTE | The species is an invasive pest of Maize (*Zea mays*) crops in Europe |

**ADULT LENGTH**
³⁄₁₆–¼ in
(4.6–5.9 mm)

566

*DIABROTICA VIRGIFERA*
# WESTERN CORN ROOTWORM
LECONTE, 1868

Actual size

The Western Corn Rootworm is one of the most devastating beetle pests in the United States, costing the economy an estimated $1 billion in lost revenue annually. It overwinters as an egg in the soil; larvae appear in the spring and begin to feed on the roots of Maize (*Zea mays*). The geographic range of the species in the United States expanded rapidly in the second part of the twentieth century, and by the end of the century it was discovered in Europe, where it is now widespread and is considered a serious pest of Maize.

RELATED SPECIES

*Diabrotica virgifera* is divided into two subspecies, the nominate and *D. v. zeae*. The only feature that allows for distinguishing them is distinct black humeral vittae on the elytra of *D. v. virgifera*. In Texas and northern Mexico, a transitional zone between the subspecies, it is impossible to separate them reliably. *Diabrotica virgifera* is also similar to *D. longicornis* and *D. barberi*. *Diabrotica longicornis* is reported to feed on various Cucurbitaceae and is not pest of Maize, while *D. barberi* is known to cause damage to Maize but is also recorded as feeding on various other Poaceae, plus Cucurbitaceae, Asteraceae, and Fabaceae species.

**The Western Corn Rootworm** has a chestnut-brown to black head with filiform, uniformly brown antennae. The pronotum is yellow or sulfur yellow and deeply bifoveate. The elytra are green in live specimens and vittate, with one sutural and one humeral vittae (often expanding to cover most of the elytra); the vittae and humeral calli are black, while the elytral epipleura are completely green.

| | |
|---|---|
| FAMILY | Chrysomelidae |
| SUBFAMILY | Galerucinae |
| DISTRIBUTION | Afrotropical: Burundi, Ethiopia, Mozambique, Rwanda, South Africa, Tanzania |
| MACROHABITAT | Savanna |
| MICROHABITAT | Natal and sub-humid lowveld bushveld |
| FEEDING HABITS | Adults and larvae feed on foliage of shrubs and trees of *Commiphora* spp. |
| NOTE | Pupae are used by Bushmen to produce poison for their arrows |

ADULT LENGTH
⅜–½ in
(9–13 mm)

*DIAMPHIDIA FEMORALIS*
# BUSHMAN ARROW-POISON FLEA BEETLE
GERSTAECHER, 1855

567

The life cycle of the Bushman Arrow-poison Flea Beetle includes oviposition on host-plant stems; free-living, leaf-chewing larvae; and pupation in the soil. Females cover their eggs with feces, which are retained by larvae during their entire development as protection from predators and parasites before they ascend to the ground for pupation. Native African San people learned of the poisonous properties of the pupal hemolymph; they dig up the pupae and apply the hemolymph as poison on arrows.

## RELATED SPECIES
Seventeen species of *Diamphidia* are known to date. They all occur in Africa and are associated with *Commiphora* plants. Based on published data, pupae of *D. nigroornata* also have poisonous hemolymph and are also used by native people to poison their arrows. The larvae of this species are greenish in color close to the anus and darker brown toward the head, and cover their bodies with feces. Biology of other *Diamphidia* species is poorly known.

Actual size

**The Bushman Arrow-poison Flea Beetle** has a large oval body similar to that of some leaf beetles in the subfamily Chrysomelinae. It is bright yellow to brownish yellow, with darker antennae and tips to the femora and tarsi. It has a wide head with small eyes situated close to the pronotum. The tibiae have a large, wide base, with denticles close to the apex.

| FAMILY | Chrysomelidae |
|---|---|
| SUBFAMILY | Galerucinae |
| DISTRIBUTION | Palearctic: Algeria, Bulgaria, Egypt, Greece, Italy, Lebanon, Portugal, southern Russia (Dagestan), Spain, Turkey |
| MACROHABITAT | Mediterranean forests, woodlands and scrub, desert and semidesert habitats |
| MICROHABITAT | Tamarisk trees (*Tamarix* spp.) |
| FEEDING HABITS | Adults and larvae feed on leaves of *Tamarix* |
| NOTE | Promising biological control agent of invasive *Tamarix* in the US |

ADULT MALE LENGTH
³⁄₁₆–¼ in
(5.3–6.8 mm)

ADULT FEMALE LENGTH
¼–⁵⁄₁₆ in
(5.8–7.7 mm)

568

*DIORHABDA ELONGATA*
# MEDITERRANEAN TAMARISK BEETLE
(BRULLÉ, 1832)

Actual size

The Mediterranean Tamarisk Beetle is being investigated in the US as a potential biological control agent of tamarisk (*Tamarix* spp.), invasive trees that have been introduced from the Mediterranean. Adults and larvae severely defoliate *Tamarix*, thus limiting the trees' abilities to spread. Adults lay their eggs on the leaves, and the emerging larvae feed on the leaf surface, making holes in the lower epidermis and parenchyma. All three larval instars are black although the second and third instars have a yellowish lateral stripe. The full-grown larvae, which can reach ⅜ in (9 mm) in length, migrate to litter on the ground or an inch (25 mm) below the soil surface to pupate.

## RELATED SPECIES

The Mediterranean Tamarisk Beetle is a member of the *Diorhabda elongata* species group, all five members of which feed on *Tamarix* species. The native Palearctic ranges of the other four species are as follows: *D. carinata*, from southern Ukraine to Iraq and western China; *D. carinulata*, from southern Russia and Iran to Mongolia and China; *D. meridionalis*, in Iran, Pakistan, and Syria; and *D. sublineata*, in France, North Africa, and Iraq. They are mostly differentiated by characters of the male genitalia.

**The Mediterranean Tamarisk Beetle** is yellowish gray with darker leg and antennae articulations, basal and apical antennomeres, and tarsi. Live specimens have greenish-yellow tinting on the elytra, which themselves are covered with randomly placed, relatively large punctures. The head is relatively broad, with small, widely separated eyes.

| FAMILY | Chrysomelidae |
|---|---|
| SUBFAMILY | Galerucinae |
| DISTRIBUTION | Nearctic, Neotropical, and Palearctic: North, Central, and South America, West Indies, Europe |
| MACROHABITAT | Forest, fields, meadows, gardens, agricultural landscapes, Potato fields |
| MICROHABITAT | Adults are found on the foliage and larvae on the roots of nightshades, including Potato (*Solanum tuberosum*) |
| FEEDING HABITS | Adults chew holes in leaves of various nightshades |
| NOTE | One of the most common flea beetles in the United States |

ADULT LENGTH
¹⁄₁₆ in
(1.5–2 mm)

*EPITRIX CUCUMERIS*
# POTATO FLEA BEETLE
HARRIS, 1851

569

The Potato Flea Beetle is one of a few leaf beetles that has migrated to Europe from its native North America. It was recorded in the Azores Islands (Portugal) in 1979, and in 2008, it was identified, together with *Epitrix similaris*, by an international team of taxonomists in the Potato fields of mainland Portugal. In its native range, *E. cucumeris* is reported to feed on 22 species of the nightshade family (Solanaceae). It was also reported on plants from other plant families, although these reports may be based on beetle misidentifications.

Actual size

## RELATED SPECIES
There are about 90 species of *Epitrix* worldwide, the majority of them (about 70) occurring in the Neotropics. Their host plants are mostly from the nightshade family. Palearctic fauna consists of 16 native and two invasive species, *E. cucumeris* and *E. similaris*. In Europe both are found in the same habitats, and it is believed that larvae of *E. similaris* are responsible for Potato tuber damage in Portugal. The third similar species, *E. tuberis*, is known only from its native rage in North America. All three species are very similar and the entire group awaits taxonomic revision.

**The Potato Flea Beetle** has a black body with no metallic tint, and light brown legs and antennae. The elytra are covered with punctures arranged in regular rows and semierect, light-colored setae. The pronotum lacks setae but is covered with coarse punctures. A relatively deep, curved furrow is situated at the base of the pronotum.

| FAMILY | Chrysomelidae |
|---|---|
| SUBFAMILY | Galerucinae |
| DISTRIBUTION | Neotropical: Puerto Rico |
| MACROHABITAT | Mountain forest |
| MICROHABITAT | Moss cushions on rocks and tree trunks |
| FEEDING HABITS | Possibly moss or plant debris |
| NOTE | One of the smallest leaf beetles |

ADULT LENGTH
¹⁄₃₂ in
(0.8–0.9 mm)

*KISKEYA ELYUNQUE*

# KISKEYA ELYUNQUE

KONSTANTINOV & KONSTANTINOVA, 2011

•
Actual size

Of the approximately 50,000 leaf beetle species worldwide, only 27 from 14 genera are known to have evolved to inhabit moss cushions. *Kiskeya elyunque* is the most abundant of these. Although moss-inhabiting leaf beetles come from different evolutionary lineages, they share important morphological features: a small, round body, robust legs, short, often clavate antennae, an absence of metathoracic wings, and marked simplification of thoracic structures. While the type series of *K. elyunque* consists of nearly 100 specimens, its biology and larvae remain unknown.

### RELATED SPECIES

There are only three species of *Kiskeya* known to date. *K. neibae* and *K. baorucae* occur in the Dominican Republic. They were discovered within moss cushions at about 2,600–4,000 ft (800–1,200 m) above sea-level in two mountain ridges (southern Sierra de Bahoruco and the more northern Sierra de Neiba) that are parallel to each other but separated by a relatively wide valley. Both species are rare, with about ten known specimens, and their larvae and biology still wait to be discovered.

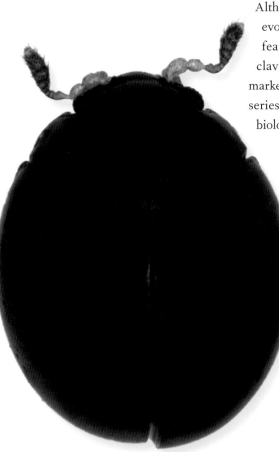

**Kiskeya elyunque** is black with a light greenish luster overall, and has dark brown to dark yellow legs and antennae. Its tiny body is round in dorsal view and convex in lateral view. The antennae are clavate and have three apical antennomeres that are much wider than the rest. The anterolateral setiferous pore is placed beyond the middle of the pronotum sides, close to its base.

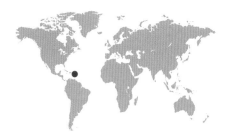

| FAMILY | Chrysomelidae |
|---|---|
| SUBFAMILY | Galerucinae |
| DISTRIBUTION | Neotropical: Puerto Rico |
| MACROHABITAT | Mountain forest |
| MICROHABITAT | Forest clearings, roadsides |
| FEEDING HABITS | Adults feed on ferns |
| NOTE | A rare example of a leaf beetle that feeds on ferns |

ADULT LENGTH
¹⁄₁₆–⅛ in
(2–2.5 mm)

*NORMALTICA OBRIENI*

# NORMALTICA OBRIENI
KONSTANTINOV, 2002

571

Actual size

Despite its relatively recent discovery (2002), *Normaltica obrieni* is common within its range, where the beetles, with their dark bodies and bright pink antennae, can easily be seen crawling on ferns. The males are markedly different from the females in that they have a much wider and longer head, long mandibles, and greatly enlarged other mouthparts. It is hypothesized that the sexually dimorphic characters function as clasping (restraining) or copulatory courtship devices rather than combat devices. This, along with examples from apionine weevils, demonstrates negative correlation between the development of sexually dimorphic external structures and the size and mechanical properties of the male genitalia.

## RELATED SPECIES
The only other known species of *Normaltica*, *N. ivie*, occurs in the Dominican Republic. Only four specimens of this species have been collected and we do not know much about its biology or feeding habits; the larvae are also unknown. Unlike *N. obrieni*, males and females of this species are very similar morphologically. They also lack metathoracic wings, and as a result have a highly simplified set of metathoracic structures.

**Normaltica obrieni** is black with a light metallic tint, pale appendages, and bright pink antennal clubs that lose their color in dry museum specimens. Its body is nearly round in dorsal view and convex in lateral view. The base of the pronotum is even, lacking transverse and longitudinal grooves, and expands backward slightly toward the scutellum.

| FAMILY | Chrysomelidae |
|---|---|
| SUBFAMILY | Galerucinae |
| DISTRIBUTION | Oriental: India (Karnataka, Kerala) |
| MACROHABITAT | Forest, parks |
| MICROHABITAT | *Terminalia* trees |
| FEEDING HABITS | Adults feed on leaves of *Terminalia cuneata* and *T. paniculata* |
| NOTE | A very recently discovered species with novel and unique behavioral trends |

**ADULT LENGTH**
¹⁄₃₂–¹⁄₁₆ in
(1.2–1.5 mm)

*ORTHALTICA TERMINALIA*
# ORTHALTICA TERMINALIA
PRATHAPAN & KONSTANTINOV, 2013

•
Actual size

*Orthaltica terminalia* and the closely related *O. syzygium* are unique among leaf beetles—and indeed beetles in general—in making use of holes preformed by larger leaf-feeding beetles on the leaves of their host trees, just as some birds nest in existing cavities produced by primary cavity-nesters such as woodpeckers. Beetles spend most of the day inside leaf-hole shelters, which offer them a roosting site, a certain degree of camouflage, and protection from various predators. They come out of their shelters to feed, forming irregular feeding trenches that radiate from the leaf hole. In some cases *O. terminalia* beetles have been observed partitioning their holes by constructing walls from fecal pellets. Until this discovery, the use of feces for the construction of defensive structures or retreats was unknown among adult leaf beetles.

## RELATED SPECIES

Seven additional species of *Orthaltica* occur in India. Only one of them, *O. syzygium*, is documented to use leaf-hole shelters. It feeds on leaves of *Syzygium cumini* (Myrtaceae) in Kerala and Karnataka. World fauna of *Orthaltica* comprises 44 named species. These feed on plants from the Combretaceae, Melastomataceae, and Myrtaceae families, and occur in the Afrotropical, Australian, Nearctic, and Oriental realms, with the majority (32 species) in the Oriental Realm.

**Orthaltica terminalia** is a shiny black beetle with yellowish-brown legs and antennae. The vertex has four long and six short setae. The sides of the pronotum are slightly uneven. The elytra are sparsely pubescent and covered in punctures arranged in regular rows. The hind femora are only weakly swollen (in the majority of flea beetles they are greatly enlarged).

| FAMILY | Chrysomelidae |
|---|---|
| SUBFAMILY | Galerucinae |
| DISTRIBUTION | Afrotropical, Australian, Nearctic, Neotropical, Oriental, and Palearctic realms |
| MACROHABITAT | Forests, meadows, swamps, agricultural fields, and gardens in mostly temperate regions of the world |
| MICROHABITAT | Adults are found on leaves of various crucifer plants, and larvae on roots of the same plants |
| FEEDING HABITS | Both adults and larvae feed on various crucifers |
| NOTE | This is one of the most widespread and common flea beetle species, and is a pest of cultivated crucifers |

ADULT LENGTH
1/16 in
(2–2.4 mm)

*PHYLLOTRETA STRIOLATA*
# STRIPED FLEA BEETLE
(ILLIGER, 1803)

573

Actual size

The Striped Flea Beetle has such a wide ecological tolerance that in a particular study of flea beetles of western Russia and the Caucasus it was found in all landscape zones, from tundra to semideserts, and in all mountain areas of this huge region. And unlike most of the flea beetles, which have narrow host-plant specialization, it is known to feed on plants from many different genera of crucifers. Because of its pest status and abundance, the biology and larvae of this species are relatively well known.

## RELATED SPECIES
The genus *Phyllotreta* contains about 230 species that are distributed worldwide, the majority of them in the Palearctic Realm. Among the approximately 100 Palearctic species, the Striped Flea Beetle is mostly similar to those whose elytra are generally black with a wide, variously shaped yellow stripe (there are about 30 Palearctic species of *Phyllotreta* with yellow-striped elytra). They feed mainly on various crucifers and are well differentiated from each other based on the color pattern of the elytra, although the most reliable characters for species identification are those of the male genitalia.

**The Striped Flea Beetle** is oily black in color with a light bronze tint, and has slightly lighter legs and antennae. A strongly curved yellow stripe runs down the middle of each generally black elytron. The head, pronotum, and elytra are covered with coarse punctures. In males, antennomere 5 is much larger than antennomeres 4 and 6; in females, these antennomeres are of similar size.

| | |
|---|---|
| FAMILY | Chrysomelidae |
| SUBFAMILY | Lamprosomatinae |
| DISTRIBUTION | Palearctic: Europe, Caucasus |
| MACROHABITAT | Forest |
| MICROHABITAT | Forest floor |
| FEEDING HABITS | In England, adults are known to feed on ivy (*Hedera* spp.) and *Astrantia* spp. Larvae are known to feed in captivity on *Hedera* spp. and in the wild are polyphagous, feeding on plants and detritus |
| NOTE | The larva lives inside a fecal case |

ADULT LENGTH
¹⁄₁₆–⅛ in
(2.3–2.8 mm)

574

*OOMORPHUS CONCOLOR*
# OOMORPHUS CONCOLOR
(STURM, 1807)

Actual size

The geographic range of *Oomorphus concolor*, as currently understood, is split between western Europe and the Caucasus Mountains. Beetles from the two regions differ from each other slightly, but research shows that they belong to a single species. In the Caucasus, adults and larvae live on the forest floor. The larvae are about ⅛ in (3 mm) long, are soft bodied, and live inside a fecal case that they build for themselves. When they are inactive, the larvae withdraw their entire body, including the head, inside the case. They are nocturnal, feeding on plants at night.

RELATED SPECIES

There are only four species of the genus *Oomorphus* in the Palearctic, with *O. concolor* being the only European species. Two species occur in China and one in Japan. All beetles have compact oval bodies with particular grooves on the ventral side. It has been observed that beetles of *O. japanus* retract their legs and antennae into these grooves when they are attacked by ants on leaves.

**Oomorphus concolor** is entirely oily black with a light bluish, copperish, or greenish tint, except for the second antennomere, which is reddish yellow. The body is oval, with short legs and antennae. The inner surfaces of the femora have grooves in which the tibiae fit. The pronotum and elytra are covered with relatively dense punctation, the larger punctures forming barely perceptible rows on elytra.

| | |
|---|---|
| FAMILY | Chrysomelidae |
| SUBFAMILY | Sagrinae |
| DISTRIBUTION | Oriental: Malaysia, Thailand |
| MACROHABITAT | Tropical forest |
| MICROHABITAT | Climbing vines |
| FEEDING HABITS | Adults feed on the leaves of host plants and larvae bore into their stems |
| NOTE | One of the largest and most colorful leaf beetles |

ADULT LENGTH
¾–1⁹⁄₁₆ in
(20–39 mm)
including tips of femora

*SAGRA BUQUETI*
# FROG-LEGGED LEAF BEETLE
(LESSON, 1831)

575

Despite the fact that the Frog-legged Leaf Beetle is one of the largest and most colorful leaf beetles in the world and that it is also commonly kept in insect zoos and reared by numerous amateurs, we do not know much about its biology in the wild. Amateurs have reported that it develops on Sweet Potato (*Ipomoea batatas*), while cocoons of the species can found on climbing vines in Asian jungles. The beetle is known for its striking sexual dimorphism, with males larger than females overall and with much larger hind legs.

RELATED SPECIES

Species of the genus *Sagra* are distributed in Asia. Most are large and similar in color to the Frog-legged Leaf Beetle. Some (e.g., *S. amethystina*) are gall-makers, which is very uncommon among leaf beetles in general. Between one and 20 larvae can be found in a single stem of their host plants. The larvae construct cocoons inside the galls, where pupation occurs.

**The Frog-legged Leaf Beetle** is brilliant metallic green with a bright metallic purple, reddish, and orange strip along the elytral suture. The pronotum is much narrower than the base of the elytra. The male hind legs are strongly enlarged. The femora are long and thick, with a few large and small denticles on the ventral side. The tibia is about as long as the femora, curved, widening apically, and with large teeth and a long, thick comb of orange setae.

Actual size

| FAMILY | Chrysomelidae |
|---|---|
| SUBFAMILY | Spilopyrinae |
| DISTRIBUTION | Australian: coastal areas mainly at border of Queensland and New South Wales |
| MACROHABITAT | Rainforest |
| MICROHABITAT | Foliage of Tuckeroo (*Cupaniopsis anacardioides*) and Guioa (*Guioa semiglauca*) |
| FEEDING HABITS | Adults feed on foliage of *Cupaniopsis anacardioides* and *Guioa semiglauca* |
| NOTE | One of the most colorful beetles of the Australian rainforest |

ADULT LENGTH
⅜–½ in
(9–12 mm)

576

*SPILOPYRA SUMPTUOSA*
# SPILOPYRA SUMPTUOSA
BALY, 1860

Despite its bright color and relative abundance in museum collections, not much is known about the biology of this species. Adults have been reported dropping to the ground from the leaves of their host plants when disturbed, without attempting to fly. The only other leaf beetle collected on the same host plants is *Platymela sticticollis*. First-instar larvae have been reared from eggs in laboratory conditions. The eggs are covered with an egg case.

## RELATED SPECIES

The genus *Spilopyra* was recently revised and contains only five species. Of these, *S. sumptuosa* has the largest geographic range. The species are differentiated by characters of the elytral humeral calli, shape of the prosternal process, and color pattern.

Actual size

**Spilopyra sumptuosa** is dark metallic purple, blue, violet, or dark green with brightly metallic colored (mostly reddish, yellow, and purple) bands and spots on the elytra, pronotum, and head margin. The mid-portions of the legs are deep reddish, while the leg apices are bright metallic green. The legs are generally long. The lateral margins of the pronotum are generally straight with protruding anterior margins.

| FAMILY | Chrysomelidae |
|---|---|
| SUBFAMILY | Synetinae |
| DISTRIBUTION | Palearctic |
| MACROHABITAT | Various forests, including taiga and northern mixed forests |
| MICROHABITAT | Adults are found on the leaves of birch trees (*Betula* spp.), and larvae in soil to a depth of about 30 in (70 cm) |
| FEEDING HABITS | Adults feed on the foliage of birch trees (*Betula* spp.), while larvae feed on their roots |
| NOTE | The larva of this species was described only as recently as 1967 |

ADULT LENGTH
³⁄₁₆–¼ in
(5.2–6.7 mm)

*SYNETA BETULAE*

# SYNETA BETULAE

(FABRICIUS, 1792)

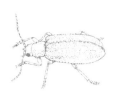

577

*Syneta betulae* is relatively common in forests in the northern Palearctic, particularly those with birch trees (*Betula* spp.). Its larva was described only in 1967, when it was found to be abundant in forests from Arkhangelsk to Kemerovo provinces in northern Russia. The larval body is thick, flattened dorsoventrally, white or cream in color, and with a slight C-shaped curvature. Females usually drop their eggs on a leaf surface, from where they fall onto the soil. The systematic position of *S. betulae* and related species is somewhat controversial: it may be in the subfamily Orsodacninae, the Eumolpinae, or its own subfamily, Synetinae.

Actual size

### RELATED SPECIES

*Syneta*, the only genus in the subfamily Synetinae, is a small Holarctic group of about 15 species and subspecies, the majority of which occur in North America. In the Palearctic, *S. betulae* is most similar to *S. adamsi*, which occurs in the Russian Far East, China, and Japan. The larva of *S. adamsi* was also described only very recently (in 1990); it differs from the larva of *S. betulae* mostly in having four pairs of long setae and one pair of short setae on the frontoclypeal suture near its middle.

**Syneta betulae** is amber in color, with sometimes lighter appendages and a dark stripe along the elytral suture. The pronotum is usually much narrower than the elytra and about as narrow as the head. Its lateral margins have a few smaller denticles and one large denticle in the middle. Its gut is relatively long, as is the case in many other foliage-feeding leaf beetles. The third tarsomere has spatulate setae.

| | |
|---|---|
| FAMILY | Nemonychidae |
| SUBFAMILY | Cimberidinae |
| DISTRIBUTION | Nearctic: southern Canada, eastern USA |
| MACROHABITAT | Boreal |
| MICROHABITAT | Male conifer cones |
| FEEDING HABITS | Feeds on the pollen of *Pinus* spp. |
| NOTE | Among the most ancient of extant weevil lineages; feeds on pine pollen |

ADULT LENGTH
⅛ –³⁄₁₆ in
(2.9–5.1 mm)

578

# CIMBERIS ELONGATA
(LECONTE, 1876)

Actual size

This species belongs to one of the oldest evolutionary lineages of weevils, dating back to at least the Jurassic. The adults and larvae of this rare weevil feed on the pollen of at least five species of *Pinus*. The larvae develop for approximately a week within the male strobili (cones) of *Pinus* species and have also been reported feeding on dead or dying shoots and stems of Jack Pine (*P. banksia*). Pollen is swept into the buccal cavity with the help of the well-articulated maxillae and mandibles, and the acutely pointed mandibles have evolved to pierce the pollen efficiently. Larvae crush the ingested pollen with their rough mandibular mola. Pupation occurs in the soil.

### RELATED SPECIES
*Cimberis* includes eight species, seven in North America and one in Europe. The adults of this genus have a prominent tooth on the inside of the mandibles, which distinguishes them from other species in the tribe Cimberidini. *Cimberis elongata* shares with *C. attellaboides*, *C. decipiens*, and *C. pallipennis* a transverse labrum with an emarginate edge. The presence of a broad median depression on the pronotum helps to distinguish *C. elongata*

**Cimberis elongata** is black, except for the red tip of the rostrum, femora, tibiae, and coxae. Elongate, erect, reddish-colored setae cover the body. The head and prothorax are narrower than the elytra, and the eyes are round and prominent. The rostrum is elongate, flattened, and widened apically, with prominent mandibles. The filiform antennae are located toward the tip of the rostrum, with the last three segments weakly expanded.

| FAMILY | Nemonychidae |
|---|---|
| SUBFAMILY | Rhinorhynchinae |
| DISTRIBUTION | Neotropical: southern Brazil (Paraná, Santa Catarina, Rio Grande do Sul) |
| MACROHABITAT | Southern temperate forests containing Paraná Pine (*Araucaria angustifolia*) |
| MICROHABITAT | Paraná Pine (*A. angustifolia*) trees, mainly on male cones |
| FEEDING HABITS | Pollen of Paraná Pine (*A. angustifolia*) |
| NOTE | This weevil is devoid of a typical rostrum and has front legs adapted to penetrating *Araucaria* cones |

ADULT LENGTH
¹/₁₆–¹/₈ in
(1.8–3.1 mm)

*BRARUS MYSTES*
# BRARUS MYSTES
KUSCHEL, 1997

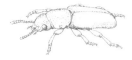

579

Actual size

When discovered, this curious little weevil was not immediately recognized as such because it has no trace of a rostrum. The adults are rare, but may be reared in relatively high numbers from larvae that develop in male cones of the Paraná Pine (*Araucaria angustifolia*). As in all *Araucaria*-associated nemonychids, these legless larvae move by crawling on their backs with the help of well-developed dorsal ambulatory ampulae. Adults have short, broad front legs for penetrating the cones.

## RELATED SPECIES

This is currently the only species in the genus *Brarus*. While highly distinct owing to the lack of a rostrum, the species shares numerous features with members of the tribe Mecomacerini. Adult Mecomacerini have elongate terminal maxillary palpi and a labrum with four or more pairs of dorsal setae. *Mecomacer* and *Araucomacer*, from Chile and Argentina and also associated with *Araucaria*, are among the closest relatives to *Brarus*. All three genera share, as adults, a smooth mesonotum with a double stridulatory file.

**Brarus mystes** is minute and yellowish brown. The body is parallel-sided and covered with mostly fine, sparse, appressed setae. The head is broad and narrows apically, but is not produced into the characteristic rostrum of weevils. Males have a larger head than females. The filiform, weakly clubbed antennae are located behind the mandibles. The scutellum is visible and the front legs are subfossorial.

| FAMILY | Anthribidae |
|---|---|
| SUBFAMILY | Anthribinae |
| DISTRIBUTION | Palearctic and Nearctic: native to northern Europe, Asia, adventive to northeastern USA |
| MACROHABITAT | Temperate forests |
| MICROHABITAT | Branches, flowers, and bark of conifers (e.g., Norway Spruce, or *Picea abies*) or deciduous trees (e.g., oaks, or *Quercus* spp.) |
| FEEDING HABITS | Feeds on the eggs of scale insects (Coccidae and Kermesidae) |
| NOTE | Larvae are endoparasitoids of female scale insects, feeding internally on eggs. Introduced to the USA for biological control of pestiferous scale species |

ADULT LENGTH
¹⁄₁₆–³⁄₁₆ in
(1.5–4.6 mm)

580

*ANTHRIBUS NEBULOSUS*
# ANTHRIBUS NEBULOSUS
FORSTER, 1770

Actual size

Among Anthribidae, or fungus weevils, only species in *Anthribus* are predaceous. The larvae feed on the eggs within female scale insects. Adults are attracted to flowers and may hibernate under the bark of trees. *Anthribus nebulosus*, which in its native range preys on more than 15 coccid species in the genera *Physokermes*, *Eulecanium*, and *Kermes*, was intentionally introduced to Virginia, USA, in 1978 for the control of pest scale insects on fruit, nut, and spruce trees. However, the discovery in 1989 of large populations of *A. nebulosus* in Connecticut, Massachusetts, and New York suggests this species entered the northeastern USA unnoticed and became established much earlier.

### RELATED SPECIES

*Anthribus* contains over 300 species found throughout the Palearctic. Other *Anthribus* species found with *A. nebulosus* in northern Europe are *A. fasciatus* and *A. scapularis*. These two species have a complete lateral carina of the pronotum, which is shortened in *A. nebulosus*. *Anthribus fasciatus* was also considered as a biological control agent of scale insects in the United States.

**Anthribus nebulosus** is brown to dark brown with a mosaic covering of dark brown and broad whitish setae. The head is broad and the rostrum short. The pronotum is transverse and the shortened lateral pronotal carina is present only basally. The elytra are oblong, with the base not much wider than the pronotum. Humeral calli are distinct. The third hind tarsomere lobes are fused.

| FAMILY | Anthribidae |
|---|---|
| SUBFAMILY | Anthribinae |
| DISTRIBUTION | Oriental and Palearctic: Ukraine, south of European Russia, East Asia |
| MACROHABITAT | Temperate forests |
| MICROHABITAT | On trees (*Styrax japonicus*, *S. obassis*, *Acer ginnala*, *A. tataricum*, and *A. campestre*) |
| FEEDING HABITS | Adults feed on leaves and fruits of host trees; larvae develop singly within seeds of host trees |
| NOTE | The species is sexually dimorphic, the males having large heads used for fighting |

ADULT LENGTH
⅛–¼ in
(3.1–6 mm)

*EXECHESOPS LEUCOPIS*
# COW-FACED ANTHRIBID
(JORDAN, 1928)

581

Aggressive mating behavior as exhibited by the males of this species is rare among fungus weevils. Comparable-size males of this curious species use their large, broad, flattened heads to push against each other on the host fruit as they compete for suitable mating sites. Mating and oviposition takes place only on the fruit. The female chews holes into the fruit to lay her eggs, usually while being guarded by her mate. Smaller males apparently avoid larger males and do not directly compete but may instead employ a different mating strategy by seeking unguarded females. Adults actively fly between host trees.

RELATED SPECIES
This genus belongs in the tribe Zygaenodini of the subfamily Anthribinae. *Exechesops* includes 35 species from the Afrotropical and Oriental biogeographic regions. All species have sexually dimorphic cephalic modifications and species are distinguished largely by the development of the male cephalic projections, or eye-stalks.

Actual size

**The Cow-faced Anthribid** is a medium-size beetle with black and whitish-gray marbled pubescence on the elytra and entirely whitish-gray pubescence on the head. The male head is large and frontally flattened, with the eyes dorsolaterally borne on conspicuous stalks. The antennae are filiform; they are almost as long as the body in males and half as long in females. While the elytra are parallel-sided, the pronotum narrows anteriorly, widening sub-basally where a raised transverse, narrow carina is present.

| FAMILY | Anthribidae |
| --- | --- |
| SUBFAMILY | Anthribinae |
| DISTRIBUTION | Australian: New Zealand (Stewart Island/Rakiura, Snares Islands/Tini Heke) |
| MACROHABITAT | At sea-level in the subantarctic zone |
| MICROHABITAT | Supralittoral lichens |
| FEEDING HABITS | Feeds on rock-encrusting lichens, predominantly *Pertusaria graphica* |
| NOTE | Lives and feeds on sea-splashed lichens |

ADULT LENGTH
⅟₁₆ in
(1.7–2.1 mm)

*LICHENOBIUS LITTORALIS*
# LICHENOBIUS LITTORALIS
HOLLOWAY, 1970

Actual size

The larvae and adults of this unique species are restricted to living on lichens growing in the spray zone of rocky seashores of the southern Snares Islands/Tini Heke and Stewart Island/Rakiura of New Zealand. The orange larva tunnels shallowly below the surface of this white lichen belt, which is composed mostly of *Pertusaria graphica*. Adult emergence begins in December, with large numbers present in February. The adults have reduced flight wings and do not fly, but are active on the surface of their host lichen.

## RELATED SPECIES

The endemic New Zealand genus *Lichenobius* includes three species, *L. littoralis*, *L. maritimus*, and *L. silvicola*. *Lichenobius silvicola* feeds on lichens growing in the bark of live trees and shrubs, and *L. maritimus*, whose adults were found in crevices with dry green algae on sea-washed rocks, may feed on a marine fungus. *Lichenobius* belongs in the tribe Gymnognathini of the subfamily Anthribinae, which includes 35 other genera. *Lichenobius* may be related to the Australian *Xynotropis*.

**Lichenobius littoralis** is small and stout bodied, and has a conspicuous short rostrum. It is mostly black with brown or yellowish legs and antennae, and the elytra have mostly iridescent silver-gray scales with usually a large spot of bronze scales. The antennae do not reach the base of the pronotum, they have a distinct club, and they are inserted on the sides of the rostrum. The pronotum is circular and lacks an antebasal carina. The elytra are parallel-sided with a steep declivity and are not mucronate.

| FAMILY | Anthribidae |
|---|---|
| SUBFAMILY | Choraginae |
| DISTRIBUTION | Cosmopolitan, primarily in tropical and subtropical regions (native to Indo-Malaya) |
| MACROHABITAT | Warehouses, agricultural settings |
| MICROHABITAT | Stored dry food-products and materials, coffee (*Coffea* spp.) and cocoa (*Theobroma cacao*) beans |
| FEEDING HABITS | Feeds on stored or living plant tissue |
| NOTE | A generalist pest of various plant products, including coffee and cocoa beans |

ADULT LENGTH
¹⁄₁₆–³⁄₁₆ in
(2.4–5.0 mm)

*ARAECERUS FASCICULATUS*
# COFFEE-BEAN WEEVIL
(DE GEER, 1775)

583

A generalist, the Coffee-bean Weevil has been reported to feed on the living and dried plant tissue of more than 49 species of plants, including 18 varieties of citrus, red peppers (*Capsicum* spp.), and beans of the Strychnine Tree (*Strychnos nux-vomica*). It is a serious pest of Cocoa (*Theobroma cacao*) and coffee (*Coffea* spp.) beans, and has become widespread through coffee- and cocoa-bean commerce. Most vulnerable are stored food-products that have not been properly dried, are soft, or are decaying. Eggs are typically laid on the surface of the infested commodity and the larvae bore into the food material.

Actual size

## RELATED SPECIES

*Araecerus* belongs in the tribe Araecerini, which includes 22 genera worldwide. *Araecerus* includes approximately 75 species from the Indo-Pacific region. To date, 650 genera are currently recognized in the family Anthribidae. The taxonomic history of this species has been convoluted because of its broad distribution. Over time, this species has been described at least ten different times as new species under different names by various experts.

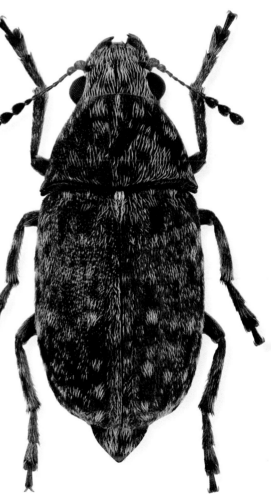

**The Coffee-bean Weevil** is a small oval beetle with fine cream or cream and brown scales. The pronotum is as wide as the elytra at its base and has a ridge on each side. The rounded eyes are prominent and the antennae are straight, originate below the eyes on the anterior surface of the head, and have three distinctly larger segments apically that form a club.

| FAMILY | Anthribidae |
|---|---|
| SUBFAMILY | Choraginae |
| DISTRIBUTION | Neotropical: Jamaica, Panama |
| MACROHABITAT | Montane cloud forest |
| MICROHABITAT | Wet bark of rotten stumps in leaf litter |
| FEEDING HABITS | Unknown |
| NOTE | A rare and unique jumping anthribid weevil |

ADULT LENGTH
¹⁄₁₆ in
(1.8–2.2 mm)

584

*APTEROXENUS GLOBULOSUS*
# APTEROXENUS GLOBULOSUS
VALENTINE, 1979

**Actual size**

This tiny, very robust weevil was previously known from a single female individual from Jamaica, and a small number of individuals from Panama are also known in natural history collections. *Apteroxenus globulosus* is flightless due to the absence of wings, but it moves around adeptly using its well-developed jumping legs. The individual from Jamaica was observed on a rotting stump that was partially buried in leaf litter. It was crawling initially and could have been confused for an oribatid mite, but when it was disturbed it quickly and actively jumped.

### RELATED SPECIES

The genus *Apteroxenus* contains a single species. It is classified in the tribe Choragini, which currently contains 15 genera from around the world, and may be most closely related to the North American genus *Euxenulus*. In all Choraginae the antennae are inserted between the eyes on the frons (in other anthribids the antennae are inserted on the rostrum).

**Apteroxenus globulosus** is a glabrous, broadly oval, convex, shiny black weevil. The head is retractile and the dorsal surface of the body is extremely convex. The pronotum has numerous small punctures and the scutellum is absent. The rostrum is almost absent and the antennae are located on the frons between the eyes. The eyes are dorsoventrally elongate and meet dorsally on the head. The legs are relatively elongate.

| FAMILY | Anthribidae |
|---|---|
| SUBFAMILY | Urodontinae |
| DISTRIBUTION | Afrotropical: southern Africa |
| MACROHABITAT | Desert or similar ecosystems |
| MICROHABITAT | Flowers and seeds of Iridaceae and Xanthorrhoeaceae species |
| FEEDING HABITS | Adults feed on flowers, and larvae on seeds, of Iridaceae species, including *Dietes*, *Iris*, and *Watsonia* spp., and on the Red Hot Poker *Kniphofia galpinii* |
| NOTE | Larvae are known to develop inside seeds |

ADULT LENGTH
⅛ –¼ in
(2.5–6.0 mm)

*URODONTELLUS LILII*

# URODONTELLUS LILII

(FÅHRAEUS, 1839)

585

Actual size

This species was originally considered to belong in the seed-feeding leaf beetle subfamily Bruchinae of the Chrysomelidae, and was also given its own family status, Urodontidae. However, a detailed study in 1943 of the larva of *Urodontellus lilii* provided evidence for the classification of urodontines within the Anthribidae. The larvae have a single ocellus, lack legs, and possess prominent ambulatory ampulae on the dorsal surface. The species appears to be closely associated with species of Iridaceae and Xanthorrhoeaceae, the larvae feeding on the seeds of these plants. Some urodontine species from South Africa complete their development in galls induced on the stem of woody Aizoaceae.

### RELATED SPECIES

Urodontinae includes eight genera, mostly from Africa except for *Bruchela* and *Cercomorphus*, which are also found in western and central Europe. *Urodontellus* was established in 1993 to include six species from southern Africa that were previously included in *Bruchela*. Externally, *U. lilii* is almost indistinguishable from *U. vermiculatus* and *U. vicinialilii* except for minor differences in the elytral color pattern and shape of the male genitalia.

**Urodontellus lilii** is an elongate-oval, black and reddish weevil with short, fine, gray-white setae throughout and a short rostrum. The head is narrow with protruding eyes and straight, relatively short antennae. The pronotum is nearly as wide as the base of the elytra. The scutellum is rudimentary. The last abdominal segments extend beyond the apex of the elytra in dorsal view.

| FAMILY | Belidae |
|---|---|
| SUBFAMILY | Belinae |
| DISTRIBUTION | Australian: southern Australia, including Tasmania |
| MACROHABITAT | Cool, Mediterranean climate; woodlands, shrublands |
| MICROHABITAT | *Acacia*, *Argyrodendron*, and *Prunus* spp. |
| FEEDING HABITS | Feeding habits of adults uncertain, larvae are wood-borers |
| NOTE | This is a pest of apricots (*Prunus* spp) |

ADULT LENGTH
⁹⁄₁₆–⅝ in
(15–16 mm)

*RHINOTIA BIDENTATA*
# TWO-SPOTTED WEEVIL
(DONOVAN, 1805)

While this species is known to feed primarily on *Acacia*, in common with many other species in the genus, it has also been reported on *Argyrodendron* and *Prunus*. The larva does extensive damage to the non-native apricot trees in Australia by boring and tunneling into the wood and eventually killing the tree. The female chews a round hole into the tree, oviposits into it, and pushes the egg to the bottom of the hole. Some species in the genus (e.g., *Rhinotia apicalis*, *R. haemoptera*, *R. marginella*, and *R. parva*) resemble beetles in the family Lycidae in shape and coloration, being orange and black dorsally; in having elongate, narrow, parallel-sided elytra; and in having dorsoventrally flattened apical antennomeres.

### RELATED SPECIES

The subfamily Belinae includes three tribes in Australia: Agnesiotidini, Pachyurini, and Belini (to which *Rhinotia* belongs). Some species of *Rhinotia* have expanded antennal segments. This Australasian endemic genus contains more than 80 species, with numerous new species awaiting description. *Rhinotia bidentata* is similar to *R. semipunctata* and *R. perplexa*, but those species lack the two large spots on their elytra.

**The Two-spotted Weevil** is elongately narrow and dorsally almost entirely black, except for white speckling and two large, well-defined white spots close to the end of the elytra. The end of each elytron narrows abruptly and extends beyond the abdomen. The underside is copiously covered in white pubescence laterally.

Actual size

| FAMILY | Belidae |
|---|---|
| SUBFAMILY | Oxycoryninae |
| DISTRIBUTION | Neotropical: Argentina (Mendoza, San Juan, San Luis, La Rioja, Catamarca, Tucumán, Córdoba, Santiago del Estero, Buenos Aires) |
| MACROHABITAT | Forests |
| MICROHABITAT | Associated with root-parasitic angiosperms in the genus *Prosopanche* |
| FEEDING HABITS | Adults feed on pollen of *Prosopanche* spp.; larvae develop inside the flowers and fruit bodies |
| NOTE | Larval development and pupation take place inside the subterranean fruiting body of the host plants |

ADULT LENGTH
⅜–½ in
(10–12 mm)

*HYDNOROBIUS HYDNORAE*

# HYDNOROBIUS HYDNORAE

(PASCOE, 1868)

587

This species is intimately associated with *Prosopanche americana* and *P. bonacinae*, subterranean, non-photosynthetic plant parasites of the roots of *Prosopis* spp. Adult weevils emerge from rotting fruit bodies of *Prosopanche* plants in early summer (January in the Southern Hemisphere). As new flowers begin to sprout and release pollen, the beetles proceed to mate, feed, and oviposit on them, and may be responsible for pollination of the host plants. During the weevil's development, the reproductive tissues (sporangia or seeds) are not damaged since the larvae consume parts of the fruit and sporophylls.

## RELATED SPECIES

The other closely related Oxycorynini genera—*Oxycorynus* (South America, four species), *Alloxycorynus* (South America, two species), and *Balanophorobius* (Costa Rica, one species)— are also associated with root-plant parasites in Balanophoraceae. The genus *Hydnorobius*, which differs from other Oxycorinini genera in having distinct longitudinal ridges on the elytra and a dorsal ridge on the front tibiae, includes three described species from Argentina and Brazil.

Actual size

**Hydnorobius hydnorae** is a moderate-size, oval, maroon-brown weevil. The rostrum is narrow and longer than the pronotum. The antennae emerge close to the head, are straight, and end in a weak club. The elytra and pronotum are almost equal in width, the pronotum being slightly narrower. The sides of the pronotum are rounded and appear explanate from above. The elytra have at least eight prominent, glossy, raised striae.

| FAMILY | Belidae |
|---|---|
| SUBFAMILY | Oxycoryninae |
| DISTRIBUTION | Neotropical: Mexico (Veracruz), introduced in USA (Florida) |
| MACROHABITAT | Wet and dry coastal tropical forests |
| MICROHABITAT | Male cycad cones |
| FEEDING HABITS | Microsporophylls |
| NOTE | A pollinator of the Cardboard Palm cycad (*Zamia furfuracea*); it has a mutualistic relationship with its host |

ADULT LENGTH
³⁄₁₆ in
(3.5–5.4 mm)

588

# RHOPALOTRIA MOLLIS

(SHARP, 1890)

Actual size

With this little weevil, mating, feeding, and oviposition take place exclusively among or within the ornamental Mexican Cardboard Palm cycad (*Zamia furfuracea*). The parenchyma, stalks, and outer ends of the microsporophyll are the only areas affected during development of the weevil within the starch-rich male cones; they do not feed on or damage the pollen. Pollination of the cycad occurs when the emerging, pollen-covered adults visit, but do not feed on, female cones. The adult weevils may be attracted to volatile chemicals or heat produced by female cones. In the wild, the cycad is highly threatened due to illegal harvesting and habitat destruction.

## RELATED SPECIES

*Rhopalotria* contains four species that are endemic to the New World. All are associated with Cycadaceae. *Rhopalotria slossonae* is native to Florida and is intimately associated with the Coontie (*Zamia pumila*). The other two species are from Mexico and Cuba. A weevil expert is currently revising this genus and this will result in the description of several new species for the first time.

**Rhopalotria mollis** is generally oval-shaped, dorsoventrally flattened, and glossy. The color is mostly blood red. The most salient features are the enlarged orange front femora, which are greater than five times the size of the middle and hind femora in males. The rostrum is about as long as the pronotum. The antennae are straight, not geniculate, a feature shared with other members of the family, and the third and second to last antennomeres are enlarged. The elytra are smooth and lack distinct striae.

| FAMILY | Caridae |
|---|---|
| SUBFAMILY | Carinae |
| DISTRIBUTION | Australian: Australia (Queensland, New South Wales, Victoria, South Australia, Western Australia) |
| MACROHABITAT | Conifer forests |
| MICROHABITAT | Adults occur on foliage; larvae are found in green cones of *Callitris* spp. |
| FEEDING HABITS | Larvae feed on the female cones of *Callitris* spp.; adult feeding habits are uncertain |
| NOTE | The remarkable *Car* larvae have unusual features such as large, long (the longest among weevils), segmented legs ending with a long, slender, curved, sharp claw |

ADULT LENGTH
³⁄₁₆–¼ in
(4–5.5 mm)

*CAR CONDENSATUS*
# CAR CONDENSATUS
BLACKBURN, 1897

589

Caridae, promoted to family status in 1991 and historically difficult to classify, has been included in Attelabidae, Belidae, and more recently Brentidae. For more than a century the immature stages of *Car* remained unknown until the very rare larva was discovered in 1992, developing in the nascent seeds of females cones of *Callitris*, a conifer in the cypress family (Cupressaceae). The female uses its straight rostrum to drill holes into the cones for oviposition. Globules of hardened resin are evident at the site of oviposition, apparently resulting in the death of most of the early-instar larvae before they penetrate the interior. Pupation takes place in the substrate.

### RELATED SPECIES
This family is found only in the Southern Hemisphere and includes six species in four extant genera. The genus *Car*, which contains three described species (*C. condensatus*, *C. intermedius*, and *C. pini*), is endemic to Australia and is closely related to the South American *Caenominurus*. Species of *Car* can be separated by characteristics of setae on their elytra, by the number of antennomeres forming the antennal club, and by their overall size.

Actual size

**Car condensatus** is a small, elongate-oval, brown to black weevil with sparse white pubescence throughout. The rostrum is narrow, parallel-sided, and almost straight. The antennae emerge from the ventral surface of the rostrum, close to the head. The elytra, which have dark markings posteriorly, are almost three times longer than the pronotum and have fine, hairlike, erect setae.

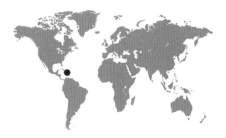

| FAMILY | Attelabidae |
|---|---|
| SUBFAMILY | Attelabinae |
| DISTRIBUTION | Neotropical: Jamaica, Puerto Rico |
| MACROHABITAT | Forests or planted trees |
| MICROHABITAT | On vegetation |
| FEEDING HABITS | Rolls the leaves of Tropical Almond (*Terminalia catappa*) for larval feeding; adults have also been taken on guavas (*Psidium* spp.) |
| NOTE | The males of this and related species have a single spine at the apex of their tibiae, whereas females have two |

ADULT LENGTH
⅛ – ¼ in
(3.2 – 5.9 mm)

590

*EUSCELUS BIGUTTATUS*
# EUSCELUS BIGUTTATUS
(FABRICIUS, 1775)

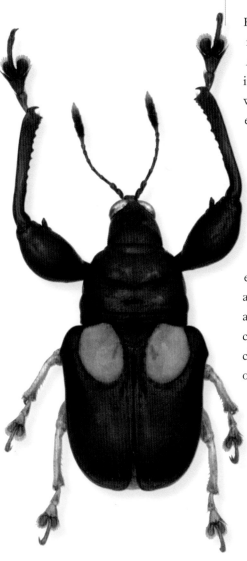

Females of this distinctive and charismatic weevil have been reported laying their eggs on leaves of young Tropical Almond trees (*Terminalia catappa*), which they then cut and intricately fold to form a barrel-shaped nidus (nest made up with a rolled-up leaf). The female uses her mandibles and enlarged front legs to prepare, restructure, and manipulate the host-tree leaf. The larva benefits from the nourishment and protection provided by the nidus. The plant is not adversely affected by the behavior and feeding of this weevil.

RELATED SPECIES

Along with four other genera, *Euscelus* belongs to the subtribe Euscelina in the tribe Attelabini. The subtribe is endemic to, and widespread throughout, the West Indies (but apparently absent from the Lesser Antilles) as well as Central and South America. The 50-plus species of *Euscelus*, which are classified into eight subgenera, can generally be separated by characteristics of their elytra, such as their color, the presence or absence of humeral spines, and their punctation.

Actual size

**Euscelus biguttatus** is a reddish-brown to dark brown weevil with yellowish-white middle and hind legs, ventral abdomen, and two large, raised oval spots at the base of the elytra. It is dorsally shiny, smooth, and finely punctured. The rostrum is shorter than the head, longer than wide, and has the non-elbowed antennae emerging near the eyes. The front femora of both sexes have a pair of projections on their ventral surface.

| FAMILY | Attelabidae |
|---|---|
| SUBFAMILY | Attelabinae |
| DISTRIBUTION | Neotropical: Mesoamerica |
| MACROHABITAT | Pastures, disturbed forests, cultivated hills |
| MICROHABITAT | Found on its host plant, *Guazuma tomentosa*, on leaves and in leaf rolls; pupates in the soil |
| FEEDING HABITS | Leaves of the medicinal plant *Guazuma tomentosa* |
| NOTE | Constructs spherical leaf rolls as an enclosure for its eggs and larvae |

ADULT LENGTH
¼–⅜ in
(7–8.6 mm)

*PILOLABUS VIRIDANS*

# PILOLABUS VIRIDANS

(GYLLENHAL, 1839)

591

This relatively common, spectacularly colored species has the unique habit among leaf-rolling weevils of creating almost perfectly rounded leaf rolls. These nests, measuring ⅝ × ⁹⁄₁₆ in (16 × 14 mm), dangle from the midrib of a leaf of the weevil's host plant, *Guazuma tomentosa*. Most other attelabids construct loose or compact cylindrical leaf rolls, not spherical ones. Oviposition takes place before leaf-rolling. It takes approximately two hours for the female of *Pilolabus viridans* to cut and roll the leaf into a ball. The larva feeds and completes its development in the maternally created leaf nest, but pupates in the soil.

## RELATED SPECIES

*Pilolabus* is the sole genus in the tribe Pilolabini and currently includes 15 species from Mesoamerica, with only four species reported south of Mexico. *Pilolabus viridans* has similar metallic colors as *P. giraffa* and *P. sumptuosus*, although the color patterns are different. Other attelabids also roll leaves, but they may have elaborate leaf-selection rituals and do not pupate in the soil.

Actual size

**Pilolabus viridans** is a brilliant metallic weevil. The head, pronotum, and elytra are red dorsally, although the pronotum and elytra also have dark green or cobalt-blue contrasting bands. A unicolored form exists as well. Ventrally, this species is dark metallic green. The body is moderately elongate and the head has a rather short, broad rostrum. The female has a pair of long, straight distal teeth on the apex of the tibiae.

| FAMILY | Attelabidae |
|---|---|
| SUBFAMILY | Apoderinae |
| DISTRIBUTION | Palearctic: Europe and Asia |
| MACROHABITAT | Deciduous forests, gardens |
| MICROHABITAT | Adults are found on leaf surfaces; larvae and pupae are protected within leaf rolls |
| FEEDING HABITS | Feeds on leaves of Hazel (*Corylus avellana*) but also known to develop on alder (*Alnus* spp.), birch (*Betula* spp.), willow (*Salix* spp.), beech (*Fagus* spp.), and oak (*Quercus* spp.) |
| NOTE | Forms cigar-shaped leaf rolls |

ADULT LENGTH
¼–⁵⁄₁₆ in
(6–8 mm)

*APODERUS CORYLI*
# HAZEL-LEAF ROLLER WEEVIL
(LINNAEUS, 1758)

The Hazel-leaf Roller Weevil exhibits a special kind of offspring care by wrapping each egg in a cigar-shaped cradle rolled from a Hazel (*Corylus avellana*) leaf. All attelabid species exhibit such behavior, but with modifications in their leaf-rolling method and cradle shape. The larvae and pupae of *Apoderus coryli* develop within these wraps. Females reportedly walk along the leaf first, presumably to measure and determine its suitability. Adult beetles emerge in the summer. The species name of this weevil, *coryli*, is in reference to its association with its host plant.

## RELATED SPECIES

*Apoderus coryli* belongs in the tribe Apoderini along with several genera primarily from the Palearctic and the Oriental realms. The only other species in the genus occurring in Europe, the similar-size and similar-shaped *A. ludyi*, is known only from Italy. Among other characters, the two European species can be separated by differences in coloration. Some related species, such as *A. tranquebaricus* in India, are minor pests.

**The Hazel-leaf Roller Weevil** has rectangular-shaped, very shiny, reddish elytra. A clear constriction exists between the bell-shaped, shiny red pronotum and the elongate black head, which bears prominent eyes. The broad elytra have distinct punctate, longitudinal striae. The rostrum is relatively short and the antennae are straight and emerge near its apex. The femora are red basally and black near their apex.

Actual size

| FAMILY | Attelabidae |
|---|---|
| SUBFAMILY | Attelabinae |
| DISTRIBUTION | Afrotropical: Madagascar |
| MACROHABITAT | Tropical wet forests |
| MICROHABITAT | On the host plant, *Dichaetanthera* |
| FEEDING HABITS | Phytophagous |
| NOTE | The long neck is used in aggressive male-to-male combat; females build nests for their eggs |

ADULT MALE LENGTH
⁹⁄₁₆–1 in
(15–25 mm)

ADULT FEMALE LENGTH
½–⁹⁄₁₆ in
(12–15 mm)

*TRACHELOPHORUS GIRAFFA*
# GIRAFFE-NECKED WEEVIL
(JEKEL, 1860)

593

Actual size

The long neck of male Giraffe-necked Weevils is used as a weapon during contests for access to females and is also waved back and forth around the female during oviposition, presumably to prevent access from competing males. The shorter-necked female builds a protective nest for each of her eggs. First she chews notches along the main veins on a single leaf from the host plant, which begins the rolling process of the leaf. Once mated, the female uses her strong legs to fold the weakened leaf in half. She then rolls the tip of the leaf into a barrel tube and lays her egg within it. A kind of Velcro strip, created by the female by biting notches along the edges of the leaf, allows the leaf nest to hold its shape. The final step is for the female to cut the leaf roll, allowing it to fall to the ground, where the larva will develop.

RELATED SPECIES

The genus *Trachelophorus* is endemic to Madagascar and contains 11 species in three subgenera, *Eotrachelophorus*, *Atrachelophorus*, and *Nigrotrachelophorus*. The Giraffe-necked Weevil belongs to the subgenus *Atrachelophorus*. The characteristic commonly shared by the five species in this subgenus is the absence of protuberances on abdominal ventrite 2 in the males.

**The Giraffe-necked Weevil** resembles a giraffe in that the pronotum and head are elongate in males. The junction between the head and pronotum is delimited by a large pronotal groove that resembles a large hinge. The neck and temples of the female head are about two or three times shorter than in males. Both males and females are entirely black except for the bright red elytra. The eyes bulge laterally and the antennae are straight and narrow.

| FAMILY | Attelabidae |
|---|---|
| SUBFAMILY | Rhynchitinae |
| DISTRIBUTION | Palearctic: China, Japan, Kazakhstan, Korea, Mongolia, Russia |
| MACROHABITAT | Forest |
| MICROHABITAT | Leaf rolls, vegetation |
| FEEDING HABITS | Host plants include species of *Malus*, *Pyrus*, *Sorbaria*, and *Populus* |
| NOTE | The males are known for their wrestling behavior |

ADULT LENGTH
¼–⁵⁄₁₆ in
(6.5–8 mm)

*BYCTISCUS RUGOSUS*
# BYCTISCUS RUGOSUS
(GEBLER, 1830)

Ritualized contests and aggressive fighting behavior are known to occur between males of species in this genus. The males extend their front legs outward while rearing up on their middle and hind legs, grabbing each other with their front legs and touching their rostra. The elongate tarsal setae may help enhance visual displays of this aggression. Females of the charismatic *Byctiscus rugosus* roll leaves into complicated cylindrical tubes for the reception of the egg. The larva feeds within the tube, where it completes its development.

## RELATED SPECIES
*Byctiscus* includes 27 species from the Palearctic and Oriental realms. Species are classified into two subgenera: *Byctiscus* and *Aspidobyctiscus*. The tribe Byctiscini has an exclusively Old World distribution and includes 12 genera in two subtribes. The related Pear Leaf-roller Weevil (*B. betulae*) is known to cause damage to grapevines, pears, and other broadleaf trees and shrubs.

Actual size

**Byctiscus rugosus** is a bright metallic, shiny green weevil with reddish reflections on the head and legs. The elytra are covered with prominently punctate striae. The pronotum is narrower than the base of the elytra, which are quadrate. The head is narrow and the rostrum is almost twice as long as the head. The antennae are not elbowed and emerge near the apex of the rostrum; the last three antennomeres are almost twice as wide as the preceding ones.

| FAMILY | Attelabidae |
|---|---|
| SUBFAMILY | Rhynchitinae |
| DISTRIBUTION | Nearctic and Neotropical: USA (Arizona, New Mexico, Texas), Mexico (Chihuahua, Sonora, Oaxaca) |
| MACROHABITAT | Oak forests |
| MICROHABITAT | Foliage, leaf litter |
| FEEDING HABITS | Epidermal tissue of fallen leaves |
| NOTE | The larvae are leaf-miners |

ADULT LENGTH
¼ in
(5.7–6.3 mm)

*EUGNAMPTUS NIGRIVENTRIS*

# EUGNAMPTUS NIGRIVENTRIS

(SCHAEFFER, 1905)

595

This species exhibits maternal care by individually placing each egg between the epidermal layers of a dead leaf of the host tree (e.g., oaks, *Quercus* spp.). In spring, a female uses her mandibles to cut an oviposition scar on a leaf that dropped to the ground the previous fall. She then oviposits a single egg into a cavity she created between the upper and lower epidermis and seals the epidermal tissue by pinching with her mandibles. The larva completes its entire development by feeding on the epidermal tissues of the dead leaf. Pupation takes place in the soil and adults emerge the following spring.

### RELATED SPECIES

There are approximately 100 species included in *Eugnamptus*. *Eugnamptus* is similar to *Hemilypus*, *Acritorrhynchites*, and *Essodius*, but can be distinguished by characters of the rostrum, distance between the eyes, length of the basal tarsomeres, prominence of the first abdominal suture, extent of dorsal punctation, and elytral length as it relates to the pygidium.

Actual size

**Eugnamptus nigriventris** is clothed in fine, erect setae and has a reddish head, pronotum, and legs, and bluish-green elytra. In the male, the length of the rostrum is shorter than the length of the head and the antennae are inserted close to the apex. In the female, the rostrum is longer than the head, and the antennae are inserted near the middle. The head and pronotum are narrower than the base of the elytra.

| FAMILY | Attelabidae |
|---|---|
| SUBFAMILY | Rhynchitinae |
| DISTRIBUTION | Palearctic: Europe, central Asia |
| MACROHABITAT | Fruit orchards |
| MICROHABITAT | Adults are found on stone fruits; larvae are found in the seeds (stones) |
| FEEDING HABITS | Adults feed on stone fruits; larvae feed on the seeds (stones) |
| NOTE | A pest of cherry, plum, and apricot trees |

ADULT LENGTH
¼–½ in
(6–12 mm)

*RHYNCHITES AURATUS*
# CHERRY WEEVIL
(SCOPOLI, 1763)

This species is one of the most important pests of cherry, Sour Cherry (*Prunus cerasus*), and related species, such as Blackthorn (*Prunus spinosa*)—it is also known as the Apricot Weevil. Adult emergence coincides with the blooming of cherry trees in the spring. The female lives approximately three months and in the course of her life may lay up to 85 eggs in the bottom of tunnels she chews in developing fruit. The larva penetrates into, and develops within, the stone. Pupation takes place in the soil. The damaged fruit will appear mottled and, if severely damaged, may drop prematurely.

RELATED SPECIES

Six tribes are recognized in the subfamily Rhynchitinae. The diverse genus *Rhynchites*, which currently includes eight subgenera, belongs in the subtribe Rhynchitina, one of two subtribes in the tribe Rhynchitini. Other species of *Rhynchites* that also occur in the Palearctic include *R. bacchus*, *R. giganteus*, and *R. heros*. *Rhynchites auratus* differs from these in having fine, erect pubescence on its body, anteriorly projecting spines on the male prothorax and small strial punctures on the elytra.

**The Cherry Weevil** is a metallic green or red beetle with fine erect setae scattered on most of its punctate body. The slightly curved rostrum is longer than the prothorax. The antennae are not elbowed and are inserted close to the apex of the rostrum. The pronotum is broadly convex and the elytra are nearly quadrate. The male has a stout anteriorly projecting lateral spine on each side of the pronotum.

Actual size

| FAMILY | Attelabidae |
|---|---|
| SUBFAMILY | Pterocolinae |
| DISTRIBUTION | Nearctic and Neotropical: Canada, USA, Mexico, Honduras, Guatemala |
| MACROHABITAT | Forested areas |
| MICROHABITAT | On leaves |
| FEEDING HABITS | An egg predator of other weevils such as *Homoeolabus analis* and *Attelabus bipustulatus* |
| NOTE | This species is an egg predator and nest thief of other leaf-rolling weevils |

ADULT LENGTH
¹⁄₁₆–³⁄₁₆ in
(2–3.7 mm)

*PTEROCOLUS OVATUS*
# THIEF WEEVIL
(FABRICIUS, 1801)

597

While most species in the family Attelabidae roll leaves to create a nest for their developing egg, this species preys on attelabid eggs and oviposits into the rolled-leaf nest of at least four other leaf-rolling weevils. Once the attelabid host parent has finished rolling the leaf nest, the Thief Weevil immediately works its way through the many, still pliable, twists and folds of the freshly made nest until it reaches the egg and eats it. The stolen leaf-roll is then used for their own larval development. This species feeds only on the eggs and invades the nests of the following, mainly oak-associated attelabids: *Attelabus bipustulatus*, *Himatolabus pubescens*, and *Homoeolabus analis* in North America, and *Himatolabus vestitus* in Mexico.

RELATED SPECIES

Two genera are included in the subfamily Pterocolinae: *Apterocolus* and *Pterocolus*. The most speciose is *Pterocolus*, with 18 described species, mostly from Mexico and Central America; *Apterocolus* contains two species. They can be distinguished by differences in size, color, the degree and location of pubescence, the bulginess of the eyes, punctation on the body, the number of exposed abdominal dorsal segments, and the presence and shape of spines on the tibiae.

Actual size

**The Thief Weevil** is a small, circular, dark metallic blue to greenish-black weevil with prominent dorsal punctations. The head is small with large eyes. The rostrum is shorter than the prothorax. The prothorax is distinctly margined on the sides and excavated beneath. The antennae are straight, with the last three segments at least three times larger than the preceding ones.

| FAMILY | Brentidae |
|---|---|
| SUBFAMILY | Brentinae |
| DISTRIBUTION | Palearctic: southern Europe, Algeria, Morocco, Israel, Syria, Iran, Russia |
| MACROHABITAT | Temperate humid forests containing predominantly oaks (*Quercus* spp.) |
| MICROHABITAT | Nests of *Camponotus*, *Lasius*, *Crematogaster*, *Pheidole*, *Tapinoma*, and *Myrmica* ants |
| FEEDING HABITS | Uncertain |
| NOTE | Myrmecophilous; has an unusual head morphology |

ADULT LENGTH
³⁄₈–¹¹⁄₁₆ in
(9–18 mm)

*AMORPHOCEPHALA CORONATA*
# AMORPHOCEPHALA CORONATA
(GERMAR, 1817)

This species is a facultative (optional) ant associate, usually of *Camponotus* but tolerated, after minor hostility, by other ant groups. When introduced to a *Camponotus* colony, these brentids face aggression by the workers until the ants discover and begin to lick glandular secretions from pubescent areas on the beetle's head. Apparently, *Amorphocephala coronata* exhibits a pseudoaltruistic behavior, whereby it regurgitates to the colony part of the food received from host worker ants. Ants have been observed tending to these brentids and actively trying to retain them in their nest. The species is gregarious, with many individuals found together.

### RELATED SPECIES

This genus belongs in the tribe Eremoxenini (which is sometimes treated as the subtribe Eremoxenina within the Brentini), an almost exclusively myrmecophilous group. Other genera in this group include *Cobalocephalus*, *Eremoxenus*, and *Symmorphocerus*. *Amorphocephala* contains 20 species from the Palearctic and Afrotropical realms. The species can be separated mainly by characteristics of the head, prothorax, and antennae.

**Amorphocephala coronata** is shiny reddish-brown beetle with a narrowly elongate body. Its most outstanding feature is its large, complex head, with the hind rostrum (just below the frons) deeply concave and bearing brushes of stiff setae. The head is sexually dimorphic, the males having a more robust front rostrum with large sickle-shaped mandibles, and the females having elongate, cylindrical mandibles.

Actual size

| FAMILY | Brentidae |
|---|---|
| SUBFAMILY | Brentinae |
| DISTRIBUTION | Nearctic and Neotropical: USA (Florida) to Paraguay |
| MACROHABITAT | Tropical and subtropical |
| MICROHABITAT | Decaying wood; under bark |
| FEEDING HABITS | Adults feed on sap or visit flowers for nectar; larvae bore into dead wood and possibly feed on sap or fungal mycelia |
| NOTE | The species exhibits sexual dimorphism and is one of the longest weevils in North America |

ADULT MALE LENGTH
³⁄₈–1¹⁵⁄₁₆ in
(9–50 mm)

ADULT FEMALE LENGTH
⁵⁄₁₆–1¹⁄₁₆ in
(8–27 mm)

*BRENTUS ANCHORAGO*
# BRENTUS ANCHORAGO
(LINNAEUS, 1758)

Most brentid species exhibit sexual dimorphism and *Brentus anchorago* is no exception: some individuals may be up to five times larger than the smallest. Both sexes engage in combat, and those with longer bodies and rostra, which are used as weapons, are more successful in securing a mate. There is an overall preference by both sexes for larger mates, thus skewing populations toward larger bodied individuals. Females chew holes into the decaying wood of primarily Gumbo-limbo trees (*Bursera simaruba*) to oviposit. Adults can be readily found in large numbers under the bark of dead logs.

### RELATED SPECIES

*Brentus* and *Cephalobarus* are currently classified in the Neotropical tribe Brentini. Thirty-seven species are included in *Brentus*. Of these, *B. cylindrus* has been reported from Polynesia (Marquesas, Tahiti), where it is possible that it was introduced. The first brentid species described by Carl Linnaeus in 1758 were *B. anchorago* and *B. dispar*, originally under the genus *Curculio*.

Actual size

**Brentus anchorago** is a greatly elongate black weevil with reddish-orange vittae on the elytra. It is one of the largest weevil species in North America. Males are strikingly longer, with the long, slender prothorax narrowing in the middle; the elongate, narrow rostrum is about as long as the prothorax. Females have a tear-shaped prothorax that broadens basally, and a rostrum that is about half the size of the prothorax.

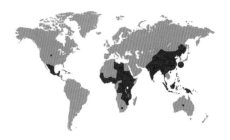

| FAMILY | Brentidae |
|---|---|
| SUBFAMILY | Brentinae |
| DISTRIBUTION | Oriental; now introduced circumtropically |
| MACROHABITAT | Tropical and subtropical areas, mainly agroecosystems |
| MICROHABITAT | Associated with Sweet Potato (*Ipomoea batatas*) and related species |
| FEEDING HABITS | Adults feed on the leaves, stems, and exposed tubers of the host plant; larvae mainly feed on tubers |
| NOTE | The most serious pest of the Sweet Potato (*Ipomoea batatas*); crop losses from weevil damage can reach up to 80 percent |

ADULT LENGTH
¼–⁵⁄₁₆ in
(5.5–8 mm)

600

*CYLAS FORMICARIUS*
# SWEET POTATO WEEVIL
(FABRICIUS, 1798)

Actual size

This infamous pest of the Sweet Potato (*Ipomoea batatas*) is responsible for major economic losses in the industry. The female Sweet Potato Weevil repeatedly chews a hole into the tuber neck, lays a single egg, and protects it by covering it with her own feces. The larvae feed and develop in the roots and stems. Their mining results in darkened, spongy, bitter, smelly tubers. Adults feed on leaves, stems, and tubers, and are long-lived. Among the current control measures, entomopathogenic nematodes appear to be successful agents for killing Sweet Potato Weevil larvae. In addition, detecting female sex pheromones is a promising way to monitor, trap, and possibly disrupt mating of adults.

RELATED SPECIES

The brentid genus *Cylas* contains 24 species. There are at least two other species commonly known as the Sweet Potato Weevil: *C. puncticollis* and *C. brunneus* from East Africa. *C. formicarius* can be distinguished from these primarily by its red prothorax; *C. puncticollis* is entirely black and *C. brunneus* is brown and smaller. The previously recognized subspecific name *C. formicarius elegantulus* is no longer used.

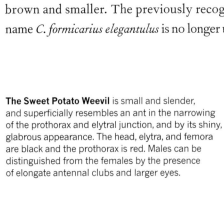

**The Sweet Potato Weevil** is small and slender, and superficially resembles an ant in the narrowing of the prothorax and elytral junction, and by its shiny, glabrous appearance. The head, elytra, and femora are black and the prothorax is red. Males can be distinguished from the females by the presence of elongate antennal clubs and larger eyes.

| FAMILY | Brentidae |
|---|---|
| SUBFAMILY | Brentinae |
| DISTRIBUTION | Australian: New Zealand |
| MACROHABITAT | Subtropical |
| MICROHABITAT | Trunk of host tree; adults hide in the canopy at night |
| FEEDING HABITS | Larvae are wood-borers of dying or recently dead trees (Araucariacea, Podocarpaceae, Asteraceae, Corynocarpaceae, Malvaceae, Meliaceae, Monimiaceae, Proteaceae); adults do not appear to feed |
| NOTE | The world's longest weevil, which has evolved complex mating behaviors |

| ADULT MALE LENGTH |
|---|
| ⅝–3½ in |
| (16–90 mm) |
| including rostrum |

| ADULT FEMALE LENGTH |
|---|
| ¹¹⁄₁₆–1¹³⁄₁₆ in |
| (18–46 mm) |
| including rostrum |

*LASIORHYNCHUS BARBICORNIS*
# GIRAFFE WEEVIL
(FABRICIUS, 1775)

601

This spectacular species is the longest weevil in the world, with some males measuring up to 3½ in (90 mm). Interestingly, males of the same species can be as small as ⅝ in (16 mm). This difference in male body size reflects the evolution of two mating strategies within Giraffe Weevils: male-to-male combat and sneaking behavior. Males with very elongate heads and rostra are successful during male-to-male combat and at fending off potential new suitors while mating. Shorter Giraffe Weevil males, on the other hand, employ sneaking behavior to circumvent a larger weevil's advantage: they slip unnoticed onto the female and mate with her while she is being guarded by the larger, unsuspecting male, effectively resulting in a weevil *ménage à trois*.

## RELATED SPECIES
*Lasiorhynchus barbicornis* belongs in the tribe Ithystenini (16 genera) and the genus contains a single species. It is related to *Ithystenus* from Australia and Vanuatu, *Mesetia* from Australia, and *Bulbogaster* from Fiji. However, *Prodector* (Pseudocephalini) from Sulawesi has been hypothesized as the closest relative to *Lasiorhynchus*.

**The Giraffe Weevil** is very long and narrow, and the scutellum is readily visible. The body color is dull, dark brown and there are usually three yellowish or reddish markings on each elytron, basally, medially, and subapically. The head, with its elongate rostrum, is as long as the rest of the body. The antennae in the males are located apically on the rostrum, while on the females they are located medially. The male antennae and underside of the rostrum are covered with setae, hence the species epithet.

Actual size

| FAMILY | Brentidae |
|---|---|
| SUBFAMILY | Eurhynchinae |
| DISTRIBUTION | Australian: southeast Australia (New South Wales) |
| MACROHABITAT | Temperate forests |
| MICROHABITAT | A borer and feeder of woody plants |
| FEEDING HABITS | Adults feed on leaves of *Persoonia* (Proteaceae); larvae tunnel into the stems |
| NOTE | The small genus *Eurhynchus* is restricted to eastern Australia |

ADULT LENGTH
½ in
(12–13 mm)

602

*EURHYNCHUS LAEVIOR*
# EURHYNCHUS LAEVIOR
(KIRBY, 1819)

The females of *Eurhynchus laevior* apparently drill holes on the underside of small twigs of *Persoonia lanceolata*, *P. laevis*, and *P. myrtilloides* for oviposition, and larvae tunnel into the stems. The larva has conspicuous brushes of setae on its mouthparts, possibly for cleaning frass (excreta) and debris from its tunnel. Mature larvae pupate toward the upper end of the larval tunnel and the adult eventually emerges through a hole chewed by the beetle. By carefully studying larval characters of species in the subfamily, scientists have been able to gain a better understanding of their evolutionary history, which has contributed toward a stable natural classification of the family.

RELATED SPECIES
*Eurhynchus* contains five species, all from eastern Australia, including Tasmania. There may be an additional six undescribed species in Australia. Two extant genera, *Ctenaphides* (two species) from Western Australia, and *Aporhina* (21 species) from Australia and New Guinea, are also included in Eyrhynchinae. The extinct *Orapaeus* (one species) from the Late Cretaceous formations in Botswana and a similar, undescribed fossil from Early Cretaceous formations in Brazil, if correctly assigned to Eurhynchinae, suggests a more widespread distribution of this ancient subfamily.

**Eurhynchus laevior** is black with white pubescence marking the body except for the apex of the rostrum. The body is narrow, with the elytra broader than the prothorax and head. The antennae are straight and emerge subapically from the rostrum. The pronotum, especially on the sides, have smooth, shiny, sparsely or shallowly punctate areas.

Actual size

| FAMILY | Brentidae |
|---|---|
| SUBFAMILY | Apioninae |
| DISTRIBUTION | Afrotropical: South Africa (Eastern Cape) |
| MACROHABITAT | Mediterranean |
| MICROHABITAT | Cycad cones |
| FEEDING HABITS | Adult feeding habits unknown; larvae feed on cycad seeds |
| NOTE | The species has a close association with African cycads in the genus *Encephalartos*, and is considered a pest of cycads |

ADULT LENGTH
³/₁₆–⁵/₁₆ in
(4–8 mm)

*ANTLIARHINUS SIGNATUS*
# ANTLIARHINUS SIGNATUS
GYLLENHAL, 1836

603

Actual size

Females of this species have one of the longest rostra among weevils, the length of which may exceed twice her body length. She uses this elongate rostrum to chew through the cycad sporophylls and reach the well-protected and concealed ovules of *Encephalartos* host plants, where she oviposits. Extracting her lancet from the now-pierced seed is often challenging, as it entails balance and extreme bending of the rostrum. Males have a much shorter rostrum. This weevil is considered a pest of its cycad host and does not significantly contribute toward its pollination. The larva is known to feed exclusively on cycad gametophytes, a behavior apparently shared with only one other insect, *Antliarhinus zamiae*.

## RELATED SPECIES

Four species are included in this genus, and the only other genus in the group is *Platymerus*, with three species. The supertribe Antliarhinitae is endemic to the Afrotropical Realm, mainly the eastern part of Africa where their cycad host plants occur. At least four recently discovered species in *Antliarhinus* and one in *Platymerus* are yet to be described.

**Antliarhinus signatus** is brown, glabrous, and dorsoventrally flattened. Females have a rostrum that can reach up to twice their body size, while the male rostrum is deltoid and much shorter, about as long as the pronotum. The pronotum is broadest in the middle. The elytra are parallel-sided with well-defined striae. The front femora are stouter than those of the middle and hind legs.

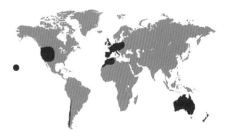

| FAMILY | Brentidae |
|---|---|
| SUBFAMILY | Apioninae |
| DISTRIBUTION | Palearctic, Australian, Neotropical, and Pacific: native to the western Palearctic; introduced to New Zealand, Australia, Chile, USA (western USA and Hawaii) |
| MACROHABITAT | In a broad range of habitats, including agricultural areas, natural forests, and rangelands |
| MICROHABITAT | Associated with Common Gorse (*Ulex europaeus*), a spiny evergreen shrub that grows in dense thickets |
| FEEDING HABITS | Adults feed on leaves and flowers of Common Gorse (*Ulex europaeus*); larvae feed on the developing seedpods |
| NOTE | Introduced intentionally to several countries as a biological control agent |

**ADULT LENGTH**
¹⁄₁₆ in
(1.7–2.4 mm)

*EXAPION ULICIS*
# GORSE SEED WEEVIL
(FORSTER, 1771)

604

Actual size

Indigenous to the western Palearctic Realm, this species has been introduced to several countries for the biological control of Common Gorse (*Ulex europaeus*), a highly invasive evergreen perennial shrub in the family Fabaceae. Initially these plants were imported as ornamentals or hedging to countries with temperate climates. The predominantly seed-feeding weevil *Exapion ulicis* partially controls the invasive weed by feeding on its seedpods in its larval stage. Females, which chew holes into the pods in order to lay their eggs, can also damage the stems and spines of the plant.

## RELATED SPECIES

The subtribe Exapiina in the tribe Apionini includes two genera: the Mediterranean *Lepidapion*, with 17 species; and *Exapion*, with 44 species and subspecies in two subgenera (*Exapion* and *Ulapion*). The slightly larger Palearctic Scotch Broom Seed Weevil (*E. fuscirostre fuscirostre*) was intentionally introduced to California in 1964 for the biological control of Scotch Broom (*Cytisus scoparius*) and has since become established along the Pacific coast of North America.

**The Gorse Seed Weevil** is very small, oval, and black, with rust-colored distal front and middle legs, scape, and funicle. The entire weevil is covered with dense, elliptical, ash-gray scales, which are slightly more prominent on the pronotum and elytra. The head is spherical and the rostrum long, cylindrical, slender, and nearly straight, with the antennae inserted close to the eyes. The dorsal margin of the scrobe of this species has a minute toothlike extension.

| FAMILY | Brentidae |
|---|---|
| SUBFAMILY | Ithycerinae |
| DISTRIBUTION | Nearctic: eastern North America |
| MACROHABITAT | Deciduous forests |
| MICROHABITAT | Soil, roots |
| FEEDING HABITS | Adults feed mainly on new growth of Betulaceae, Juglandaceae, Fagaceae, and cultivated fruit trees (Rosaceae); larvae feed in the soil on the roots of the same host plants |
| NOTE | Regarded as an occasional pest of orchards and nurseries |

ADULT LENGTH
½–¹¹⁄₁₆ in
(12–18 mm)

*ITHYCERUS NOVEBORACENSIS*
# NEW YORK WEEVIL
(FORSTER, 1771)

605

Once included in its own family, this eastern North American species has been difficult to classify among weevils. It is now included within the family Brentidae. Females of the New York Weevil lay eggs covered in fecal matter in small depressions in the soil, e.g., at the base of its host plant. The legged larva develops in the soil by feeding on the lower surface of lateral roots of its host plant while traveling on its back and generating a tunnel. Pupation takes places at the expanded end of these tunnels. Adults are known to feed on the bark of shoots, leaf petioles, leaf buds, and acorn buds of their host plants.

## RELATED SPECIES

*Ithycerus noveboracensis*, which is the only species in the subfamily Ithycerinae, differs from other weevils by its unique male genitalia and the venation of its flight wings, in addition to its distinctive color pattern. The number of Malpighian tubules (structures associated with the gut of beetles) is reduced in larvae and adults, which is a characteristic feature of other members of the family Brentidae.

**The New York Weevil** is large, covered with scalelike setae, and has a distinct mottled dark and light color pattern. The rostrum is short and broad, with the straight antennae emerging near the apex. The pronotum is almost as wide as the head and narrower than the base of the elytra. The anterior corners of the elytra are right-angled and the elytral apices are narrowed, forming a pair of distinct rounded lobes.

Actual size

| FAMILY | Brentidae |
|---|---|
| SUBFAMILY | Microcerinae |
| DISTRIBUTION | Afrotropical: Angola, Botswana, Namibia, South Africa, Zambia, Zimbabwe |
| MACROHABITAT | Xeric (very dry) environments |
| MICROHABITAT | Under stones on coarse gravel or compact soil, at the base of plants |
| FEEDING HABITS | Larvae feed on roots of Arrowleaf Sida (*Sida rhombifolia*); feeding habits of adults uncertain |
| NOTE | Species in this genus are ground-dwelling, cryptically colored weevils and are broadly distributed sub-Saharan Africa |

**ADULT LENGTH**
⅝–¹¹⁄₁₆ in
(15.5–16.5 mm)

*MICROCERUS LATIPENNIS*
# MICROCERUS LATIPENNIS
FÅHRAEUS, 1871

The subterranean C-shaped white larva of this species is known to girdle the taproot of *Sida rhombifolia*. The adults are cryptic ground-dwelling weevils, usually found under stones on various kinds of substrates, from soft, loose sand to compact gravelly soil. The ovipositor of the female has strongly sclerotized blades and therefore it is hypothesized that eggs are laid in the soil. Adults are reported to be most active during twilight or in shady areas during the day. These weevils superficially resemble root weevils in the Curculionidae subfamily Entiminae, particularly due to the presence of their short rostrum.

RELATED SPECIES
Three genera are included in the exclusively Afrotropical subfamily Microcerinae: *Microcerus*, with 23 species; *Episus*, with 42 species; and *Gyllenhalia*, with two species. Within *Microcerus*, *M. spiniger* and *M. retusus* are most similar to *M. latipennis*, but can be distinguished based on features of the rostrum, tuberculation on the pronotum, and differences in the shape of the elytra. *Microcerus borrei* can also be confused with this species, but *M. latipennis* has less protuberant eyes and the rostrum and elytra differ.

**Microcerus latipennis** is a moderately large, elongate, ovate weevil with light brown to dark brown scales covering its body. The head, pronotum, and elytra are covered with tubercles of various sizes, facilitating a cryptic lifestyle on the ground. The broad rostrum ends posteriorly in a V-shaped groove between the slightly protruding eyes. The antennae are relatively long and stout, and are covered with scales and setae.

Actual size

| FAMILY | Brentidae |
|---|---|
| SUBFAMILY | Nanophyinae |
| DISTRIBUTION | Palearctic and Nearctic: native to the Palearctic; intentionally introduced to Canada (Manitoba, Ontario, Quebec) and USA (northern states) |
| MACROHABITAT | Wet habitats |
| MICROHABITAT | On flower buds, fruit, and leaves of its host plants |
| FEEDING HABITS | Adults and larvae feed on Purple Loosestrife (*Lythrum salicaria*) and *L. hyssopifolia* |
| NOTE | Introduced intentionally to North America as a biological control agent against the invasive weed Purple Loosestrife (*Lythrum salicaria*). In its native range, this widespread species has been described under more than 30 different names in the scientific literature |

ADULT LENGTH
$\frac{1}{32}$–$\frac{1}{16}$ in
(1.4–2.2 mm)

*NANOPHYES MARMORATUS MARMORATUS*
# LOOSESTRIFE SEED WEEVIL
(GOEZE, 1777)

607

✦

Actual size

In North America, the broadly distributed Purple Loosestrife (*Lythrum salicaria*) is an invasive wetland perennial with a Eurasian origin. The tiny weevil *Nanophyes marmoratus marmoratus* is one of the beetle species introduced to the region for the biological control of this weed (along with species in *Hylobius* and *Galerucella*). Adults and larvae feed on unopened flower buds and adults also feed on the developing leaves. A single larva completes development within a single bud. Mature larvae form pupal chambers at the bottom of the bud. Feeding on the flower buds prevents the production of seeds in the host.

## RELATED SPECIES
Sometimes given the rank of family, the subfamily Nanophyinae currently consists of approximately 30 genera and 300 species. Adults of most species measure $\frac{1}{8}$ in (2.5 mm) or less, and careful dissection of genital structures is usually required for accurate identification. *Nanophyes* includes more than 35 species and subspecies from the Palearctic Realm. One other subspecies of *N. marmoratus* is recognized: *N. m. miguelangeli* from the Russian Far East and Japan.

**The Loosestrife Seed Weevil** is a tiny oval beetle whose rostrum is longer than its pronotum. The color of the body is variable but usually dark brown to black, with variably sized orange-yellow markings on the elytra, and reddish-brown legs and antennae. Adults are covered with scattered whitish setae.

| FAMILY | Dryophthoridae |
|---|---|
| SUBFAMILY | Dryophthorinae |
| DISTRIBUTION | Nearctic: North America |
| MACROHABITAT | Temperate forests |
| MICROHABITAT | Forest litter and under the bark of *Pinus* spp. |
| FEEDING HABITS | Adult feeding habits unknown; the larvae are borers in decaying wood |
| NOTE | Associated with moist, dead wood |

ADULT LENGTH
¹⁄₁₆–¹⁄₈ in
(2.4–3.1 mm)

*DRYOPHTHORUS AMERICANUS*
# DRYOPHTHORUS AMERICANUS
BEDEL, 1885

Actual size

This species is associated with moist, dead wood and is also found in forest litter. It is not surprising, therefore, that it usually dirt-encrusted and has a soiled appearance. Adults and larvae have been associated with species of *Pinus*. The larvae are found in partly decayed wood and have mandibles that are internally granular for chewing wood. Adults are most often encountered under bark. This is the only species of the genus found in North America. It is not considered a pest, even though the generic Greek name means "oak-destroyer."

RELATED SPECIES

*Dryophthorus* and the four other genera in the subfamily Dryophthorinae were, until recently, classified under the subfamily Cossoninae in the family Curculionidae. *Lithophthorus* and *Spodotribus* are known only from Oligocene fossils. The extant *Stenommatus* is also found in the New World, while *Psilodryophthorus* is from New Guinea and the Philippines. *Dryophthorus* includes approximately 37 species found in all biogeographic regions. Of these, six species are also known from the New World.

**Dryophthorus americanus** is small, brown, and subcylindrical. Most of the body is covered with deep, wide, and usually dirt-encrusted punctations. The elytral interstriae are narrow and prominently raised. The tarsi have five segments. The antennae have a four-segmented funicle and the last segment is glabrous, except for the spongy tip—a trait that it shares with other dryophthorids.

| FAMILY | Dryophthoridae |
|---|---|
| SUBFAMILY | Orthognathinae |
| DISTRIBUTION | Neotropical |
| MACROHABITAT | Where palms grow; host species include *Cocos* spp., *Diplothemium caudescens*, *Attelea* spp., and *Elaeis guineensis* |
| MICROHABITAT | In or on palms |
| FEEDING HABITS | Larvae feed in wood of host palms; adult feeding habits uncertain |
| NOTE | Large, charismatic weevil with distinct rostral pubescence |

ADULT LENGTH
$^7/_{16}$–1¾ in
(11–45 mm)

*RHINOSTOMUS BARBIROSTRIS*
# BEARDED WEEVIL
(FABRICIUS, 1775)

609

This interesting-looking species, males of which have a rostrum resembling a colorful bottle brush, is one of the largest weevils in the world. The elongate front legs and rostrum of the adult male are used during combat with other males. The thick brush of setae may be advantageous during courtship, when the male wipes and strokes the dorsal surface of the female. The female prefers to oviposit in the bark of weakened or stressed palms. The larva develops inside the host. This species is a serious pest of the Coconut Palm (*Cocos nucifera*).

RELATED SPECIES

*Rhinostomus* contains eight species in the tropical regions of the world. The genus belongs in the tribe Rhinostomini, which also contains the North American genus *Yuccaborus*. *Rhinostomus barbirostris* is very similar to the African *R. niger*, but differs in punctation and pubescence of the legs, the morphology of the head, and the shape of the male genitalia.

**The Bearded Weevil** is a large black weevil covered with rough, deep punctures. The males have an elongate, dorsally dentate rostrum with reddish-gold setae that can give the appearance of a beard. Females have tubercles on the dorsal surface of their shorter rostrum, which lacks pubescence. Males have longer front legs than the females. The antennae emerge from the middle of the rostrum and the last antennomere is narrow, velvety, and very long.

Actual size

| FAMILY | Dryophthoridae |
|---|---|
| SUBFAMILY | Orthognathinae |
| DISTRIBUTION | Palearctic and Oriental: Indian subcontinent east to Japan and Peninsular Malaysia |
| MACROHABITAT | Temperate forests |
| MICROHABITAT | Under bark or logs |
| FEEDING HABITS | Adult feeding habits unknown; the larvae are borers in Pinaceae, Moringaceae, Fabaceae, Myrtaceae, and Moraceae trees |
| NOTE | A large, charismatic wood-boring weevil, with a potentially high risk for accidental introduction and establishment into non-native temperate regions |

ADULT LENGTH
½–1³⁄₁₆ in
(12–30 mm)

*SIPALINUS GIGAS GIGAS*
# JAPANESE GIANT WEEVIL
(FABRICIUS, 1775)

610

This charismatic species is associated with unhealthy, dying, or felled trees from numerous families and is usually found under bark or logs. If the larvae occur in large numbers they may destroy their host tree. The holes and tunneling caused by adults and larvae may damage wood used for commercial purposes. While not yet established outside of its native range, this species has been intercepted in North America and New Zealand from wooden packing material such as dunnage, crating, and pallets. Given its associations with logs and fallen trees, it may also readily disperse over water.

RELATED SPECIES
*Sipalinus* includes seven species, two from Eurasia and Australasia, and five from Africa. The species can be distinguished primarily by the sculpturing of the pronotum. Additional diagnostic characters are the shape and punctation of the rostrum, the shape of the antennal club, particularly the spongy apical part, the length of the second tarsomere, the ventral covering of the tarsi, and the genitalia.

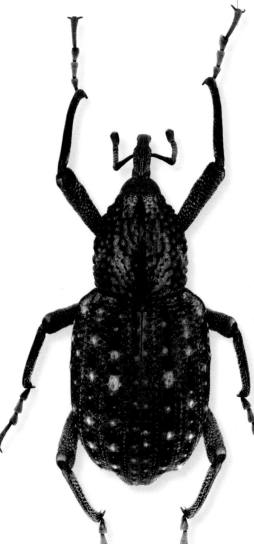

**The Japanese Giant Weevil** is brownish, large and robust, with a crusty appearance. It is heavily tuberculate, a feature that makes it stand out among most Old World weevils. The rostrum is as long as the pronotum. The pronotum is widest near the middle and tuberculate on the disk, except for a narrow median vitta or stripe. Short velvety stripes alternate, along the interstices, with whitish areas with light setae.

Actual size

| FAMILY | Dryophthoridae |
|---|---|
| SUBFAMILY | Rhynchophorinae |
| DISTRIBUTION | Nearctic and Neotropical: USA (southern California, southern Arizona), Central America, Peru, Brazil, Colombia |
| MACROHABITAT | Dry, warm areas (desert-like environments) |
| MICROHABITAT | Cacti |
| FEEDING HABITS | Associated with Saguaro (*Carnegiea gigantea*), *Ferocactus* spp., *Opuntia* spp., *Hylocereus* spp. and other Cactaceae |
| NOTE | Previously used as a biological control agent against invasive cacti; a pest of cactus-based commodities, such as dragonfruit, in some countries |

ADULT LENGTH
⁹⁄₁₆–1 in
(15–25 mm)

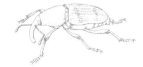

*CACTOPHAGUS SPINOLAE*

# CACTUS WEEVIL

(GYLLENHAL, 1838)

611

This species feeds on cacti (Cactaceae) and in some countries is a serious pest of commodities such as dragonfruit (*Hylocereus* spp.) and nopal (*Opuntia ficus-indica*). In 1946, more than 17,500 of these weevils were introduced to South Africa to help control prickly pears (*Opuntia* spp.), an invasive weed. The destructive larva feeds and burrows through the woody segments and "trunk" of the cactus, eventually causing it to rot and collapse. The larva builds a fiber cocoon inside the pear segment or near the joints. While successful at controlling prickly pears, the species did not become established there due to the colder South African climate. The adult nibbles on the pears and is not harmful.

## RELATED SPECIES

*Cactophagus* includes approximately 40 species distributed from the southern USA into South America, but is absent in the Antilles, Argentina, Chile, Paraguay, and Uruguay. *Cactophagus spinolae*, the only species in the genus that occurs in the United States, is very similar to *C. fahraei*, but differs primarily in having very fine, shallow, and rather dense punctures forming the elytral striae.

Actual size

**The Cactus Weevil** is the largest weevil in California. It is entirely black, or black with red to orange-red spots on the front of the pronotum and four transverse stripes (fasciae) on the elytra. The surface is shiny to dull and lacks pubescence. The rostrum is stout and almost as long as the pronotum. The antennae emerge close to the head. The strial punctures on the elytra are small, close together, and shallow.

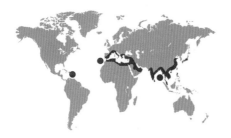

| FAMILY | Dryophthoridae |
|---|---|
| SUBFAMILY | Rhynchophorinae |
| DISTRIBUTION | Oriental, Palearctic, and Neotropical: native to Southeast Asia; introduced to Asia, Africa, Middle East, Mediterranean Europe, Aruba |
| MACROHABITAT | Tropical and subtropical |
| MICROHABITAT | Wood-borer of palms |
| FEEDING HABITS | Larvae feed and develop inside at least 23 species of palm trees; adults feed on palms too |
| NOTE | One of the most destructive pests of palms; also a delicious snack |

ADULT LENGTH
1–1½ in
(25–38 mm)

*RHYNCHOPHORUS FERRUGINEUS*
# RED PALM WEEVIL
(OLIVIER, 1791)

612

The broad host preference and severity of damage caused by the Red Palm Weevil to healthy or weakened palm trees makes this species one of the most destructive pests in the world. Both ornamental and commercial palms are impacted. This weevil is not entirely negative, however. In its native territory, all life stages—but particularly the large and juicy larvae commonly called Sago Worm—are considered nutritious and delicious. Culinary practices using Red Palm Weevil are currently being explored to perhaps assist in curbing hunger and nutrition shortfalls in developing regions of the world.

RELATED SPECIES
*Rhynchophorus* contains approximately ten species, which are variable in coloration and may be easily confused with one another. Studies comparing DNA sequences of *R. ferrugineus* populations across its entire range suggests the existence of at least one cryptic species, *R. vulneratus*, historically considered a junior synonym of *R. ferrugineus*.

**The Red Palm Weevil** is large, shiny, and oval-shaped. Coloration is very variable, with some individuals being completely black with minor reddish-orange markings on the pronotum to mostly reddish-orange with black markings on the pronotum. Punctations are not apparent and the elytral striae are well defined.

Actual size

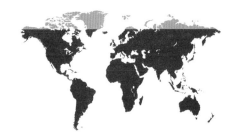

| FAMILY | Dryophthoridae |
|---|---|
| SUBFAMILY | Rhynchophorinae |
| DISTRIBUTION | Originally from the Oriental Realm, now cosmopolitan |
| MACROHABITAT | Cereal grains |
| MICROHABITAT | Adults and larvae typically feed on stored grain-products (corn, barley, rye, wheat, rice, etc.) but can also attack cereal plants in the field |
| FEEDING HABITS | Feeds and develops within a seed kernel or equivalent |
| NOTE | One of the most damaging grain pests in the world |

ADULT LENGTH
$\frac{1}{16}-\frac{1}{8}$ in
(2–3 mm)

*SITOPHILUS ORYZAE*
# RICE WEEVIL
(LINNAEUS, 1763)

613

From its native India, this small weevil has accompanied humans around the globe, becoming one of the most serious and widespread pests of stored grain-products. The presence and impact of this and other species in *Sitophilus* date back at least to the times of ancient Egypt (2300 BCE) and Roman playwright Plautus (*c.* 254–184 BCE). They were also aboard Captain Cook's ships during his round-the-world voyages. When left unchecked, Rice Weevil infestations can soon become a significant problem, as exemplified in Australia, where an estimated 40 tons of wheat was spoiled and up to a ton of *S. oryzae* needed to be swept up and destroyed during World War I.

RELATED SPECIES

The genus *Sitophilus* contains 18 species. Both the Granary Weevil (*S. granarius*) and the Maize Weevil (*S. zeamais*) belong in this genus and closely resemble the Rice Weevil. In the past, the Maize and Rice weevils were considered to be a single species; the two can readily be distinguished by the shape of the male genitalia.

Actual size

**The Rice Weevil** is a small, dark brown beetle with two distinct reddish to reddish-yellow patches on each elytron, basally and subapically. The surface of the integument is rough due to the deep punctations marking the pronotum and elytra.

| FAMILY | Brachyceridae |
|---|---|
| SUBFAMILY | Brachycerinae |
| DISTRIBUTION | Afrotropical: southern and eastern Africa |
| MACROHABITAT | In habitat characterized by lengthy dry periods and severe droughts |
| MICROHABITAT | Ground-dwelling, on clay soil |
| FEEDING HABITS | Feeds on foliage of the Karoo Lily (*Ammocharis coranica*) |
| NOTE | A charismatic weevil, used as amulet, and sometimes also referred to as Moose Face Lily Weevil or Elephant Weevil |

ADULT LENGTH
1–1¾ in
(25–45 mm)

614

*BRACHYCERUS ORNATUS*
# RED-SPOTTED LILY WEEVIL
(DRURY, 1773)

This charismatic flightless African weevil feeds on the leaves of the Karoo Lily (*Ammocharis coranica*) and is closely associated with it. The female excavates a hole in the soil adjacent to the bulbs, where she eventually oviposits. Up to three larvae develop within each bulb and pupation takes place in the soil in a smoothly lined chamber constructed by the weevil. Perhaps because of the red spots on this weevil and its host-plant association, it was used as decorative magical beads and strung into amulets worn by African Bushmen.

## RELATED SPECIES

Many species in the *Brachycerus* are large and colorful. Some species, such as the Garlic Weevil (*B. muricatus*), are serious pests of *Allium* spp. in parts of Europe and northern Africa. Approximately 500 species are classified in *Brachycerus*, ranging across Africa and most of the Palearctic Realm. Species can generally be separated based on the sculpture of the head, prothorax, and elytra.

Actual size

**The Red-spotted Lily Weevil** is massive, bulbous, and black, with red dots on the elytra and additional markings on the pronotum. The disk of the pronotum and the rostrum are uniquely sculptured with grooves and bumps, and the sides of the pronotum are tuberculate. The surface of the rounded elytra is relatively smoother. The rostrum is short and broadened apically.

| FAMILY | Brachyceridae |
|---|---|
| SUBFAMILY | Erirhininae |
| DISTRIBUTION | Neotropical, Nearctic, Afrotropical, Oriental, and Australian: native to South America (Argentina, west to Bolivia and north to northern Brazil); introduced to the USA, West Africa, India, Australia |
| MACROHABITAT | Freshwater ecosystems |
| MICROHABITAT | In or near water |
| FEEDING HABITS | Feeds on Water Hyacinth (*Eichhornia crassipes*) |
| NOTE | Introduced for the biological control of the invasive Water Hyacinth in the USA |

ADULT LENGTH
³⁄₁₆ in
(3.5–5.0 mm)

*NEOCHETINA BRUCHI*
# CHEVRONED WATERHYACINTH WEEVIL
HUSTACHE, 1926

615

The larval and adult stages of this weevil feed on Water Hyacinth (*Eichhornia crassipes*), which has led to its introduction from Argentina to several parts of the world to control this invasive weed. The weevil lives in or near fresh water and the adults have water-repellent scales on their body for the formation of a plastron, a portable air bubble that the weevil uses to breathe underwater. Under high magnification, specialized appressed-perforated and plumose scales are noticeable. The appressed-perforated scales cover most of the dorsal and ventral surfaces, while the plumose scales and setae are present at points of articulation.

## RELATED SPECIES

The genus *Neochetina* includes six species in the New World and belongs in the tribe Stenopelmini, which includes 26 genera. Species of *Neochetina* can primarily be separated by differences in structures on their pronotum and elytra. The related Mottled Waterhyacinth Weevil (*N. eichhorniae*) also feeds on Water Hyacinth and is used to control this weed.

Actual size

**The Chevroned Waterhyacinth Weevil** is a broad, oval beetle, densely covered with gray, yellow, and brown scales that are closely pressed against the surface. The elytra typically have a distinctive lighter-colored V-shaped (chevron) band, although color patterns can be variable. Elytral striae are narrow yet prominent. The rostrum is almost as long as the pronotum. The female has a slightly longer rostrum with the tip devoid of scales.

| FAMILY | Brachyceridae |
|---|---|
| SUBFAMILY | Raymondionyminae |
| DISTRIBUTION | Nearctic: USA (California, in and around Mendocino County) |
| MACROHABITAT | Temperate forests |
| MICROHABITAT | Coniferous leaf litter |
| FEEDING HABITS | Unknown |
| NOTE | An eyeless weevil endemic to California |

**ADULT LENGTH**
¹⁄₁₆–¹⁄₈ in
(1.7–2.9 mm)

616

*ALAOCYBITES CALIFORNICUS*
# ALAOCYBITES CALIFORNICUS
GILBERT, 1956

Actual size

This small, eyeless species is endemic to the northern coast of California and lives as an adult in coniferous, specifically redwood, leaf litter. The larva and its biology remain unknown. The immature stages of the related *Raymondionymus perrisi* were found in the soil and it is plausible that *A. californicus* larvae are also terricolous. This and other leaf- and soil-dwelling organisms are commonly collected by sifting and washing deep humus or soil. Anophthalmy (absence of one or all eyes) may be an adaptation to life in the dark leaf-litter environment, where eyesight is unnecessary.

RELATED SPECIES

*Aloacybites* consisted of *A. californicus* and *A. rothi* until *A. egorovi* was discovered in 2007 from leaf-litter samples collected in the Russian Far East. The genus also includes a Pliocene (3 million-year-old) *Alaocybites* fossil from Alaska's Lost Chicken Creek gold mine, suggesting either a broader ancient distribution of the genus or collecting bias. *Schizomicrus* is sympatric with *A. californica*, but species in *Schizomicrus* can be distinguished by the presence of a distinct prosternal depression. The Venezuelan *Bordoniola* may be closely related.

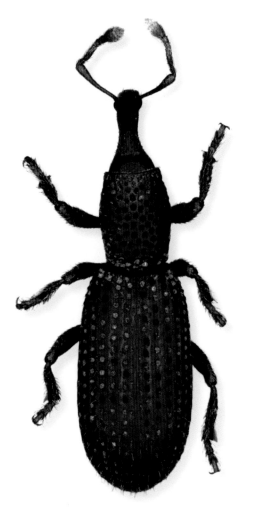

**Alaocybites californicus** is tiny and eyeless. The body is shiny, elongate, relatively narrow, and mostly a translucent, light red-brown in color. The head is not hidden by the pronotum, the antennae are geniculate, and the rostrum is evenly curved and slightly shorter than the pronotum. The elytral interstices are covered with sparse, erect yellow setae. The pronotum and elytra have prominent punctures that are usually encrusted with dirt. The legs have only four tarsomeres instead of five as in other members of the family.

| FAMILY | Curculionidae |
|---|---|
| SUBFAMILY | Curculioninae |
| DISTRIBUTION | Neotropical: Belize, Panama |
| MACROHABITAT | Forest |
| MICROHABITAT | Leaf surfaces |
| FEEDING HABITS | Adult feeding habits are uncertain; larvae are presumably leaf-miners |
| NOTE | The odd combination of morphological structures of this weevil has led to problems with its classification |

ADULT LENGTH
³⁄₁₆ in
(4–4.5 mm)

*CAMAROTUS SINGULARIS*

# CAMAROTUS SINGULARIS

CHAMPION, 1903

617

Actual size

Adults of the unusual-looking and rather rare *Camarotus singularis* superficially resemble leaf beetles of the subfamily Cassidinae in that the lateral sides of the elytra project outward on each side of the body. The shortened rostrum and apparently straight antennae of *Camarotus* species, on the other hand, bear a resemblance to features of weevils in the family Attelabidae. This strange combination of morphological structures has led to problems in determining the correct classification of the species in the past. Based on observations for other species of this genus, *C. singularis* larvae presumably mine leaves of Melastomataceae or similar plants.

### RELATED SPECIES

*Camarotus* is the only genus in the subtribe Camarotina of the tribe Camarotini, and includes 40 species in three subgroups distributed throughout tropical America. *Camarotus singularis* is included in the *C. cassidoides* group, along with 18 other species. *Camarotus dilatatus* from Guatemala is the species that most closely resembles this species but differs in having a black, not brick-red, ventral surface.

**Camarotus singularis** is a short, stout, dull brick-red weevil with the sides of the elytra extremely expanded laterally. The males have enlarged front femora bearing an anterior row of sharp, serrated teeth. The rostrum is short and robust, and the antennae, which are inserted at the middle, superficially appear straight with the basal segment elongate and curved. The pronotum is almost twice as broad as it is long, and is considerably narrower anteriorly.

| FAMILY | Curculionidae |
|---|---|
| SUBFAMILY | Curculioninae |
| DISTRIBUTION | Australian: New Caledonia |
| MACROHABITAT | Rainforest |
| MICROHABITAT | On foliage of *Sloanea* spp. |
| FEEDING HABITS | Unknown; the host plant is *Sloanea lepida* (and possibly other *Sloanea* spp.) |
| NOTE | Adults possess a long, curved prothoracic helmet (hornlike structure) |

ADULT LENGTH
³/₁₆–¼ in
(4–5.5 mm)

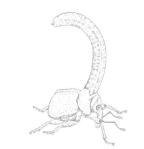

*CEROCRANUS EXTREMUS*
# CEROCRANUS EXTREMUS
KUSCHEL, 2008

618

Actual size

This bizarre-looking species belongs to the tribe Cranopoeini, a group of weevils that excrete waxy thoracic and elytral secretions that harden to form solid, yet soft, structures, such as the long, hollow, curved thoracic horn displayed by this species. Both males and females have these structures and the secretions start as soon as the adult emerges from the pupal stage. The presence of such a large horn does not impede the weevil from taking flight—it is, in fact, an agile flyer. The wax is secreted by glands concealed in a loop of dense, short, soft setae on the prothorax.

RELATED SPECIES

*Cerocranus* contains a single species. The tribe Cranopoeini includes 19 species in 11 genera from the Pacific (e.g., Mariana, Marquesas, and Cook islands), Australia, and Papua New Guinea. Aside from *Cerocranus*, Cranopoeini includes the genera *Blastobius*, *Cranopoeus*, *Docolens*, *Cranoides*, *Onychomerus*, *Spanochelus*, *Enneaeus*, *Swezeyella*, *Fergusoniella*, and *Cratoscelocis*. Species in the tribe can be separated by structures on their legs, by their elytra, and by characteristics of the male genitalia.

**Cerocranus extremus** adults are dark brown, with some reddish brown on the legs and ventral surface. The prothorax has a long, curved hornlike process that is sometimes more than twice the length of the entire body. The elytra are convex, wider than the base of the prothorax, and have a pair of short tubercles near the center. The female rostrum has a large pit with a glabrous rim and wax-producing setae in front of the eyes.

| FAMILY | Curculionidae |
|---|---|
| SUBFAMILY | Curculioninae |
| DISTRIBUTION | Nearctic: northeastern North America |
| MACROHABITAT | Eastern deciduous forest |
| MICROHABITAT | On chestnut trees (*Castanea* spp.) |
| FEEDING HABITS | Larvae feed inside nuts of various species of *Castanea*, including *C. dentata*, *C. mollissima*, and *C. pumila*; adults feed on young nuts of the same hosts |
| NOTE | The largest species in the genus *Curculio* in North America |

ADULT LENGTH
¼–⅝ in
(6.5–16 mm)

*CURCULIO CARYATRYPES*
# LARGER CHESTNUT WEEVIL
(BOHEMAN, 1843)

619

This large and iconic weevil is intimately associated with the American Chestnut (*Castanea dentata*), a tree almost extinct due to chestnut blight, a disease caused by the invasive fungus *Cryphonectria parasitica*, which was accidentally introduced from Japan in the twentieth century. The Larger Chestnut Weevil has experienced a radical decline and is now rare throughout its historical range, possibly surviving only on other species of native and introduced chestnuts. Several weevil larvae may feed on a single chestnut kernel and eventually exit through an almost perfectly circular hole. Pupation takes place in the soil.

## RELATED SPECIES

This is one of almost 345 species in the diverse, seed-feeding genus *Curculio*. They feed on seeds and gall formations of Fagaceae (beeches), Betulaceae (birches), and Juglandaceae (walnuts). Some *Curculio* species are serious pests of Pecan (*Carya illinoinensis—Curculio carya*), Hazel (*Corylus avellana—Curculio nucum*), and chestnuts (*Castanea* spp.— *Curculio elephas*). Variation in *Curculio* rostral length may correlate with the variation in the host-plant seed size, contributing to the high diversity of *Curculio* species.

Actual size

**The Larger Chestnut Weevil** is an elliptical, dark reddish-brown beetle with a dense covering of golden-yellow to gray, mottled and striped pubescence, and a very thin, elongate, curved rostrum that is almost as long as the rest of the body in females and slightly shorter in males. The rostrum is continuous with the frons. The antennae are greatly elongate and emerge approximately midway on the rostrum in males and closer to the head in females.

| FAMILY | Curculionidae |
|---|---|
| SUBFAMILY | Curculioninae |
| DISTRIBUTION | Neotropical: Argentina, Bolivia, Uruguay, Brazil (Belém, Manaus), French Guiana, Suriname, Paraguay |
| MACROHABITAT | Vegetation along rivers and ditches |
| MICROHABITAT | Aquatic environments on stems of Water Hyacinth (*Eichhornia crassipes*) |
| FEEDING HABITS | Adults and larvae feed on the eggs of grasshoppers (*Cornops* spp.) |
| NOTE | Unusual in that, unlike other weevils, it feeds on other insects rather than plant tissues |

ADULT LENGTH
¼–⁵⁄₁₆ in
(7–8 mm)

620

*LUDOVIX FASCIATUS*
# LUDOVIX FASCIATUS
(GYLLENHAL, 1836)

This weevil is peculiar in that it feeds exclusively on the eggs of *Cornops* grasshoppers oviposited inside stems of the Water Hyacinth (*Eichhornia crassipes*). The female weevil also utilizes the Water Hyacinth as its oviposition host plant. The larva develops, feeds, and pupates within the grasshoppers' ootheca (egg masses). Suitability and availability of grasshopper oothecae is assessed by the female weevil with her elongate rostrum. Adult *Ludovix fasciatus* are capable of swimming on the surface of the water and employ a kind of six-legged simultaneous breaststroke, with the body suspended on the surface and the legs submerged and providing the thrust.

### RELATED SPECIES
This species belongs in the tribe Erodiscini, a relatively depauperate Neotropical tribe containing slightly more than 100 species classified in eight genera. The majority of species in the tribe are associated with aquatic or semi-aquatic plants. *Ludovix* includes only two species. This tribe is closely related to the ant-mimicking species in the tribe Otidocephalini, and in the past both tribes have been combined.

Actual size

**Ludovix fasciatus** is shiny, narrow, and elongate. It is reddish brown with a transverse darker band near the middle of the elytra. The pronotum is rounded along the sides. The appendages are narrow and elongate, as is the rostrum, which is curved and as long as the rest of the body. The apex of the femora is swollen.

| FAMILY | Curculionidae |
|---|---|
| SUBFAMILY | Bagoinae |
| DISTRIBUTION | Oriental and Nearctic: native to Bangladesh, India, Pakistan, Thailand; introduced to the USA |
| MACROHABITAT | Semi-aquatic; found in freshwater ecosystems |
| MICROHABITAT | In or near water, on water plants |
| FEEDING HABITS | Exposed tubers of Hydrilla (*Hydrilla verticillata*) |
| NOTE | Introduced to the USA as a biological control agent against a devastating invasive aquatic plant |

ADULT LENGTH
⅛ – ³⁄₁₆ in
(2.8–4 mm)

*BAGOUS AFFINIS*
# HYDRILLA TUBER WEEVIL
HUSTACHE, 1926

621

Actual size

This weevil species, originally from Asia, was released into the United States to control Hydrilla (*Hydrilla verticillata*), an invasive aquatic plant frequently used in aquariums and native to Asia, Europe, Africa, and Australia. This weed outcompetes aquatic plants indigenous to coastal areas of North America and herbicides are not effective for its control. Adults of *Bagous affinis* feed on plant parts above the ground surface, while the larvae feed within tubers. Development and feeding by the Hydrilla Tuber Weevil depends on suitable water levels and habitat conditions, which may limit the species' success.

## RELATED SPECIES

Species in the weevil subfamily Erirhininae, also found in aquatic and semi-aquatic environments, superficially look very similar to species in Bagoinae, but lack a channel on the ventral surface of the prothorax. Most species in the cosmopolitan genus *Bagous* are associated with freshwater plants and can generally be separated by features of their elytra, prothorax, and legs, as well as structures of the male genitalia.

**The Hydrilla Tuber Weevil** is a medium-size elongate-oval black beetle with gray and brown markings, and usually whitish longitudinal stripes on the prothorax. Its smooth, shiny appearance is due to the broad, appressed scales densely covering the body. The legs are long and slender, and the elytral striae are well defined. This species has a median longitudinal channel on the ventral side of the prothorax for the reception of the rostrum.

| FAMILY | Curculionidae |
|---|---|
| SUBFAMILY | Baridinae |
| DISTRIBUTION | Neotropical and Nearctic: native to Central America, Mexico, Panama; introduced to USA (Broward and Miami-Dade counties, Florida) |
| MACROHABITAT | Tropical |
| MICROHABITAT | On host vine species |
| FEEDING HABITS | Adults and larvae feed on Possum Grape Vine (*Cissus verticillata*) |
| NOTE | A charismatic and colorful baridine species, thought to have been inadvertently imported into Florida through trade in live plants or plant products |

**ADULT LENGTH**
³⁄₁₆–¹⁄₄ in
(4.5–7 mm)

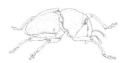

622

*EURHINUS MAGNIFICUS*
# EURHINUS MAGNIFICUS
GYLLENHAL, 1836

Actual size

This stunning weevil belongs to the distinctive genus *Eurhinus*, whose members have a metallic appearance. All developmental life stages of *Eurhinus magnificus* are associated with the Possum Grape Vine (*Cissus verticillata*). A gall is induced by the female at the site of oviposition on the stems of the host vine. The larvae complete five instars within this gall before pupating. Minor damage is caused to the host plant, including loss of the affected stem. This weevil has become inadvertently established in southern Florida, with the first records dating back to 2002. It is unknown if it finds other related species of vine, such as cultivated grapes (*Vitis* spp.), to be suitable hosts.

## RELATED SPECIES

*Eurhinus* includes 23 species from the tropical regions of America. All are metallic and brilliantly colored. *Eurhinus magnificus* is very similar in color to *E. festivus*, *E. cupripes*, and *E. yucatecus*. The differences among these species lie in the shape and pubescence of an abdominal depression and structures of the male genitalia. *Eurhinus magnificus* has been described at least six times as different species, five by a single author.

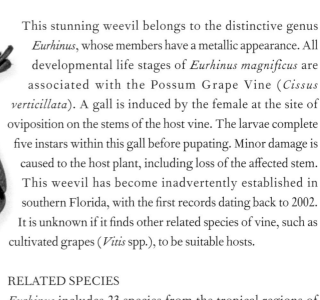

**Eurhinus magnificus** adults are brilliant, metallic blue-green with areas of metallic cupreous red on the head, anteriorly on the pronotum, the humeri and apices of the elytra, and proximal areas of the legs. Coloration is variable. The weevil is relatively large and robust, with obvious sharp humeral angles. Punctations are not evident, except for those along the elytral striae. The rostrum is roughly the size of the pronotum.

| | |
|---|---|
| FAMILY | Curculionidae |
| SUBFAMILY | Baridinae |
| DISTRIBUTION | Neotropical: French Guiana, Peru, Panama, Costa Rica, Bolivia |
| MACROHABITAT | Forest |
| MICROHABITAT | Adults are usually found on herbaceous plants; larvae are unknown |
| FEEDING HABITS | Unknown |
| NOTE | The adult is a remarkably armored and colored weevil, with sharply pointed spines on the elytra that can be painful if it is not handled carefully |

ADULT LENGTH
³/₁₆ – ¼ in
(5–6 mm)

*PTERACANTHUS SMIDTII*

# PTERACANTHUS SMIDTII

(FABRICIUS, 1801)

623

Actual size

More than 60 species in five beetle families occurring in the Neotropical Realm share a similar unusual color pattern, which is thought to be a form of fly (Diptera) mimicry. In these beetles the head and anterior portion of the prothorax is generally bright red, the rest of the prothorax and basal part of elytra is entirely black, and the apical half of the elytra is more or less uniformly golden-yellow to pale gray. The co-occurring, abundant, understory lauxaniid fly *Xenochaetina polita* is hypothesized to be the model that adults of *Pteracanthus smidtii* mimic. Evolutionary-selection pressures that led to this stunning mimicry complex between flies and beetles are not well understood.

## RELATED SPECIES

The diverse subfamily Baridinae consists of approximately 550 genera in ten tribes. *Pteracanthus* is a monotypic genus belonging to the largely Neotropical tribe Ambatini. Scientists believe that the current arrangement of tribes in the Baridinae is rather meaningless and that much more work is needed to elucidate the relationships of genera and species.

**Pteracanthus smidtii** is a spiny, medium-size, mostly black weevil with a bright red head and anterior half of the pronotum. The elytra have four large, broad, acutely pointed spines, two emerging near the base (directed laterally) and two near the apex (directed posteriorly). The abdomen is covered with bright white scales ventrally, as is the rostrum. A small, sharp tooth is present on the ventral edge of each femur.

| FAMILY | Curculionidae |
|---|---|
| SUBFAMILY | Ceutorhynchinae |
| DISTRIBUTION | Palearctic and Nearctic: native to the western Palearctic; introduced intentionally to Canada |
| MACROHABITAT | Pastureland, open fields |
| MICROHABITAT | Roots and shoots of plants in the family Boraginaceae |
| FEEDING HABITS | Roots and shoots of Houndstongue (*Cynoglossum officinale*) and other Boraginaceae |
| NOTE | Introduced to Canada for the biological control of Houndstongue |

**ADULT LENGTH**
⅛ –³⁄₁₆ in
(3–4 mm)

624

*MOGULONES CRUCIFER*
# MOGULONES CRUCIFER
(PALLAS, 1771)

Actual size

This robust, compact shoot- and root-feeder was introduced to Canada in 1997 to assist in the biological control of Houndstongue (*Cynoglossum officinale*), a Eurasian weed accidentally introduced more than 100 years ago through contaminated seed. The weed is found in pasture and rangeland over most of North America and is highly toxic to livestock. While primarily associated with Houndstongue, *Mogulones crucifer* also feeds on other species of *Cynoglossum* and *Solenanthus*. The deliberate collection, transportation, and release of this weevil in the United States is a federal crime, because of the risk it poses to native Boraginaceae, some of which are rare and endangered.

### RELATED SPECIES

*Mogulones* contains 67 species, all of which are associated with Boraginaceae. The majority of the species are found in the Mediterranean region. The genus belongs to the Ceutorhynchini, the most diverse tribe (with approximately 70 genera) in the subfamily Ceutorhynchinae. *Mogulonoides* resembles *Mogulones* but the two genera differ in characteristics of their elytra, and by the size and shape of toothlike setae on their front tibiae.

**Mogulones crucifer** is an oval-shaped, dark-colored weevil with white pubescence mainly on the ventral side and the elytra. White scales on the elytra form a distinct cross-shaped pattern, hence the species name *crucifer*. The rostrum is almost as long as the pronotum. The pronotum is broadest posteriorly, where it meets the elytra. The widest part of the weevil is near the middle of the elytra.

| FAMILY | Curculionidae |
| --- | --- |
| SUBFAMILY | Conoderinae |
| DISTRIBUTION | Australian: Papua New Guinea (Huon Gulf) |
| MACROHABITAT | Rainforest |
| MICROHABITAT | Dead trees, logs |
| FEEDING HABITS | Phytophagous |
| NOTE | A rare case of a beetle that superficially looks like a spider |

ADULT LENGTH
¹¹⁄₁₆–¾ in
(17–19 mm)

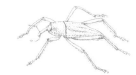

*ARACHNOBAS CAUDATUS*
# SPIDER WEEVIL
(HELLER, 1915)

625

*Arachnobas caudatus* superficially resembles a spider, as its genus and common names suggest. Species in *Arachnobas* are generally slow-moving and tend to drop and play dead when disturbed. They usually occur on dead trees or logs with large, leafy lichens, mosses, and/or fungi, and it is hypothesized that their long legs have evolved to navigate this terrain. The fringe of setae running along the legs of males of *A. caudatus* and related species is longer than on the legs of females, which points to the possible usage of the legs for communication between mates before and/or during copulation, although this has yet to be demonstrated.

RELATED SPECIES
The Papuan region endemic *Arachnobas* includes approximately 60 known species with possibly many more waiting to be described. *Arachnobas* and *Caenochira* from New Guinea are included in Arachnopodini, one of 15 tribes in Conoderinae. *Caenochira* includes only one species, *C. doriae*, which has been challenging to classify within Curculionidae and whose current placement in Arachnopodini is suspect.

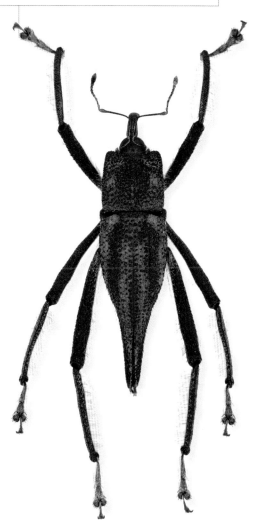

**The Spider Weevil** is black with lighter-colored areas on the pronotum and elytra. It has an elongate body and long, slender, setose legs, giving it a spider-like appearance. The body is widest at the junction where the pronotum and elytra meet. The legs are equal in length and longer than the body. The rostrum is about as long as the pronotum.

Actual size

| FAMILY | Curculionidae |
|---|---|
| SUBFAMILY | Conoderinae |
| DISTRIBUTION | Neotropical: Central and South America |
| MACROHABITAT | Forests |
| MICROHABITAT | Adults are found on leaf surfaces; larvae are found in pods, buds, and possibly stems |
| FEEDING HABITS | Feeds on Pigeon Pea (*Cajanus cajan*); also on *Canavalia*, *Dolichos*, and *Phaseolus* in the family Fabaceae |
| NOTE | This charismatic weevil is a pest of Pigeon Pea |

ADULT LENGTH
³⁄₁₆ in
(3.5–4.2 mm)

*COPTURUS AURIVILLIANUS*
# CLOWN WEEVIL
(HELLER, 1895)

626

This attractive tricolored species belongs to a group of weevils that as larvae bore into wood, thus carving galleries into the branches or trunk of their host plant. In some cases, the damage and infestation may lead to the death of the host plant. Weevils in this and related tribes are active during the day and are readily encountered moving about in a peculiar short, quick, nervous series of movements on the leaf surface. The Clown Weevil is considered a pest in Peru of the high-protein legume commonly known as Pigeon Pea (*Cajanus cajan*). Oviposition and larval development take place in the pods and buds of the host.

RELATED SPECIES
*Copturus* is included in the tribe Lechriopini, which contains 19 genera. It is restricted to the New World and contains approximately 50 species, with a large number awaiting description. In Mexico, the related Avocado Branch Weevil (*Copturus aguacate*) is a serious pest of Avocado (*Persea americana*), causing foliar damage and death of branches or entire trees from wood-boring activities.

Actual size

**The Clown Weevil** is a small seed-shaped weevil that is covered in broad, flattened black, red, and cream to white scales. The head and prothorax have red scales with black spots medially and laterally, although the bright red scales often appear faded on preserved individuals. The rostrum, legs, and most of the elytra are black. White scales cover most of the ventral surface and form six spots on the elytra. The eyes are large, encompassing almost the entire head dorsally.

| FAMILY | Curculionidae |
|---|---|
| SUBFAMILY | Cossoninae |
| DISTRIBUTION | Nearctic: Canada (southern Ontario and Quebec), USA |
| MACROHABITAT | Forest floor |
| MICROHABITAT | Under bark or leaf litter, or in rotting wood |
| FEEDING HABITS | Wood-feeding |
| NOTE | A small weevil, often encrusted with dirt |

ADULT LENGTH
³⁄₁₆ in
(3.5–4.5 mm)

*ACAMPTUS RIGIDUS*

# ACAMPTUS RIGIDUS

LECONTE, 1876

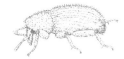

627

*Acamptus rigidus* is commonly found in large numbers in rotten wood, under bark, or in forest litter. It has been found in association with *Populus* species, but may also occur on other tree species. Adults resemble small pieces of bark or rotten wood and may be easily overlooked by the casual observer. As with other cossonines, all developmental stages can typically be found feeding and living together within the wood. The related species *A. cancellatus* has been unintentionally introduced to the South Pacific islands of Samoa and Fiji from tropical America.

## RELATED SPECIES

Eight genera are included in the Acamptini. Two of these, *Acamptella* and *Trachodisca*, are from Nepal, *Pseudocamptopsis* is from Tanzania, and the remainder (*Acamptus*, *Acamptopsis*, *Choerorrhynchus*, *Menares*, and *Prionarthrus*) are from the Americas. *Acamptus* includes seven species. *Acamptus rigidus* may be confused with the sympatric *A. texanus*, but features of the antennae differ between the two species.

Actual size

**Acamptus rigidus** adults are elongate, brown weevils with white mottling, and have broad, erect scales. Some individuals may be encrusted with dirt. The rostrum is short and rests on the front coxae in a ventral channel. The tibiae are stout, sinuate on the inner side, and strongly hooked at the tip. The tarsi are not dilated or spongy beneath, and the antennal club is pubescent only near the tip. Species in the genus are highly variable. As with other cossonines, the end of the hind tibiae of this species has a large hook-like tooth and lacks an apical comb of setae.

| FAMILY | Curculionidae |
|---|---|
| SUBFAMILY | Cryptorhynchinae |
| DISTRIBUTION | Neotropical: Central America |
| MACROHABITAT | Tropical forest |
| MICROHABITAT | Forest floor; larvae develop inside fallen logs |
| FEEDING HABITS | Adult feeding habits are uncertain; larvae feed on decaying wood |
| NOTE | The enlarged tibiae of males are used in combat |

**ADULT LENGTH**
³⁄₈–⁷⁄₁₆ in
(10–11 mm)

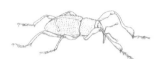

628

*MACROMERUS BICINCTUS*
# MACROMERUS BICINCTUS
CHAMPION, 1905

Actual size

The elongate, swollen front tibiae of *Macromerus bicinctus* males are used for signaling and as weapons during competition with other males for females. During fights, the front legs are used as clubs to deliver forceful blows against opponents. The female drills holes into a log for oviposition, and as she is doing so males usually attempt to copulate with her; this is when male fighting also occurs. Copulation is short, lasting 5–28 seconds, although the male usually remains with the female until she begins oviposition.

RELATED SPECIES

The genus *Macromerus* includes approximately 40 described species distributed throughout tropical America. Two subgenera are currently recognized: *Macromerus* and *Neomacromerus*. The genus is classified in one of the largest subtribes in the Coleoptera, the Cryptorhynchina, which includes at least 205 genera globally. Species in this genus are mainly separated by their color pattern as well as differences in the male legs.

**Macromerus bicinctus** is a moderate-size black weevil. The males have modified elongate front legs, with front femora that are almost as long as the elytra, and front tibiae that are long, curved, and swollen near the apex. The pronotum is deeply punctate and the elytra have large punctures arranged longitudinally. Two narrow, transverse reddish-yellow bands of scales decorate the elytra.

| FAMILY | Curculionidae |
|---|---|
| SUBFAMILY | Cyclominae |
| DISTRIBUTION | Australian: Australia (Western Australia) |
| MACROHABITAT | Ground-dwelling |
| MICROHABITAT | Adults crawl on the ground; larvae live under the soil surface |
| FEEDING HABITS | Larvae feed on roots, and adults feed on stems, of *Lepidobolus preissianus* |
| NOTE | A remarkable armor-plated, ground-dwelling weevil |

ADULT LENGTH
1⅛–1¼ in
(29–32 mm)

*GAGATOPHORUS DRACO*
# GAGATOPHORUS DRACO
(MACLEAY, 1826)

629

The Australian endemic tribe Amycterini contains weevils that are large and robust, with a very short rostrum. The female of the well-armored, terricolous *Gagatophorus draco* lays her eggs in the soil with the help of a specialized ovipositor that has a pair of strong, glabrous, claw-like processes called styli. As with other species in the tribe, the larva lives in the soil and feeds on roots of its host plant, in this case *Lepidobolus preissianus*. The very prominent spikes on the dorsal surface of adults presumably provide this beetle with camouflage or protection from predators.

## RELATED SPECIES

*Gagatophorus* is one of 39 genera in the tribe Amycterini, which includes approximately 400 species. *Gagatophorus* contains six species, all endemic to Western Australia. The species largely resemble each other in being tuberculate and generally black, but they are distinguished by differences in the placement of tubercles on the pronotum and elytra, as well as the overall shape of the prothorax.

Actual size

**Gagatophorus draco** is a large, shiny, and remarkably well-armored weevil, whose dorsal surface is covered with spikes, giving it the appearance of a medieval spiked club. The weevil is black with minute patches of gray pubescence or scales. The head has a wide, deep groove and the rostrum is very short. The species is flightless and the elytra are fused. The prothorax is elongate and robust, and the disk is decorated with prominent ridges and tubercles. The elytra are granulose between the rows of tubercles, and toward the end there are six or seven tubercles on each side.

| FAMILY | Curculionidae |
|---|---|
| SUBFAMILY | Entiminae |
| DISTRIBUTION | Australian: New Guinea and adjacent islands |
| MACROHABITAT | Tropical forest, plantations |
| MICROHABITAT | Adults are found on leaf surfaces; larvae are found with roots of host plants |
| FEEDING HABITS | Phytophagous; recorded host plants include species in the families Urticaceae, Euphorbiaceae, and Selaginellaceae |
| NOTE | This genus includes some of the most colorful and charismatic species of all weevils |

**ADULT LENGTH**
⅞ in
(21–23 mm)

630

*EUPHOLUS SCHOENHERRII*
# EUPHOLUS SCHOENHERRII
(GUÉRIN-MÉNEVILLE, 1838)

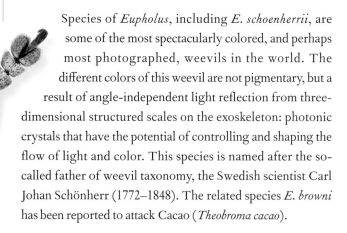

Species of *Eupholus*, including *E. schoenherrii*, are some of the most spectacularly colored, and perhaps most photographed, weevils in the world. The different colors of this weevil are not pigmentary, but a result of angle-independent light reflection from three-dimensional structured scales on the exoskeleton: photonic crystals that have the potential of controlling and shaping the flow of light and color. This species is named after the so-called father of weevil taxonomy, the Swedish scientist Carl Johan Schönherr (1772–1848). The related species *E. browni* has been reported to attack Cacao (*Theobroma cacao*).

## RELATED SPECIES
*Eupholus* belongs to the tribe Eupholini, which includes six additional genera. The entire tribe is restricted to the Oriental and Australian realms, with *Rhinoscapha* being most widespread and *Eupholus* occurring in New Guinea and the Maluku Islands (Moluccas). *Eupholus* contains approximately 60 species and subspecies, including four subspecies in *E. schoenherrii*: *E. s. schoenherrii*, *E. s. petiti*, *E. s. mimikanus*, and *E. s. semicoeruleus*.

**Eupholus schoenherrii** is a brilliant metallic blue to green weevil with five transverse black elytral bands, where scales are absent. The rostrum is relatively long—almost the same length as the pronotum—and the pronotum is narrower anteriorly. The antennae are relatively long, and the last three antennomeres are black. The tarsi are broad and prominent.

Actual size

| | |
|---|---|
| FAMILY | Curculionidae |
| SUBFAMILY | Entiminae |
| DISTRIBUTION | Australian: mainland New Guinea |
| MACROHABITAT | Moss forests or alpine shrubbery on mountains 6,600–8,200 ft (2,000–2,500 m) |
| MICROHABITAT | On leaves |
| FEEDING HABITS | Leaves of woody plants such as *Rhododendron* spp. |
| NOTE | This weevil has a close association with lichens (*Anaptychia* and *Parmelia* spp.), which grow on its dorsal surface, resulting in the formation of a living "lichen garden." It is listed as "Vulnerable" by the International Union for Conservation of Nature |

ADULT LENGTH
⅞–1¼ in
(23–31 mm)

*GYMNOPHOLUS LICHENIFER*
# LICHEN WEEVIL
GRESSITT, 1966

631

This curious weevil carries on its back a small community of organisms, such as lichens, nematodes, diatoms, rotifers, psocids, and phytophagous mites. Both the weevil and the lichen benefit and may depend on each other for survival. While the lichen obtains from the weevil a suitable, presumably protective, substrate for anchoring and nutrients, it in turn offers the weevil camouflage. A dense covering of lichens grows on the fused elytra and pronotum of this flightless weevil. Lichen Weevils are long-lived, some living longer than five years. Owing to deforestation of its natural habitat, this species is considered vulnerable to extinction.

## RELATED SPECIES
Seventy-one species are currently included in *Gymnopholus*. At least 13 families of autotrophic organisms, such as fungi, algae, lichens, and liverworts have been observed living on beetles of the subgenus *Symbiopholus*, which includes *G. lichenifer*.

**The Lichen Weevil** is large and black with reddish-brown femora. The dorsum is considerably rough and usually has a dense covering of lichen growth, including sometimes fruiting areas and mites and psocopterans concealed in pits and folds. The head, including the elongate and apically widening rostrum, is longer than the almost square prothorax. The disk of the pronotum has a prominent tubercle on each side. Specialized scales are present on the elytra.

Actual size

| FAMILY | Curculionidae |
|---|---|
| SUBFAMILY | Hyperinae |
| DISTRIBUTION | Palearctic and Nearctic: native to the Mediterranean region; introduced to southwestern USA |
| MACROHABITAT | Riparian tamarisk (*Tamarix* spp.) groves |
| MICROHABITAT | Generally on the leaves of *Tamarix* spp. |
| FEEDING HABITS | Adults probably feed on leaves and branches of the host plant based on data from related species; larvae feed externally on the host plant |
| NOTE | Pupation takes place in a loosely woven cocoon |

ADULT LENGTH
⅛–³⁄₁₆ in
(3–4 mm)

632

*CONIATUS SPLENDIDULUS*
# SPLENDID TAMARISK WEEVIL
(FABRICIUS, 1781)

Actual size

This charismatic Mediterranean weevil species feeds on tamarisk (*Tamarix* spp.), highly invasive small trees that have displaced native willows and cottonwoods in the southwestern USA. Only the Tamarisk Leaf Beetle (*Diorhabda elongata*) has officially been released in the United States for the biological control of *Tamarix* species, but the Splendid Tamarisk Weevil, while not authorized for release, has recently been found in *Tamarix* stands in the southwest. Larvae in the subfamily Hyperinae are unusual among weevils in that they feed externally on their host plant. Pupation takes place in a perforated, rounded silken enclosure attached to the host leaf or stem.

## RELATED SPECIES

*Coniatus* is included in the tribe Hyperini, along with 18 other genera (e.g., *Adonus*, *Brachypera*, *Hypera*). Twelve species are included in the genus *Coniatus*, all of which are believed to be associated with species of *Tamarix*. Two species, *C. repandus* and *C. tamarisci*, have been considered for release to help control *Tamarix* in the United States. *Coniatus splendidulus* belongs in the subgenus *Bagoides*. The size of the rostrum and the eyes, as well as differences in coloration, are helpful to separate the species.

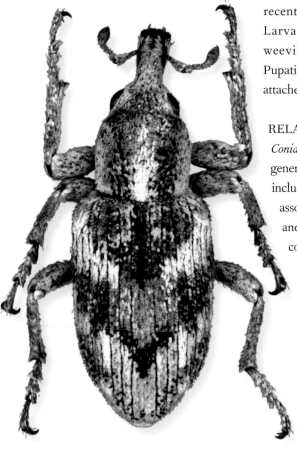

**The Splendid Tamarisk Weevil** is multicolored, with scales of various shades of green, yellow, pink, and black. The elytra have two black arrow-like bands, one close to the scutellum and the other near the middle. The antennae emerge near the middle of the rostrum, which is about as long as the pronotum. The eyes are vertical-oval and located near the base of the rostrum.

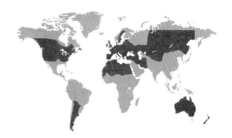

| FAMILY | Curculionidae |
|---|---|
| SUBFAMILY | Lixinae |
| DISTRIBUTION | Palearctic, Nearctic, Neotropical, and Australian: native to Europe and western Asia; introduced to Canada (British Columbia, Alberta, Saskatchewan, Ontario, Quebec, Nova Scotia), USA, South America (Argentina), Australia, New Zealand |
| MACROHABITAT | Grasslands, roadsides, riverbanks, disturbed areas |
| MICROHABITAT | Thistle flowers (*Carduus*, *Cirsium*, and *Silybum* spp.) |
| FEEDING HABITS | Feeds on *Carduus*, *Cirsium*, and *Silybum* spp. |
| NOTE | Introduced intentionally for the biological control of invasive thistles |

ADULT LENGTH
³⁄₁₆–⁵⁄₁₆ in
(5–8 mm)

*RHINOCYLLUS CONICUS*

# THISTLE-HEAD WEEVIL

(FRÖLICH, 1792)

633

The Thistle-head Weevil was introduced to North America in 1968 for the biological control of the noxious, non-native Nodding Plumeless Thistle (*Carduus nutans*), found in pastures, rangelands, and croplands, and along highways. The life cycle of this weevil is tightly synchronized with the development of its host, therefore this biological control program was very successful, reducing thistle by 80–95 percent in some sites. The female oviposits almost 100 eggs on the flower bracts and covers them with chewed plant material. The legless larva feeds through the bracts into the buds and receptacle, preventing the production of viable seeds. Unfortunately, *Rhinocyllus conicus* has been found also attacking native and sometimes rare and threatened *Cirsium* species in North America.

## RELATED SPECIES

The genus *Rhinocyllus*, which includes nine species native to Eurasia, is classified in the subfamily Lixinae along with several related genera such as *Bangasternus*, *Larinus*, and *Nefis*, which was described in 2013. Characters to separate the species in this group of weevils include the shape and length of the rostrum, as well as patterns of setation on the body.

Actual size

**The Thistle-head Weevil** is a medium-size oval black weevil with mottled yellow and black setae on its dorsal surface. The rostrum is relatively short, less than the length of the pronotum, and is ridged laterally. The antennae are short and located near the apex of the rostrum. The antennal club has shorter, more compact pubescence. The elytra are parallel-sided and about three times the length of the prothorax.

| FAMILY | Curculionidae |
|---|---|
| SUBFAMILY | Molytinae |
| DISTRIBUTION | Nearctic: North America |
| MACROHABITAT | Conifer forests |
| MICROHABITAT | On tree leaders in the forest canopy |
| FEEDING HABITS | Adults feed on the inner bark and cambium of their host; larvae develop in the terminal leader of their host, where they feed on phloem |
| NOTE | A significant North American pest of young spruce (*Picea* spp.) and pine (*Pinus* spp.) trees |

**ADULT LENGTH**
³⁄₁₆–¼ in
(4–6 mm)

*PISSODES STROBI*
# WHITE PINE WEEVIL
(PECK, 1817)

634

Actual size

This North American weevil is a serious pest of young conifers, including Eastern White Pine (*Pinus strobus*) and Sitka, White, and Norway spruces (*Picea* spp.). The adults, which can live for up to four years, overwinter in the leaf litter. The adult female chews a cavity in the phloem of the host plant, oviposits, and subsequently plugs the hole with a fecal pellet. The larva feeds on the inner bark and cambium in the terminal leader of the host and then moves down the stem, destroying the growth of the previous two to four years. The related Lodgepole Terminal Weevil (*Pissodes terminalis*) causes damage to Lodgepole (*Pinus contorta*) and Jack Pine (*Pinus banksiana*) in western North America.

## RELATED SPECIES

The genus *Pissodes* is broadly distributed in the northern hemisphere, with 18 species in the Palearctic Realm (e.g., *P. castaneus*, *P. harcyniae*, and *P. pini*) and 29 in North and Central America (e.g., *P. nemorensis*, *P. fiskei*, and *P. rotundatus*). The distribution of the genus follows that of their principal host trees in the family Pinaceae. Because of the economic importance of this group, several characters are often used to differentiate the species, such as the morphological structures of adult and immature stages, as well as molecular data.

**The White Pine Weevil** is small, oval, and dark brown, with irregular brown and white scales on the elytra, pronotum, and legs, giving it a lichenous appearance. The rostrum is narrow and about as long as the pronotum, with the medium-size antennae emerging almost in the middle. The elytra are twice the length of the pronotum. The legs are proportional and all of equal size.

| FAMILY | Curculionidae |
|---|---|
| SUBFAMILY | Molytinae |
| DISTRIBUTION | Australian, Nearctic: native to Australia; accidentally introduced with cycads to some other areas (e.g., USA: California) |
| MACROHABITAT | Dry, open areas |
| MICROHABITAT | On cycads (e.g., *Macrozamia macdonnellii*) |
| FEEDING HABITS | Feeds on caudices and trunks of cycads |
| NOTE | A pest of cycads in some areas, with an interesting taxonomic history |

ADULT LENGTH
³⁄₁₆–¼ in
(5–6 mm)

*SIRATON INTERNATUS*
# SIRATON INTERNATUS
(PASCOE, 1870)

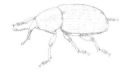

635

This species bores into cycad caudices (swollen stems) and trunks, and generally attacks weakened or stressed cycads in gardens and nurseries. The weevils, which have been transported over long distances concealed and protected within the thick trunks of cycads, have on occasion become serious cycad pests (e.g., in California). This species was treated and described as native to central Italy and not recognized as an invasive species there until recently, when it was identified as a well-known Australian cycad weevil.

### RELATED SPECIES

One other species is included in the genus: *Siraton roei*. Both *Siraton* species resemble *Demyrsus meleoides*, which has a similar biology. An additional four genera belong in the Australian molytine *Tranes* group: *Howeotranes* (one species), *Milotranes* (two species), *Paratranes* (one species), and *Tranes* (four species). A number of new species await description. The other genera are associated with either Zamiaceae (cycads) or Xanthorrhoeaceae (grasstrees).

Actual size

**Siraton internatus** is medium-size, shiny black weevil. Excluding the rostrum, the body is roughly oval. The rostrum is approximately the size of the prothorax and parallel-sided. The prothorax is slightly narrower than the base of the elytra, with gently arched sides and a notably punctate pronotal disk. The elytral striae are well developed and the interstriate sections rugous.

| FAMILY | Curculionidae |
|---|---|
| SUBFAMILY | Orobitidinae |
| DISTRIBUTION | Neotropical: Paraguay, Argentina |
| MACROHABITAT | Subtropical wet forest |
| MICROHABITAT | Presumably on foliage |
| FEEDING HABITS | Phytophagous |
| NOTE | A rare and bizarre-looking weevil with a hunchbacked appearance that is capable of stridulating |

ADULT LENGTH
⅛ in
(3.1–3.3 mm)

636

*PAROROBITIS GIBBUS*
# PAROROBITIS GIBBUS
KOROTYAEV, O'BRIEN & KONSTANTINOV, 2000

Actual size

Very little is known about the biology of this curious little weevil. It is one among a few weevils that produce sound by striking a narrow stridulatory file under the subapex of the elytra against blade-like ridges on the dorsal surface of abdominal segment 7. Both sexes in this species stridulate, indicating that the sound is produced when the insect is alarmed, or for communication between the sexes before and during mating. Stridulation mechanisms in weevils vary and may have evolved independently several times within the group.

## RELATED SPECIES

Two genera are included in the Orobitidinae: *Orobitis* and *Parorobitis*. The Palearctic *Orobitis* includes just two species, the more broadly distributed *O. cyanea*, which develops in seed capsules of *Viola* spp.; and *O. nigrina*, which occurs only in the Balkans. *Parorobitis* also includes two species, both from southern South America: *P. gibbus* and *P. minutus*. The two species can be distinguished based on color pattern and several genitalic characters of the male and female.

**Parorobitis gibbus** is a small, rounded weevil with a hunchbacked appearance and two well-developed pronotal swellings, hence the species name *gibbus*, meaning "hump." The dorsum is densely covered with elongate white and brown scales, these darkest where the pronotum and elytra meet. The head capsule is small and the rostrum is almost as long as the pronotum. The antennae are inserted on the rostrum one-third of the distance along from the head, and the antennal club is short and oval.

| FAMILY | Curculionidae |
|---|---|
| SUBFAMILY | Scolytinae |
| DISTRIBUTION | Palearctic, Afrotropical, Neotropical, Oriental, and Pacific: native to Africa; spread through introduction to most coffee-producing regions of the world |
| MACROHABITAT | Tropical forests, plantations, orchards |
| MICROHABITAT | Fruiting bodies of possibly only coffee (*Coffea* spp.) |
| FEEDING HABITS | Adult feeding habits are unknown; larvae feed within coffee berries |
| NOTE | The most devastating insect coffee-pest worldwide |

ADULT LENGTH
¹⁄₃₂–¹⁄₁₆ in
(1.2–1.8 mm)

*HYPOTHENEMUS HAMPEI*
# COFFEE BERRY BORER
(FERRARI, 1867)

637

Actual size

As the common name aptly suggests, females of this tiny beetle bore galleries into coffee berries to lay their eggs. These galleries may be lined with fungi that have evolved symbiotic associations with this species of ambrosia beetles. Upon hatching, the larvae feed within the coffee berry, causing extensive damage. Mating occurs within the berry among siblings shortly after eclosion. The long-lived females emerge from the berry, already inseminated, and search for oviposition sites on developing coffee berries. Males have reduced wings and do not fly. The cryptic life history of these beetles makes them very challenging to control. The boring activity of the adults and larvae reduces coffee yield and quality. Resulting lesions to the berry are entry points for secondary bacterial and fungal infections.

### RELATED SPECIES

*Hypothenemus* contains 179 species globally and belongs in the scolytine subdivision of ambrosia beetles. The Coffee Berry Borer (CBB) may be confused with the Black Twig Borer (BTB; *Xylosandrus compactus*) and the Tropical Nut Borer (TNB; *Hypothenemus obscurus*), which may also be found on coffee. These beetles may be distinguished by the morphology of their dorsal setae: BTB has long, thin setae on its dorsum; TNB has broad, round-ended setae; and CBB has rigid, pointed, straight setae.

**The Coffee Berry Borer** is minute and black. The head is marked by a deep, long median groove and the antennae are clubbed. The pronotum is globular and bears anteriorly four (rarely six) coarse teeth and an additional 25 rasp-like teeth on the center. The elytra are smooth and shiny. The body is covered by erect setae, each emerging from strial punctures.

| FAMILY | Curculionidae |
|---|---|
| SUBFAMILY | Scolytinae |
| DISTRIBUTION | Palearctic, Nearctic, Neotropical, and Australian: native to Europe, the Middle East, and northern Africa; accidentally introduced to Canada, USA, Argentina, Brazil, and Australia |
| MACROHABITAT | Temperate and boreal forests |
| MICROHABITAT | Phloem of primarily elm (*Ulmus* spp.) |
| FEEDING HABITS | Phloeophagous (feeds on phloem) |
| NOTE | Accidentally introduced to several countries, and vector of the Dutch elm disease fungus |

ADULT LENGTH
¹⁄₁₆–⅛ in
(1.9–3.1 mm)

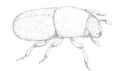

638

*SCOLYTUS MULTISTRIATUS*
# SMALLER EUROPEAN ELM BARK BEETLE
(MARSHAM, 1802)

Actual size

This species is the main culprit for the spread of Dutch elm disease, acting as a vector for the fungus *Ophiostoma novo-ulmi*, which causes the disease, and resulting in the almost total demise of American elms (*Ulmus* spp.). A European beetle, it was first recorded in 1909 in Boston, Massachusetts, and has since spread across all continental US and southern Canada. Spores of *O. novo-ulmi* are transmitted to the phloem of healthy trees in the spring by the emerging adults after they have overwintered as larvae. The female attacks unhealthy trees and constructs a uniramous gallery under the bark, from which larval galleries radiate almost perpendicularly.

### RELATED SPECIES

Approximately 124 species of *Scolytus* are known. In North America, the genera *Scolytopsis* and *Cnemonyx* are most similar to *Scolytus*. *Scolytus multistriatus* greatly resembles the European Banded Elm Bark Beetle (*S. schevryrewi*), but may be distinguished by the shape of the male genitalia.

**The Smaller European Elm Bark Beetle** is small, dark reddish brown, and shiny. It is cylindrical in shape, with a noticeable large median ventral knob arising from the anterior part of abdominal ventrite 2 that points toward the rear. The presence ventrally of small tubercles on the posterior sides of the margin of abdominal segments 2–4 is also a diagnostic character for this species. The eyes are long and narrow. The prothorax is slightly shorter than the elytra. The abdomen visibly ascends in lateral view.

| FAMILY | Curculionidae |
|---|---|
| SUBFAMILY | Platypodinae |
| DISTRIBUTION | Australian: Australia (New South Wales and Victoria) |
| MACROHABITAT | Forests |
| MICROHABITAT | Bores into the wood of healthy, undamaged *Eucalyptus* trees |
| FEEDING HABITS | Feeds on ambrosia fungi |
| NOTE | Displays eusocial behavior, which is rare among beetles |

ADULT LENGTH
¼ in
(5.5–7 mm)

*AUSTROPLATYPUS INCOMPERTUS*

# AUSTROPLATYPUS INCOMPERTUS

(SCHEDL, 1968)

639

Actual size

This ambrosia beetle is currently the only known eusocial insect outside of termites and ants, bees, and wasps. The species forms large cooperative colonies of overlapping generations in live eucalyptus trees, where a single egg-laying female and her brood are tended and protected by unfertilized female workers. All ambrosia weevils have a nutritional symbiotic relationship with ambrosia fungi, which they carry with them in mycangia, or specialized structures; in the case of this species, the mycangia are on the female prothorax. The sterile working caste cultivates ambrosia gardens along a complicated tunnel system within their colony.

## RELATED SPECIES

*Austroplatypus* includes a single species and is classified in the tribe Platypodini of the subfamily Platypodinae. It has a three-segmented maxillary palp which was incorrectly described as a four-segmented palp in the original description of the genus. Platypodini includes 24 genera worldwide and the subfamily contains approximately 300 species. These beetles are collectively called ambrosia beetles. The common name, however, is also used for a number of independently evolved fungus-farming weevils in the subfamily Scolytinae.

**Austroplatypus incompertus** adults are elongate, cylindrical, brownish-red weevils with short, strongly clubbed antennae. The species is sexually dimorphic: the females are relatively large, and have mycangia on the pronotum, ridges basally along the suture of the elytra, and a spiny, abrupt elytral declivity; the males are smaller, they lack mycangia, and the elytral apices and base are simple.

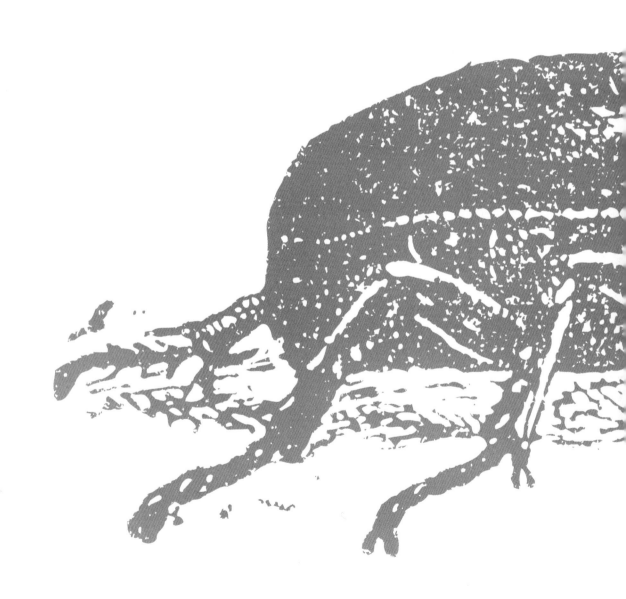

# APPENDICES

# GLOSSARY

**Aedeagus** Male genital structure.

**Algivorous** Feeding on algae.

**Angiosperm** Flowering plant.

**Antennation** To touch with the antennae.

**Antennomere** Antennal article.

**Aposematism** The use of a distinctive color pattern or behavior by a species to warn a predator of its distastefulness or toxicity.

**Apterous** Lacking flight wings.

**Asperate** Rough or uneven.

**Australian Realm** One of the seven biogeographical areas of the world, covering Australia, New Guinea, New Zealand, and surrounding islands.

**Batesian mimicry** Form of mimicry in which a harmless species has evolved to resemble a harmful species in order to avoid predation (cf. Müllerian mimicry).

**Bidentate** Having two teeth or teethlike processes.

**Binominal name** Formal species name comprising two parts, the genus name and the species name, e.g., *Goliathus regius*.

**Biofilm** Group of microorganisms stuck to one another to form a thin layer.

**Biogeographical region** Terrestrial region of the Earth characterized by the species it contains. The seven biogeographical regions used in this book are the Nearctic, Neotropical, Palearctic, Afrotropical, Oriental, Australian, and Pacific realms.

**Bioluminescence** Emission of light by a living organism, e.g., a firefly.

**Biomimetics** Imitation of nature for the purpose of solving complex human challenges, e.g., the bombardier beetles' spray mechanism inspired the creation of micromist-spray technology.

**Bipectinate** Appearing like a bird's feather, with each segment bearing two prolonged extensions.

**Biramous** Having two branches, as in an appendage that splits into two, each branch being made up of a line of segments (cf. uniramous).

**Brachypterous** Having reduced or rudimentary flight wings.

**Bryophagous** Feeding on mosses.

**Callus (pl. calli)** A swelling—an antennal callus is a swelling at the front of the head above the antennal attachment.

**Cantharidin** Defensive chemical secreted by beetles in the families Meloidae and Oedemeridae that causes the skin of humans to blister.

**Capitate** Having a swollen head-like tip.

**Caraboid larva** Somewhat resembling the larva of a ground beetle in the family Carabidae, i.e., highly mobile with long legs and a prognathous head.

**Carina (pl. carinae)** Raised ridge or keel.

**Cerambycoid larva** Somewhat resembling the larva of a ground beetle in the family Cerambycidae, i.e., with a parallel-sided, somewhat flattened or cylindrical, distinctly segmented body.

**Cervical sclerites** Paired plates between the posterior head margin and anterior pronotum margin.

**Chorion** Outer shell of an egg.

**Clavate** Club-shaped; a clavate antenna thickens gradually toward the tip.

**Clypeus** Shield-like plate at the front of the head between the labrum and the frons.

**Coleopterist** Person who studies beetles (order Coleoptera).

**Commensalism** Relationship between two organisms in which one benefits and the other receives neither benefit nor harm.

**Compound eye** Eye that is made up of numerous separate visual receptors called ommatidia, each containing a lens and light-sensitive cells.

**Conglobulation** Ability to roll up into a ball.

**Connate** Fused or joined to form a single unit.

**Cosmopolitan** Occurring worldwide.

**Costa (pl. costae)** A rib-like structure.

**Coxa (pl. coxae)** First, basal section of the leg.

**Crepuscular** Active mainly at dawn or dusk.

**Crypsis** Ability to remain undetected, either through behavior or camouflage.

**Curculionoid larva** Somewhat resembling the larva of the superfamily Curculionoidea, i.e., thorax without legs, and body unpigmented and soft.

**Denticle** Toothlike projection.

**Detritivore** Feeding on detritus. Detritivores often play an important ecological role, acting as decomposers.

**Diapause** Period when growth slows or stops as a result of a change in environmental conditions, e.g., a drop in temperature.

**Diurnal** Active during the day.

**Dorsal** Relating to the dorsum.

**Dorsum** Back or upper surface (cf. ventrum).

**Eclosion** Emergence of a larva from an egg, or an adult from a pupal case.

**Elytral disk** Dorsal surface of the elytra, sometimes flattened.

**Elytral suture** Longitudinal midline along which the closed elytra meet.

**Elytron (pl. elytra)** Hardened forewing modified to act as a protective wingcase for the hind wing in most beetles.

**Endemic** Found only in a specific geographic location.

**Entomophagous** Feeding on insects.

**Endocarina** Raised ridge or keel on the inner side of a structure.

**Epicranium** Upper part of the head.

**Epipleuron (pl. epipleura)** Outer, downward-folding edge of an elytron.

**Estivation** Period of dormancy or torpor to avoid stress during hot, dry summers.

**Eusociality** The highest level of animal sociality, in which the animals cooperate in the care of young and have social divisions of labor, e.g., *Austroplatypus incompertus*.

**Exoskeleton** The external skeleton.

**Exotic** Not native to the region.

**Explanate** Spread out, flattened.

**Falciform** Shaped like a sickle.

**Family** Taxonomic rank above genus and below order (or superfamily). Some families are further divided into subfamilies and tribes.

**Femur (pl. femora)** Third, and usually largest, section of an insect's leg.

**Filiform** Shaped like a filament or thread; usually applied to antennae.

**Flabellate** Shaped like a fan; usually applied to antennae.

**Frass** Excreta of insects; it may be solid or liquid.

**Frontoclypeal suture** Suture or groove between the frons and the clypeus on a beetle's head.

**Fovea** Small pit or groove.

**Frons** Front part of the head above the clypeus and between the eyes.

**Fungivorous** Feeding on fungi; also referred to as mycophagous.

**Funicle** Antennomeres between the club and basal segment, or scape.

**Fynbos** Ecoregion of South Africa's Western Cape province, characterized by wet winters and hot, dry summers, and with a high level of endemism.

**Galea** Modified plate at the outer margin of the maxilla.

**Gena (pl. genae)** Large cheek-like plate on the side of the head behind and below the eye.

**Genal** Relating to the gena.

**Geniculate** Abruptly bent, like a knee; usually applied to antennae.

**Genus (pl. genera)** Taxonomic rank below family and above species, sometimes further divided into subgenera. In a species' scientific name, the genus name forms the first part of the binominal.

**Gibbosity** A bulge or hump.

**Gill** Respiratory organ used for breathing under water in aquatic beetle larvae (see also microtrichial gills).

**Gin-trap** Pinching structure of some beetle pupae, e.g., in the family Tenebrionidae, used as a defensive mechanism.

**Glabrous** Smooth and lacking setae.

**Gular** Relating to the ventral region of the head, or gula.

**Holarctic Realm** The combined Palearctic and Nearctic realms (cf. Nearctic Realm; Palearctic Realm).

**Holometabolism (adj. holometabolous)** A complete metamorphosis, in which the beetle has four stages to its life cycle: the egg, larva, pupa, and adult.

**Holotype** A single physical specimen originally used to describe a species or subspecies.

**Homonym** An identical name used for different taxa. The rules of the International Code for Zoological Nomenclature state that the first usage of the name takes priority, and that taxa ascribed the same name subsequently should be renamed.

**Humerus (pl. humeri)** Outer basal angle of the forewing, or elytron.

**Hydrofuge setae** Water-repelling hair-like setae that surround the bodies of some aquatic Coleoptera that hold a film of air that allows them to breathe underwater (cf. plastron).

**Hydropetric** Relating to the film of water on a rock surface.

**Hypermetamorphosis** A form of holometabolism in which some larval instars differ in appearance, e.g., as seen in blister beetles (family Meloidae).

**Hypertrophication** Abnormal increase in volume.

**Hypognathous** Vertical orientation of the head, with the mouthparts pointing downward (cf. prognathous).

**Impunctate** Smooth and lacking punctation.

**Inquiline** Species that lives in the home of another, forming a commensal relationship with its host, e.g., *Cephaloplectus mus* is an ant (*Formica* spp.) inquiline.

**Instar** Stage between molts of the larva; the first instar is the stage between the egg and first molt.

**Integument** The outer covering or cuticle of the beetle's body.

**International Code of Zoological Nomenclature (ICZN)** Code of rules, governed by the International Commission on Zoological Nomenclature, regulating the scientific naming of animals.

**Invasive** Exotic, or non-native, species that has a negative impact on the environment it has invaded.

**Kairomone** Chemical substance emitted by one species that benefits the receiver but not the emitter, e.g., stressed trees produce ethanol, which attracts ambrosia beetles.

**Labium** Lower "lip" of an insect's mouth.

**Labrum** Upper "lip" of an insect's mouth.

**Lamella (pl. lamellae; adj. lamellate)** Plate-like structure.

**Larva (pl. larvae)** Stage of a holometabolous insect that follows the egg and precedes the pupae.

**Larviform female** Adult female that resembles the larval form of the species, e.g., as seen in some fireflies (Lampyridae).

**Maculate (n. maculation)** Spotted.

**Major male** Large male form of some species, with disproportionately long horns, e.g., *Onthophagus taurus*. Major males engage in aggressive fighting behavior with other major males in competition for females (cf. minor male).

**Malpighian tubules** Kidney-like excretory and osmoregulatory organs that are closed at their distal end and open into the junction between the midgut and hind gut.

**Mandibles** Paired biting jaws of an insect, often modified depending on the food favored by the species. They are also used in attacking and defensive behaviors.

**Maxillae (sing. maxilla)** Paired structure below the mandibles, used to hold and manipulate food during chewing.

**Mentum** Basal part of the labium.

**Mesothorax** Middle (second of three) segment of the thorax to which the middle pair of legs is attached.

**Mesoventrite** Ventral portion of the mesothorax.

**Metathorax** Posterior (third of three) segment of the thorax to which the hind pair of legs is attached.

**Metaventrite** Ventral portion of the metathorax that articulates anteriorly with the mesoventrite and posteriorly with the first abdominal ventrite.

**Metepisternum** Episternum of the mesothorax.

**Microsetose** Bearing very small setae.

**Microtrichial gills** Air pocket used for breathing and trapped within the minute, dense setae (microtrichia) on the integument of an aquatic insect.

**Mine** Feeding tunnel of an insect larva within a leaf or other part of a plant.

**Minor male** Small male form of some species, with reduced horns, e.g., *Onthophagus taurus*. Minor males use sneaking behavior to copulate with females (cf. major male).

**Mola** Grinding part of a beetle's mandibles.

**Moniliform** Shaped like a string of beads; usually applied to antennae.

643

**Monotypic** Taxonomic group with only one member, e.g., a monotypic genus contains only one species.

**Müllerian mimicry** Form of mimicry in which two poisonous species that share a predator, or several predators, have evolved to resemble one another to avoid predation (cf. Batesian mimicry).

**Mycangium (pl. mycangia)** Structure adapted to contain and transport fungal spores, e.g., the pits found in bark beetles.

**Mycophagous** Feeding on fungi; also referred to as fungivorous.

**Myrmecophile** Organism that lives with ants, often sharing their nest.

**Myrmecophagous** Feeding on ants.

**Nearctic Realm** One of the seven biogeographical realms of the world, covering most of North America and Greenland.

**Neoteny (adj. neotenic)** Retention of juvenile characteristics into adulthood.

**Neotropical Realm** One of the seven biogeographical realms of the world, covering Central and South America, and the Caribbean.

**Nidus** A nest.

**Notopleural suture** Suture between the propleuron and pronotum in some beetle groups.

**Ocellus (pl. ocelli)** Small, simple eye with a single lens (cf. compound eye).

**Ocular canthus** Upper or lower extremity of the compound eye. In some beetles the clypeus or genae extend over the eyes, partly or completely dividing them so that the beetle appears to have four eyes.

**Ommatidium (pl. ommatidia)** Individual visual unit of the compound eye.

**Ootheca** Egg mass or egg case.

**Oriental Realm** One of the seven biogeographical realms of the world, covering the Indian subcontinent, Sri Lanka, and Southeast Asia

**Ovipositor** Abdominal structure in females used to lay their eggs. Oviposition is the process of laying eggs via the ovipositor.

**Ovoviviparity (adj. ovoviviparous)** Form of reproduction in which the eggs are fertilized, incubated, and hatch inside the female, which gives birth to live young.

**Pacific Realm** One of the seven biogeographical realms of the world, covering Melanesia, Micronesia, and Polynesia.

**Palearctic Realm** One of the seven biogeographical realms of the world, covering Europe, Africa north of the Sahara Desert, and Asia north of the Indian subcontinent and Indochina.

**Palp** Paired sensory appendages associated with the maxilla and labium, used for touch and taste.

**Palpomere** Article of a palp.

**Parasitoid** An external or internal parasite that ultimately kills its host.

**Parthenogenesis** Type of asexual reproduction in which the offspring develops from an unfertilized egg.

**Parthenogenetic pedogenesis** Form of asexual reproduction that involves parthogenesis in larvae.

**Pectinate** With teeth-like projections resembling a comb; usually applied to antennae.

**Pheromone** Chemical substance secreted by an organism that influences the behavior of other members of the species, e.g., used to attract a mate.

**Phloeophagous** Feeding on the phloem tissue of the inner bark.

**Phoresy (adj. phoretic)** Form of commensalism in which one animal attaches itself to another for transportation, causing its host no harm in the process.

**Phylogenetics** The study of the evolutionary relationships between organisms through morphological and DNA analyses that result in hypotheses of their shared evolutionary histories.

**Phytophagous** Feeding on plants.

**Pilose** Having a covering of usually soft, fine setae.

**Plastron** Thin layer of air trapped by specialized structures (e.g., setae, scales) extending from the cuticle of some aquatic beetles while they are underwater enabling them to breathe.

**Pleuron (pl. pleura)** Lateral section, or plate, of a thoracic segment.

**Predaceous, predacious** Feeding by catching live prey.

**Pretarsus** Last segment of the insect leg that bears a claw or claws.

**Procoxal cavity** Cavity in the prothorax into which the front coxa is inserted. The shape of the cavity and whether it is open or closed are useful identification characters.

**Proepipleuron** Outer, downward-folding edge of the prothorax.

**Prognathous** Horizontal orientation of the head, with the mouthparts projecting forward (cf. hypognathous).

**Pronotum** Dorsal plate of the prothorax (cf. prosternum).

**Propleuron** Lateral sclerite of the prothorax externally visible in some beetle groups.

**Propygidium** Dorsal section of the abdomen anterior to the pygidium.

**Prosternum** Ventral plate of the prothorax (cf. pronotum).

**Prothorax** The anterior of the three segments that make up the thorax, to which the first pair of legs is attached.

**Pubescence** Having a covering of soft, closely set setae.

**Punctation (adj. punctate)** Pitted with small holes or depressions (punctures).

**Pupa (pl. pupae)** Life stage of a holometabolous insect that follows the larva and precedes the adult.

**Pygidium** Hardened abdominal tergite exposed beyond the apex of the elytra in some beetles.

**Pyrophilous** Adapted to thrive in recently burned environments, e.g., *Melanophila acuminata* can detect fires with infrared receptors and lays its eggs under recently burned tree bark.

**Raptorial** Adapted to hold prey during feeding.

**Ramus (pl. rami)** A branch, or a projecting process.

**Red-rotten decay** Stage of decomposition in wood that is favored by some beetle larvae.

**Reflex bleeding** Defensive mechanism in which the beetle "bleeds" a noxious liquid from its joints to deter predators.

**Riparian** Relating to the bank of a stream, river, lake, or wetland.

**Rostrum** Snout- or beak-like projection extending from the head of an insect; weevils in particular are known for their rostra, which in some cases are extremely long.

**Rugose** Having wrinkles.

**Saprophagous** Feeding on dead or decaying organic matter, and thereby playing an important role in the decomposition process.

**Saproxylic** Dependent on dead or decaying wood.

**Saproxylophagous** Feeding on dead or decaying wood.

**Scale** Flat seta on the body wall that occurs in various shapes and colors.

**Scarabaeiform larva** Somewhat resembling the larva of a beetle in the superfamily Scarabaeoidea, i.e., a thick-bodied, C-shaped larva with well-developed legs and head.

**Sclerite** Hardened plate that together with others forms the exoskeleton of an insect.

**Sclerophyll** Vegetation type common to parts of Australia, South Africa, the Mediterranean, California, and Chile with hot, dry summers and mild, wet winters. Plants are characterized by hard leaves that are adapted to dry conditions and are unpalatable to many animals.

**Sclerotin** Protein produced by insects that hardens as it matures, thereby stiffening the insect's cuticle.

**Sclerotized** Part of the body that has been hardened with sclerotin.

**Scrobe** Shallow groove, e.g., into which the antenna of some weevils is inserted.

**Scutellary striole** Short striae, or lines, near the scutellum.

**Scutellum** Posterior projection of the mesonotum, which in beetles is positioned between the bases of the elytra.

**Securiform** Triangular and compressed in shape; usually applied to palps.

**Serrate** Having a notched margin, like the teeth of a saw; usually applied to antennae.

**Serrulate** Having a very finely notched margin; minutely serrate.

**Seta (pl. setae)** Bristle- or hairlike structure.

**Setal brush** "Brush" of setae, often on the mouthparts and used to aid feeding.

**Setiferous pore** Bristly pore or tiny surface opening.

**Setose** Bearing setae.

**Sinuate** Having a wavy edge or margin.

**Species** Taxonomic rank below genus and comprising a group of similar individual organisms capable of breeding with one another to produce similar fertile offspring.

**Spermatheca** Cavity or receptacle in the female reproductive system for receiving and storing sperm.

**Spiculate** Covered in spicules.

**Spicule** Narrow, pointed, hardened prickle-like projection.

**Spiracle** External tracheal opening on the side of the insect's thorax and abdomen through which air and water vapor pass in and out during respiration.

**Stria (pl. striae)** Fine impressed line.

**Stridulation (vb stridulate)** Producing a noise by rubbing together specialized body parts.

**Stridulatory file/organ** Finely ridged structure across which another part of the body is rubbed to create a noise.

**Stylus (pl. styli)** Needle-like projection or spike.

**Subelytral cavity** Protected space between the dorsal surface of the abdomen and fused elytra that serves several functions, principally to reduce transpiration in beetles that inhabit dry environments or capture air bubbles to allow some aquatic beetles to breathe underwater.

**Subfamily** Taxonomic rank below family and above tribe and genus.

**Subglabrous** Almost smooth; only slightly setose.

**Submentum** Anterior ventral region of the head capsule below the mentum.

**Subsocial** Form of social behavior in which the adults cooperate to care for their young.

**Subspecies** Taxonomic rank below species level and referring to a usually geographically distinct group that differs in appearance and other characters.

**Subtribe** Taxonomic rank below tribe and above genus.

**Sulcate** Having long, narrow longitudinal grooves or furrows.

**Sulcus (pl. sulci)** Furrow or groove.

**Superfamily** Taxonomic rank above family and below order.

**Suture** Seam or rigid join between two separate parts.

**Symbiosis (adj. symbiotic)** A long-term and dependent relationship of members of one species with those of another (symbionts) to the benefit of one or both.

**Sympatry (adj. sympatric)** In which populations of two different species live together in the same geographic area but do not breed with one another.

**Synanthropic** Related to wild (i.e. not domesticated) animals living near, and benefitting from, human-influenced habitats.

**Synonym** In taxonomy, a synonym is a scientific name for a species or other taxon correctly known by another name.

**Systematics** Study of the diversity of living organisms and their evolution, and the relationships among them.

**Tarsal formula** The number of tarsomeres of a tarsus on the front, middle, and hind legs (e.g., 5-5-4); a useful identification character for various groups of beetles.

**Tarsomere** An article of the tarsus. Beetle tarsi usually have one to five tarsomeres.

**Tarsus (pl. tarsi)** Fifth segment of an insect's leg.

**Taxon (pl. taxa)** A group within taxonomy, the hierarchical system of biological classification, e.g., a genus, or a species.

**Taxonomy** The science and practice of recognizing, describing, and naming species.

**Tergite** A sclerite, or plate, that covers the tergum.

**Tergum (pl. terga)** Dorsal surface of a body segment of an arthropod.

**Terricolous** Living on, or beneath, the ground surface.

**Tessellated** Formed from plates or other shapes that fit together without gaps or overlaps in a mosaic-like pattern.

**Tibia (pl. tibiae)** Fourth section of an insect's leg.

**Tomentose** Covered with tomentum.

**Tomentum** A form of pubescence composed of short, matted, woolly hair-like setae.

**Tribe** Taxonomic rank below subfamily and above genus; it may be further subdivided into subtribes.

**Trichome** Very fine bristle- or hairlike structure.

**Tridentate** Having three points or processes.

**Triungulin (pl. triungula)** First instar, or larval stage, of a species that undergoes hypermetamorphosis (e.g. blister beetles, family Meloidae); it is mobile and seeks out a host on which it and subsequent instars feed.

**Trochanter** Second section of the leg, between the coxa and femur.

**Trochantin** Present on the outer side of the coxa in some groups of beetles, e.g., visible on hind legs of Archostemata.

**Troglobite** Animal adapted to live in dark cave environments.

**Trophallaxis** Transfer of food between social insects.

**Tubercle** Knobby protuberance.

**Uniramous** Having a single branch (cf. biramous).

**Univoltine** Producing one brood of offspring per year.

**Urogomphus (pl. urogomphi)** Process extending from the terminal segment of some larvae, sometimes taking the form of paired "horns."

**Ventral** Relating to the ventrum (cf. dorsal).

**Ventrite** Visible sclerite, or plate, covering the ventrum.

**Ventrum** In a beetle, its lower surface.

**Vernal** Relating to spring.

**Vertex** Upper, or dorsal, surface of the head.

**Vitta (pl. vittae)** Stripe of color.

# CLASSIFICATION
## *of the* COLEOPTERA

Below is a classification of the world beetles down to the rank of family (based on Bouchard et al. 2011 and Ślipiński et al. 2011). Suborders, superfamilies, and families known only from fossils are excluded. Families followed by an asterisk (*) are those represented in *The Book of Beetles*. The approximate number of described extant species is given in square brackets after each family (although note that these numbers can vary from source to source, and that new species continue to be described on a regular basis). See the Classification and Resources sections (pages 16–17 and 648–49, respectively) for additional information.

**ORDER COLEOPTERA**

**Suborder Archostemata**
Family Crowsoniellidae* [1]
Family Cupedidae* [31]
Family Micromalthidae* [1]
Family Ommatidae* [6]
Family Jurodidae* [1]

**Suborder Myxophaga**
SUPERFAMILY LEPICEROIDEA
Family Lepiceridae* [3]

SUPERFAMILY SPHAERIUSOIDEA
Family Torridincolidae* [65]
Family Hydroscaphidae* [22]
Family Sphaeriusidae* [19]

**Suborder Adephaga**
Family Gyrinidae* [882]
Family Trachypachidae* [6]
Family Carabidae* [40,350]
Family Haliplidae* [218]
Family Meruidae* [1]
Family Noteridae* [250]
Family Amphizoidae* [5]
Family Aspidytidae* [2]
Family Hygrobiidae* [5]
Family Dytiscidae* [4,015]

**Suborder Polyphaga**
SUPERFAMILY HYDROPHILOIDEA
Family Hydrophilidae* [3,400]
Family Sphaeritidae* [5]
Family Synteliidae* [7]
Family Histeridae* [4,300]

SUPERFAMILY STAPHYLINOIDEA
Family Hydraenidae* [1,600]
Family Ptiliidae* [650]
Family Agyrtidae* [70]
Family Leiodidae* [3,700]
Family Silphidae* [200]
Family Staphylinidae* [56,000]

SUPERFAMILY SCARABAEOIDEA
Family Pleocomidae* [50]
Family Geotrupidae* [920]
Family Belohinidae [1]
Family Passalidae* [800]
Family Trogidae* [300]
Family Glaresidae [57]
Family Diphyllostomatidae [3]
Family Lucanidae* [1,489]
Family Ochodaeidae [110]
Family Hybosoridae [573]
Family Glaphyridae [204]
Family Scarabaeidae* [27,000]

SUPERFAMILY SCIRTOIDEA
Family Decliniidae* [2]
Family Eucinetidae* [53]
Family Clambidae* [170]
Family Scirtidae* [800]

SUPERFAMILY DASCILLOIDEA
Family Dascillidae* [80]
Family Rhipiceridae* [70]

SUPERFAMILY BUPRESTOIDEA
Family Schizopodidae* [7]
Family Buprestidae* [14,700]

SUPERFAMILY BYRRHOIDEA
Family Byrrhidae* [430]
Family Elmidae* [1,500]
Family Dryopidae* [300]
Family Lutrochidae* [11]
Family Limnichidae* [390]
Family Heteroceridae* [300]
Family Psephenidae* [290]
Family Cneoglossidae* [10]
Family Ptilodactylidae* [500]
Family Podabrocephalidae* [1]
Family Chelonariidae* [250]
Family Eulichadidae* [30]
Family Callirhipidae* [150]

SUPERFAMILY ELATEROIDEA
Family Rhinorhipidae* [1]
Family Artematopodidae* [45]
Family Brachypsectridae* [5]
Family Cerophytidae* [21]
Family Eucnemidae* [1,500]
Family Throscidae [150]
Family Elateridae* [10,000]
Family Plastoceridae* [2]
Family Drilidae* [120]
Family Omalisidae* [8]
Family Lycidae* [4,600]
Family Telegeusidae* [10]
Family Phengodidae* [250]
Family Rhagophthalmidae* [30]
Family Lampyridae* [2,200]
Family Omethidae* [33]
Family Cantharidae* [5,100]

SUPERFAMILY DERODONTOIDEA
Family Derodontidae* [30]
Family Nosodendridae* [50]
Family Jacobsoniidae* [20]

SUPERFAMILY BOSTRICHOIDEA
Family Dermestidae* [1,200]
Family Endecatomidae* [4]
Family Bostrichidae* [570]
Family Ptinidae* [2,200]

SUPERFAMILY LYMEXYLOIDEA
Family Lymexylidae* [70]

SUPERFAMILY CLEROIDEA
Family Phloiophilidae* [1]
Family Trogossitidae* [600]
Family Chaetosomatidae* [12]
Family Metaxinidae [1]
Family Thanerocleridae* [30]
Family Cleridae* [3,400]
Family Acanthocnemidae* [1]
Family Phycosecidae* [4]
Family Prionoceridae* [160]
Family Mauroniscidae* [26]
Family Melyridae* [6,000]

SUPERFAMILY CUCUJOIDEA
Family Boganiidae* [11]
Family Byturidae* [24]
Family Helotidae* [107]
Family Protocucujidae* [7]
Family Sphindidae* [59]
Family Biphyllidae* [200]
Family Erotylidae* [3,500]
Family Monotomidae* [250]
Family Hobartiidae* [6]
Family Cryptophagidae* [600]
Family Agapythidae* [1]
Family Priasilphidae* [11]
Family Phloeostichidae [14]
Family Silvanidae* [500]
Family Cucujidae* [44]
Family Myraboliidae* [13]
Family Cavognathidae* [9]
Family Lamingtoniidae* [3]
Family Passandridae* [109]
Family Phalacridae* [640]
Family Propalticidae* [30]
Family Laemophloeidae* [430]
Family Tasmosalpingidae* [2]
Family Cyclaxyridae* [2]
Family Kateretidae* [95]
Family Nitidulidae* [4,500]
Family Smicripidae* [6]
Family Bothrideridae* [400]
Family Cerylonidae* [450]
Family Alexiidae* [50]
Family Discolomatidae* [400]
Family Endomychidae* [1,800]
Family Coccinellidae* [6,000]
Family Corylophidae* [200]
Family Akalyptoischiidae* [24]
Family Latridiidae* [1,000]

SUPERFAMILY TENEBRIONOIDEA
Family Mycetophagidae* [130]
Family Archeocrypticidae [60]
Family Pterogeniidae* [26]

Family Ciidae* [650]
Family Tetratomidae* [150]
Family Melandryidae* [420]
Family Mordellidae* [1,500]
Family Ripiphoridae* [400]
Family Zopheridae* [1,700]
Family Ulodidae [30]
Family Promecheilidae [20]
Family Chalcodryidae* [15]
Family Trachelostenidae [2]
Family Tenebrionidae* [20,000]
Family Prostomidae* [30]
Family Synchroidae [8]
Family Stenotrachelidae [19]
Family Oedemeridae* [1,500]
Family Meloidae* [3,000]
Family Mycteridae* [160]
Family Boridae [4]
Family Trictenotomidae* [13]
Family Pythidae* [23]
Family Pyrochroidae* [167]
Family Salpingidae* [300]
Family Anthicidae* [3,000]
Family Aderidae* [900]
Family Scraptiidae [500]

SUPERFAMILY CHRYSOMELOIDEA
Family Oxypeltidae* [3]
Family Vesperidae* [75]
Family Disteniidae* [336]
Family Cerambycidae* [30,080]
Family Megalopodidae* [350]
Family Orsodacnidae* [40]
Family Chrysomelidae* [32 500]

SUPERFAMILY CURCULIONOIDEA
Family Nemonychidae* [70]
Family Anthribidae* [3 900]
Family Belidae* [375]
Family Caridae* [6]
Family Attelabidae* [2 500]
Family Brentidae* [4,000]
Family Dryophthoridae* [1 200]
Family Brachyceridae* [1 200]
Family Curculionidae* [48 600]

647

# RESOURCES

The following is a selection of useful books, scientific journal articles and websites currently available to those with an interest in beetles.

## BOOKS

Arnett, R. H. Jr. and M. C. Thomas (Eds). *American Beetles. Volume 1. Archostemata, Myxophaga, Adephaga, Polyphaga: Staphyliniformia* CRC PRESS, 2001

Arnett, R. H. Jr., M. C. Thomas, P. E. Skelley and J. H. Frank (Eds). *American Beetles. Volume 2. Polyphaga: Scarabaeoidea through Curculionoidea* CRC PRESS, 2002

Beutel, R. G. and R. A. B. Leschen (Eds). *Coleoptera, Beetles. Volume 1: Morphology and Systematics (Archostemata, Adephaga, Myxophaga, Polyphaga partim). Handbook of Zoology. Arthropoda: Insecta* WALTER DE GRUYTER, 2005

Booth, R. G., M. L. Cox and R. B. Madge. *IIE Guides to Insects of Importance to Man. 3. Coleoptera* INTERNATIONAL INSTITUTE OF ENTOMOLOGY, 1990

Campbell, J. M., M. J. Sarazin and D. B. Lyons. *Canadian Beetles (Coleoptera) Injurious to Crops, Ornamentals, Stored Products, and Buildings* AGRICULTURE CANADA, 1989

Cooter, J. and M. V. L. Barclay (Eds). *A Coleopterist's Handbook* (4th edition) AMATEUR ENTOMOLOGISTS' SOCIETY, 2006

Crowson, R. A. *The Biology of the Coleoptera* ACADEMIC PRESS, 1981

Downie, N. M. and R. H. Arnett Jr. *The Beetles of Northeastern North America. Volumes 1–2* SANDHILL CRANE PRESS, 1996

Evans, A. V. and C. L. Bellamy. *An Inordinate Fondness for Beetles* UNIVERSITY OF CALIFORNIA PRESS, 2000

Evans, A. V. and J. N. Hogue. *Introduction to California Beetles* UNIVERSITY OF CALIFORNIA PRESS, 2004

Hatch, M. H. *The Beetles of the Pacific Northwest. Parts 1–5* UNIVERSITY OF WASHINGTON PRESS, 1953–1971

Klausnitzer, B. *Beetles.* EXETER BOOKS, 1981

Klimaszewski, J. and J. C. Watt. *Coleoptera: Family-group Review and Keys to Identification. Fauna of New Zealand No. 37* MANAAKI WHENUA PRESS, 1997

Lawrence, J. F. (Coordinator). *Order Coleoptera*. Pp. 144–658 *in*: Stehr, F. (Ed.). Immature Insects. Volume 2 KENDALL/HUNT PUBLISHING COMPANY, 1991

Lawrence, J. F. and E. B. Britton. *Australian Beetles* MELBOURNE UNIVERSITY PRESS, 1994

Lawrence, J. F. and A. Ślipiński. *Australian Beetles: Morphology, Classification and Keys* CSIRO, 2013.

Leschen, R. A. B. and R. G. Beutel (Eds). *Coleoptera, Beetles. Volume 3: Morphology and Systematics (Phytophaga). Handbook of Zoology. Arthropoda: Insecta* WALTER DE GRUYTER, 2014

Leschen, R. A. B., R. G. Beutel and J. F. Lawrence (Eds). *Coleoptera, Beetles. Volume 2: Morphology and Systematics (Elateroidea, Bostrichiformia, Cucujiformia partim). Handbook of Zoology. Arthropoda: Insecta* WALTER DE GRUYTER, 2010

Löbl, I. and A. Smetana (Eds). *Catalogue of Palaearctic Coleoptera. Volumes 1–8.* APPOLO BOOKS [1–7] / BRILL [8], 2003–2013

McMonigle, O. *The Ultimate Guide to Breeding Beetles. Coleoptera Laboratory Culture Methods.* COACHWHIP PUBLICATIONS, 2012

New, T. R. *Beetles in Conservation* WILEY-BLACKWELL, 2010

Pakaluk, J. and S. A. Ślipiński (Eds). *Biology, Phylogeny, and Classification of Coleoptera. Papers Celebrating the 80th Birthday of Roy A. Crowson. Volumes 1 and 2* MUZEUM I INSTYTUT ZOOLOGII PAN, 1995

## FIELD GUIDES

Bily, S. *A Colour Guide to Beetles* TREASURE PRESS, 1990

Evans, A. V. *Beetles of Eastern North America* PRINCETON UNIVERSITY PRESS, 2014

Evans, A. V. and J. N. Hogue. *Field Guide to Beetles of California* UNIVERSITY OF CALIFORNIA PRESS, 2006

Hangay, G. and P. Zborowski. *A Guide to the Beetles of Australia* CSIRO, 2010

Harde, K. W. *A Field Guide in Colour to Beetles.* OCTOPUS BOOKS, 1981

Lyneborg, L. *Beetles in Colour.* English edition supervised by Gwynne Vevers BLANDFORD PRESS, 1977

Matthews, E. G. *A Guide to the Genera of Beetles of South Australia. Parts 1–7* SOUTH AUSTRALIAN MUSEUM, 1980–1997

Papp, C. S. *Introduction to North American Beetles with more than 1,000 Illustrations* ENTOMOGRAPHY PUBLICATIONS, 1984

White, R. E. *A Field Guide to the Beetles of North America* HOUGHTON MIFFLIN CO., 1983

## SCIENTIFIC JOURNAL ARTICLES

Bouchard, P., Y. Bousquet, A. E. Davies, M. A. Alonso-Zarazaga, J. F. Lawrence, C. H. C. Lyal, A. F. Newton, C. A. M. Reid, M. Schmitt, S. A. Ślipiński and A. B. T. Smith. Family-group names in Coleoptera (Insecta). *ZooKeys* 88: 1–972 (2011)

Lawrence, J. F. and A. F. Newton Jr. Evolution and classification of beetles. *Annual Review of Ecology and Systematics* 13: 261–290 (1982)

Lawrence, J. F., S. A. Ślipiński, A. E. Seago, M. K. Thayer, A. F. Newton and E. Marvaldi. Phylogeny of the Coleoptera based on morphological characters of adults and larvae. *Annales Zoologici* 61: 1–217 (2011)

Peck, S. B. The beetles of the Galápagos Islands, Ecuador: evolution, ecology, and diversity. *Journal of Insect Conservation* 12: 729–730 (2008)

Ślipiński, S. A., R. A. B. Leschen and J. F. Lawrence. Order Coleoptera Linnaeus, 1758. *In*: Zhang, Z.-Q. (Ed.) Animal biodiversity: an outline of higher-level classification and survey of taxonomic richness. *Zootaxa* 3148: 203–208 (2011)

649

## NATIONAL AND INTERNATIONAL ORGANIZATIONS DEDICATED TO THE STUDY OF BEETLES

**Asociación Europea de Coleopterologia [Spain]**
www.ub.edu/aec

**The Balfour-Brown Club**
www.latissimus.org/?page id=24

**The Coleopterists Society [USA]**
www.coleopsoc.org

**Coleopterological Society of Japan [Japan]**
www. kochugakkai.sakura.ne.jp/English/index2.html

**Wiener Coleopterologen Verein [Austria]**
www.coleoptera.at

## USEFUL WEB SITES

**Beetles (Coleoptera) and coleopterists**
http://www.zin.ru/animalia/coleoptera/eng/index.htm

**BugGuide**
http://www.bugguide.net

**Coleoptera**
http://www.coleoptera.org

**Systematic Entomology Laboratory, United States Department of Agriculture, Coleoptera World Wide Web Site**
http://www.sel.barc.usda.gov/Coleoptera/col-home.htm

**Tree of Life Web Project. Coleoptera**
http://www.tolweb.org/coleoptera

# NOTES *on* CONTRIBUTORS

PATRICE BOUCHARD is a research scientist and curator of Coleoptera at the Canadian National Collection of Insects, Arachnids, and Nematodes in Ottawa. He has published more than 50 scientific papers, books or book chapters, including the 1,000-page *Family-group names in Coleoptera* and the award-winning *Tenebrionid Beetles of Australia*. Patrice is also on the editorial board of *The Canadian Entomologist*, *ZooKeys*, and *Zoological Bibliography*.

*Contributions:* pages 306–7, 310, 312, 314–15, 461–4, 466–7, 469–500, 502–13, 646–7. With Yves Bousquet: pages 33, 43, 49, 113, 300, 303, 305, 308–9, 313, 465, 468. With Arthur V. Evans: pages 6–29. With Arthur V. Evans and Stéphane le Tirant: pages 56, 58, 199, 224, 240.

YVES BOUSQUET pursued his undergraduate studies at the College Bourget in Rigaud, Quebec, where he developed a strong interest for beetles at the age of 12. He obtained his Ph.D. from the University of Montreal, Canada, in 1981. Since then he has been a research scientist at the Canadian National Collection of Insects, Arachnids, and Nematodes in Ottawa. He is the author or co-author of six books and more than 100 scientific papers or book chapters on the taxonomy and biology of beetles, particularly those of the families Carabidae, Monotomidae, and Histeridae.

*Contributions:* 34, 57, 60, 63–8, 73, 76–9, 82–9, 92–100, 103, 106–7, 110–11. With Patrice Bouchard: pages 33, 43, 49, 113, 300, 303, 305, 308–9, 313, 465, 468.

CHRISTOPHER CARLTON grew up in Arkansas, USA, where he developed an early fascination for insect diversity. He received his undergraduate degree from Hendrix College (Conway, Arkansas) and his graduate training at the University of Arkansas (Fayetteville, Arkansas), where he also served as Curator of the University of Arkansas Arthropod Museum. He moved to Baton Rouge, Louisiana during 1995 to join the entomology faculty at the Louisiana State University Agricultural Center. He directs the Louisiana State Arthropod Museum and leads the training program in systematics. He has described or co-described approximately 200 species of Coleoptera, mostly belonging to the family Staphylinidae.

*Contributions:* pages 114–88, 249–60, 301–2, 304, 311, 365, 454–60.

MARIA LOURDES CHAMORRO is a research entomologist with the Systematic Entomology Laboratory at the National Museum of Natural History in Washington, D. C. She has authored more than 15 scientific publications on the taxonomy, relationships, and comparative morphology of adult and larval forms of beetles and caddisflies. These include a 250-page monograph of Neotropical *Polyplectropus* and book chapters for the *Handbook of Zoology: Coleoptera*. She currently serves as Chrysomeloidea editor for the journal *Zootaxa*. Maria is an avid field-collector and curator; among her scientific discoveries are one new tribe of beetles, four new genera, and more than 60 new species.

Contributions: pages 578–639.

HERMES E. ESCALONA earned his Ph.D. in Entomology from the Universidad Central de Venezuela (UCV) in 2012. He is interested in the systematics and evolution of Coleoptera, with current projects on Australian longhorn beetles (Cerambycidae) and beetle families within Cucujiformia. He is currently affiliated with the Museo del Instituto de Zoología Agrícola-UCV and is a visiting scientist at the Australian National Insect Collection-CSIRO.

*Contributions:* pages 316–17, 319, 321, 326, 328–9, 331–5, 337–45, 347–50, 352, 354–9, 376–7, 380, 383–8, 390–4, 396–405.

ARTHUR V. EVANS is an author, lecturer, and broadcaster. He is research associate at the Smithsonian Institute, Washington, D. C., and adjunct professor at Virginia Commonwealth University, University of Richmond, and Randolph-Macon College. Arthur has published more than 40 scientific papers and over 100 popular articles and books on insects and other arthropods, including *Beetles of Eastern North America*.

*Contributions:* pages 35–41, 44–6, 50–5, 59, 61–2, 69–72, 74¬–5, 80–1, 90–1, 101–2, 104–5, 108–9, 189–92, 195, 197–8, 202, 205, 208–9, 214–15, 220, 226, 228, 230–1, 238, 261–3, 270, 276, 278, 284, 287–8, 293, 318, 320, 322–5, 327, 330, 336, 346, 351, 353, 378–9, 381–2, 389, 395, 501, 648–9. With Patrice Bouchard: pages 6–29. With Patrice Bouchard and Stéphane le Tirant: pages 56, 58, 199, 224, 240.

ALEXANDER KONSTANTINOV graduated from the Department of Zoology of the Belorussian State University in Minsk in 1981, and received a Ph.D. in entomology from the Zoological Institute in St Petersburg, Russia, in 1987. He taught biology in elementary, middle, and high schools and, after completing his dissertation on the taxonomy and fauna of flea beetles of the European part of the former U.S.S.R. and the Caucasus, taught zoology of invertebrates, taxonomy and ecology of animals at the Belorussian State University. From 1995 he has studied the taxonomy and biology of leaf beetles at the Systematic Entomology Laboratory in Washington, D. C. He has published over 100 papers and five books on leaf beetle taxonomy. His current research includes the classification and biology of flea beetles in the Oriental Realm for which, in recent years, he has traveled extensively in Bhutan, China, India, Japan, and Nepal.

*Contributions:* pages 547–77.

RICHARD A. B. LESCHEN is a researcher at Landcare Research in New Zealand. He has authored more than 150 publications on beetle systematics, evolution, and natural history and is a co-editor of the *Handbook of Zoology: Coleoptera*. He has studied the world over, traveled from the subantarctic islands to deep Amazonian rainforests, and promotes the study of beetles by participating in workshops, teaching, and collaboration. He is also a musician and songwriter.

*Contributions:* pages 360–4, 366–75, 406–53.

STÉPHANE LE TIRANT is curator of the Montreal Insectarium, one of the world's largest museums devoted entirely to insects. He is an expert in cultural entomology and exhibitry. He is the author of numerous papers on insects and the co-author of *Papillons et chenilles du Québec et des Maritimes*, a book on the butterflies and caterpillars of Quebec and the Maritimes. Stéphane has served as an international consultant for many projects including the Shanghai, Hong Kong, Newfoundland, and Audubon insectariums. He has helped to create more than 12 butterfly houses around the world. He was the entomological advisor for the acclaimed series *Insectia*, which was purchased by the National Geographic and Discovery channels. Six species have been named after him.

*Contributions:* 193–194, 196, 199, 200–1, 203, 204, 206, 207, 210–13, 216–19, 221–3, 225, 227, 229, 232–7, 239, 241–8, 264–8, 269, 271–5, 277, 279–83, 285–6, 289–90, 291–2, 294–9. With Patrice Bouchard and Arthur V. Evans: pages 56, 58, 199, 224, 240.

STEVEN W. LINGAFELTER received his Bachelor and Master of Science Degrees in Biology at Midwestern State University (Wichita Falls, Texas) in 1989 and 1991, respectively. He received his Doctorate in Entomology from the University of Kansas (Lawrence, Kansas) in 1996. Since that time, he has been a Research Entomologist with the Systematic Entomology Laboratory, United States Department of Agriculture, and based at the Smithsonian Institution's National Museum of Natural History in Washington, D. C. He has published more than 60 papers and four books on beetle systematics and taxonomy, with an emphasis on Neotropical longhorn beetles.

*Contributions:* pages 514–46.

PHOTOGRAPHER AT THE CANADIAN NATIONAL COLLECTION

ANTHONY DAVIES A student of H. F. Howden and S. B. Peck, Anthony Davies has been providing curatorial and research support for CNC coleopterists since 1971, including J. M. Campbell, A. Smetana, and P. Bouchard. He was a contributing author in the *Checklist of Beetles of Canada and Alaska*, the *Reclassification of the North Temperate Taxa Associated with* Staphylinus *Sensu Lato* (with A. Smetana), the *Catalogue of Palaearctic Coleoptera*, *Family-group Names in Coleoptera*, and two volumes of *Adventive Species of Coleoptera Recorded from Canada*. He recently provided photographs for *Tenebrionid Beetles of Australia*, and the *Insects and Arachnids of Canada* series.

651

653

655

# ACKNOWLEDGMENTS

## CONTRIBUTOR ACKNOWLEDGMENTS

Significant input regarding information on the distribution, biology, taxonomy, literature and nomenclature associated with various species was received from our colleagues from all over the world. We are indebted to the following people for their insightful comments and for sharing their data with us: R. Anderson, M. Angel Moron, W. Barries, L. Bartolozzi, V. Bayless, C. Bellamy (deceased), L. Bocák, M. Bologna, S. Brullé, M. Buffington, J. Cayouette, C. Chaboo, D. Chandler, A. Cline, D. Curoe, A. Davies, H. Douglas, T. Durr, M. Ferro, G. Flores, F. Francisco Barbosa, M. Friedrich, R. Foottit, R. Fouquè, F. Génier, M. Gigli, B. Gill, M. Gimmel, R. Gordon, H. Goulet, V. Grebennikov, J. Hammond, G. Hanguay, L. Herman, M. Ivie, E. Jendek, I. Jenis, P. Johnson, A. Kirejtshuk, P. Lago, T. Lamb, D. Langor, S. Laplante, J. Lawrence, C.-F. Lee, L. LeSage, N. Lord, T. C. MacRae, C. Maier, C. Majka, M. Monné, P. Moretto, A. Newton, R. Oberprieler, A. Payette, S. Peck, J. Pinto, S. Policena Rosa, D. Pollock, J. Prena, B. C. Ratcliffe, C. Reid, J. M. Rowland, W. Schawaller, G. Setliff, W. Shepard, A. Ślipiński, A. Smetana, A. B. T. Smith, A. D. Smith, W. Staines, Jr., W. Steiner, A. Sundholm, D. Telnov, M. Thayer, T. Théry, D. Thomas, A. Tishechkin, P. Wagner, C. Watts, K. Will, N. Woodley, H. Yoshitake, D. K. Young, N. Yunakov.

A large number of photographs were generated specifically for this book. The following institutions and individuals made their (often rare) specimens available to us and facilitated our visits: American Museum of Natural History, New York City, USA (L. Herman, A. D. Smith), Australian National Insect Collection, Canberra, Australia (C. Lemann, A. Ślipiński), California Academy of Sciences, San Francisco, USA (D. Kavanaugh, N. Penny), Canadian Museum of Nature, Ottawa, Canada (R. Anderson, F. Génier), Field Museum, Chicago, USA (J. Boone), Florida State Collection of Arthropod, Gainesville, USA (P. Skelley), Kansas University Biodiversity Institute, Lawrence, USA (C. Chaboo, Z. Falin), Museum of Comparative Zoology, Cambridge, USA (P. Perkins), Queensland Museum and Sciencentre, Brisbane, Australia (S. Wright), Smithsonian Institution, Washington, D. C., USA (T. Erwin, D. Furth, C. Micheli, E. Roberts, F. Shockley), A. Desjardins, M. Ivie, I. Jenis, S. Laplante, A. Smetana, A. D. Smith, D. Telnov. Processing of several image files was performed by M. Saeidi. The tireless and surgeonlike efforts of A. Davies to clean, remount, and photograph dozens of often old, rare, and minute beetle specimens are sincerely acknowledged; this project could not have been completed without him.

René Limoges from the Montréal Insectarium is sincerely acknowledged for his enthusiasm towards the project. Richard Leschen was supported in part by the Core funding for Crown Research Institutes from the Ministry of Business, Innovation and Employment's Science and Innovation Group.

We sincerely thank the staff at Ivy Press for their vision, guidance and sustained support throughout the project. Editors and reviewers, some of which spent a significant amount of time editing the contents, improved the overall quality of the book greatly. Our institutions have permitted us to use the necessary resources (specimens, camera equipment, libraries, etc.) in order to make this project feasible; the production of this book would not have been possible without their important support. Lastly, but most importantly, we would like to thank our families for their constant encouragement.

## PICTURE CREDITS

The publisher would like to thank the following individuals and organizations for their kind permission to reproduce the images in this book. Every effort has been made to acknowledge the images, however we apologize if there are any unintentional omissions and would be grateful if notified of any corrections that should be incorporated in future reprints or editions of this book.

KLAUS BOLTE 294, 522, 524, 528, 531, 534, 540, 542–3, 547, 558, 638. JASON BOND AND TRIP LAMB 479. LECH BOROWIEC 42–3, 47, 107, 130, 134, 150, 173, 229, 234, 251, 329, 349, 357, 371, 374, 442, 453, 489, 496–7, 500, 505, 561, 565, 567, 604, 607. KAROLYN DARROW © THE SMITHSONIAN INSTITUTION 61–2, 68–9, 71–2, 77, 79, 83. ANTHONY DAVIES, COPYRIGHT © HER MAJESTY THE QUEEN IN RIGHT OF CANADA AS REPRESENTED BY THE MINISTER OF AGRICULTURE AND AGRI-FOOD 5, 11, 15T, 32–3, 35 (© President and Fellows of Harvard College), 36–40, 44, 50–1, 57, 60, 63, 66, 85 (© President and Fellows of Harvard College), 88–9 (© President and Fellows of Harvard College), 92 (© President and Fellows of Harvard College), 97, 99–102, 110–11, 114, 115 (© President and Fellows of Harvard College), 116–18, 120–1, 123, 125–9, 131, 133, 135, 137–46, 148, 151–66, 168–72, 174–83, 185–92, 194–5, 202–8, 210–11, 214, 216–17, 220–1, 223. 225–7, 230–2, 235, 238–9, 241–7, 250, 252–61, 265, 268–9, 281, 286–7, 290, 296, 300–8, 309 (© President and Fellows of Harvard College), 311, 313–14, 316, 317 (© President and Fellows of Harvard College), 318, 322, 326, 330–1, 335–6, 338–9, 343–6, 348, 350–3, 355, 359, 360 (© President and Fellows of Harvard College), 362–9, 370 (© President and Fellows of Harvard College), 372–3, 377, 380–1, 383–4, 386–7, 396–8, 400, 402 (© President and Fellows of Harvard College), 403, 408, 410–15, 417–20, 422–4, 426–8, 431–3, 437, 439, 444, 446–52, 455, 457–8, 460–1, 463–5, 469–71, 475, 477, 482, 484–6, 490, 493, 499, 503–4, 507–8, 509 (© President and Fellows of Harvard College), 510, 511–12 (© President and Fellows of Harvard College), 513–14, 520–1, 525, 532, 537, 541, 550, 554, 557, 559, 562, 564, 569–73, 576, 579, 581–82, 584–91, 593–7, 599–603, 606, 609–11, 614–18, 620, 622–3, 625–6, 628–32, 636–7, 639. ARTHUR V. EVANS 24T, 25TR. HENRI GOULET, COPYRIGHT © HER MAJESTY THE QUEEN IN RIGHT OF CANADA AS REPRESENTED BY THE MINISTER OF AGRICULTURE AND AGRI-FOOD 8L, 48–9, 52–5, 64–5, 67, 70, 74–6, 80–2, 84, 86, 90–1, 93–4, 96, 104, 109, 149, 337, 358, 409, 416, 421, 425, 429–30, 434, 436, 438, 440–1, 443, 454, 459, 467, 483, 488, 491, 494, 516, 518, 578, 605, 608, 612, 621, 627, 634. PAUL HARRISON 23B. INSECTARIUM DE MONTRÉAL / Robert Beaudoin: 28T; / René Limoges: 19TR; / Jacques de Tonnancour: 21C, 26. IVO JENNIS 312. KENJI KOHIYAMA 6, 7B, 15b, 478. VITYA KUBÁŇ AND SVATA BÍLÝ 277, 288, 297. STÉPHANE LE TIRANT 199–200, 224, 544–5. RENÉ LIMOGES 1, 3, 12T, 13, 14, 197, 219, 222, 527. KIRILL MAKAROV 41, 122, 132, 193, 213, 248–9, 299, 319, 334, 354, 356, 405–7, 462, 498, 501, 506, 580, 583, 633. COSMIN MANCI 485. FRANCISCO MARTINEZ-CLAVEL 212. MARCELA A. MONNÉ 22B. R. SALMASO, ARCHIVES OF THE MUSEO DI STORIA NATURALE OF VERONA 34. WOLFGANG SCHAWALLER 487. UDO SCHMIDT 73, 78, 103, 106, 108, 119, 228, 376, 530, 538, 549, 560, 563, 566, 592, 598, 613, 624. SCIENCE PHOTO LIBRARY / Pascal Goetgheluck 18BL; /Natural History Museum London: 9. SHUTTERSTOCK /Four Oaks: 20T; /Karel Gallas: 18BR; / Pablo Hidalgo: 29; / King Tut: 28B; /Georgios Kollidas: 16; /D. Kucharski, K. Kucharska: 21T; /Henrik Larsson 25CR; /Morphart Creation: 641–1; /Hein Nouwens: 30–1; / stable: 27CR; /think4photop: 27TR; /Vblinov 23T; /Czesznak Zsolt: 10. MAXIM SMIRNOV 2, 8R, 95, 112–13, 196, 198, 201, 209, 218, 233, 236–7, 279, 289, 575. LAURENT SOLDATI 480–1, JULIEN TOUROULT 328. © TRUSTEES OF THE NATURAL HISTORY MUSEUM, LONDON 45–6, 59, 87, 98, 105, 124, 136, 147, 167, 184, 215, 271, 295, 298, 310, 315, 332, 340, 342, 347, 361, 375, 379, 382, 385, 435, 473, 476, 492, 502, 515, 529, 535, 539, 574, 577, 635 (photographer: Harry Taylor). ALEX WILD 7T, 12BL, 12BR, 19TL, 20B, 22T, 24B. CHRISTOPHER C. WIRTH 56, 58, 240, 262–4, 266–7, 270, 272–6, 278, 280, 282–5, 291–3, 320–1, 323–5, 327, 333, 341, 378, 388–95, 399, 401, 404, 445, 456, 466, 468, 472, 474, 517, 519, 523, 526, 533, 536, 546, 548, 551–3, 555–6, 568, 619. GINNY ZEAL © IVY PRESS LIMITED 17.

Thanks also to Roger Booth, Beulah Garner, Michael Geiser, Malcolm Kerley, Christine Taylor, and Max Barclay, Curators of the Coleoptera Collections at the Natural History Museum, London.